1st 10ᵘ

A
PSYCHIATRIST'S
WORLD

A
PSYCHIATRIST'S
WORLD

The Selected Papers of
KARL MENNINGER, M.D.

Edited, with an Introduction, by
BERNARD H. HALL, M.D.

Foreword by
MARION E. KENWORTHY, M.D.

NEW YORK   THE VIKING PRESS   MCMLIX

Contents

PART ONE: THE MAN

PART TWO: THE CLINICIAN

Studies of Psychological Reactions to Infectious Diseases

Neurological Studies

Studies of Clinical Syndromes

Psychosomatic Studies

PART THREE: THE THEORIST

PART FOUR: THE TEACHER

Public Education

Medicine and Psychiatry

Psychiatric Education

PART FIVE:
THE PSYCHIATRIST AFIELD

Crime and the Law

PART SIX: THE HISTORIAN
OF PSYCHIATRY

Acknowledgments

The members of a committee, chosen to represent their colleagues, made a selection of writings for this book. The committee consisted of Dr. D. Bernard Foster, chairman, Dr. Philip Holzman, Dr. Herbert Klemmer, Dr. Harry Levinson, Dr. Herbert C. Modlin, and Dr. Gardner Murphy. After the committee made their selections, they invited me to act as their editor. For the selections that are included here, for the final editing, and for the commentaries preceding the individual sections, I must assume full responsibility.

I am deeply indebted to many. The members of the committee have always been generous in giving me their assistance and guidance. Mr. Les Roach, Mr. Basil Cole, and nearly all of my colleagues at The Menninger Foundation have assisted me in one way or another. Mr. Nelson Antrim Crawford has provided me with valuable editorial advice. My thanks to the typists who helped prepare copy. Especially I wish to thank the secretaries, Mrs. Hilda Donnelly, Mrs. Margaret Wingett, and Mrs. Virginia Eicholtz, and the Menninger Clinic medical librarian, Miss Vesta Walker, for their assistance. Mr. Denver Lindley of The Viking Press generously provided me with his very able and distinguished editorial counsel.

My particular thanks go to one who did more than any other in assisting to make this book possible, Mrs. Mary Douglas Lee. Mrs. Lee is the assistant to the editors of the *Bulletin of the Menninger Clinic*. For months now, as secretary to the Committee, she has been busy accomplishing all those complicated, detailed editorial tasks necessary before the appearance of the printed page.

My thanks also to all of the editors of the various journals who repeatedly encouraged us in the preparation of the book, and who graciously granted permission for the reprinting here of a number of articles.

—B.H.H.

Foreword

Many years ago it was my privilege to be one of the group of men and women who received our first real stimulus toward the eager learning of the dynamic possibilities of psychiatry under the tutelage of Elmer Southard at the Boston Psychopathic Hospital.

Here in this setting of warm friendliness, Elmer Southard created an atmosphere of exciting scientific adventure. Here it was that I first met Karl Menninger, an eager, serious-minded young doctor with an infectious sense of humor and a warm-hearted interest in the welfare of people. In those days, as at present, this young man was always busy working at something that was important to do.

One of the many bits of advice Southard often reiterated was certainly important for all of us to follow. Perhaps this wise teacher was aware of our self-doubts, and knew the wisdom of reassurance. He would say, in his warm, genial, persuasive fashion, "It is important for young psychiatrists to get into the habit of writing. Write about your cases. Whether you feel you have anything to say that has new significance or not, it is important for you to write. You must share with others what you have learned, and the task of writing clarifies your own thinking."

I have no direct knowledge from Karl Menninger himself whether this kind of direct stimulus from Southard helped him to pursue his writing efforts so consistently. He, more effectively than all the rest of us in that group, has followed Southard's precepts.

In his speech given in Boston in November 1958, on the occasion of the twenty-fifth anniversary of the founding of the Boston Psychoanalytic Society and Institute ("Footprints," p. 856), he recalled that Southard advised his return to Topeka, "where the very lack of many things in Boston is an advantage because you can get them started right, without the handicaps of traditions, prejudice, and vested interests." For those of us who have had the opportunity to observe first-hand what a contribution Karl Menninger has made to psychiatry and psychoanalysis, through Topeka as the center of his efforts, he has fulfilled in a practical way the prophetic vision of Elmer Southard.

As I look through the list of papers selected for these collected writings, I am struck anew with the conviction, long felt, that what Karl Menninger has learned about people he has shared with the world through his writings and teachings. The fields of psychiatry and psychoanalysis have been enriched through his efforts.

These volumes permit the student of human nature to savor the wide range of interests needed by a good physician of the mind.

Karl Menninger, as a man, as a clinician par excellence, as a scientist, teacher, and administrator, represents the best kind of deep dedication to the study of the welfare of mankind.

—Marion E. Kenworthy, M.D.

Introduction

The writings published here are from the world of one psychiatrist, the world in which Karl Menninger has lived and practiced medicine. His world is a busy and exciting one filled with many people and many things. He is interested in and tries to understand everything in it. In fact, he consistently tries to make his world, and thereby the world of others, a better one.

A number of his friends and colleagues who have shared this world with him became imbued with the idea of conveying some of its depth and color and versatility to others. To some extent this has been done in his books. But these, each one of which has been written and rewritten dozens of times over a period of years before first publication, are only partially representative of his world. They are the weighed and considered product of thousands of quick passages, flashing observations, sympathetic insights, and tilts with prejudice and complacency. To those of us who know him best, he is most alive in motion—in memorable sentences, irrelevancies and fragments, insights, and occasions when he cuts the Gordian knots of daily medical practice.

With this in mind we began to plan this book, as a labor of love, in honor of his sixty-fifth birthday. We recognized the impossibility of conveying the emotional quality of his daily life. But we remembered that there were hundreds of notes and articles written over the years, often for special occasions, often hasty or even impromptu, written under pressure of a busy life, which had been tossed aside and forgotten. No attempt had ever been made to compile them or to relate them to one another. Perhaps if these were brought together and re-read by a committee of colleagues, some pattern would emerge or some suggestion of the quality of the man off-guard would appear.

This we have tried to do. If nothing else is apparent, we believe that the regard in which we hold Karl Menninger and the honor we wish to do him will be clear to the reader.

Karl Menninger happens to be a psychiatrist. He is also a physician, a psychoanalyst, a teacher, a writer, an administrator, a theorist, and a researcher. As a man he is, as well, a son, a brother, a husband, a father, a grandfather, and a Presbyterian. He is, in addition, a militant conservationist, an able historian, a compulsive collector of books, a sometimes serious bridge and chess player, a laboring horticulturist, and an omniverous reader. He is a lot of other things, too.

Since Karl Menninger has written during most of his life about his world, his writings when studied chronologically are biographical. They reveal how he explored his world and what he found there, and what he tried to do with and about his discoveries. The writings show the evolution of his convictions as a man and as a physician.

His world defies compartmentalization. Since he is more than somewhat distrustful of the categorization of anything, it does him an injustice to attempt to classify his writings under headings, but such an attempt has been made here. The result is as arbitrary as he contends any such efforts necessarily are. But, gentle reader, accept the arbitrary categories in which his writings have been placed for convenience of arrangement and for that alone. In everything he writes he is all that he is, not now a teacher and later a clinician or still later a theorist. He is all of these simultaneously.

Karl Menninger was born a physician's son in what was then (1893) a small town in Kansas. As he has been busily growing during the last sixty-six years, so has Topeka. In fact, their lives became closely intertwined. He tells about it in "My Town." He was reared in a home where his parents daily sought to know, to love, and to serve God. There he learned the pleasure of work and there he also learned the pleasure of study. The pursuit of questions of "how" and "why" about the world around him began there under the tutor-ship of his parents, both of whom had been schoolteachers. Such was his curiosity that he entered the scientific world. But the stamp of his parents was to direct him to choose a career which at that time was not considered very scientific. He thought it was, and with time he helped to make it more so.

He attended Washburn University in Topeka, then the University of Wisconsin in Madison, where he was graduated. Later he com-pleted medical school *cum laude* at Harvard University. After hav-ing been commissioned in the United States Naval Reserve Force, he returned to the Midwest to serve his internship at the Kansas City General Hospital. It was during his internship that, still undecided about the direction of his career as a physician, he became interested in neurology and psychiatry.

Medical practice in those times frequently included the diagnosis and treatment of syphilis, which was then a common disease. Not only was it common but it has had the notorious ability to simulate nearly all other diseases. Nearly every differential diagnosis there-fore included the consideration of syphilis. The dictum of the great Osler, "He who knows syphilis in all of its manifestations, knows all of medicine," was such an integral part of medical teaching that it rang from the amphitheater, the lecture hall, and the corridors of hospitals.

During the time that Karl Menninger was interning, the gold-sol test for the diagnosis of neurosyphilitic conditions and Salvarsan therapy for the treatment of these conditions were becoming a part of medical practice. There is perhaps nowhere an excitement that equals the discovery of a specific in medical pharmacology—a specific that makes rational medical treatment possible. And the young physician inflamed by that excitement could visualize its impact upon the future of medicine. He busied himself with the use of these new methods, and his interest in neurology and psychiatry grew because syphilitic conditions of the central nervous system were then a major part of the practice of the neurologist and the psychiatrist. But an even more decisive event was about to occur in his life. Like so many events that shape our lives and spin them irretrievably into a deter-

mined direction, the circumstances of its occurrence appeared fortuitous.

While at Harvard he had, with others, helped establish there a
chapter of the Phi Beta Pi Medical Fraternity. During his internship
in Kansas City he was visited by one of the officers of that fraternity,
Dr. Lawson G. Lowrey. These men discussed the young intern's increasing interest in neurology and psychiatry, and Dr. Lowrey told
of the work that was being done in these specialties at the Boston
Psychopathic Hospital, where he was a staff member. He urged Karl
Menninger to come there to study. The Naval authorities approved
this program, and in July 1918 he journeyed back to Boston, scarcely
aware of what was to happen to him there or how his life was about
to be given a new purpose.

The professor of psychiatry at Harvard University, who was also
the superintendent of the Boston Psychopathic Hospital at that time,
was an unassuming man named Elmer Ernest Southard. Despite his
modesty, he had that quality which when possessed by a good teacher
is a power of inestimable force—the ability to inspire. And Karl
Menninger was at that moment in his life when his future could
be decisively influenced by an inspired teacher. In large measure this
book is a product of the inspiration of Elmer Ernest Southard. He
had a dream of what psychiatry could become. And Karl Menninger
grasped the significance of that dream. The die was cast. For the
rest of his professional life Karl Menninger would be dedicated to
the implementation of Southard's dream. And in so doing he became
a dreamer himself and expanded even Southard's hopes for psychiatry.

Southard was a writer as well as a physician; and his students
wrote. Karl Menninger began to write in Boston. He didn't search
around for something to write about; he wrote about what he was
doing, about his everyday experiences with patients. As he wrote he
studied, and he learned, and he taught, and he developed his ideas.
And a continuity began. In his first paper questions were raised that
would trouble him throughout his clinical career. He continued to
write in his attempt to find answers to those questions.

In the preface to his first book, *The Human Mind,* he describes how he seized moments from his busy life as a physician to write: "One can't stop living to write a book, and I've had to put together this manuscript under difficulties. I have rolled off pages of it in the cabooses of freight trains and in the lounge of the Twentieth Century. Parts of it were conceived in railroad depots and in the wards of the hospital. There are passages that still retain the flavor of the coal-oil lamp on the farmer's kitchen table. There have been so many interruptions. No one but doctors and mothers know what it means to have interruptions."

From the Boston Psychopathic Hospital he returned to Topeka and entered the practice of medicine with his father, Dr. Charles Frederick Menninger. Together they dreamed of the development of a group for the associated practice of medicine, an idea then in its infancy. And Karl Menninger tried something else that was new —the private practice of psychiatry. He called himself a "neuropsychiatrist," as was fashionable at the time. But at first he practiced more neurology than psychiatry, because few people thought of themselves as psychiatric patients. Few people had even heard of psychiatry, and an even smaller number had ever seen a psychiatrist. He soon realized that if he were to help implement Southard's dream for psychiatry he would have to tell people about psychiatry and explain what it is. He began what was to become a kind of career for himself—the interpretation of psychiatry to others.

He taught at Washburn University in Topeka, where he told college students about psychiatry. He talked to physicians about it. He never missed an opportunity to address lay groups about it, and he even interpreted Southard's dream about psychiatry to other psychiatrists. And he wrote about psychiatry.

His first papers are like those of any physician—articles written for professional medical journals about the diagnosis and treatment of clinical problems. But in his earnestness to tell others about psychiatry, he began a different kind of writing. He wrote for medical journals— articles in which he attempted to teach psychiatry to other physicians. In addition, he began to write articles for a different audience than that for which most physicians write—the general public. These were published in popular magazines, and through them he attempted to tell millions of Americans about mental health, mental illness, and the work of the psychiatrist. He wrote books about psychiatry and addressed them to the laity. While teaching a class in mental hygiene at Washburn University he found there was not an adequate textbook for the course. So he wrote one. The result was *The Human Mind,* published in 1930. It probably remains the most widely sold book on psychiatry for the general public that was ever written.

In his early clinical papers he recorded his meticulous observations of various clinical phenomena. He attempted to abstract generalizations from the clinical material that he studied. His attention was directed primarily to the behavioral manifestations of reactions of human beings to infectious diseases. He attempted to find the causes of these behavioral manifestations and found the offending microorganism that caused the infection hardly adequate to explain the patient's behavior. Thus crippled by a lack of theoretical formulations for the understanding of human behavior, he was led to give more than a cursory look at the then not so popular theories which a physician in Vienna had formulated from his own clinical studies of patients. For Karl Menninger, the concept of the unconscious seemed as basic and as practical as Harvey's theory of the circulation of the blood. At last he had a theoretical concept with which he could translate the behavior of his patients into its original meaning and purpose.

He began to look at his patients with new eyes. And he began to see what Freud and others were seeing. Using the theoretical concepts proposed by Freud, he began a series of studies which now would be called psychosomatic studies. He hardly thought of them as that. He was simply attempting to study sick people whose illnesses traditionally had been thought of as physical. However, he began to study the symptoms and signs of these illnesses from the standpoint of their psychological meanings. He made several attempts to study certain psychiatric syndromes, and wrote about a few of these. But his major interest for a long time remained the study of patients not thought of as needing to see a specialist in psychiatry. He discovered the writings of Georg Groddeck and for a time was perhaps more influenced by Groddeck than he was by Freud—a physician taking a fresh look at human suffering with the insights discovered by Freud. As he studied the psychological aspects of a great number of physical illnesses, he wrote about them, and a number of these articles are included here.

When he started the private practice of psychiatry, he had very few patients, but he imagined a practice of psychiatry including many patients. He thought of prisoners as patients. Very early in his career he began to write for his profession, and the public as well, telling them that our treatment of prisoners is primitive, and he spoke of rehabilitation and treatment, rather than imprisonment and punishment, as the intelligent approach to the offender. He thought of students who flunked out of college as patients. He thought about many who suffer and who never consult a physician as patients.

He wondered about the patients who seemed to resist doctors' efforts to help them. And his attention was drawn repeatedly to the recognition that a man is often his own worst enemy. When Freud wrote in *Beyond the Pleasure Principle* about man's destructiveness, Karl Menninger needed no convincing. Freud's formulation of the basic energies available to man made so much practical sense and seemed so obvious that Karl Menninger often has been impatient with those who could not accept Freud's ideas about life and death instincts so readily.

He began to study man's destructiveness, particularly his self-destructiveness. He recognized that few people who commit suicide are ever seen by a psychiatrist, or by any physician, for that matter. But this did not keep him from attempting to understand that peculiar combination of a wish to die, a wish to kill, and a wish to be killed which ends in self-destruction. But as he studied suicide he came to recognize that those who actually succeed in killing themselves represent only a small fraction of the protracted suicides that go on daily. He began to study the partial suicides, and he recognized that many diseases from which man suffers may be in the service of the man's own self-destructiveness. He wrote about his studies, and published *Man Against Himself*. A lot of people read the book, but few of them believed what was written there. It is not a comfortable book to read. It stands as one of the most searching studies of man that ever has been written. He writes that when man looks inward, not all that he sees is flattering.

Never did he forget the other of the life instincts, Eros, wherein lies the psychological salvation of man. Eros, the constructive instinct, was recognized by him as the reason for hope for man, and the reason for the psychiatrist's sustained efforts to help the patient find another way of life for himself. He wrote about it in *Love Against Hate*.

When he joined with his father and brother in the development of the Menninger Clinic he began to put into clinical practice his understanding of the constructive life instincts. With his colleagues he began to develop methods to help patients win their private battles with their own destructiveness. Techniques were developed for using the hospital environment in the treatment of patients; diagnostic and treatment methods using a multi-disciplined team of personnel were formulated for use with both inpatients and outpatients.

Karl Menninger was one of the first physicians in the United States to complete psychoanalytic training—he owns certificate Number 1 issued by the Chicago Institute for Psychoanalysis—and it had a major impact upon his theoretical and clinical work. Psychoanalysis is three things: It is most commonly known as a treatment method; it is also an organized body of theories about human behavior, and as such is also a system of psychology. When used as a treatment method it becomes a valuable research tool and thus enables further knowledge to be added to the theory of psychoanalysis.

While practicing psychoanalysis he became convinced that its theories of human behavior are sound and offer the best formulations known for understanding people with mental suffering. He is always moved to try to teach others those principles about which he has become convinced. Thus he was instrumental in establishing an Institute for Psychoanalysis where others could be taught about it. This Institute was established in Topeka, Kansas; never before or since has there been such an institute in so small a town. Its faculty has taught men and women, many of whom have become leaders in psychiatry and psychoanalysis. During the time he was helping to train psychoanalysts in the Topeka Institute he was also assisting a number of them to develop additional institutes in other parts of the United States.

Because he believed that every psychoanalytic treatment provided an opportunity for clinical research, he made frequent contributions to the psychoanalytic literature based on his clinical experience. He became a vigorous participant in psychoanalytic meetings and was elected president of the American Psychoanalytic Association. Another man might have been content to continue in the daily practice of psychoanalysis, but not Karl Menninger; perhaps he is too restless to remain a practicing psychoanalyst.

Karl Menninger is the champion of the individual; yet he is also mindful of the forest of men. One of the attractions that psychoanalysis had for him was its almost singular emphasis upon the individual patient. More than many, however, he has seen a danger in psychoanalysis—a tendency for its practitioner to treat the few while millions suffer, and he is annoyed by this. Because psychoanalysts are among the best-trained psychiatrists, their services as teachers and clinicians are sorely needed in many areas, particularly in the development of modern treatment programs in the large public mental hospitals. As one of their leaders he has attempted to arouse psychoanalysts to assume a greater sense of social responsibility.

Recognizing the enormity of the national need for psychiatric care, he has often appeared to underrate the importance of psychoanalysis. No one believes more in the efficacy of the psychoanalytic treatment method than he, but he is also concerned about those for whom psychoanalysis is not the treatment of choice.

As a psychiatrist he observed many times that the physician is often not the person who is most helpful to the patient; often it was an attendant, or a gardener, or a maid, or a nurse whom the patient found most helpful. He saw that the psychiatrist's task was primarily to create an environment in which many personnel were available to assist the patient in his recovery. Such experiences affected him deeply—he saw that psychiatric treatment is bigger than any individual physician, that it is a group endeavor. These experiences eventually led him to conceive with others the development of The Menninger Foundation.

Karl Menninger was not content with his accomplishments as a leader in psychoanalytic education. He foresaw that many physicians would not become psychoanalysts and that the greatest contribution of psychoanalysis would be not through its use as a treatment method but through the application of its principles about human behavior. He thought that psychiatrists particularly should learn these principles. Under his leadership psychoanalytic concepts, which for many years were taught only in psychoanalytic institutes to a limited few, were introduced to a large number of young physicians during their residencies in psychiatry. He has pioneered in the belief that these principles can be taught even earlier when the physician is a medical student. Psychoanalysis has since become a basic science for the physician and, as well, for social workers, psychologists, anthropologists, ministers, and many others. And Karl Menninger had a lot to do with this.

By 1938 Karl Menninger was recognized as an able and thoughtful spokesman for American psychiatry, and he perhaps made his official debut in that capacity when Harold Stearns asked him to write about psychiatry for a book which he published in that year called *America Now*. The book was a study of contemporary American civilization and Karl Menninger had come of age as a psychiatrist. Greatly assisted by his efforts, psychiatry had also come of age in the United States.

The years that have followed might well be called "the years of maturity." The essential first steps for the implementation of Southard's dream for psychiatry had been taken. But in Karl Menninger's world, pleasure comes from the expenditure of effort and not in arriving at the goal. He is a starter of things. Southard once told him, "There are lots of people who can finish things; the job is to find someone to start things." *

Along with his father, his brother, William C. Menninger, and others, particularly Robert P. Knight, Karl Menninger could visualize

---

* Gay, Frederick P. *The Open Mind*. New York, Normandie House, 1938.

the potential that The Menninger Clinic could have in developing psychiatry for the public good. He had learned from his pioneering days in psychiatry that as the public recognized what psychiatry had to contribute to the welfare of man, that same public would become militant in demanding psychiatric services. Long before many, he anticipated that a greater public demand for psychiatry was coming and that the profession was ill equipped to meet that demand. And so, under his imaginative leadership, The Menninger Clinic was transformed into a nonprofit foundation. Despite the fact that The Menninger Foundation was financially poor, the members of its staff were inspired, and the fact that that inspiration was put to work in an old barn or an old farmhouse seemed irrelevant.

From the very beginning of The Menninger Clinic, its staff members had engaged in educational and research activities as well as in clinical work. One of the reasons for the inception of The Menninger Foundation was to provide training for badly needed psychiatrists, psychologists, social workers, nurses, psychiatric aides, and adjunctive therapists. And so the Menninger School of Psychiatry was conceived in 1945. By this time others began to see what Karl Menninger had seen earlier and the Veterans Administration was the first to ask The Menninger Foundation for assistance in the training of psychiatrists. Karl Menninger left his consultation office for the office of an administrator—the manager of the new Winter Veterans Administration Hospital. Later, as he predicted, when Kansans were informed about psychiatry and the low status of care in their mental hospitals, those same Kansans demanded of their legislators appropriations adequate to reform the state hospitals of Kansas. So he left his administrative position with the Winter Veterans Administration Hospital to become the chief consultant to the state hospitals of Kansas. He knew that the mentally ill get well through people and that these people, the personnel of the hospital, must be educated for the work. He pioneered the development of educational programs for personnel representing all the disciplines associated with psychiatry.

As he emerged as a leader and a reformer, he also emerged as a theorist. His ideas, derived initially from clinical experience, found their way through the pen to paper as he described methods for the examination of the patient and developed theoretical constructs, particularly ones having to do with our very conception of illness and health. And thus it has come to pass that the practitioners of the latecomer to medicine—the Cinderella of medicine, as Thomas Salmon called psychiatry—may in the end contribute most to the writing of the very philosophy of medicine and thus of health and disease.

But this book is not meant to be biographical, at least not any more so than any man's writings are autobiographical. And the biography is far from complete, because its subject has "a heap of living" to do yet. Many of his theoretical ideas are now being drafted into manuscript form. He hopes to be able to contribute to the changing of the fate of prisoners. He hopes to help to abolish capital punishment. He hopes to help improve our schools. He hopes to pass on to many more what he has learned from his world.

The scene of American psychiatry today is very different from what it was when he began. At that time there were only a few who, like him, attempted to develop it. Now there are many throughout the United States dedicated to similar goals and objectives. Southard's dream remains far from a reality even yet. But there are many more now who have grasped the significance of that dream and have been inspired by it. They may not even know the source of their inspiration. But Karl Menninger knows.

And so, Doctor Karl, we salute you! We, your friends and colleagues, cherish your inspiration and leadership. Because we love you, we want others to know you as we do. We think our words inadequate to tell others about your world. Recognizing that frailty, we have chosen your own words.

—BERNARD H. HALL, M.D.

A
PSYCHIATRIST'S
WORLD

PART ONE

The Man

When a searching curiosity and a restless, boundless type of vigor are mixed in proper proportions and rigorously disciplined, two things result—a staggering breadth of engagements with life and a prodigious productivity. Therein is the secret of the catholic scope of the writings of Karl Menninger. Regardless of his profession, Karl Menninger, the man, might well have written about many of the subjects explored in this section. In some of these writings he states simply his personal views or opinions about a variety of topics. In others he writes with an air of militancy. In still others he essays the philosophical more than the scientific subject.

But these are not the writings of a psychiatrist dislodged from his moorings as a clinician. When he views the masochistic self-concept of the Kansan with a clinical surveillance, he does so not only because of his clinical curiosity but because he is defensive about being a Kansan. Similarly, he explores the sources of our attitudes toward the soil, "the dirt beneath our feet." Often he is stimulated to write about such subjects in an attempt to understand them. What sometimes is even more important to him is the attempt to understand a problem well enough to be able to "prescribe" a solution which will lead to its change and improvement. Once he feels that he understands a problem, that he has an explanation or even a solution to propose for it, he has to tell others about it.

Not always is he precise; he sometimes appears to retreat into an annoying vagueness. Thus he skirts a forthright answer when asked, "What is your favorite tree?" Apparently he favors slightly that graceful giant, the sycamore, but as if avoiding a horticultural favoritism he quickly names other trees and ends with a declaration of fondness for them all.

This apparent vagueness is not accidental. He prefers risking being considered vague to forfeiting his right to change his mind when he is uncertain or undecided. And he changes his mind often.

He will be concerned by the publication of this book. He will be fearful that the reader will fail to recognize, as he well recognizes, that many papers reprinted here do not include the changes he has made in his own thinking as a result of further study and thought. Of all things that Karl Menninger is, he is not orthodox. In one of the Reading Notes he contrasts himself to another by saying, "he is prejudiced against prejudices and I'm prejudiced against prejudice against prejudice!"

For many years now he has made notes as he has read. Certainly nowhere is his broad range of interests more clearly in evidence. He often becomes so excited about what he reads that he must share his pleasure or displeasure with others. These Reading Notes, however, have another origin. Reading for Karl Menninger is a luxury, an activity which must be woven into those precious moments when he is not engaged in some other way in his busy world. But he has to write about his reading to justify the expenditure of time and effort.

In one of these notes he mirrors his deep feelings about "defective" children seen at a Christmas party where he was a guest. His compassion is called forth by the twisted, often contorted bodies of little children sadly different, often grotesquely so, unbeautiful forms of life, dignified all the same in their aliveness. Not all of the creation is beautiful. For him, not to admit this is only evidence of another kind of insensitivity. But the unbeautiful, the different, the lonely, the unloved, the neglected, the forlorn, the forgotten—all belong to the creation and he is their advocate.

With deftness and with gentle wisdom he writes of his reverence for life, the plight of the Indians, the defense of the trapped and hunted animal, the beauty of trees, the majesty of his ninety-year-old father, the meaning of a hospital, and the town of his heritage. Perhaps nowhere is his personal philosophy of life more directly expressed than in two short papers included in this section—"Take Your Choice" and "Reverence for Life." In his world there can be only contempt for the zealous pursuit of peace of mind. In his world, reverence for all things living is, indeed, the highest ethic.   —B.H.H.

1. Take Your Choice

"God offers to every mind its choice between truth and repose. Take which you please—you can never have both."

—Ralph Waldo Emerson, "Intellect"

To me it is a strange and dismal thing that in a world of such need, such opportunity, and such variety as ours, the search for an illusory peace of mind should be so zealously pursued and defended, while truth goes languishing.

Unrest of spirit is a mark of life; one problem after another presents itself, and in the solving of them we can find our greatest pleasure. The continuous encounter with continually changing conditions is the very substance of living. From an acute awareness of the surging effort we have the periodic relief of seeing one task finished and another begun, and the comfort of momentary rest and nightly sleep.

But a querulous search for a premature, permanent "peace" seems to me a thinly disguised wish to die. As I have said elsewhere, in paraphrase of Freud, man is a creature dominated by an instinct in the direction of death, but he is also blessed with an opposing instinct which battles heroically with varying success against its ultimate conqueror. This magnificent drama of conflict sets us our highest ideal—spiritual nobility and social achievement.

For most people in this rugged world, the problems of reality

Reprinted from *This Week* magazine, Oct. 16, 1949.

are sufficient in power and prevalence to preclude all complacency. But for many others it is not the problems of reality or the problems of other people which most painfully disturb peace of mind; it is lovelessness.

Their cry for peace is a cry for unearned love, in the face of the wisdom of Jesus and Lao Tse and many others who taught that we get love only by giving it.

To seek after peace of mind is to forsake this truth for an illusion. It is the *search* to which I object, because striving for personal peace means turning one's back on humanity and its suffering, losing one's life in trying to save it.

On the other hand, peace or something near it is often achieved by those who do not seek it, who, seeking truth, forget themselves.

2. My Favorite Tree

Like many of the previous contributors to this series I feel uncomfortable about naming one favorite from among the many trees I know. I shall feel guilty of a certain disloyalty and unfairness which my friends, the trees, might resent. Trees seem very human to me, not in some fanciful way but in a deeply emotional way. I speak with some diffidence of this emotion because I perceive that there is a wide variance among people with regard to such a feeling. To see a tree chopped down for utilitarian purposes, valuable as these may be, pains me sharply, to the astonishment of some of my friends. The sight of the felling of great trees, which seems to thrill the average movie audience, arouses in me only the most unpleasant sensations, similar to those more conventionally experienced when the hero of a story finally loses his life. Journeys I took some years ago through parts of the states of Oregon, Washington, and the upper peninsula of Michigan left me depressed for weeks: inconsiderate destructiveness as a trait of human beings seemed too nakedly revealed.

As a psychiatrist I am interested in the way people (including myself) feel about things. Reactions such as I have described can be called by different names—sentimentalism, neuroticism, pantheism, totemism, identification. They are bound to be ridiculed by the practical man who regards trees only as so much lumber from which so many useful things can be made. But when I think of the destruction of the top soil and the devastation of floods which

Reprinted from *American Forests*, 56:4, 39, June 1950.

have followed so regularly the application of this "practical" principle, I wonder if it isn't in part an illusion and in part an excuse for cupidity. Recently one of my neighbors—a very "practical" man —cut down a beautiful walnut tree and transformed it into boards for a corral for his horses. I asked him about it, because he is intelligent and approachable. He was astonished that I concerned myself. "A tree is a tree," he said.

Having this deeply emotional reaction toward trees, I cannot name a favorite tree. Instead I shall mention several which are especially endeared to me, but in different ways. The sycamore has always impressed me with its grandeur and its uniqueness. The massiveness of its trunk and the majestic sweep of its branches give this tree a truly grand architecture, unsurpassed by any other tree. The sycamore is also one of my oldest acquaintances among the trees, for its spectacular, dappled branches and white trunk, and the round seed pods swinging from its branches all through the winter, stamped its identity upon my mind during early school days.

Of the less common trees the yellowwood is one of my favorites, producing quite different emotional reactions of an aesthetic sort. Its smooth, clean bark, the airy grace of its foliage, and its occasional display of fragrant white flowers combine to create an effect of delicate beauty. Although it is a hardy little wild tree, it attains its richest beauty of foliage and flowers only under cultivation—a circumstance which is particularly gratifying to the cultivator of trees.

And of the common trees I love the cottonwood because, like us Kansans who have named it the official tree of our state, it withstands both adversity and prosperity. To the thousands who live on the great prairies of the Southwest, the groves of cottonwoods represent "the forests," and often provide the only natural shade for many miles for men and beasts.

I am tempted to mention other favorite trees, for it seems to me that trees, like music, have the power to evoke feelings and moods. And who can name his favorite mood? But I was invited to write a page, not a book.

3. Listen!

Thinking about your seventh annual meeting put me into a historical mood, possibly because this is your second time to meet in Topeka where, recently, we had the annual meeting of The Menninger Foundation. Perhaps, in a way, that is why you are here, because The Menninger Foundation is the present form of a group of people who are interested in doing something that you are interested in, namely, the endeavoring to bring some kind of alleviation or improvement into the lives of people with the kind of illness which most of the world has for a long time shunned and ignored. I say this because I assume that most of you are thinking of therapeutic music in connection with psychiatry. I realize there are other areas in which music can be applied for a therapeutic effect, but am I wrong in thinking that most of the audience are connected with psychiatric therapies?

It is an interesting fact, is it not, that something as important and beautiful, as constructive and helpful as music should have come into the area of the most unpopular, the most feared, in a sense the most tabooed, formerly the most shunned and avoided of all patients? Can you imagine how odd you would have looked two or three hundred years ago offering your services?

You can say, "Well, it happened back in the time of Saul." Cer-

Transcription of a banquet address given in Topeka, Kansas on Oct. 18, 1956, at the Seventh Annual Conference of the National Association for Music Therapy. Reprinted from *Music Therapy 1956*, E. Thayer Gaston, ed. Lawrence, Kansas: National Association of Music Therapy, 1957.

tainly it did. But only here and there through history was there very much reference to it. The general attitude of the public—I was going to say a few hundred years ago but I could almost say a few years ago—was that the mentally ill are talking nonsense and are not reachable by any means of communication that we ordinarily use. And yet, look at you, this great crowd of people, compared to what you were seven years ago. Can some of you remember the first meeting? Can you remember the one four years ago? Can you imagine what this group is going to look like, let us say, thirty years from now? (Some of you will not be here, you know.) Do you think this would be a big enough room for them?

I was thinking in connection with our Foundation last week—and I repeat the same thought—that now you are seven-year-old children and people may say, "Oh! How much you have grown this year!" Well, now we are saying that too, but what one really means—it is rather patronizing—is that you are still just a little kid and do not forget it. Your organization will go through that stage, will it not? You will go through the experiences a seven-year-old child experiences. There will be a joke about someone having lost a bag or a hat. Now these little jokes, so human, so natural, so intimate, in a way so unrelated to the big subject, help make the convention.

These little things are so much more important than they seem because we know each other, we know our purposes, we know our goals, we know our common discouragements, and we are hoping we will gain more self-confidence, more and more strength. We hope to arrive at a point where we will not have to defend that for which we stand. We will not have to keep explaining to people. That will be taken for granted.

Well, suppose it is. What will you go on to next? Have you thought about that? I assume you have. I assume you realize that if the organization is going to grow in doctrine, the substance of what you are doing is going to have to grow. That does not mean merely more therapists, more musicians, or even better salaries, much as I hope you get that, too, but you need some kind of es- sential development in your thinking, in the purposes for which you conceive the special applications of music. You will have to begin to think of what relationship your therapy has to the function of all therapies. You will have to do some studying about this because it is very likely that you take it for granted, as most people do, that music therapy is a therapy added on to an already established body of therapy. Somebody has to remind you, as they have to remind us all from time to time, that the whole question of therapy is a puzzling one.

Exactly what do you think therapy means? Just think to yourself what treatment means. If a child bumps his knee and it bleeds, and his mother puts on a Band-Aid, is this treatment? If you are downhearted or in a bad mood, and the neighbor smiles cheerily at you, is this treatment? Is it treatment when a friend pats you on the back and tries to encourage you? You see, we have to say no to all those questions in the frame of reference in which you and I are operating. Ordinarily we have to limit treatment to that which a selected group of individuals, like yourselves and like doctors, are performing with a specific object in mind to a specifically selected group of people.

I think it is helpful to remember how medicine started. While the normal, healthy, able-bodied people were fighting or working, from time to time, there would be somebody hurt or wounded. Then presumably there must have been some women about, who, having finished with the food preparation, ministered to the wounded men. Now it must have been that there were some old men or weak men who may have helped these women. One can presume that originally the people, at least the men, who were set apart for the care of the wounded and sick must have been men who were helping the women. Later we turned that around, you know, and the doctors got the nurses to help them.

Be that as it may, before long a certain group of men became set apart. Whether it was because they were not strong enough to fight or for some other reasons, these men became interested in ministering to those who were disabled. The sick were already a somewhat extruded group, a somewhat isolated group, and have been ever since, in a way. (To be sick is to be immediately out of circulation, be in a hospital, be in a home, and so forth.) Then similarly, those who took care of the sick became detached, in a sense, from the main body of people, and it is the ministrations of this detached group to the other detached group that began to be the basis of treatment.

You cannot have a patient without a physician. No matter how sick a man is, he is not considered a patient until he has consulted a physician. This is by definition. The treatment begins after he has become a patient. I remind you of this because you can see that for a long time the medical profession did not have the prestige that it now does. It was not popular to be a therapist. After the fall of Greece and throughout the first few hundred years of the Christian era, every well-to-do Roman—and, of course, most Romans were well-to-do, largely through the acquisition of slaves—had his own private slave physician. The physicians were mostly Greeks, occasionally Egyptians, or Jews from the other side of the Mediterranean.

You have to remember that the present status of medicine is something that is bewildering, even to us doctors. While few of us can remember that far back, most of us do realize that medicine came up a very hard way, forbidden, as you know, to experiment, forbidden to make any dissections, any examinations, fought against by various civil and ecclesiastical authorities for a long time.

During the Hasmonaean period of Jewish history, the revolt of the Maccabees, a hundred and some years before Jesus lived, there was written a very famous collection of the wisdom of the Hebrews. This is unfortunately not in the Protestant Bible. It is considered by the theologians a more pious and more spiritual work than its sister book, Ecclesiastes. I am referring now to The Wisdom of Jesus Ben Sirach, or Ecclesiasticus. In this there is a very famous passage sometimes cited in medical journals and at medical meetings entitled "Honor a Physician." It goes on for about fifty verses telling the people why they should honor a physician. Doctors quote this, sometimes a bit sentimentally, showing that the Bible, at least the Catholic Bible, says a physician should be honored.

Some might ask why the people had to be enjoined to honor the physician. What did the physicians do in those day for which the people had to be grateful? They did not have penicillin. They did not even have aspirin. What do you think the doctors did hand out in those days other than consolations? Actually they handed out quite a little, and they got paid rather like small merchants, if they were not slaves. If they were slaves they did it for nothing. If they were in business their fees were regulated by law—a practice which the Jews and Romans took over from the Babylonians who, by law, said how much might be charged for certain procedures. Actually they did not have a great many therapeutic procedures.

Gradually, in less than the last one hundred years, the role of the physician has been changing. Even within my memory the family physician rode around in a little old buggy, not a very prosperous man, usually not one of the wise men of the community, too busy to be on the school board, etc. The family physician was very different in those days from the present-day scientist who knows a great deal about all kinds of antibiotics and who has had training in biochemistry, chemistry, physics, etc., none of which the old family physician had.

Think of therapy, as you know therapy outside of music. What do you think of? You think of penicillin, perhaps. You may think of psychoanalysis, but very likely you will think of electroshock, quinine for malaria, which is not so recent, and you will think of various surgical operations and such. Think of all these things as therapeutic means which physicians have developed. Realize what we compete with when we who believe in it say that music has a place also. Do not you doctors realize what effect music has on you and that it could have a helpful effect on other people? Some doctors do sense that and some do not.

A lot of doctors do not see any sense in psychotherapy. Some doctors do not see any sense in this therapy or that therapy because they have not had personal experiences or observations with it. But you and I have with music. We have had personal experiences. We know we are affected, and we know patients are affected. We believe in it. We believe in it here in Topeka. We use it. We consider this along with various other things that we can do for patients, other than direct medication and other than direct psychotherapy, as helpful to them. Now we still believe this, and we believe it just as firmly as we did seven years ago. We believe it even more so, and we want to see it develop. But I think now we have to make further steps and be a little more specific.

You are established now. It seems to me you no longer have to prove your right to exist, but we have gotten together to exchange views. You have new conceptions of music therapy, new techniques for it. Some of the researches that Dr. Gaston and others of you are carrying on are going to go farther, and you are not going to remain the small, intimate, friendly little group you are now. You are going to grow. There are going to be disadvantages to this, but it is inevitable. There are going to be more people working in the things that you believe beneficial, because you have aligned yourself with this little group, this somewhat extruded group of people working to change the condition of other people.

You are listening to me right now. You think that I am supposed to speak from a great supply of supposed knowledge and that to hand out some to you will change you, but that I will not change. That is as wrong as possible. What happens, you know, is that a two-party situation is always set up so that the person who is doing it may get more benefit out of it than the person to whom it is done. Music therapy, in other words, is something which helps you as well as the patient. Not only is it a way to earn a living, but it is also a way for you to express what you believe is most important.

I have a long poem I was going to read which I read at our Foundation meeting. It is a poem on "listening." I shall not read it, because I would rather do some listening than just read you a poem about it. The meaning of this poem, called "The Eleventh Commandment," [1]* is that when Moses came down from the mountain he had another commandment which he did not put on the stone but he told everyone about it. This eleventh commandment was: Listen! Listen! I think every music therapist should know it by heart. You do something creative when you listen. How well you play the piano when there is someone to listen to

---

* Numbered reference notes begin on page 877.

you play! In listening, you stimulate the other person to do his best. This effect of listening may be one of the techniques music therapists need to develop, since many of us tend to emphasize letting someone else listen to what we do. The emphasis of this poem and the suggestion I throw out is that we have underesti- mated the therapeutic effect of listening.

Recently I was very impressed when a friend who had been quite ill asked if he could not come back and play for me. He did not say, "I want you to see how much better I am." He did not say, "I am better." He did not say anything about himself. He said, "I want to come back and play for you sometime. Would you listen?" I said, "Certainly I will listen." This time I did not hear anything about symptoms, I just heard music. My listening meant a great deal, and it had something to do with the furtherance of his recovery. This kind of experience is an aspect of music therapy that I would like to think about a lot more. If you will read that poem in *Harper's,* which I will not take the time to do now, I will feel that it is a part of my message continuing to you after I sit down. Read it when you go home. It is the Harvard Phi Beta Phi prize poem this year, and its essence is that there are many beautiful things about listening.

This reciprocal effect I want you to think about all year, to see if we are making the most of it in music therapy and whether here is an area that needs further exploration, further development. Not just music appreciation, but person appreciation, not just are we music therapists appreciated ("Do they realize how much good we do?") but do we appreciate what an opportunity this is for our personalities to have their maximum effect and stimulation by the things we have the privilege of doing?

If this sounds a little mixed up, let me put it another way. It seems to me that in every field you have to keep reminding your- self of certain things. I hope you will not laugh at me when I tell you that I try to get out of making speeches. I am not very good at speeches and I try to convince you that I am not. One of these days I will convince you, and then I am going to be very depressed because there will be no one to listen to me.

4. Bleeding Kansas

Sometimes, when I have just returned from the mountains or the seashore, friends who meet me on the street exclaim sympathetically but enviously about my trip, "Were you not sorry to leave?" They ask, "Isn't it hard to come back from such beautiful places into the drab monotony of our Kansas scenery?"

When they say such things I cannot answer them; I cannot even look at them for fear of betraying my thoughts. I look at the ground or I look past them to the horizon. Inwardly I recall the words of a famous Kansan who wrote to his wife on December 10, 1854: ". . . Our food is mush, molasses, and bacon, mixed plentifully with dirt three times a day. Thus we live in Kansas. *A more lovely country I certainly never saw*—and yet it looks worse now than at any other season. I am told by those who know that in the spring and early summer when the grass and shrubbery and flowers appear it is beautiful beyond conception. So I think it must be. And in a few years when civilization by its magic influence shall have transformed this glorious country from what it now is to the brilliant destiny awaiting it, the sun in all his course will visit *no land more truly lovely and desirable than this. . . .*" [1]

This man was one of the truly great Kansans because he had vision, a vision not only for the future, but for the present realities. And he had come to Kansas from one of the most beautiful states in the union, Pennsylvania.

I am well aware that the other side of the road looks smoother

Reprinted from *Kansas Magazine*, December 1939.

and the grass in the opposite field greener, but I believe this inability of some Kansans to appreciate their own state has a far deeper psychological origin. It is observable in so many different ways. I have sometimes called it, in our professional jargon, a characteristic feeling of inferiority. We seem to share it with Arkansas, which is also a beautiful and creditable state, but whose citizens are often ashamed of having originated there. I see the self-depreciation of Kansans exhibiting itself in the form of a sense of uneasiness, an apologetic manner when in the association of representatives of older and wealthier states, and in a tendency to join with them in a bantering ridicule of our state instead of recognizing how much this represents a defense of their own ignorant provincialism. But more serious, I think, is a kind of asceticism, a willingness to accept as our fate and lot a far less comfortable and joyous existence than could be ours almost for the asking. This, too, springs from our self-depreciation.

No one could ask for a better illustration of this than the prohibition sentiment of the state. I know, as everyone else knows, that there are relatively few total abstainers in Kansas, but to keep up appearances we must not buy or sell liquor publicly. We must smuggle it in from Missouri to the cynical but gratified amusement of our less hypocritical eastern neighbors. We comfort ourselves with the logic that because some men are fools all men must be martyrs. The fact that there may be joy in wine is forgotten in the face of the fact that there may be tears in rum. Kansans have no sense of superiority about their prohibition. Some comfort themselves with a puritanical sense of self-righteousness, but it is cold comfort. For the same energies that have prohibited the open sale of liquor would have gone much farther had they been invested in the promotion of beauty, the improvement of highways, the enlargement of parks, the fostering of music and art.

Not but what we have done fairly well with music and art. I am proud of what we have done. But I am afraid that most of my fellow Kansans are not. They are not proud of it because they realize that it is so much less than we could have done had we not had an ascetic disapproval of joy or anything that would make it appear that we were a happy, progressive, successful state. We want to be "bleeding Kansas." When someone calls us a typical prairie state we get angry, not because we think we have been misunderstood but because we fear we have been understood too well and our shame publicly exposed.

I would be happy to believe that our feelings of inferiority are only the expression of an innate modesty, a feeling of revulsion against the flamboyant, bombastic egotism of California and the similar arrogance of a few other states. Unfortunately I cannot believe this. Kansas does not refrain from announcing that it has the best of this or the best of that because of our essential good taste; Kansas does not announce it because Kansas does not believe it. When I tell friends that I think our scenery is beautiful and that our climate is delightful (Cyrus Holliday said that it was better than that of sunny Italy) my friends think I am ironic or a little "touched." They would much rather read in the paper that we had broken a heat record so that they could use it to prove their martyrdom than to reflect that hot weather is the healthiest weather of all and that fewer people die from the effects of climate in Kansas than in almost any other state. Yesterday it was 97 in Los Angeles; it was 70 in Topeka. But I am sure this fact was not headlined by any Kansas newspapers, and I am more certain that it was not headlined by any California papers. Last week New England was ravaged by a terrific wind storm which did more damage in one hour than all the tornadoes have done in Kansas since the dawn of civilized history, but I am sure that this was not noted by any Kansas newspapers nor by any of the eastern newspapers which still play up "Kansas cyclones."

Not long ago the son of a colleague came to me for advice in regard to entering my Alma Mater, the Harvard Medical School. He was afraid that he would not be admitted. I remarked that the fact that he was a Kansan would probably be to his advantage in his consideration by the committee. "Well," he exclaimed, "that will be the first time that coming from Kansas ever did me any good!" I could not think of any reply to this. He was a handsome young fellow, a member of the third generation since the pioneers.

His family has prospered (in Kansas!) and he was as nattily dressed, as sophisticated in manner as the boys I have known from Harvard and Hopkins, and Pennsylvania. But the poor fellow does not know it. He labors under a sense of inferiority which is pitiful. He goes to college with a sensitiveness which will probably make him either a recluse or a noisy eccentric.

I am fairly familiar with the physicians of America, and I can honestly say that I believe that we have within the confines of our state medical men quite as capable as those in most other comparable localities. Ambitiously we endeavor to maintain a medical school, but we do not trust it to be staffed by Kansas doctors. The students of the medical school of the University of Kansas are instructed by men borrowed from Missouri, Missouri doctors from Kansas City.

The phenomenon of the city of "Kansas City, Missouri," is perhaps the most brilliant illustration of my thesis. Poor Kansas City is an orphan town; it has no parent state. Missouri disowns it as a metropolis; St. Louis is the Missouri city, and Kansas City should be the Kansas city, but it isn't. Rather, it is and it isn't. It is located largely in Missouri, populated largely with ex-Kansans, depends upon Kansas for its economic existence, supplies Kansas with traveling salesmen, truck drivers, and racketeers, instructs Kansans how to vote, and considers Kansas its great backyard. Kansans, nonetheless, think it is a great metropolis and speak of it reverently as "the city."

Think of a state smart enough to issue a magazine like this one! Think of a state with people wise enough to abolish capital punishment fifty years ago. Think of a state with people in it capable of erecting a structure like the Santa Fe Railroad or an organization like the Capper press. Think of a state with a Historical Society such as ours. We have heard a lot about wheat, but consider the trees; we are the only state in the union without a national forest, and yet we are also the only state in the union with more trees in it than at the time it was settled. Think of a state with people in it like William Allen White and Ed Howe and Nelson Antrim Crawford, William Herbert Carruth and Esther Clark, John James Ingalls,

Charles M. Sheldon, Kirke Mechem, and W. G. Clugston, Birger Sandzén, and many others. You know this is not a state of mediocrities. The same humility of spirit is to be observed in the Kansas intellectuals, in the Kansas voters, and in the Kansas press. In their eagerness to be broadminded, tolerant, democratic, they have listened receptively to many prophets, some false, some true, and have followed them fervently. This fervent response—a response sometimes bordering on fanaticism—is regarded by many Easterners as characteristic of the people of Kansas. In abolition, prohibition, Populism, antitobacco legislation, Brinkley worship, Winrodism, etc., they have gone off the deep end with desperate seriousness, and in so doing earned for themselves the name of being a humorless, puritanical people, incapable of joy and grudging in their attitude toward those happier than themselves.

This is not a pretty reputation and naturally one shrinks from accepting this description of oneself and his friends and neighbors. Oddly enough, however, we do accept it almost unanimously and meekly endure the opprobrium and ridicule of other states. This I believe to be due to a humility and self-distrust so great as to be crippling to our energies.

For the fanaticism of Kansans is due, I believe, not so much to puritanical self-righteousness, the desire to reform and inhibit, as to a wish to identify themselves with the best, the most idealistic and fruitful ways of life. And because they feel pathetically unequal to maintaining these ideals and to living at the high pitch at which they conceive other more gifted people to be living, they fence themselves about and reinforce their tense strivings with laws and prohibitions.

In discussing Kansans it is usually assumed that their strictness is aimed at coercing other people to their beliefs, to reform the wicked. The reformer's psychology is often described as being a desire to keep others from the sinful pleasures he secretly indulges in or at least burns to indulge in. This unsympathetic portrayal of the reformer as a hypocrite and a dog in the manger has some truth in it; but this very intolerance of the intolerant betrays an unconscious hypocrisy in the hypocrite-hater. To put away the temptation to indulge in more paradoxical but perhaps confusing expressions, let us state it more plainly by saying that at heart everyone is a reformer in the sense that he must curb certain antisocial tendencies in himself which he openly deprecates but yearns to indulge. We say that his attitudes are unconscious because he is not aware of such yearnings and would probably develop all kinds of defensive symptoms if he began to be aware of the strength of unlawful desires in himself. The activities of the zealot who rushes about making life miserable for other people may be considered as one form of defensive symptom of this type. His activity therefore is chiefly directed against himself, in spite of its apparent direction toward the world in general. The world may avoid him, trip him up, laugh at him, and find many ways of overcoming the discomfort he causes, but he has no way of circumventing his own unrelenting harshness toward himself which drives him to take desperate measures to reinforce his failing defense against antisocial urges.

I began by saying that we live in a beautiful state, a state settled by brave, intelligent, and far-visioned people; then I had to add that our intelligence and our vision do not seem to have prevented us from developing a vast inferiority, not a real inferiority but a feeling of inferiority. I related this inferiority to feelings of over-conscientiousness which in turn I think may be an echo of the pioneer struggles of our immediate ancestors. We need writers and artists to proclaim the beauty of Kansas and to demonstrate the intelligence of the majority and not the eccentricity of the lunatic fringe.

The members of the press have a special responsibility in this matter. I have long felt that the newspapers could modify the unfavorable opinions of the outsiders if they would modify the feelings of Kansans about themselves. For the men of the press reflect this attitude of inferiority; indeed they encourage it; they exploit it. They like to brag about breaking heat records and raising freaks. They feel a little shamefaced in writing about our cultural attainments. The newspaper reporters seem to feel impelled to pull a wisecrack if possible, and the desk man would rather think up a funny headline than an accurate one. They deceive themselves into thinking the people like this. The truth of the matter is that too many of the newspapermen do not take their own work seriously. They do not take their state seriously. If the Wichita newspapers, for example, would give more space to the glories of Kansas and less to the iniquities of Topeka; if the Topeka newspapers would give more space to the cultural activities of the city and less to the political goings-on in the State House, and if all the editors of all the papers would read *The Kansas Magazine* and print excerpts from it instead of lifting paragraphs from the *Kansas City Star,* we would have an even better state than we have now, and we would have more fun living in it or visiting outside of it.

5. Orpheus and Psyche

There is no silence; in the secret places of the heart
There is always music. And the merry voices of the leaping past
Ring faintly in the memory, unstilled and unassuaged
By the blaring blasts and the hoarse insistent clangs of now.
Music there is of soul and tones of thought,
Chords and arpeggios of happiness and sorrow,
Dancing and luring and lulling us to sleep,
Oblivious to the world's dumb chatter.

Love moves on with a relentless sweep,
Driving before it man and mate,
Beauty and beastliness and all that separate
These stark polarities of life's endeavor.
What is it to be deaf, or blind, or dull
To the smirking lies of man's communications?
Love has no need of senses, nor has life,
And God is love, and life.

There are those, hampered in the narrow prison of their souls,
Clutching the bars they have themselves erected
Or have permitted to endure unshaken,
Who, finding God at fault in this short measure,
Cry out to heaven—not of the bars that bind their hearts
But of the straw that falls across their path,

Reprinted from the *Volta Review*, January 1924.

This minor deprivation of the senses
Too all-abundantly provided,
And mourned from envy, not from need,
Finding the most of men have more—
Seduced to lay upon the back of Christ
A cross to represent their own infirmity
Of spirit—not of ears!

Nor ears nor stars, "but in ourselves
That we are underlings"!
For there inheres within the powers of self-direction
The crushing of the chains of prejudice,
Of faulty self-restraints, taboos, and predilections,
Freeing a spirit like Prometheus, bound;
Whose powers transcend all deafness of the ears,
Granted a sense of hearing in the heart.

Nor need our love take refuge now in phantasy,
Deserting the market place of life—
The concourse of the burden bearers,
Some of them laughing like Italian girls
Bearing their onerous tasks upon their heads
With unimprisoned souls, and some
Groaning and clamoring underneath a load
Not only self-imposed, but unacknowledged
In its true nature, magnified
To compensate for inner poverty
Of love and joy by heaping up
A pinnacle of pity and
A shrine to ego worship.

Exalting then this lustful adoration,
These mortals cast upon their mates a narrowed glance
Of this suspicion and of hate,
Distrustful, hence distrusted, and the bars

And bolts creak with ominous contraction,
Steadily growing smaller till the jail has crushed the jailor,
Filled with a bitter ego dead of its own disease.

Others, indeed, whose piteous struggles
Within these self-erected or perpetuated bars,
Unaided by escape to love of man or maid
Or task or toil or monument of beauty,
Dash them in agony and pain against unyielding steel,
Steel that the truth can melt though flesh can never break.
Bleeding and bruised and broken in a vast and lonely dungeon,
These are the hearts whose woe and melancholy
Achieve an end of sad despondency,
Cheating the world of some fine flower
Whose seed was planted but whose blossoms
Wilted in an unseen sun.

What though the world can never understand our sorrows,
Our petty deprivations and our lacks,
Our wistful struggles in the race of man?
What if the world can never understand or know or care?
What if—indeed what if?
What do we know of the world's struggles?
The pains and envies, degradations and despairs
Of each and every heart that feels the throb
Of the all-pervading love of life
In a world of obstacles?

Who in this world is altogether free?
Who is not bound by some faint limitation of the flesh,
Some thorn which may well spur instead of stab,
Impelling to success, not mere permission?
This is the great accomplishment of over-compensation,
Vicarious expression of a pain,
Pain that was known to Jesus

Writhing upon a cross, and to David
Crouching within a cave and singing,
"For He remembereth that we are dust"!
What of mere deafness! There is no silence
In the secret places of the untrammeled soul,
Where music of the mind reverberates
Forever.

6. The Dirt Beneath Our Feet: Why Do We Despise It?

I have looked up some early records of agricultural goings-on. It is recorded that:

"Abel was a keeper of sheep, but Cain was a tiller of the ground.

And in process of time it came to pass, that Cain brought of the fruit of the ground an offering unto the Lord.

And Abel, he also brought of the firstlings of his flock and of the fat thereof. And the Lord had respect unto Abel and to his offering:

But unto Cain and to his offering he had not respect. And Cain was very wroth, and his countenance fell.

And the Lord said unto Cain, Why art thou wroth? and why is thy countenance fallen?

If thou doest well, shalt thou not be accepted? and if thou doest not well, sin lieth at the door. And unto thee shall be his desire, and thou shalt rule over him.

And Cain talked with Abel his brother: and it came to pass, when they were in the field, that Cain rose up against Abel his brother, and slew him.

And the Lord said unto Cain, Where is Abel thy brother? And he said, I know not: Am I my brother's keeper?"

About seven thousand years ago, in the era which this incident

Reprinted from *The Land,* Winter 1943. An address given to Friends of the Land in Chicago, Illinois, in November 1943.

describes, perhaps allegorically, three or four cities were arising along
the valleys of three rivers lying between four deserts. As you go
from West to East, there is, of course, the Sahara Desert, then the
Valley of the Nile. At the head of that valley was the ancient city
of On. Then there is the narrow desert between that and the Red
Sea and beyond that the larger Arabian Desert between the rivers
of the Euphrates and the Tigris, near the mouth of which the city
of Ur was discovered. Then there is the large desert of Baluchistan
and Iran, and the Indus River separates that desert from the Indian
Desert farther to the east.

Along these valleys, surrounded by enormous expanses of arid
land, civilization was born. This is a curious circumstance. There
were many more fertile areas, far more richly endowed by nature.
Illinois, for example, or even Kansas, in which I live, or Iowa, or
Massachusetts, or the South of this country, to say nothing of the
Mediterranean areas, offered richer sites. Civilization was born on
comparatively lean land, back there about the time of the murder of
Abel by Cain.

A great deal of importance was going on in these three valleys
around these old cities of Ur and On and Kish seven thousand years
ago. One thing was that the intelligence of the human occupants
rose a notch. Instead of pursuing and killing and destroying and
driving away the wild oxen or the wild boars or the wild asses,
people captured a few of them and entered into a cooperative plan.
They made nutrition a little more available to some of these wild
animals, and the wild animals, in exchange, gave a little milk or
a little service and, occasionally in the case of the males, their lives.
This domestication of animals was probably the first step in the
definite crystallization of what we now call civilization. And at
the same time these people were depending less upon the wild
grasses which they opportunistically plucked as they happened to
find them growing in the moister or more protected areas; they
began to save and store up the seeds of these grasses and subsequently to plant them, and take some care of the soil. Wheat and
barley and millet were definitely cultivated seven thousand years
ago. Rice and oats and rye came a little later.

A third step in civilization was a rude plow probably developed from the old digging sticks. At the same time, the wheel was introduced, a calendar was developed, a written language was formulated and, unfortunately, cities were formed. And this was the beginning of civilization.

II

All my life I have been interested in what might be described philosophically or categorically as "conflict," the opposition of forces; for example, the forces represented by Cain versus those represented by Abel.

What does that mean? Does it mean the country man versus the city man? Conflict between the people who live in the country and the people who live in the city is something actually far more serious than we allow ourselves to admit.

Seven thousand years ago practically no one lived in the cities. Then a few people came to live in the cities and the cities were destroyed. The country remained. Then new cities were formed and those cities were destroyed, and new cities formed. Then wars began and all kinds of cities were formed. New country was discovered, and cities were formed, and the country spread. People moved from the country into the city, and so it went on.

The general trend is for the multiplication of the cities, whereas the amount of agricultural land cannot be multiplied. The productivity of land, on the other hand, can be destroyed; so that there is all the time more land available for cities and all the time less land available for farmers and the countrymen.

Now, from the standpoint of the psychiatrist—and I ought occasionally to speak as one, since that is my profession—the city is a very unhealthy place. Many people assume the farmers must be pretty crazy or they would not want to live on those bleak old farms and do all that hard work, while all the normal people live in the city. The farmers, for their part, think the most of the crazy people must gravitate to the cities, since everything else does. Most of the crime is committed in the cities, farmers say, and why do people want to live where it is so crowded, so uncomfortable? And so on.

These are opinions. What are the real facts? Well, most psychiatrists would say that, however commendable the social impulses
that have some influence in creating the cities, maybe the city
dwellers overdo it a little bit and that, as far as mental health is
concerned, farmers have it all over city people.

But is this really a question of the conflict between the city
dweller and the country dweller? Is it, perhaps, a representation of
an ancient feud between the rancher and the farmer? I happen to
live in the region not so long ago called the "open range," and this
feud between those "cattle people," as the farmers refer to them, and
those "dirty farmers" as the rangers refer to them, is still fresh in
the memories of my mother and father and some of my uncles, and
remnants of the conflict are still observable in local practices. The
conflict between animal husbandry and agriculture has been the
theme of a good many plays and stories, and it is supposed to have
been the allegorical significance of the story of Cain and Abel.

I do not think that is correct, and I want to say why. We have
heard a great deal about it, especially those of us who have been
interested in conservation. The question of the buffalo versus the
hog is still a painful question in Kansas and Iowa. I am not so sure
we made a good trade when we lost the buffalo and got the hog;
perhaps we did. I live in Topeka, in a city to the north of which is
corn country and orchard country; to the east of which is potato
country; to the west of which is wheat country; and to the south
of which is cattle range, for many, many miles. So in my community
we have all four of these elements: the truckers, the orchardist, the
corn growers, and the wheat growers and ranchers. They get along
together just about as well as oil and water or some other four, if one
can think of four kinds of immiscible substances.

I have been interested in their conflicts. I have thought of them
in terms of those elements that are represented by the word "keeper,"
such as keeping and saving and preserving and conserving and
sustaining and supporting and retrieving and so on, in relation to
another list of antonymns such as wasting, destroying, discarding,
and consuming.

What do these mean in psychological terms? How are these

represented in human beings? What should we look for in a human personality that corresponds? That is, of course, a subject of theological disputes and philosophical discussion and has been for many centuries. I will only try to tell you my own beliefs about the matter, and my beliefs as a psychiatrist are largely influenced by the discoveries of a physician, a psychologist, by the name of Sigmund Freud.

Two of Freud's discoveries, I think, are of enormous significance to friends of the land. First, he found that in every human being there are aggressive, destructive impulses and potentialities. These destructive impulses are not limited to certain bad boys, certain wicked men, certain inhabitants of Germany or Japan; they reside also in you and in me and in every human being.

The church, of course has held that for a long time. When I say "the church" I mean not just the Catholic Church but the Christian church and many other churches and Judaism and Mohammedanism. All religions recognize the fact that human beings are capable of being bad; that is acknowledged, and what they do about it is variously prescribed and interpreted. But now, from the psychological standpoint, we are not thinking of this in a moral sense—whether it is good or bad to be destructive. I leave that to you. At any rate, it would seem as if every human being had the same potentialities for destructiveness as every other human being. But certainly some human beings master that aggressiveness and destructiveness much better than others do.

Religion believes and psychiatry believes that there is some point in recognizing this aggressiveness and making a deliberate effort to control it. Some philosophies, such as that of the National Socialist Party of Germany, believe that it is better to exploit it and glorify it; they say that shows you must be powerful, you must be cruel, you must be destructive—that really shows that you are a superman, and so on.

Consider, on the other hand, the other point of view—the faith that such aggressive and destructive tendencies in human beings can be mastered and controlled by certain devices.

The devices differ according to the different schools of thought.

I won't discuss those, but I do point out that perhaps the real question is not farming versus ranching or city people versus country people, but between good farming versus destructive farming, constructive and creative farming versus destructive farming, constructive ranching versus destructive ranching.

Think over the implications of this. Let him who runs read, and he who can think for himself go on thinking. The making of power dams by greedy power and light companies, dams that destroy all the fish, for example, can be done destructively and can be done constructively. You can destructively construct a dam, kidding yourself, perhaps kidding most of the people, but certainly not kidding the thoughtful person that you are doing something constructive—making for the citizens a great deal of power, it is going to be one cent cheaper, and so forth and so on. And meanwhile you destroy billions of dollars worth of fish and fowl and make more mosquitoes. "Who cares?" say those who are destructively minded. But if you are constructively minded, you do care.

I think the Cain-and-Abel conflict is really not, then, a question of the animal husbandry versus farming but a question of the destructive element versus the constructive element. I am the son of a pioneer family, third generation, practically, now, and I was brought up on stories about the pioneers. My mother published a book describing the early experiences of her mother and herself and others, and I am very much interested in the pioneers, and I don't mean it in any disrespectful way if I tell you that I think in certain respects they are grossly overrated. I think they suffered enormously, and I think there were some brave, some courageous, some honest, some industrious and hard-working people among them; but there were also a great many destructive, wasteful, aggressive, sneak-thief, ex-convict fellows among them; and many of them achieved a subsequent glory which they ill deserved.

Horace Greeley made a trip through the West in 1856 or thereabouts, and was particularly impressed by it. Let me quote part of what he wrote then—an unpleasant truth. He stood on land which now is part my farm and he said, "If the Garden of Eden exceeded this fertility I pity Adam for having to leave it."

He went on to describe how excessively cruel the people were to their buffalo, to the cattle, to the oxen who dragged the carts, and how long they made them go without water and how much they seemed to enjoy beating them.

"I noticed with sorrow that the oxen which draw these great supply-wagons are often treated cruelly, not merely in respect to beating and whaling which every human brute delights in bestowing on every live thing over which he domineers, but with regard to food and drink. Here were cattle that had stood in the yoke all that hot, dry day with nothing to eat or drink; and, when they came down to the river mad with thirst, they were all but knocked down for trying to drink. I was assured that oxen are sometimes kept in the yoke, without food or drink, for two days, while making one of these river crossings. There can be no excuse for this. Those which have long to wait ought to be taken off and driven a mile or more if necessary to grass and feed there; at all events, they should be watered at least twice a day. How can a competent train-master—to say nothing of humanity—overlook the policy of this?

"An unpleasant truth must be stated: There are too many idle, shiftless people in Kansas. I speak not here of lawyers, gentlemen speculators, and other nonproducers, who are in excess here as elsewhere; I allude directly to those who call themselves settlers, and who would be farmers if they were anything. To see a man squatted on a quarter-section in a cabin which would make a fair hog pen, but is unfit for a human habitation, and there living from hand to mouth by a little of this and a little of that, with hardly an acre of prairie broken (sometimes without a fence up), with no garden, no fruit trees, 'no nothing'—waiting for someone to come along and buy out his 'claim' and let him move on to repeat the operation somewhere else—this is enough to give a cheerful man the horrors. Ask the squatter what he means, and he can give you a hundred good excuses for his miserable condition: he has no breaking-team; he has little or no good rail timber; he has had the 'shakes'; his family have been sick; he lost two years and some stock by the border-ruffians, etc., etc.

"And it is bad to note that hardly half the settlers make any sort of provision for wintering their cattle, even by cutting a stack of prairie hay, when every good day's work will put up a ton of it. If he has a cornfield, the squatter's cattle are welcome to pick at that all winter; if he has none, they must go into the bottoms and browse through as best they can. Hence his calves are miserable affairs, his cows unfit to make butter from till the best of the season is over. His oxen, should he have a pair, must be recovering from their winter's famine just when he most urgently needs their work. And this exposing cattle all winter to these fierce prairie winds is alike inhuman and wasteful. I asked a settler the other day how he could do it. 'I had no time to make a shelter for them.' 'But had you no Sundays? Did you not have these at your disposal?' 'Oh, yes. I don't work Sundays.' 'Well, you should have worked every one of them, rather than let your cattle shiver in the cold blasts all winter—it would have been a work of humanity and mercy to cut and haul logs, get up a cattle stall, and cover it with prairie hay, which I will warrant to be more religious than anything you did on those Sundays.' "

I wonder if a considerable heritage of that destructiveness is not still to be seen in the way farming is done.

I live in the country. I have no other home. I am impressed by certain things about farmers. One of them is their destructiveness. One of them is their total lack of the appreciation of the beautiful —in the main. There are exceptions. Some of them have an exquisite, sensitive perception of the beautiful which they did not learn in school.

III

A second discovery of Freud's was that self-love, real self-interest, is not opposed to the love of others, as many people think. You can't say, "Oh, they are just selfish farmers." Greedy, selfish people are not so bad, you know; self-love and the love of others can't be made antagonistic that way. Self-love is not opposed to the love of other people. You cannot really love yourself and really do yourself a favor without doing other people a favor, and vice versa.

Really, the thing that interferes with love is not love of yourself but hate, and hate is the common enemy of self-love or the love of anybody else. So all destructiveness is self-destructiveness, and all love is, in a sense, self-love. The new conception of psychology does not get into those endless arguments about when you are unselfish. Are you unselfish if you do a favor for your child, whom you love? Every kind of love is love, and the opposite of love is hate. The concomitant action for love is constructiveness and the concomitant action for hate is destructiveness.

"Am I my brother's keeper?" "Have I got time to pay attention to somebody else?"

Perhaps at the time Cain asked it, this was a personal question. Then it became a moral question, and in 1944 it is a political question. It is very prominent in newspapers of your own city and elsewhere— this question, "Am I supposed to help somebody else? The hell with them. I haven't got time to do that." But you can't divide people up that way. Anything you do for somebody else is a help for yourself, and vice versa.

This is not a moralistic conclusion. It is a psychological conclusion. It does not make any difference to me. I can't live long enough and you won't, either, to know what is going to happen when all the land is ruined. Whom are you doing this for? What does this organization exist for, this Friends of the Land? There will be enough land for as long as you and I live. What is Dr. Bennett so worried about? What are the rest of these conservationists so disturbed about? Use it all up, if you want to. Or do you want to? What is the real motive for conservation?

Well, what motivation, in the long run, will you consider? In all the years since Jefferson proposed this, what has been going on, in these one hundred and fifty years? You have agricultural colleges scattered all over the country. What have they been teaching, for the love of Heaven? What have they been teaching these boys? I don't know. I am a doctor. I don't know what is going on in the field of agriculture except what I read in the paper and my agricultural journals. But I wonder what they teach. What do the county agents instruct them in?

I wonder. And I keep wondering.

Here are a few hundred people, and there are three or four million people in Chicago; and I couldn't find anything in the paper this morning about this meeting. Who really cares about this? Is this a little group of fanatics that I am talking to? I wonder who these people are who are fanatical enough, like myself, to ride a thousand miles or so to go to a meeting and talk about something that is so obvious as conserving the soil, and why doesn't everybody take an interest in that?

Well, as Hugh Bennett said, "The plain truth is that Americans, as a people, have never learned to love the land." Why is this? We were all brought up on it not so very far back. Why don't Americans love the land, I wonder? Because it is dirty, or what? Why must agriculture be, as it seems to me, a life of drudgery, with the farmers sneered at for poor people who have not enough civilization to live in a steam-heated apartment on the North Side? Why must we be taken for poor, ignorant, hard-working drudgery-loving people, who are sneered at by the city dwellers? Or else, why must farming be the hobby of men and women with city incomes who can spend their week ends doing it, as I do? Or else, why must it be a political bludgeon, to be called by a fancy name and used in Congress for obtaining something that most farmers don't want? Why is agriculture obliged to fill those extraordinary roles?

I am just a doctor. I don't know. I don't see how something can be called a bloc that has no relation to the people that make up the adjective or noun that is supposed to define a bloc.

What are the real difficulties in cultivating some kind of love of the soil—saving it, making nice terraces, running these underground plows through it? What is the real question of making people love the soil? Think about it liberally. I have some ideas born out of clinical practice. There is the fact that we now have changed "dirt" to "soil" and to "land," and in a lot of curious puns that one can make they all have meaning. After all, "soil," the same word that we are all now extolling, is also now a bad word— "soiled" and "dirty," and many people believe, and most doctors would rise up righteously and confirm the idea that dirt means disease, that disease comes from dirt and things that are dirty.

Belatedly we have discovered, of course, that a tremendous anti-bacterial element is contained in the soil. When I was a child and worked on the farm and my uncle would cut his fingers and rub them in the dirt, I would tell my father. He was a physician, and he would shake his head and look half-disgusted and say, "It is only a question of time until I have to amputate my brother-in-law's arm." He never did amputate that arm and his brother-in-law got along all right with his wound sterilized by dirt, which I was religiously taught in medical school to take away from the patient immediately, regardless of how much pain it caused the individual to be scrubbed.

What is really the nature of the soil? Is it the dirt? Is civilization largely built on overcoming it, or built up on a taboo of dirt, overcoming a natural affection for it? Is it overcoming a natural affection we have for dirt, for the soil? Is it necessary to be so clean? People come out to see me at my place; oh, yes, they certainly want to see the chrysanthemums and all the dogwood flowers. They take a short walk and come back and sit in the house. "Oh, I haven't got on the right shoes." So what? If you walk on the leaves in the woods you get dust on your shoes. What is the psychology of that?

7. To My Father
on His Ninetieth Birthday

JULY 11, 1952

It falls to my lot with a sadly increasing frequency these days to write some words of appraisal in connection with the passing of a colleague or a friend. At such times I attempt to review in my mind the chief contributions to their fellow men and the pervading spirit of their lives, and set them down on paper. We do this partly to comfort ourselves for our lost friend, and partly to convey to the family a confirmation of our affection and our sympathy.

It is a very different matter to undertake an appraisal of one who is still with us after many years of living and working, and whom we hope to have with us many years yet, without blinking the inevitability of our ultimate separation. This is a far more joyous task and a more grateful one, through the knowledge that what we have to say will come to his living ears as a part of that always unfulfilled debt that we all owe to one another in the way of acknowledgment and testimonial. We cannot live without each other; there is in life a constant giving and taking, and perhaps we too seldom reflect upon the balance of debits and credits until it is too late.

And so it is my special honor and my pleasurable duty to formulate what is in the hearts of my brother and my sister, my wife and myself—and no doubt of many others. But I am the eldest son of

A tribute given at a dinner attended by relatives and close friends gathered to honor Dr. C. F. Menninger. Not previously published.

the man we are talking about. I have known him intimately longer than anyone else. I am more in his debt than anyone else. So I am grateful for the opportunity to acknowledge this for myself and for my brothers.

I have read in the papers and I have heard from the lips of friends and I have seen in the telegrams and letters the many fine things you think my father has done. But we who have lived close to him know so many fine things that no one knows that he has done. The infinitely many little occasions of simple kindnesses, personal thoughtfulness, gentle encouragement, generous giving, and the courage of bearing infirmity with dignity and patience. Not only do I know of all this through observation and through infinitely many contacts and experiences, but I know it deep in the core of my personality. Whatever good my brothers and I may have accomplished, for which we get so many kind words of praise, my father and the two women who have been his wives made possible.

My earliest memory of Father is of his leaving a Sunday afternoon outing, just as we were starting, to take care of a patient who had been hurt in an accident, and who was brought to our cottage. I have many more memories, on the one hand of his taking us on outings into the country and on the other hand of his sacrificing his personal pleasure to his professional duty. Still another early memory is that of my father sitting at his desk at night studying medical books. To study, to be with his family, and to be faithful to his professional obligations were three of the principles that my brothers and I grew up with.

You have read sketches of his life. You know how he first came to Kansas to help found a college and teach, and how, when he returned again to Kansas, he straight off organized a medical study group. You know how he soon became a civic leader, spearheaded the Board of Health in its concern for better public-school hygiene, helped to reorganize the Chamber of Commerce, proposed and developed a nationally famous rose garden, helped in the teaching at our local medical school, and participated in the medical activities of Christ's and St. Francis Hospitals, and in the county and state societies.

You know, too, how he preached the gospel of cooperation by doctors. You have heard that it was the inspiration he derived from the Mayo Clinic that led to the development of the Menninger Clinic. Sometimes I hear him say that it was I and not he who developed the Clinic and the Sanitarium and the psychiatric center. Let me explain to this group of intimate friends why this is not so; it is the essential part of this tribute I want to pay him. When Ernest Southard died in Boston and I returned to Topeka, Father had been in practice thirty years. Most men who had had this much experience and so well-established a career would not have taken kindly to the bumptious, eccentric, and impulsive gyrations executed by a youngster scarcely out of his internship, particularly this youngster. Most men would have said "Do this," "Do that," "Take this case, take that case," "Use this treatment and use that treatment." Not Father. All he said to me was, "Let's work together. I will help you in any way I can. Feel free to leave town as often as you can and see what other doctors are doing; I'll carry on for us here. Attend medical meetings. Take all the journals and read them, and if you write for some of them send reprints to doctors who may not take the journals."

I proposed a laboratory. He was delighted. He had always tried to have one and did the laboratory work himself, but we got Mildred Law! I proposed a secretary, and later an office nurse and a psychologist. With every proposal I made he agreed with enthusiasm.

It happened that, because of my interest in a new specialty at a particularly prosperous time in the world's history, I almost immediately got quite a few patients of my own, and sometimes my income during those early months was almost as great as his. With the magnanimity and maturity and dignity and the real love that characterized him, he reacted not with envy, or discomfiture of any kind, but only with pride and pleasure.

Having seen many young doctors since then, I can visualize now how arrogant and presumptuous and cocksure and self-centered and really ignorant I was. When I think of some of the mistakes I made, I marvel at the patience and gentle forbearance of the most wonderful partner a man ever had. I remember some times when, through some error of mine or some decision of the Almighty, things looked very dark. I remember that at those times he gave me from his wisdom and experience the greatest comfort that could be received. I have quoted some of the things he told me in those early days to many successive waves of students, who will, I am sure, pass them on to their students and their children so that, without his knowing it, Father's words are probably already immortal.

I have often wondered in recent years how Father could have put up with me. But he did more than put up with me. He encouraged me and counseled me and helped me. "We must work together," he always said. "Let us do it thoroughly, honestly, and the best we can. Let it be said that anything the Menningers undertake to do, they do well." Having made these points, my father crystallized the spirit of working together in a group by the most magnificent and eloquent self-effacement. He stepped quietly into the background. He surrendered everything he had done, every personal ambition, to the goal of having a group of doctors working together with one purpose.

It is this capacity for living in the present with an eye to the future but never a glance to the past that has made him actually, really, truly, the founder and spirit of the Menninger Clinic. More than anyone else I know, he is described by the passage so difficult to understand, but so true, "Let him who would be the greatest among you be the servant of all."

I do not believe my father thinks of himself as "the servant of all." I do not think he thinks about himself at all. He is just interested in the infinite phenomena of life, in learning all he can about it, and he loves to examine it piece by piece. He is the perennial student, and the greatest naturalist I have ever known, but this preoccupation with the details of nature has never kept him from having a warm personal interest in every human being he meets. He is as gentle and kindly and gracious in talking with a stranger or a friend as he is in his gentle, warm, personal handling of a chip of rock or a rose or a shell.

Recent studies by scientists into the processes of aging have reversed some popular notions about the progressive loss of our natural powers. It has been observed that some individuals continue to grow as long as they live, and that after sixty years some powers are actually greater than in earlier years. I think my father illustrates this phenomenon. Physically, of course, he is not quite as strong as he once was, but his memory remains resonant. His interest in everything in the world continues unabated. His reverence for the mystery of the universe and its Creator deepens.

I want him to know from my lips what my brothers and I trust he has long since realized from our actions, that he is the great inspiration of our lives—ours and many others'. Each of us could say that our highest ambition can be only to reach the age of ninety with our vision as undimmed as his, our purposes as unchanged, our affection for God and his creatures as unswerving. And I hope that then—or even now—my children and grandchildren and foster children can feel half as fervently and tenderly toward me as we, today, feel toward our father, Charles Frederick Menninger.

8. My Town

My name is Karl Menninger. I'm a doctor. I'm here in New York attending a medical meeting. I live in Kansas, but I have also lived in Wisconsin, in Boston, in New York, and in Chicago. For a long time now I have lived in the Kansas town in which I was born. It's my town. I would like to tell you about it.

My town is Topeka. It's the capital of a great state. Topeka was founded ninety-nine years ago this very day by a shivering group of ten idealistic young men who had spent the night in a crude log cabin on prairie-grass beds. After they had viewed, as they recorded, "The beautiful conformation of the land spread out before us," their chairman sat down upon a sack of flour and they drew up the Articles of Association. That night their cabin caught fire and burned to the ground.

The young Pennsylvania engineer who sat on the sack of flour had previously surveyed Minnesota and Missouri before deciding that Topeka was the most beautiful and promising area for the development of his dreams. He planned the city of Topeka, and he planned a railroad to run north to Atchison, and west across Kansas, *maybe* as far as Santa Fe, New Mexico. His friends laughed at this, and considered him a visionary fool. But Cyrus K. Holliday was a genius, and his railroad and his city have outgrown even his vision.

Topeka isn't a very big town. When I was a boy, we used to

An address given on Dec. 5, 1953, over the radio network of the National Broadcasting Company. Reprinted from the *Menninger Quarterly*, Winter 1954.

watch the census figures and look forward to the time when we
would pass thirty thousand population and be a big city! It is more
than triple that now, but it is still not a big city! I hope it never
will be. Sometimes I wish it were only thirty thousand again.

My parents were pioneers in Kansas, and in Topeka. They came
west because of certain ideals. This part of the country was really
developed by idealists, you may remember. It was tough going
then . . . pretty primitive. Lots of hard work. Not many amuse-
ments. But lots of hope.

Not many streets were paved in my town when I was born. I can
remember the mud. My father was a real horse-and-buggy doctor,
and I often rode along with him on his calls. I can remember the
horse cars, too . . . and the buggies and gigs and phaetons and
carriages. The pioneers planned wide streets for Topeka, and planted
lots of trees along them. They seemed big to me, even when I was a
boy, playing under them or climbing them. And lots of trouble
to trim around when we mowed the lawn.

In those days, our town was a publishing center. The state capitol
was here and the headquarters of a great railroad. But printing and
publishing and education—they were our local pride. I have forgotten how many millions of copies of our papers and magazines
go out all over the world every month.

We still publish and we still have the Santa Fe, and the Rock
Island and Union Pacific and Missouri Pacific, too. We have an
airport and some factories and a county lake and a big air base
and a supply depot and a municipal university. Several insurance
companies head up in Topeka. It is surrounded by beautiful coun-
tryside of fertile farms and ranches. (And, by the way, we do *not*
raise wheat or pump oil—that's farther west and south. We grow
alfalfa and apples and beef and chickens.) Pretty country. Hillier
than you think. Out of my office windows I see trees and meadows
and hills in the distance; summer and winter, there are birds flitting
about near the window. I like that kind of an office.

When I was a boy, my brothers Edwin and Will and I used to
dream of organizing a sight-seeing bus for Topeka such as we had
seen in San Francisco and Salt Lake City. We thought we could

meet people at the railroad stations and give them quite an interesting tour. We knew about some sights that most visitors never saw. Interesting too. We could show them where they trained Dan Patch, the great race horse. We could show them an oak tree all twisted around with a hackberry. We could show them an elm tree that reached out nearly three hundred feet in all directions. Biggest elm in the world, we thought.

We could show them a haunted house and several Indian graves and the Mound, where old Jim Burnett used to live; he was an Indian that weighed four hundred pounds and had a pony that pulled him in a cart without reins. We could show them the old Underground Railway stations—two of them. We might even take them by the insane asylum. That was a mysterious place where most people never ventured. It had a big wooded park around it, and some of us fellows had been in there, hunting walnuts or just peeking at the wild men. We had seen the great stone castles with the barred windows. Occasionally we actually saw some of the "crazy people," marching along in groups with guards beside them who motioned to us to stay back. It was scary. But quite a sight.

That was a long time ago.

I sometimes feel as if my boyhood dream about running a sightseeing bus had almost come true. Hundreds of vistors come to Topeka today—I guess I should say thousands. People come to consult our great historical library and museum and they come to speak at our university and they come on business and to conventions. But perhaps most of them come to visit our hospitals, especially our psychiatric hospitals. Several of our people do little else but show visitors around, every day. We might go with them for a few minutes tonight, if you like.

I am sure that they would show you all the things I have mentioned; and our beautiful high school and churches and pretty homes and lawns and our municipal rose garden that my father started, and the new library and the Kaw River. They would show you a lot of things.

But finally, they would get around to showing you our hospital. It is funny how this little publishing town, this railroad town, this state capitol town, should have turned into such a hospital city. There is the big Santa Fe Hospital and the tuberculosis hospital and the fine Catholic hospital. We have one of the finest medium-sized general hospitals in the world, really owned by the city although it is a private hospital. The farsightedness of the Episcopalian pioneers who set aside the ground, plus the generosity of one of the early doctors and the vision of Dr. Merrill Mills, our senior surgeon, were supported by the contributions of every citizen of the community. Then there is a private psychiatric hospital, too, which began twenty-five years ago, and is just completing a new building that has all the modern features that could be discovered anywhere in the world. We are proud of it, too, because it was contributed to us, contributed by people all over the United States.

Then I am sure that your guides would show you the Winter Veterans Administration Hospital because it is kind of special. General Omar Bradley and General Paul Hawley started a training program for young psychiatrists at this hospital right after the close of World War II, and more of those young doctors have been trained here than in any place in the world. This training is still going on, too, in spite of the fact that the old Army-hospital pavilions are just about to fall down. With nearly a section of land to build on, however, and an appropriation from Congress last year, there will be a magnificent new psychiatric hospital there to replace the old one, and it will still be the Veterans Administration's chief training hospital. Lots of people come to see it.

Your guides would probably tell you how thousands of people moved to Topeka to help operate this hospital, to take care of other thousands of people who came to Topeka to be cared for in it, or to study or attend lectures. They will probably tell you how many thousands of Topekans—businessmen, housewives, college students, store clerks, lawyers, and plumbers come out on Saturday afternoon and Sunday and evenings and mornings and holidays to do volunteer service. Some have given over seven thousand hours service to it, and twenty-seven organizations have regular working representatives. One of our volunteers, who has come for seven years, is blind, and one comes out in a wheelchair.

It's the same at the State Hospital. And I'm sure our guides would take you over to see that. Because it is a part of the system. Topeka is the only city in the world, I guess, where the federal government and the state and the county and the city and private organizations all work together cooperatively and harmoniously in one integrated unit.

You will be surprised when you see our state hospital. Its buildings are pretty old but its beautiful grounds look like a college campus. You'll be welcomed and you won't see any wild men walking around with guards. You will see lots of people out on the grounds, playing baseball, sketching on easels, sitting under trees talking, mowing the lawns, making bouquets from the garden, or picking strawberries, nurses in white here and there. You would even see children playing around on the grounds, too, because there is a Children's Department. You won't believe these are patients—but most of them are.

You will have a hard time parking because there are lots of cars there now. Didn't used to be *any*. There is an Out-patient Department where people from all over Kansas come for psychiatric advice, without any implication of their being called "insane" or some other damning word. And relatives of patients who were once frightened away and discouraged from coming are now encouraged to come, and often. The patients give parties for their relatives right on the wards, and a good time is had by all. This makes for a good deal of popular education, too. There is a big canteen on the hospital grounds; people lunch in it and have Cokes and coffee, and the Junior League girls of Topeka are the cooks and waitresses. Good food, too. There are tree clubs and bird clubs and sewing classes and art classes among the patients. A professor of music from the university comes down every week end and supervises a staff of musicians and musical programs which have been organized in various parts of the hospital with an orchestra and a band and various choruses and quartets. Oh, it is a lively place, the State Hospital! And it is a part of the community. That's the important thing.

For example, you know how at Christmas time some towns have

a municipal Christmas tree. Well, in Topeka our municipal Christmas tree is located on the State Hospital grounds! It has a big Santa Claus on top, and the patients help decorate it. At the foot there is a big box and the people of the town drive through the grounds to see the lights and the Santa Claus, and they drop gifts in the box, thousands of them. Every patient gets presents at Christmas.

Some of our patients at the State Hospital only sleep there; in the day time they work in various stores and factories and hospital kitchens and other places. This is often the first step in their moving out of the hospital and returning to normal life. For from that institution, formerly called the insane asylum, now the great majority of our new patients leave within twelve months to return to their homes or to useful work. And the people of Topeka know this, now. They know that most mentally ill patients get well if they are treated right—treated with kindness and patience and love and skill, not only by doctors and nurses and aides and therapists but by the whole community. The people in my town are no longer afraid of patients. They know too many of them. And they feel responsible for them.

Some of our patients have been in the hospital for quite a while, so long that they have almost forgotten how to live outside. So, when they do get well, they are a little shy about various social amenities. A group of women in our town started a club for patients who were soon to leave the hospital, to help retrain them in social living. The club meets at the homes of various women about town for teas and luncheons and little parties. They have lots of fun relearning how to be with people in the outside world. Its originator, Mrs. George Bishop, was written up in the *Ladies' Home Journal*.

But she is only one of many citizens who have discovered that it is not only the sick people who are benefited when a town becomes interested in psychiatric illness. There is something about work with sick minds and hearts that makes ordinary people more sensitive to suffering, more tolerant, more human—even to each other.

They discover that love cures people, the ones who receive love and the ones who can give it, too.

I don't mean to say that the people in my town are better than the people in your town, but I think we are better than we used to be, partly because of living so close to our sick people, and seeing them get well, with such a little help from us.

The thing I am trying to emphasize here is that it is a two-way process. There is a woman in our town who for years led the life of an invalid, although she wasn't any one's *patient*. She never went out socially but stayed at home, lonely, frightened, and depressed. She heard about the club I was describing and somehow they managed to get her to invite them to her home. She was so amazed that these nice people were actually mental patients that she became one of the regular sponsors of the club, and went everywhere with it. Well, in the course of things she regained her own mental health completely and has a real zest for life now and takes part in lots of other things. The patients themselves catch on to this phenomenon, and feel proud to think that the ones that are helping them are also being helped by it.

At Winter Hospital we have a nationally known artist who gave up her personal career in favor of teaching painting to our patients. The chef of one of our hotels was badly burned one day through the clumsiness of one of our patients who was working as his helper, but before he was taken to the doctor for treatment, he took time to comfort the patient and assure her that he knew it was only an accident and could happen to anyone and for her not to feel bad.

I was buying a suit recently and noticed one of our patients sitting in the corner of the store, doing nothing. I asked the manager about him, and he said, "Oh, yes, I hired him; most of the time he is a pretty good clerk, but the last few days he has been a little depressed and hasn't done much. But we'll carry him along, and he'll be back on the job shortly."

There is a leading banker in our town who is now one of the officers of The Menninger Foundation. I have often heard him confess, in his earnest appeals to audiences in other cities, how he used to scoff at the whole psychiatric business. He tells his listeners that they will wake up some day, as he did, and realize that the stone rejected by the builders has become the head of the corner.

Just before I came here I was walking through the State Hospital and I saw one of our local store owners helping a group of patients make Christmas decorations. His downtown store was jammed with shoppers, I am sure, right then, but that didn't interfere with his regular weekly visit to his group at the State Hospital.

I can't prove it, but I am pretty sure that when people overcome their fear and prejudice against mental illness, they become healthier-minded, and hence more tolerant in other ways. None of our hospitals makes any differentiation with respect to race or sex or color among patients or employees or volunteers. This came about very naturally. It rubbed some people the wrong way at first, but no one stopped coming and I think everyone likes it better now. They are even proud of themselves.

I am proud of them, too. I am proud of all this, and grateful, too. Because, as you see, the people in my town have been very good to me. I mean they listened to what we told them a long time ago, and there is nothing so nice as to have people listen to you! Oh, there were some skeptics and scoffers; it was kind of tough sometimes in the early days. And, to tell the truth, we didn't think of ourselves as missionaries. It was a good town and my brother and I wanted to come back here to it, after living in the East a while. We have been as surprised as anyone else at the result. We didn't start out to convert anyone.

We just started out with an ideal. It was mostly my father's. He celebrated his ninety-first birthday last summer, and everyone loves him. They've named a street after him in Topeka, and talk of naming other things for him. Long ago he had the ideal of doctors working together. He said if we would work together and strive for the highest standards, people would be grateful and come here from everywhere. He used to be a general practitioner, but way back before 1918 he had been specially interested in psychiatry. He greatly admired the wonderful Ernest Southard of Harvard.

Southard believed that people who recognized their own mental problems and tried to do something about them were often the finest and wisest people in the world. Something can be done for *them*.

The ones to worry about are those who don't ever suspect *themselves* of any mental infirmity but are always sure that it is all the *other* people in the world who are crazy or wicked or disloyal. Some of these people whom no one calls crazy might well be locked up somewhere for life; it might prevent a few kidnapings and other crimes. But a long way from Topeka, if you please; because our conception of psychiatric hospitals here is not confinement; we think they are places to get well in, places in which to be treated, places in which to learn to understand one's self, to learn how to live.

It may strike you as odd for me to call psychiatry learning how to live, but all you have to do to realize how many people don't know how to live is to look about you. And a good many of them do come to us. One out of every twelve children born in this country goes to a mental hospital some time during his life. That's about two hundred and fifty thousand people a year somewhere in our country. One out of every two patients going to a doctor or to a general hospital for what he calls a physical illness is suffering from a condition which is at least partly mental. It costs us more than a billion dollars a year in tax funds just to take care of these patients as inadequately as we do now. All this is to say nothing about crime and vandalism and juvenile delinquency and industrial sabotage and absenteeism and drunkenness and divorce, all of which we psychiatrists regard as evidence of not knowing how to live very well.

It is an awareness of these problems that has sustained the members, governors and trustees of The Menninger Foundation in their efforts to develop in Topeka a center of psychiatric work—treatment, education, and research in the field of mental illness. I have said a good deal about the help my fellow townsmen have given me. I haven't said much about how the people of Milwaukee and Chicago and Los Angeles and San Francisco and Dallas and

Houston and Minneapolis and Wilmington and New York and
Washington have helped us. I haven't described how our governors and trustees come to Topeka regularly for our meetings,
sending their money ahead of them and after them. And I haven't
said much about the visitors from Canada and Peru and Baghdad
and Siam and Calcutta and Copenhagen that keep coming all the
time to see what we are doing or to join us for a time in Topeka.
I haven't said much about my father, who inspired all this, or
about my brother Will, who has always been my partner. He has
devoted himself for the last few years to the *national* community
—trying to show perceptive men and women in business, industry, medicine, and the home that psychiatry is *their* business—not
the esoteric specialty of a few doctors, but the proper study of
all of us by all of us.

I haven't mentioned our American psychiatric colleagues who
have given us so much help by visits and lectures and counsel.
Nearly five hundred of them are members of The Menninger
Foundation. I haven't said much about the professional men and
women on the staffs of our clinics and hospitals in Topeka, who
carry on all this work. When they are not working, they are playing in our Civic Orchestra or acting in our Civic Theater or teaching in our Sunday schools or working in our Art Institute and
our Audubon Club and our Parent-Teacher Associations, and all
the rest.

What I have been talking about has been the joint and united
effort of all these people. There are over ten thousand of us in
Topeka directly connected with psychiatry, either as patients or
relatives or as doctors or nurses or aides or secretaries or gardeners
or something! There are ten thousand more who are indirectly
connected with us in helping people to learn to live and *indirectly*
learning to live themselves.

So you see Topeka has changed since I was a boy. It has become
rather psychiatric. But I don't believe even our worst enemies would
call it a "crazy" town. No, it is a pretty nice town. It is a friendly
town. It is a busy town. It is an intelligent town. I love it. When
I finish with this broadcast, I'll get on the train and go back to it.

It's where I belong, there with those "dear hearts and gentle people, the folks in my home town."

My father had an idea and an ideal; my brother and I worked at it, but *everybody* helped develop it. We're all proud, together. I couldn't begin to tell you how many people helped. Still do. I'd like to call out some of their names over the radio right now, and say, "Hello, Dave! Hello, Laird! Are you listening to this? Have I told the story right? This is the way we did it, isn't it?"

But I can't call all the names; there are so many. Some of them are asleep now; some of them are lying in our Mount Hope Cemetery. That includes my mother; she helped, too; still does.

And, since last Monday, it includes my wonderful father.

It includes some of the fellows with whom I picked up walnuts out there on the grounds of the "insane asylum," a long, long time ago.

Well—that's our town. I am proud of it. This is my tribute to it. We grew up together. It has changed in half a century—so have I. Psychiatry has changed Topeka, and perhaps Topeka has helped to change psychiatry.

We have no "insane asylum" any more. We have a psychiatric community, in a wonderful American town. Come out and see it sometime!

9. The Meaning of the Hospital

Among the dualities that characterize our universe—light and dark, heat and cold, up and down, good and bad—perhaps the most all-embracing is the duality of substance and meaning. We sit in the shadow of a building which is called a hospital; it has a purpose, it has a history, it has a form and structure that we are proud of. These bricks and windows which were once a dream—a long, long dream—have assumed a reality, a reality which will last longer even than the dream. Before the bricks and the mortar came the vision and the faith; but with the bricks and the mortar here, there is still vision and faith.

For even as we sit and look at these walls, and touch them with our hands, walk upon the solid floors, and admire the physical beauty, we know that all this is not the hospital. Like the corrupting mortal flesh in which eternal spirits are housed, a hospital building is only a shell in which the meaning of a hospital can be realized.

So what is the meaning of this hospital? The meaning of this hospital is embodied in the fabric of the personalities, the human beings who work together in it. I wish it were possible to convey this in realistic terms, this service in the spirit of love. I wish I could make a montage of pictures that would convey the real spirit, the real totality of an infinite number of homely details. Can you see a kindly nurse bringing a glass of water to a restless patient?

Words spoken at ceremonies dedicating the C. F. Menninger Memorial Hospital on May 8, 1954. Reprinted from the *Menninger Quarterly*, Summer 1954.

An aide smoothing a pillow? An engineer trudging through the corridors checking the heat? A secretary patiently typing long records? A therapist listening to labored piano lessons, or untangling a snarled loom? A doctor checking a blood-pressure reading? A buyer hunting a place to park downtown in order to buy two pairs of stockings, four shades of lipstick, a pair of blunt-end scissors? A waitress faithfully wiping the surface of a hundred plates? Of course I haven't touched upon some important things—no mention of psychotherapy, or electroshock, or research. But you see I *have* touched on *the* important thing. It is such people as these, who have caught this vision, working together to help somebody get well, to help him to help himself get well. That is what the hospital is.

And I don't mean only those who dedicate their lives and their daily work to the relief of suffering and the development of human potentialities. I would include those temporarily incapacitated fellow human beings whose earnest efforts to make use of the help that is offered them combine to make up the spirit of cooperative human endeavor that constitutes the meaning of a hospital.

Time was when a hospital was a place in which to die. It was not a place of mercy and of healing, but one of endurance, charity, and pity. But the meaning of the modern hospital is quite different. It is no longer an asylum, no longer a pest house, no longer a hotel on the way to God. It is a beacon, a lighthouse—and, for all its scenes of suffering, it is a place of joy. It is a place in which people come, not to die, but to cease dying—a place in which to get well. Temporary refuge it may be, and, in another sense from the original, truly a "hotel of God"—a way station, not on the way to death, but on the way to life.

Nevertheless, some day its strong walls will crumble, and what we look upon so proudly today as new and fresh and beautiful will be old and worn and tawdry. Some of the folks here then will be saying, "What shall we do with the old building?" "The old building," they will call it—the low-vaulted past, for which a new temple, nobler than the last and with a dome more vast, will be in the making.

We shall be gone by then, most of us. But the meaning of the
hospital will outlive us all. It will outlive this building—it will
outlive the memories of this glorious opening day. The vision and
the faith of a kindly man, who loved rocks, and flowers, and trees,
and shells, and books—and, most of all, loved people and believed
that they could help one another—this vision and faith carried on
by a thousand sons and daughters—this will live forever.

The meaning of this hospital can be said to lie in the answer
to the question, What difference does it make? What difference
will this hospital make in the lives of the people that come here
to be helped? What difference will it make in the lives of those
who come to help? What difference will it make in the lives of those
who have already helped to make *this* possible? Who can find words
in his heart to answer such questions? Who would trust his imagination to go far enough in envisioning the possibilities? What
calculating machine would be powerful enough to compute the
total worth of the lives which will be revolutionized here by help
received, or by help given, by lessons learned and by lessons taught?

As one contemplates the vista of human potentialities, of hope
made real by love, its solemnity and awesomeness sobers one for
a moment, even on a joyful occasion. I hope it will not sound ir-
reverent if I say that in a sense I feel as if we stood upon holy
ground. The faces of friends pass before me who could not be here
for the opening of this hospital, but whose lives helped to determine its meaning. In spirit they are here—John Stone is here, Sam
Cobb is here, Dick Hall is here. And my father, Doctor C. F.—I
am sure he is here. Two years ago, on the occasion of the ground-
breaking ceremony for this new hospital, my father made this
prayer: "Almighty God, Father of mercies and God of all comfort, we believe that Thou hast put it into our hearts to erect this
building for the help and healing of the children of men. Look
upon us with favor, we pray, as we dedicate it to that end. Bless
all who come here sick and troubled. And bless, we pray, all who
labor here to relieve affliction. Direct us, we beseech Thee, with
thankful hearts, in Thy way of righteousness and peace, and to
Thee be glory and praise, now and forevermore. Amen."

Some of you were not yet born when they began thinking about this hospital, this new and beautiful building. Thousands of hours of planning and tedious re-planning by them and others here—especially Miss Mildred Law—have gone into this wonderful building. It is well built, it will last a long time.

10. Looking Backward

With due recognition of my grey hair, which always surprises me when I see it in the mirror each morning, they have assigned me the task of directing your thoughts backward in time toward the traces of our development as a Foundation. I shall try to do this, alternating inconsistently—I fear—between justifiable pride and becoming humility, for one must have both.

Where shall I begin? With the part most of you remember—the end of World War II when the Veterans Administration (and many others) suddenly awakened to the need for training more doctors in psychiatry, which we had urged in vain for ten preceding years? Shall I begin with General Hawley's appeal to us to help him in his magnificent program of nation-wide graduate medical training? With the subsequent development of the Winter Veterans Administration Hospital and the Menninger School of Psychiatry, including the transformation of the Topeka State Hospital?

But all this part of our history you know—it is still all around us. I will go back another five years—to 1940. Jean Menninger—and later Maurice Finkelstein—had had the inspiration and vision of our conversion into a nonprofit corporation, and it was in this year finally organized. Then came the war; Dr. Will and many other staff members and employees departed for the services and at the

Remarks made at the annual dinner meeting of The Menninger Foundation, Oct. 21, 1951. Reprinted from the *Menninger Quarterly*, Spring 1952.

same time the flow of patients increased. All construction had been stopped by the war but through the genius of Mildred Law, a garage, a hotdog stand, and a barn were combined into an office building. The same year the stockholders and partners decided to offer all of their possessions to The Menninger Foundation as a gift.

But all this you know, too. So let me start farther back, twenty years earlier, when first Father, and then I, and then Dr. Will and Mildred Law and John Stone were starting in a very humble way something unheard of in the midwest, a psychiatric clinic. With the help of David Neiswanger, Sam Cobb, Dick Hall, the Neeses, and some generous but skeptical fellow citizens, we occupied a farmhouse on a hill, in a cornfield at the edge of town. It was slow and painful going at first, and the community of Topeka regarded it as amusing, absurd, preposterous or damn-foolishness, according to their lights and tolerance. Psychoanalysis, for the official recognition of which Topeka became responsible over an area comprising all the states west of the Mississippi, was considered a fad, a fraud, or a farce—again according to various interpretations. The dignity and sobriety of our Robert Knight, Charles Tidd, and other psychoanalysts did something to counteract these notions.

It was not until 1933 that the American Medical Association designated the Menninger Clinic a psychiatric training center and young student doctors began arriving, some of whom have since become leaders in American psychiatry in various parts of the country. Some patients and employees began working together to remodel the old cow barn on the grounds into a recreational center and Adjunctive Therapies Building, which was to serve its new purpose for seventeen years and in so doing demonstrate an ideal that has gone round the world and come back to us in 1951 in the form of a brave new building.

This is recent, too, however, for if we look farther and farther back, we see a handful of men, camping in tents at a point about half a mile north of where we sit together tonight. It was a little later in the year than now, and much colder. One of these men had big ideas, and was considered a fool—by fools. But the fool was a leader, and a man of vision. Here, he said, is the best place

for a city. And Topeka was thus born—ninety-seven years ago. But
even Cyrus Holliday little dreamed, I am sure, that he was founding a world medical center. A few years later the same fool said,
"This is the beginning of a great railroad"—and the Atchison,
Topeka and Santa Fe Railroad was born.

Within this decade, but seven hundred miles east, another idealist
was born; his earliest memory is of being flooded from his home
by the surging Ohio River. He was scheduled to become a lawyer.
But new ideas in education were astir in the land, and a project of
founding a new type of university in the west brought him, with
some fellow idealists, to Holton, Kansas, thirty miles north of
where Cyrus Holliday had settled. A few years later he had returned to Chicago for medical schooling, and thence to Topeka
with the bride who had taught school to pay his tuition.

For ten years this young doctor worked and studied and saved
before he and his wife could afford to have children. He became
known for his wide reading and deep learning in medical sciences.
He brought many technical medical instruments to Kansas for the
first time. He became president of the city Board of Health and
introduced the first program of school hygiene in Topeka. He taught
in the Kansas Medical School, which later became the University
of which he had dreamed. A few years later—it was 1910—he
bought his first automobile; his sons, who had "kept" his horses,
were now in high school.

You know the rest.

We have gone back nearly a hundred years. The little encamp-
ment on the Kaw became a village and then a town and then a
city. The little office at 727 Kansas Avenue was moved a few miles
west, where you dedicated a new building this afternoon.

Does it seem like a long span of time? No—only a ripple in a
stream, a vagrant breeze, a flash of light. Let me tell you of a waking dream I had recently that puts it all in a different perspective.

I saw some moving pictures recently made by the time-lapse
camera method. This technique enables us to study motion too
slow to be observed by the human eye. You have seen them, I am
sure: a whole season's growth shown in a few minutes, with plants

leaping out of the ground, shooting up like sky rockets, exploding into blossom, maturing into seed pods, and then withering away. I have recently seen another film—this one concerned with living brain tissue—photographed by this remarkable time-lapse technique, with pictures made every five minutes or so for a period of three months. On the screen I saw seemingly rigid cells moving, pulsating, stretching, struggling—as I had never conceived of them before.

Well, let me ask you to imagine that a film of this type had been made by the men of another planet who began their picture 750,000,000 years ago when they first spotted our earth through their telescopes. They decided to make a film history of us, taking a picture every year—not every five minutes, mind you, but *once a year*. This was the fancy of a forester named James C. Rettie who wrote about it in the autumn of 1948 issue of the magazine in which I have been interested since its inauguration by the Friends of the Land. The magazine is called *The Land*. Mr. Rettie's article was originally entitled *A Flash in the Pan*. I have taken many liberties with his version, but the main idea and many of the paragraphs as they stand are his.*

The people of that far-away planet, thought Mr. Rettie, had continued to work faithfully in making this time-lapse film. Recently they had become worried at the way things seemed to be going, and had decided to send a copy of the film to the Earth so that we might see what was happening to us. Let us suppose, you and I, that they have made arrangements for a group of intelligent people, such as ourselves, to sit down and look at this rapid-fire, capsule film of history.

You will have to arrange to take some time out to see it. The picture will begin at midnight, New Year's Eve, and will continue day and night without stopping until midnight of the next New Year's Eve. There will be 24 pictures per second so that time will seem to move at the rate of 24 years per second, which is about

---

* In my efforts to reach Mr. Rettie, I learned that *his* article, in *The Land,* was in turn inspired by a bulletin, "To Hold This Soil," written for the federal government in the 1930s by Russell Lord, who is editor of *The Land*. Mr. Lord, who gave Mr. Rettie permission to adapt the time-movie idea in his article, has graciously consented to allow me to adapt it further in my own.

1400 years to the minute, or 86,000 to the hour, and 2,000,000 years to the day. The normal life span of a man will occupy about three seconds. The full period of earth history will thus be unfolded upon the screen from Pre-Cambrian times to the present.

If you are going to get any sleep during this year-long film, you should do it during the first three months, for that will be a rather dull period. Mostly it will be a desolate, dreary, monotonous picture of violent geologic eruption and erosion, mountains rising and melting away like boiling butter, the land masses constantly changing in size, shape, and location.

Early in April, after you have watched the picture for three months, you will see some indication of the presence of single-celled organisms in some of the warmer, sheltered waters, and by the end of the month some of these organisms will have become multi-cellular, and a few of them encased themselves in shells— the trilobites. By the end of May, the first vertebrates will appear, although they will still be aquatic creatures. In June, about sixty per cent of the land area that we know as North America will be under water and one broad channel will occupy the space where the Rocky Mountains now stand. Great deposits of limestone and of oil and gas will be in the process of formation under shallow seas. On land there will still be no signs of vegetation. About the middle of *July* the first land plants will appear and begin the tremendous job of soil-building. Very slowly the mat of vegetation will spread, battling for its life against the devastation of erosion. The increasing vegetation will pave the way for the land animals, which will come much later. Early in August the seas will be teeming with fish, some of them breathing by lungs. Later that month some of these will venture ashore, and the first crude lizard-like amphibians will appear.

If you are not too tired by now, you will see, early in September, the first insects, some of them very large. Heavy vegetation, rapidly growing, is laying down layer upon layer of what we shall later call coal. Now seed-bearing plants and the first reptiles appear. And by the end of the month the first dinosaurs come; they will dominate the animal realm for about two months, and then disappear.

In October the Appalachian mountains will arise. Some small and pretentious animals will feed their young upon milk secreted by the female. The emergence of these animals will be recognized as one of the great events in the total picture.

November will bring pictures of a sea extending from the Gulf of Mexico to the Arctic in space now occupied by the Rocky Mountains. One of the flying reptiles will become conspicuous because of a wingspread of fifteen feet. But the dinosaurs will disappear, and there will be a rapid development of modern flowering plants, trees, and insects. Toward the end of the month there will be a tremendous eruption in the West, and the Rocky Mountains will rise out of the sea.

As the picture runs on into December, it will show the mammals in command of animal life. By now seed-bearing trees and grasses have covered most of the land with a heavy mantle of vegetation. Erosion will be confined to localized areas and most of the streams will be crystal clear.

On Christmas Day a stream flowing to the southwest will begin the cutting of what we now know as the Grand Canyon of the Colorado.

Christmas is past. The picture has run on through the latter days of December and there is still no sign of mankind. We spectators have become alarmed lest somehow man has been left out.

But not so. Around noon, on the thirty-first day of December, there will appear a stooped, massive creature of manlike proportions—Pithecanthropus, the Java ape man. For tools and weapons he uses stones and wooden clubs. He and his children live a precarious existence threatened on the one side by hostile animals and on the other by tremendous climatic changes. Ice sheets—in places four thousand feet deep—will form in the northern parts of both North America and Asia. Four times this glacial ice will push southward to cover half of the continents. With each advance the plants and animal life will be swept under or pushed southward. With each recession of the ice, life will struggle to re-establish itself in the wake of retreating glaciers.

The picture will run on through supper time of December 31, with still very little evidence of man's presence on earth. It will be eleven o'clock at night before the Neanderthal man appears, and half an hour later will come the Cro-Magnon man, living in caves and painting crude pictures on the walls of his dwelling. Fifteen minutes more will bring the Neolithic man, who learns how to chip stone to produce cutting edges for spears and tools. In a few minutes more he has domesticated the dog and the sheep.

The dawn of civilization will not begin until about five or six minutes before the end of the picture. The Egyptians, the Babylonians, the Hebrews, the Chinese, the Greeks, and the Romans in turn will arise and recede during the fourth, third, and second minutes before the end.

At fifty-eight minutes and forty-three seconds past eleven o'clock, just one minute and seventeen seconds before the end, Jesus will be born; he will urge men to love one another, and die after one and a half seconds. For the next sixty seconds his adherents will be seen to increase in great numbers to the north and west and with this increase will come much bloodshed over details of doctrine concerning him. Then, less than one-half minute before the end of the film, Columbus will discover the new world. The Declaration of Independence will be signed just seven seconds before the final curtain.

And now the film is flickering through the last seven seconds! Human beings seep across the face of the North American continent, driving before them the primitive redman who had lived there. The landscape is changing more radically than it has ever changed before in a comparable period of time. The great virgin forests disappear before ax and fire. The soil, covered for aeons by its protective mantle of vegetation, is laid bare to the ravages of water and wind erosion. Streams that have been flowing clear once again take up a load of silt and carry it toward the ocean. Humus and mineral salts vanish at a terrifying rate. Highways and cities spring up in the United States, as they did a few seconds earlier on the other side of the globe, where now human beings can be seen picking up cow dung and scraps of straw to serve as fuel with which to cook and keep warm; the dense forests formerly there are gone without a trace. Here and there dust storms will darken the landscape; over other wide areas devastating floods wash away billions of acres and many habitations. Men will be seen counting what they call wealth in terms of bits of printed paper, representing a relatively useless metal kept buried in strong vaults. Meanwhile the soil, the only real wealth that can keep mankind alive on the face of this earth, is being torn loose from its moorings and washed into the seven seas.

It is a few seconds before midnight.

These human beings who arrived on earth only a few minutes before twelve o'clock are multiplying at an astonishing rate; their food supply is diminishing. Each second there is an additional half-billion of them! There are now less than two acres of tillable land for each of them. More than half of them are hungry, some of them are starving. They engage in repeated exhausting wars against one another, which cease only while preparations are made for greater wars. Some of them systematically exterminate others. And all through the mass of struggling humanity, there are cripples and stragglers, hoarders and parasites, vandals and pillagers. There are petty destroyers, and destroyers on a grand scale. Some are playing, some are slaving, some are loafing, some are dying. Many are confined in great prisons and hospitals.

But there are also builders, toilers, leaders, and repairers. There are soil savers and soul savers, as well as destroyers. Forces of construction and conservation and salvation are at work, opposing the forces of waste and devastation and destruction. These little people, these ants, frantically scurrying about in the last few seconds of our year-long picture, are playing a part in a titanic contest. Until they came, the constructive forces of nature were—very slowly—gaining against the destructive forces. When man came, *his* destructiveness turned the tide back again; destruction gained ground. The outcome is still in the balance.

It is three seconds before midnight.

During these three seconds you and I were born, The Menninger Foundation was born.

And now the thought comes to me: What will the result of our labors look like in this film? Will it be lost in the dreadful scene of destruction? Or will it appear, if only for a second, as a bright flash of light, illuminating and guiding and spreading. Will it grow, or will it be extinguished after a few more seconds?

Will there be, in that irreversible film, enough men and women here and there in the surging mass—enough men and women with courage and idealism and vision to stem the tides of destructiveness, to oppose not only the ravages of nature but the evil within man himself, and turn defeat into victory?

We have so little time left—and so much to do. We can only do it *together. How shall we look in this picture when the next great roll of film is shown?*

11. Reverence for Life

It may be because of my medical background that I notice it, but I have the impression that one effect of our more mechanized living is to diminish the identification of young people with Hiawatha's brothers and Hiawatha's chickens. I realize that nature study and many manifestations of an interest in wildlife have their following, but it seems to me they are too little concerned with the unnecessary suffering of animals. Take, for example, the whole business of killing for pleasure, whether it be in the form of the so-called sport of hunting or the so-called business of trapping. These are hideously cruel performances, and it seems to me as I talk to them not one boy or girl in a dozen knows anything about them or cares anything about them from the standpoint of the moral question of whether it is right to inflict pain for fun.

I think there must be millions of girls wearing furs without having given a thought to how they were obtained—there are millions of boys who think they are getting back to nature in a healthy, masculine way when they go out and knock something in the head with a bullet. Albert Schweitzer has made the central plank of his faith revolve around the concept of reverence for life. It seems to me we could extend it somewhat and say that the highest ethic is not only a reverence for life but a reverence for the comfort of others, including everything that the Lord created.

A statement prepared for the Ninth Annual Conference for School Administrators, Mount Rainier National Park, June 1954.

12. Reading Notes

Someone sent me a magazine called *The National Magazine*. The name made me suspicious. As I looked it through, with its nice print and many pictures of elephants, bears, kangaroos, dogs, etc., I was increasingly intrigued. Then I came upon an incredible cartoon of a dog standing on its hind legs on a laboratory table, its front legs being pulled in opposite directions by a system of ropes and pulleys, and a bald-headed, leering man in a white coat smoking a drooping cigarette, surrounded by bottles and so forth, observing the dog's frantic resistance to being pulled in two. The caption of this cartoon is ". . . So That Humanity (?) May Benefit."

Then I looked more carefully, and in very fine print on page one it does say that this magazine is published monthly by The National Anti-Vivisection Society with editorial offices in Chicago. As a psychiatrist, I can understand fanaticism; as a fanatic myself in various respects, I can even forgive it. But dishonest and hateful propaganda of this kind, so identical with that used by the Nazis regarding the Jews and everyone else they didn't like, seems to me to be a kind of wickedness that even this fanatical psychiatrist cannot understand or forgive.

These notes appeared originally in the following publications: *Bulletin of the Menninger Clinic*, the *Menninger Library Journal*, the *Menninger Quarterly*, TPR (The Menninger Foundation employees' publication), and the Menninger School of Psychiatry *Alumni Bulletin*.

Psychiatrists with a vision of the importance of administration will be interested in rereading the eleventh chapter of Numbers. Dr. Orlo Choguill recently preached a sermon regarding the reactions of a great leader, Moses, to the constant griping of his followers. In his distress he cried to God that he could no longer handle such a large and querulous multitude unassisted, and was instructed to get himself seventy assistants, who were then given appropriate training in their leadership functions. It seems that two members of the body politic were not invited to join this administrative council but nonetheless went about on their own enunciating the principles to which the total assembly were dedicated. Now Moses had a right-hand man who was very zealous and he became much exercised about these irregular and uninstructed exhorters and urged Moses to put a stop to it immediately. It was at this time that Moses replied with a famous exclamation, one which Lincoln paraphrased many centuries later. "Would to God," he said in substance, "that there were more of them, who would take this responsibility without having it forced upon them." It might have improved Freud's study of the psychology of the group to have reflected upon this incident.

A recent book has been published entitled *Best Articles—1953*.[1] It contains an article, which is reprinted in *Omnibook* for October, about a Hindu fakir who not only walks across glowing coals in the presence of a psychiatrist, a surgeon, and a professor of physics from London University, but has demonstrated the ability to *see,* in some curious way, through his skin rather than through his eyes. Now don't call me credulous; I am just telling you what the man says. Even if it is a trick, it is a mighty good one and the description of the demonstration sounds as if the fellow himself does not know how he does the trick.

A phenomenon like this ought to be studied. I am firmly against shutting our eyes to phenomena that we cannot explain and comforting ourselves by the assumption that it probably didn't occur. I hope some one runs this down. I want to see this fellow!

Adult Leadership for November 1953 has an article on "Role Playing at Home" in which such things as this are described: They can't get the young son to come to the supper table promptly. So the father proposes to him that they play a game, exchanging roles, and the young son now takes upon himself the task of getting his recalcitrant father to come to the table. Of course, it works (in a way that will surprise you) but the question is, why? What is this thing "responsibility" anyway?

Dr. Harry Tiebout after a long study of alcoholic addiction proposes in an important article in the *Quarterly Journal of Studies on Alcohol* for March 1953 that the difference between benefit and nonbenefit in treatment of alcoholics relates to a distinction between compliance ("My alcoholism is getting me. I have to have help. I will do whatever you say") and surrender, which is more than a compliant bowing of the head. I am in agreement with this and am very interested in the "conversion point." It seems to me that this is the difference between false and true humility as well as between false and true cure of alcohol addiction. I think it is involved to some extent in all psychiatric treatment, and in religious attitudes also. I have often thought that the meaning of "My head is bloody but unbowed" is generally misunderstood. A little bowing of the head might be less spectacular and narcissistic but also less self-destructive. It is a hard problem, this question of pride versus humility. You have to have a certain amount of both, and the question is just how to construct the best pattern.

In the Abbott Laboratories publication *What's New?* there is a report of an article appearing in *The Lancet,* April 1955, called "Diagnosis by Slide Rule." This English physician has devised a mechanical gadget whereby certain differential diagnoses can be arrived at by an addition of symptoms indicated by slide-rule markers. This interested me, because I began to work on something of that kind in the year 1916, at which time I was a junior in the medical school at Harvard. I hadn't arrived at the slide-rule stage, but I had been very much interested in Leftwich's extraordinary book *Index of Symptoms,* which, if you don't know it, you would be most interested in. One should, I thought, be able to arrive at a diagnosis by slide-rule methods, and I am glad someone has carried out this project logically, if for no other reason than to show up the limited concept of diagnosis represented by this approach, the naming of something identified by parts. It makes me think of those childhood days when, emulating our elders, we were prone to organize clubs, called by any convenient name, and very likely to change names and constituents a half-dozen times during the year, and to vanish entirely at the end of the semester.

Last night I read Morris L. Ernst's new book *Utopia 1976,* which Rinehart will bring out in November 1955. Morris is a thinker and here he has tried to think ahead, in the way which anyone in any organization that believes in planning must do to the best of its abilities. I am willing to accept his predictions and base some of my plans on them. But some, such as the thirty-hour week, horrify me. (*Must* we abandon what we enjoy doing?)

And he says nothing about the consequences of the parabolic curve of increase in alcohol consumption which might do something to impair the more roseate aspects of his Utopia!

Reread FitzGerald's translation of Omar again last night—the regular one and then a very early edition. Funny what a hold it has on us, isn't it? But how different it reads than it used to! I believe I used to think it was a poetic version of "Eat, drink, and be merry, for tomorrow we die" (especially the "drink"). A maudlin justification of alcoholism, I guess I thought. Today I see it as a kind of an effort to be brave in the face of existentialist anxiety, an exhortation to seek the best in life, and promptly. Consider how he begins: "Wake." Then the third stanza, "Open, then, the door." Then those famous lines:

> The wine of life keeps oozing, drop by drop;
> The leaves of life keep falling, one by one.

These move us all, do they not? And yet they are so trite! And so dreadful!

I hope everyone reads the article by Dorothy Van de Mark in *Harper's* for March 1956, entitled "The Raid on the Reservations: A new program to 'help the Indians' turns out to be just another slick scheme to hand their last refuge over to the landgrabbers." Miss Van de Mark is in charge of a private Indian center in Chicago. I talked to her while up there. She told me that something like five thousand Indians have been moved to Chicago, many of them practically kidnaped from their reservations, because it was the wish of the Great White Father in Washington for them to get located in the cities, get busy in industry, and break off with their tribal traditions and friends. When Hitler and the Russians did things like this, we screamed; but when we do it, all in the best interests of the Indian, of course, who screams? Quite a few of us, but who listens? Not Washington.

It says in *Time* (February 20, 1956) that during Passover time Orthodox Jews must beware of using soda pop containing food coloring made from an alcoholic base which may have been manufactured from *leavened grain!* It is because of stipulations like this that many psychoanalysts throw out the baby with the bath and regard all religion as a compulsion neurosis or a "racket" or both. They forget that religious reformers from the time of Micah through Jesus and many since Him have inveighed against making the symbol more important than the thing. How consistent should one be? How scrupulous should one be? One thing I remember with pleasure about Schweitzer was the wry smile he gave me when, in speaking of his diet, he added, "But look! I am not consistent in my vegetarianism, for I *love* eggs!"

I have previously mentioned the *Mattachine Review,* a periodical published in Los Angeles devoted to the problems of the individual with dominant homosexual proclivities. A friend has just sent me three issues of a very similar magazine called *One,* also published in Los Angeles, which frankly labels itself "The Homosexual Magazine" (not quite correct English, in my opinion, but clear). It is well edited and in good taste. There are quotations from Plato's *Symposium,* short articles, letters, editorials, etc., reminding us of the attitude of the people of that epoch toward homosexuality. I think magazines of this kind may do much to relieve the distress and loneliness of incurable (if they will forgive the word) homosexually inclined individuals. One is aware in reading them under what fear these individuals live. "Citizen's rights in the case of arrest" are detailed at length, for example. The editorial position of these magazines is that homosexual inclination is no crime. Right! Homosexual seduction, homosexual rape, and homosexual offenses against public decency are just as reprehensible (criminal) as heterosexual offenses of the same kinds, and in just as bad taste. Homosexual relations as such which are not displayed, not advertised, not permitted to be in any way publicly offensive should not be considered criminal. But since they *are,* it is up to each individual whether he can bring himself to take the steps necessary to a personality change which is expensive, painful, difficult, and prolonged, or whether he elects a life of covert satisfactions within a small group, involving clandestine law-breaking.

Curious how our philosophies and emotional attitudes change! Every once in a while someone speaks to me about "mellowing" and I never know whether this is a compliment or an insult. In looking over some of my old correspondence, I find a memo to some of my colleagues here and in New York, dated April 8, 1948. I seem to have been very much exercised about an article in the *British Journal of Medical Psychology,* Volume 21, by Jane Darroch on "An Interpretation of the Personality of Jesus," based upon Schweitzer's interpretation of his life (*Quest of the Historical Jesus*) [2] picturing him as seeking death to punish himself for claiming to be the Messiah which he knew to be false, wishing to hurt his mother, etc. She was particularly interested in his identification with sinners. Well, the article *is* rather amateurish and what we psychoanalysts call "wild." What interests me now is that it shocked and annoyed me so much eight years ago! I don't believe the position of either

Jesus or Freud will be much affected by such quixotic tilts. Perspective is a great thing, and I don't know whether mellowing is anything more than the accumulation of perspective!

Dr. Tom Szasz contributed an article on malingering to the very respectable if somewhat ponderous *AMA Archives* (October 1956). I think his main point is correct, that the word expresses the physician's attitude, but I think what he scotomatized throughout is the *reason* for the doctors' attitude of irritation and moral condemnation of the malingerer. It was this which I was at some pains to examine in *Man Against Himself*. My point was that malingering is not only self-destructive but *also* extremely aggressive, unconsciously aggressive in one way and consciously aggressive in another way. These aggressive intents combine to tease, mislead, and deceive the physician, and hurt his *amour propre*. At the same time they mislead other people too. But while from some people they win for the patient pity and even money, from the physician they elicit first apparent stupidity—that is, blundering—and then anger.

For this total syndrome we need a word, and I sympathize with Szasz in thinking that "malingering" should be dispensed with as a designation of this peculiar behavior pattern. This is exactly what "schizophrenia" is, in my opinion, and this is what "epilepsy" is, and this is what "psychopathic personality" is. None of these are diagnoses.

For twenty-six years I have been perpetrating an error.

I have asked people what is the largest state east of the Mississippi and after they have named New York, Virginia, etc., I finally tell them "No, you are all wrong; it is Georgia!"

Well, it is *not* Georgia. It has not been Georgia since early in
March of 1940 when a man who was a prospector, a geologist, a
millionaire, a philanthropist, a metallographer, a zoologist, an orni-
thologist, a publisher, a theologian, an honorary Boy Scout, and a
one-time governor of Michigan convinced the Census Bureau that
its computation of the areas of the states had been incorrect, and in
the revised figures another state became the largest east of the Mississippi. Which one, and what was the name of this extraordinary
man?

Answer: Chase Salmon Osborn; state of Michigan.

George Corner is a distinguished American anatomist and
embryologist. His book of autobiography and selected essays
(*Anatomist at Large*. New York: Basic Books, 1958) demonstrates
the reason for his great success as a teacher, as a scientist, and as a
gentleman of kindness and culture. As a kind of teaser question,
based on one of his essays, let me ask: What famous remedy was
named after a king, contemporary with Julius Caesar, who killed
himself? It was used by physicians for nearly twenty centuries. In
one edition of the Bible (1568) a familiar verse was translated, "Is
there no tryacle in Gilead?" The balm referred to as treacle was
this drug. Thousands of doctors have prescribed it; hundreds, at
least, have denounced it. What were the names of this treacle?

Answer: Mithridatium and Theriac.

Children Limited is a publication I imagine most of you haven't
seen. I hadn't until this year. The December 1954 issue is a sixteen-
page tabloid-format newspaper. It is published by the National

Association for Retarded Children, a nonprofit organization of parents and friends of the mentally handicapped.

This was all the more interesting to me because, of all the Christmas parties I ever attended, the one given by the local association of these tops the list in certain respects. As the children arrived with their parents at the Foundation's Hopkins Building, which had been beautifully decorated for the occasion, they were greeted by some of the parents who had gotten there early. They looked around at the tree and the decorations and then sat stiffly and demurely in their chairs, waiting for the movie and the eventual Santa Claus and the ingeniously contrived sleigh full of gifts. The children weren't crying—far from it, and neither were the parents. But there were a few helpers and visitors for whom it was too much. There were wheelchair children and children with protruding tumors of the brain. There were overgrown babies and undersized adolescents. I really didn't look at the children so much; I looked at those brave, brave, brave parents. Some of them were young folks, some older folks; some evidently with means and some certainly without much. But all of them had a problem. Outside, the rest of the world was having eggnog parties and Christmas dances and Yule logs and whatnot—but here in this room were those wistful little faces and clumsy little bodies, and standing behind them were those faithful parents. I started home three times but I only got a few feet each time; I had to go back.

Intelligent people know that most hawks are immensely beneficial birds. This is quite aside from their beauty, sitting or sailing gracefully through the sky in the evening. Thousands have been autopsied and their stomachs contain ninety-five per cent rodents, beetles, and such things. Nevertheless they are persistently slaughtered by a few ignorant farmers who are convinced that they kill chickens, and even label them all "chicken hawks." There is no

such thing as a chicken hawk. They are also killed occasionally
by teen-agers and other trigger-happy gunmen. They are killed
in a few places, directly contrary to law, by the owners of game
farms who set up traps on top of tall poles to which hawks are attracted by the flutter of the young quail and pheasants in the
pens.

But the most incredible thing is the slaughter of thousands of
hawks made from blinds in the brush on certain ridges in the Pennsylvania mountains along which the hawks are known to migrate.
Hawkshooting is an organized sport there and has been going on
for at least seventy years. The state once unfortunately offered a
bounty for the scalp of the goshawk, which is indeed a destructive bird but which is comparatively infrequent. The hawks are
lured by tied pigeons and are shot at, left and right. Many are left
crippled, broken-winged, and dead all over the ground. There
are only a few "hunters" who violate the laws by digging into
this bloody sport, but there are over three hundred shooting sites
along the Blue Mountain, furthered of course by local "businessmen" (beer taverns, sporting goods stores, etc.) in spite of such
efforts as the Pennsylvania game wardens have exerted. See the
article by Maurice Brown, "Pennsylvania's Bloody Ridges," in
Nature magazine for June–July 1956.

In New Orleans I was able to obtain two numbers missing in
my collection of the *Transactions of the Kansas State Historical Society,* one for the year 1900 and the other the year 1890. There is
some excitingly interesting material in the former about the burning of Osceola and the raid on Lawrence, numerous articles by
Charles Gleed (the uncle of Mrs. Pendleton Miller), a biography
of Governor Charles Robinson, and an article on the first Kansas
railway, which was *not* the Santa Fe, but the Atchison and Pikes
Peak Railway, organized the same month as the Santa Fe.

In the 1890 issue, which is even bigger, there are, among other

things, lists of the enormous number of periodicals and newspapers on file in our Historical Museum, something many people
haven't any idea of. Almost every newspaper published in every
city in the United States, from way back when. Like a lot of this
old historical stuff, the big problem is how to find (in spite of the
excellent indexes) what there is of importance without spending
too many hours of poring over the unimportant.

I am very much interested in coincidences. Last Saturday at my
colloquium I dug out a piece by Mencken to read to the Fellows.
That evening his death was announced in Baltimore. Sunday I
picked up a book by Jung that has been lying on my dresser for
nearly a year (I was supposed to review it for the *Bulletin* and
had overlooked it). It turned out to be a study of *coincidences!*
Well, next, when I laid it down, I opened the new issue of the
International Journal of Psycho-Analysis which had just arrived,
and the first article is one by Jule Eisenbud, "On the Use of the
Psy Hypothesis in Psycho-Analysis," illustrated by extraordinary
"coincidences" or something of the kind; e.g., a patient had a
presentiment one day that he would see a certain rare warbler in
New York at a time when this warbler didn't belong there. Well,
you know the answer; he did.

Then—in case this isn't coincidence occurrence enough—the
next morning I went to Dr. Levinson's seminar on industrial
psychiatry, and one of the most sagacious members of the group
quietly handed me the verbatim account of four annual sessions of
a group in New York in which the discussants heard from one
another experiences in nonscientific diagnosis and treatment, including "spiritual healing." I may comment on some aspects of the
latter another time, but right now I am emphasizing the coincidence. Actually there was still a fifth one, but I have probably
taxed your credulity too far already!

Natural History for September 1955 is unusually interesting. It gives a vivid picture of the efforts being made to dispose safely of radioactive refuse; it has a nostalgic résumé of the life of Sequoia; it describes in detail the tortuous route of the vanilla bean from Madagascar vines to American palate. It reminds us by the reproduction of an old plate of the shocking brutality of whaling—this picture showing the neat trick of certain whalers who harpooned baby whales so they would rush off in agony to their mothers, who open their mouths to seize the little whales and hold them against the steel and rope and craft of those mammals aboard ship who were created in the image of God.

Time magazine says Joe Krutch discusses in his new book the old but unanswered reflection that the approach of a human being is more feared by other creatures than anything else in the world. This is a far cry from the spirit of Saint Francis of Assisi and Hiawatha and Schweitzer.

John Bartlow Martin is a kind of Lincoln Steffens or Albert Deutsch of the penology field. He is trying to stir up the public about prisons. I hope he is successful. He has written half a dozen books, at least three of them about crime and prisons. *Break Down the Walls* (New York: Ballantine Books, 1954) is his best yet, although it is somewhat unbalanced in that over one-third of it is about the Jackson Prison riots. His discussion of the American prison system is not textbook stuff; it is good newspaper reporting. It is obvious that he has gone to see and knew what to look for. His impressions of Joliet and some of the other prisons described coincide with my own impressions. The whole prison business stinks, to use a vulgar word for an even more ugly situation; it is making more crime than it is curing. It is sadistic and medieval. It defeats its own purpose. It costs us lots of money.

I used to think that public indifference to such things as this stemmed from a distrust of experts. I have changed my mind. I think the public puts too much faith in anybody who calls himself an expert. Those of us who are quite sure that we are experts have never taken the trouble to get the information about these things to the public in the right form at the right time. Why? Because *we experts* don't trust other experts. By other experts this time I mean good newspaper reporters, like Martin. These fellows are doing their best but they have got to be supported by us. How many psychiatrists have ever come out and said a good word for Albert Deutsch's book on *Our Rejected Children?* Years ago Albert Bein wrote a book on *Youth in Hell* about the same problem. Did any psychiatrist boost it or supply copies to all members of his legislature? Frank Wright, Jr. collected some amazing verbatim records of the goings-on in some state hospitals in 1947; the National Mental Health Foundation published it. Try to buy a copy today.

I am glad Martin's publishers have gotten out a fifty-cent paperback. I hope it sells a million. I don't agree with every statement in it, but I agree with the spirit. And I trust it.

Will Herberg contributes an article to the July 16, 1954, issue of the *Commonweal* maintaining that anti-Semitism is no longer decent, respectable, or American, but he goes on to say that Jews are different—inner-directed, hence unadjusted and unadjustable, and disturbing to all conformity.

I don't agree either that anti-Semitism is no longer respectable or that Jews are compelled to be chronically irritating to other people. Lots of people know more about it than I do, but I don't like Herberg's doctrine that a Jew is the very "embodiment of non-adjustment." I know a few individuals like that but they are not all Jews!

At last I have found somebody who seems to very much resemble Ernest Southard. Lucien Price, one of the editors of the *Boston Globe,* got the same perennial stimulation from hearing Whitehead talk that I used to get from hearing Southard talk. "I would come away at midnight after four or five hours' lively interchange with him, exhilarated as with a raging flame of life. Did he emanate an electricity of the spirit? It used to puzzle me that other guests could take that flood of powerful and original ideas, to all appearances, so coolly. . . . There was his face, serene, luminous, often smiling, the complexion pink and white, the eyes brilliant blue, clear and candid as a child's yet with the depth of the sage, often laughing or twinkling with humor."

I know exactly how Price felt. I thought everything that Southard said was a pearl. Now Whitehead was a greater man than Southard; perhaps he is the nearest to a modern Plato that we have ever had. But everything that Plato said was not a pearl, and this is even more true of Whitehead. I am glad Price did this book, and I enjoyed reading it (*Dialogues of Alfred North Whitehead.* Boston: Little, Brown, 1954). But what it conveys to me is that Whitehead did emanate an electricity of the spirit that there is no way to record. So did Southard.

To the *Bulletin of the Menninger Clinic* for January 1954 I contributed some correspondence of mine with a patient who had been a clinical psychologist but had "lost my mind" in 1918 and had been in hospitals for many years. "I am like the picture of your patient in a recent magazine, sitting on floor, head bowed. Long ago they took materials away in Occupational Therapy because I ruined them. . . . We hardly know we are alive at all after years of shock treatment and all the rest. Pray for our death," she said.

This was in January 1954. I noticed an article in one of our technical journals recently written by this woman. I shall not tell the name nor the content of her excellent article because this note might embarrass her, but she knows who I mean, and I want her to know I am proud of her, and various friends and readers of mine will be as astonished and pleased as I am, and maybe revise their pessimistic notions.

Dr. Joseph Ashbrook of Yale is said to have determined the length of the day for the planet Mars down to the figure of 24 hours, 37 minutes, and 22.6679 seconds, which is about $\frac{1}{100}$ of a second longer than the presently used value. Brouwer, also of Yale, claims that our own planet has in recent years taken 64 ten-thousandths of a *second* longer than it used to to make a complete rotation.

For me, such precision in regard to vast movements (and in the case of Mars at such vast distances from us) is amazing—no, that is not a strong enough word—*breathtaking,* to the point of incredibility. I am almost irresistibly tempted to find out how this is done, and only the fact that I am already late to a clinical conference prevents my dashing off a few letters to the *Astronomical Journal* and the Yale Observatory. Let us take it on faith and bow our heads in admiration of our scientific colleagues in this discipline. (See *Science News Letter* for January 16, 1953.)

In the January 23, 1953 issue of *The New Yorker* Peter De Vries, who has contributed several humorous ribbings of the sententious patter about wines which Schoonmaker and others issue, tops his record with a skit on "A Case of Piesporter." A well-intentioned bloke lugs home a case of wine which he sees on sale and which, of course, the wine store as usual will not deliver, for a surprise birthday present for his wife. She doesn't appreciate it very much. That's all there is to it, but if you read it you will laugh long and often. It made me think of a similar occasion in my own life on which I carried home a couple of packages just as he did, plus an especially fine bottle of wine under my arm which had been presented to me and which I intended to re-present to my wife and allow her to think that in a burst of great generosity I had purchased it for her. I couldn't get a taxi and trudged across town about thirty blocks (in New York City). I hired bellhops and luggage carriers galore and got it all as far as Kansas City. There, with the great conveniences now offered by the railroad, whereby one has to jump off one train at seven o'clock in the morning and struggle up an escalator, run down a corridor and clamber down another pair of steps to get on another train in order to continue in the same direction in which the first train is going, I managed to drop the damn thing right on the hard floor of that most inconvenient and inelegant of all Union Stations.

Mr. De Vries may think his story was imaginary but I can tell him it wasn't. But how did he know?

I read the first story in Bertrand Russell's new book of fiction, *Satan in the Suburbs* (New York: Simon and Schuster, 1953) and I didn't like it and I don't recommend it. He says he doesn't know what impels him to write short stories, but if this first one is any sample I could give him a few hints. He wants to caricature and ridicule his own super-ego and, along with it, the ego ideals of many other people. Despite his brilliance, he has an amazing incapacity to grasp how other people feel and what men live by. This comes from a great admirer of Bertrand Russell, the philosopher and mathematician, not the novelist, or the man.

If you want to know what the first story is about, I can tell you in a few words. Human beings are corrupt at heart and need only a little encouragement to overcome their hypocritical efforts to be decent. But evil is a necessity and to stamp it out would be considered insane.

Existential Psychoanalysis. By Jean-Paul Sartre. New York: Philosophical Library, 1953.

This reviewer can only record his dismay at discovering that although he was hitherto interested in and somewhat acquainted with existentialism, and although this book is written in English (translated) and although there are few unfamiliar words, he has no idea what the author is trying to say. It certainly has nothing to do with psychoanalysis as officially defined and customarily used. Sample: "The obscenity of the feminine sex is that of everything which 'gapes open.' It is a summons to being as all holes are." Provocative obscurantism of this sort (also modern poetry) may be *art,* but it's not science, in *my* opinion, nor art to *my* taste.

One of the finest things the Group for the Advancement of Psychiatry ever did was the devotion of one whole meeting to the psychological problems arising from the compulsory loyalty oath, now in print as *GAP Symposium No. 1,* dated October 1954, which includes an extensive bibliography. Excerpts of opinion from the fields of law, business, sociology, psychiatry, economics, and philosophy are given. Professor Kallen was impressed that the whole meeting testified to a "civic conscience among psychiatrists." Prosecuting Attorney von Moschzisker of Philadelphia said a cogent thing when he remarked that as a prosecutor he knew something about capturing conspirators, and then told a few of the methods, and added "[but] we are not going to catch them [disloyal people] by getting them to stand up and swear they are loyal." Elsewhere he remarked, "I think blind fear of Russia is something we have great need to be concerned about. . . . I don't see how anyone in this room who has not been there has the faintest idea of what goes on [in Russia]."

Just finished *The Black Swan* (New York: Knopf, 1954) which Mr. Knopf sent me. I met Thomas Mann once with Logan Clendenning in Kansas City, and Mrs. Menninger and I saw him again with Fred Hacker in California. He told me at that time that he had gotten all of material for *The Magic Mountain* during an incredibly short visit—seems to me he said a week—at that sanitarium in Switzerland. All of which leads up to some remarks about *The Black Swan*. There is an unbelievably stiff, hypocritical, loaded dialogue between mother and daughter. The daughter is crippled, realistic, artistic, forbearing. The mother is a simpleton and a sentimentalist. She falls in love with a young American. She decides to proposition him and does, but before the date comes off, extensive pelvic carcinoma is discovered which kills her. Thus it is a psychosomatic treatise, hinting that if clubfoot can "cause" frustration (daughter), frustration can "cause" carcinoma (mother). You all know what I think of "causings."

Arthur Upfield, the Australian who has turned out sixteen mystery stories, has now written one, *Death of a Lake* (New York: Doubleday, 1954) in which the murder is of minimal importance. The whole story is written about the gradual evaporation, in continuous heat and drought, of a large lake in Western Australia. Everyone knows it is soon going to be a dry hole, and the increasing human anxiety plus the concentration of wildlife of all kinds makes it very, very eerie. It gives one a horrific impression of Australia. Even our local heat was coolness after reading this.

One psychological detail: The author never mentions *smell*. Can you imagine what the complete progressive evaporation of a five-mile lake would mean in the way of dead fish, turtles, and so forth? He describes vividly the death of literally millions of birds and rabbits and fish but, as I say, never one word about the smell!

I was about to buy a new 1955 car (still driving my 1941 Ford) but the frenetic advertising disgusted me. I did try out a few but every one of them knocked my hat off when I got in and then the steering wheel punched me in the belly. Besides that, they are all too big. I don't want to drive a bus; I want to drive a little car that I can get into without breaking my neck.

Question: Why, with all this publicity about engines being too powerful and the highways too dangerous and cars being so inconvenient (*The New Yorker* has yowled for years about this) why has not one single company had the courage to come out with an ad like this:

Ours is a car for people who want to get from one part of the city to another conveniently and safely and park with maximum ease. Our car will not go over fifty miles an hour and it is not low, swanky, sneaky, sloozey, etc. but has enough head room so that you can get in without breaking your back, neck, or hat. It goes fifty miles to the gallon of gas. To keep the price down to a reasonable figure, it is made in one color only. And, while there is room in the rear for a couple of extra tires, there is not enough room for a couple of steamer trunks, a baby carriage, and a bicycle; hence you can get the garage door closed. We have a two-door model for one- or two-person families and a station wagon for those who want to take all the children and in-laws on every shopping trip.

I picked up the Topeka newspaper this morning and read about the death of one of the leading women of this city in a hunting accident. Wonderful husband; two fine young children. He was helping her through a fence and the dog ran up. I don't believe that all the fun of hunting added together can possibly equal the suffering and tragedy it causes. I apologize for persisting in my fanaticism in this matter. Sure, accidents can happen anywhere, but hunting isn't necessary.

And we Americans may consider ourselves at least semicivilized, but we haven't got this transportation problem licked. I am beginning to get phobic about riding in a car, especially outside the city limits. Two cars crashed on a lonely country road here at Christmas and killed or injured fourteen people. Where can you go safely with a car?

The *Management Newsletter* from the National Foremen's Institute of New London, Connecticut, devoted its December 1954 issue to an analysis of the defects in the company Christmas party. Why did they suddenly become so popular? And then suddenly so unpopular? Mr. Croft hasn't said the last word here, but he has made some interesting suggestions about the effect of the Scrooge pattern; i.e., meanness all year with a sudden burst of generosity at Christmas. Incidentally I could never see why people were so happy about Dickens' *A Christmas Carol* because I never had any confidence that Scrooge was going to be different the next day.

There is a famous German aphorism which contains a quadruple pun. Here it is:

> *Eifersucht ist eine Leidenschaft*
> *Die mit Eifer sucht was (?) Leiden schaft.*

I have been playing around with a device to partially render this pun into English and I've given up. I get as far as "Jealousy is a way to suffer which seeks with zeal to make things tougher," and then I despair. Anyone who enjoys translation and finding the *mot juste* can play with this and no doubt improve upon it. Let me know what you come up with.

Among my Mother's papers I have found some most interesting things. For example, she had started a collection of the last (recorded) words of famous people, dividing them into "believers" and "unbelievers." Comes now Professor Le Comte of Columbia with a book, the *Dictionary of Last Words* (New York: Philosophical Library, 1955) which makes most interesting, if somewhat gloomy, reading.

Got started on a novel by Virginia Chase, about eleven o'clock last night, entitled *The End of the Week* (New York: Macmillan, 1953). Sorry I did. First, I couldn't put it down and stayed up until I had finished it; secondly, it disturbed me. Made me realize that teachers are human beings. We psychiatrists entertain the comfortable illusion that no one has emotional problems except our patients. Gosh, wouldn't it jolt the nation if the parents of all the children who are entrusted to these earnest, patient, frustrated teachers were suddenly to realize that those teachers are human beings? Virginia Chase used to be one, and like myself, she had a mother and a grandfather and some farther back who were all teachers; also five of her brothers and sisters. She knows what she is talking about, and she can write. I kept getting tearful throughout the book. That idealistic little teacher, Caroline Treat, who got invited to the wedding of former students and was so happy, only to find that it was a mistake. She had bought herself a new dress and made a long trip to attend it. On the way home she comforted herself by finding in her scrapbook one of the many maxims she had saved: "A good teacher must have a willingness to be forgotten." She kept saying it over and over to herself. A great man, a professor at Harvard, had said it. "A good teacher must have a willingness to be forgotten. A good teacher . . ."

Or the little cross-eyed boy with a not-very-high IQ who importuned his teacher, troubled by her marital problems, to stay after school and help him prepare for the spelling match. When, out of curiosity, she asked him why he was so determined to compete in it (she felt that he was certain to lose) he didn't answer. "Why, Freddy?" she repeated. He dropped his eyes, and when the answer came it was in a whisper. "So somebody will look at me," he said.

Or the wistful girl who put everything she had into teaching but kept hoping she would meet a man and got a telephone call from an old friend who made a date, the first one the poor thing had had in four years. Her preparations and free associations during the subsequent conversation are almost too painful to read—makes one think of Dorothy Parker. It turns out that the boy friend is trying to sell her some insurance, but I oughtn't to tell you that.

If you have children in school, you had better get this book and study your lesson!

The Trouble with Cops. By Albert Deutsch. New York: Crown Publishers, 1955.

Albert Deutsch has never made any secret of the fact that he was interested in the "underdog"—the misunderstood, the neglected, the handicapped, the mistreated. That is why he surveyed the care of the mentally ill in America and then the care of so-called delinquent boys in state institutions, and that is precisely why he has now concerned himself with policemen, yes, *policemen* of all people. And this really isn't strange at all, for there is no question that the police are misunderstood, looked down upon, unfairly treated, ridiculed, criticized, overburdened, underestimated, and generally given a bad go of it in America. This is in sharp contrast to the situation in England, and in sharp contrast to what should be the case if we truly wish to make use of them in the control of crime in America. This is a reporter's book, a survey of the situation in many places, done with the characteristic penetration, directness, and fearlessness of Albert Deutsch. The police will love it, and so will everyone who wants to see a better America, although they will be shocked at some of its revelations. Until politics, bribery, low pay, and the low morale and low prestige of the police are changed, we cannot expect proper protection.

Eugen Kogon's *The Theory and Practice of Hell: The German Concentration Camps and the System Behind Them.* (New York: Farrar, Straus. The German edition was published in 1946. This American edition is dated 1950.) The author was a scholar, writer, editor, and banker. He is a devout Catholic. He was a prisoner of the Gestapo for eighteen months, and then was taken to Buchenwald where he remained six years, and was there at the time of the liberation. Since then he has been publisher of a literary journal in Frankfort. This is a systematic, thorough, documented description of one of the most terrible exhibitions of human wickedness on a mass scale in all history. If anyone has any doubt about the existence of an inherent instinct of aggression, theologically known as original sin, he should read this book even though he has heard all about the dirty evil business in piecemeal accounts.

The New Yorker for January 10, 1953, opens with a clever editorial which probably reflects the thinking of thousands of writers
at the moment: "Well, stuffiness is on the increase. . . . We were
sitting here thinking about the McCarran-Walter Act and the way
it assumes that all foreigners are suspicious characters. But we don't
plan to write anything about it, because Senator McCarran says
that critics of the law are either Communist-inspired or ignorant,
and we've taken it off our list of things that can be discussed. Too
risky. Thank heaven we can still discuss the shape of taxicabs.
The roof is too low."

Courage is generally regarded as a virtue, and we psychiatrists
think of it as an acquired virtue. The characterology of the redoubt-
able Kingbird (*Tyrannus tyrannus*) as beautifully described by
Charlton Ogburn, Jr., in *Audubon* for May–June 1953, would make
it appear that courage is neither acquired nor a social tradition in
all cases but may be an inherited species characteristic. What do we
do with that fact in our theories? (For non-ornithologists, the
Kingbird regularly attacks only larger and more dangerous birds
than itself and does so with zest and effectiveness.) Perhaps, says
Ogburn, more than any other living creature, he possesses "that
mysterious something that makes life the irrepressible miracle of
the universe." I often observed, as a boy on the farm, exactly the
phenomena described by Mr. Ogburn in this interesting article.
Children will love it.

Reading matter formerly seemed to descend upon me like heavy
rain. Then it began to hail. And now I have no metaphors left. My

reading has become dishonest; I read the articles only about one-third of the way through. For instance, the excellent practical tests one should use in purchasing binoculars or the thrilling account of rattlesnake collecting or the centenary notice of the birth of Charles Lathrop Pack, pioneer nature conservationist—all in *Nature Magazine* for May 1957—or the beautiful poem by Stanley Kunitz in *The Nation* for May 4, 1957, entitled "The War Against the Trees," describing the devastation preceding the erection of a new filling station, the alarming account of our dying oak trees in the *Scientific American* for May 1957, or the excellent description of the reticular activating system in the brain (same issue as the latter). You know that story about the mule who was supposed to respond so wonderfully to gentle care and quiet commands, and when it didn't, the former owner asked "Well did you get its attention first by hitting it with a ball bat?" Apparently this is what the reticular formation does. It also serves as a kind of integrating machine. It may turn out to be the nearest physical parallel to the ego.

And in the *New Republic* for April 29, 1957, the Washington correspondent for a leading Toronto paper and London journal shows how inevitable is a closer relationship between United States and Canada despite our rudeness, their clumsiness, or any other inadvertencies. We are symbiotic and will grow more so.

American Forests for September 1954 is a special issue because of the approaching convention of the American Forestry Association and contains among other things an excellent illustrated long article entitled "This Is Forestry." I recognize that I am vulnerable whenever I mention trees but this time I have a wonderful rationalization. We psychiatrists are continually put in the position of being vocational counselors and I wonder how many of us recommend forestry, with all its exciting and absorbing and constructive elements, as a true occupational therapy for specific patients. Now if we don't recommend it, is it because (1) we really don't know what forestry

is, or (2) we forget it, or (3) we haven't thought about this therapeutic opportunity, or (4) we don't believe in it? Don't answer, but
just remember that this is in the September issue. And if you have a
young adolescent who doesn't know what he wants to do, let him
read it.

The October 1954 issue of *American Forests* is chiefly remarkable
for its review of the observations made by the convening members
of the American Forestry Association interested in reforestation in
the Northwest. What I saw on my own visit to Washington and
Oregon about 1935 was so horrifying that I have never wanted to go
back. Evidently others have felt the same way and this convention
did a lot to reassure members of the American Forestry Association
that the Northwest has seen the error of its ways and has been attempting to mend them. Somewhere in this issue or the preceding
one—I can't find it at the moment—there is a pair of before-and-after
pictures, with captions to the effect that this is the way it looked fifteen years ago; the author says in the caption, "I never wanted to see
it again, but I happened to and this is the way it looks now. Hope
has returned to my heart!"

While you are at it, take a look at the article on pet raccoons in
this issue. If you read it, you will never be able to look a raccoon
coat in the face again.

Against all my principles and resolutions, I dived into a 950-page
book, printed in small type, and plowed on through it to the end.
Not as a Stranger (New York: Scribner, 1954) was written by
Morton Thompson, author of the novel about Semmelweiss, *The
Cry and the Covenant,* which made quite a sensation in 1949.

I read the book partly because of my interest in the motives for
studying medicine; along these lines I learned absolutely nothing.
I am reminded of one or two individuals I have known who had

this similar doctor aspiration before the age of six, as the hero and apparently the author did. It is a beautiful illustration of how conscious rationalizations and the known data of childhood do not always explain powerful conscious drives.

There is a paradox in the book which was disturbing to me. The hero is portrayed as a highly conscientious, ethical man who is shocked and angry at the derelictions of his friends and colleagues and speaks up about them courageously. He is gentle and tender to his patients; he is courteous and respectful to his teachers. But toward his wife he was boorish beyond words; he seemed unable to master waves of hatred which arose every time he approached this gentle, generous, well-meaning girl who had saved his life. Whether his hatred arose from his sense of guilt for having married her for money (she didn't have much), or because he was thus put in a humiliating position, or because she was of the same sex as his mother who was so cruel to him in an exquisite but subtle way, could be argued. But in a person who would not be called neurotic by anyone, the paradox between his gentleness with patients and his ruthlessness with his wife is hard to understand.

One other thing about the book. There are some evil individuals in the medical profession, and some reprehensible practices, but I very seriously doubt the truth of a few of the episodes the author has used, for example that of moving elderly patients into very cold rooms in the hope that they will get pneumonia and die more quickly and thus release beds. At least, if such a thing as this were done, it wouldn't be defended so blatantly as it is here. Perhaps symbolically the episode means something; we all know how easy it is to relegate elderly patients to nursing homes in which the medical profession has taken very little interest; but obvious and outright manslaughter I doubt.

Hearing so much of the beautiful new Catholic translation of the Bible called the Knox, I obtained one from England (London:

Burns and Oates). His New Testament translation was first published in 1945, the Old Testament four years later, the one-volume edition only in 1955.

The translator Knox is nowhere identified other than as Monsignor Knox. He certainly wasn't John! I finally found his first name on the cover of the box—Ronald! His Archbishop, Cardinal Griffin, writes an introduction in which he praises the translation for its freshness of approach, its lively language, and for the ease with which it may be read. I don't agree with the ease of reading. In some places, passages are definitely clarified for the Catholic reader (who, after all, has not had the advantages of the Revised Standard Version). But for some reason or other the translator takes a compulsive pleasure in inverting his sentences, putting objects before subjects, adverbs before verbs, e.g., "The bean stalk tall quickly did Jack then climb." Occasionally this gives a quaint and poetic effect, but more often it is just plain clumsy.

There are many helpful footnotes explaining manuscript variations, discrepancies, and contradictions. Psalm 25 is set up as "The Alphabet of Trust," with the first sentence beginning with "All," the second with "Belie," the third with "Can," the fourth with "Direct," etc. He does the same thing with each of the four chapters of Lamentations.

But you won't like his version of the Twenty-third Psalm, e.g., "As in honor-pledged but sure paths He leads me; dark be the valley about my path; hurt I fear not while He is with me . . . envious my foes watch. . . ."

Now and then there is an outright blunder detectable even by an amateur in a quick survey. On page 880, a letter from the Syrians to the high priest Onias reads, "Appraised of this, we would fain know how you do; pray tell us." Presumably the Monsignor meant to write "Apprised." Father Francis Furlong tells me that in the American edition (New York: Sheed and Ward) it has been altered to the correct word (apprised).

And in the famous first lines of the Second Isaiah, contrary to all the texts and all my information about the Hebrew text, Knox seems to think that the first lines are addressed to the people who are to be comforted, rather than to those leaders who are enjoined to do the comforting. In the familiar translation, "Comfort ye my people," "my people" is in the accusative; Knox insists on putting it in the appositional nominative.

In spite of these captious details, it is a beautiful translation and in many places helpful and clarifying.

Some time ago I submitted a paper to the Topeka Psychoanalytic Society on the general problem of recovery. In it I developed the idea that medical, social, psychological, and subjective criteria were involved in the determination of what is health or lack of health. I suggested that there might be a fifth category, something for which I didn't have a very good name because of the taboos in scientific circles on such terms as "spiritual."

My timidity is not shared by Dr. John A. Blake, chief psychologist at the Central State Hospital of Petersburg, Virginia. In *Mental Hygiene* for July 1953 he submits the existence of a fifth category of personality needs which he frankly designates as the spiritual. He describes it as an almost universally acquired need. He points to religious paranoiacs as individuals whose needs in this respect have become distorted, and to those with suicidal depression, the conviction of unpardonable sinfulness, as violators of spiritual laws.

I am not convinced by these and other examples he cites, but I ran into the same difficulties myself when I considered trying to illustrate in medical terms the sort of thing I had in mind. So I take off my hat to Dr. Blake, not just because he agrees with me, but because he had the courage to call it by name. We psychiatrists live in a curious semantic world; I have often thought how shocked the average medical audience would be to hear words like "spiritual" brought into a discussion, just about as shocked as a group of churchmen might be if a pastor or priest began to swear in church. It just ain't done! (Yet I have written an article citing numerous psychiatric authorities that swearing is sometimes good for one's mental health, and a good many people have assumed that spirituality was a trait of human personality. Are the clergy against mental health? And are the doctors oblivious to personality traits?)

The Eli Lilly Physicians' Bulletin for November–December 1952 contains an article on functional heart disease by Dr. Meyer Friedman which develops the unusual idea that a general uncertainty in religious faith has favored feelings of insecurity to an extent reflected by the increase in functional heart disease. This brief summary does not do justice to the thoughfulness and practical nature of the article, which is commended to all psychiatrists because the principles invoked apply to many forms of psychiatric illness. Consider this description of narcissism quoted from Buddha: "He who looks at his own navel looks straight into hell."

I have a collection of opinions about prejudice published by the *Baltimore Sun* (October 1954). Dr. Will, Margaret Mead, Reinhold Niebuhr, Mrs. Franklin Roosevelt, and many others say what they think about it. I didn't read every one, but those I did read were fine, although they all said just about what you would expect. They said prejudice is an evil thing and does a lot of harm and makes no logical sense, but comes from earlier acquired misapprehensions, unhappy experiences, and distortions of thinking.

I suppose quite a few people will quit speaking to me after I have written this down, but the truth is I rather believe we are apt to blame too many things on prejudice. Prejudice is, usually, just an impressive name for the other fellow's negative attitudes. I am against hunting, for example, also against boogie-woogie, Frenchmen, public gum chewing, and arson. You'd say I am *prejudiced* against them. Well, is this an evil? It may be necessary for the integrity of my psychological system.

Now, don't tell me I am being captious and that I understand perfectly well what is meant by prejudice. The continuous confusion of prejudice with anything that our side doesn't like bothers me. Hitler wasn't prejudiced; he was deluded. Charles Angoff, the novelist, reviews Professor Gordon Allport's book on prejudice in the *New Republic* for January 3, 1955, and spends half of it talking about personal experiences which show that someone or other doesn't like some Jews or other. Is prejudice synonymous with anti-Semitism, for Heaven's sake? Angoff sticks his neck way out and declares that "the Jewish world is in an uproar" over Toynbee's disparagement of Judaism as a religion. This, Angoff thinks, is sheer prejudice! Nonsense! Thousands of people have publicly disparaged Christianity, Buddhism, Catholicism, Masonry, the Republican Party, and the British Empire, and no world has gotten into any uproar over it. Furthermore, Angoff knows, and I know, that "the Jewish world" is *not* in any uproar over what Mr. Toynbee says about Judaism as a religion, and it is ridiculous to drag this into a review of a book written by a psychologist. He is prejudiced against prejudice and I'm prejudiced against prejudice against prejudice!

I have just read two beautiful biographical studies made by a former student of mine at Washburn, who now has his Ph.D., I believe, and is working in psychiatric social work in California. The one analysis, the life of Emily Dickinson, shows how extremely odd and embittered and inhibited she was. Chained to an extremely rigid life routine, imprisoned by herself within her own home, hurt by the rejection of her strange poems by her greatly admired friend, the editor of the *Atlantic Monthly,* she nevertheless persisted in writing fragments of feeling whose intrinsic beauty ultimately made them the admired property of the cultural world.

The other study is about Florence Nightingale. Here again I
was greatly impressed by the inner suffering, the bitterness again,
the hatred for her mother, and physical invalidism. Just to pick up
a minor point, here was a woman who was almost constantly ill
throughout her life, who "collapsed time after time, who was expected to die repeatedly, who suffered innumerable depressions, who
at the age of 52 had been an invalid for 16 years, expecting death
each day, who ultimately lost her vision and died at the age of 90!"

Perhaps in the author's concentration on the hidden things in
these women's lives, the backside of the tapestry, so to speak, he has
somewhat underemphasized the beauty of the façade. We must
remember that out of the one life came beauty and comfort for
many lonely souls, and out of the other came mercy and an awakening of social consciousness regarding the little things that are needed
along with medicine to relieve pain and promote recovery from
illness. Both are wonderful illustrations of that old principle, *bonum
ex nocentibus,* that Ernest Southard used to make us think about
so often.

It was Emily Dickinson who wrote:

> If I can stop one heart from breaking
> I shall not live in vain.
> If I can ease one life the aching,
> Or cool one pain
> Or help a fainting robin
> Unto his nest again
> I shall not live in vain.

I have just read every word in the *Federal Reporter* (214, Series
2, p. 862) of Durham *vs.* United States, No. 11859, the United States
Court of Appeals, District of Columbia Circuit, argued in March
1954, and decided July 1, 1954 (by Judge Bazelon). It is the famous
decision amending the old M'Naghten ruling of 100 years ago. I

have always protested that anyone who attempted to form an opinion as to someone else's knowledge of right and wrong was ignorant, stupid, or dishonest. First of all, there is no universal agreement about the rightness and wrongness; secondly, there is no reason to believe that any act is either entirely right or entirely wrong; third, there is no way of knowing for sure that someone else believes or knows about rightness and wrongness; and fourth, there is no way to know whether and to what extent another individual feels and is guided by what he believes to be more right or less right or by what some one else considers to be more right or less right.

Anyway, all this has been scotched for once and all in American courts by Judge Bazelon's intelligent proposal that we move on to a more logical proposition; namely, that the question of whether or not an individual guilty of a certain act prohibited by law should be punished in a stereotyped way or whether he should be regarded as in need of treatment should be determined by the opinion of the jury (based on the evidence, of course) as to whether or not the unlawful act was the "product" of mental disease or mental defect.

All this means that we now agree that it does no good to *punish* a man for a fever or a convulsion or an irrational impulse to kill. We may have to shut him up, for his sake or our own, but in calling it sickness we recognize something beyond the complete control of our will (ego). This really means then that the law finally comes around to admitting that we are not as free as the law has always presumed that we were.

I recently quoted an old discounted book about psychological factors in cancer. Now comes a report by LeShan and Worthington, two psychologists working with Dr. Ravich of the Institute of Applied Biology in New York. Using 152 patients with cancer and 125 without, they studied psychological inventories and found a preponderant frequency in the cancer group of (1) the loss of an important relationship with no satisfactory replacement, (2) an inability to express hostile feelings in any way (I doubt this), (3) persistent tension over the death of a parent, often in the distant past.

On the basis of their studies of these cases, the authors attempted some predictions as to whether certain newly admitted patients had cancer or not, based solely on the presence or absence of the three factors just mentioned. Correct predictions were made in 24 of the 28 cases attempted.[3]

Again I repeat: one of these days the cancer-research people who have had such enormous financial support and who have worked so frantically and intensively on the problem for the past thirty years will wake up to the fact that *psychology has an influence on tissue cells,* a proposition which they have consistently regarded even until now as a preposterous heresy.

I have purchased and am placing in our library, where I hope it will always remain, another documented account of the policy of sadism and extermination practiced by the Nazi officials and employees toward the Jews, Slavs, Jehovah's Witnesses, liberals, and other "enemies." This is the volume titled *Harvest of Hate* (1954) by Leon Poliakov, who has made a scholarly investigation of the horrible business from the beginning to the end. It is published by the Syracuse University Press with a foreword by Reinhold Niebuhr, acting dean and professor of Christian ethics at the Union Theological Seminary. The next fellow who questions the existence of an instinct of hate and destructiveness will be referred to this book.

A cartoon that should be framed and hung on the wall of certain lumber companies appears in *The New Yorker* for July 31, 1954.

Standing in front of a great fallen tree, a couple of big boys are saying, "We may not be able to make 'em, but we can sure as hell cut 'em down."

Many of us who have long been interested in the therapeutic effects of music will view with mixed emotions the editorial in the *J.A.M.A.* for September 1953, page 219. Evidently the editors have just heard about it. They found an article by a doctor in the *West Virginia Medical Journal* and looked up the literature, noting two articles, one about the effect of music on mental defectives and one on the use of a magnetic recorder. If this exhibition of naïveté weren't so pathetic, it would be funny. I suppose we ought to be congratulating ourselves that the *J.A.M.A.* at least notices it at long last.

I tried to pass it up but it was too good an article—Morton Sontheimer in the *Saturday Review* for September 18, 1954, on magazine articles. Clever style, and lots of sense. He quotes the old gag about magazine articles being classified into these three:

"Oh the glory of it!"

"Oh, the shame of it!" and

"Oh!"

Same with these notes!

The Clinician

STUDIES OF PSYCHOLOGICAL REACTIONS TO INFECTIOUS DISEASES

A national misfortune provided Karl Menninger an opportunity for the clinical research which led to his first published paper. During the influenza pandemic of 1918 he was studying with Elmer Ernest Southard at the Boston Psychopathic Hospital. Once, during the long hours of work necessitated by the pandemic, Southard said to him, "Why do you not in your exhausted moments, between patients, dictate off all sorts of most general comments on influenza and its relation to psychiatry and neurology?" * With this suggestion Karl Menninger began his career as a writer.

One hundred patients admitted to the Boston Psychopathic Hospital between September 15 and December 15, 1918, provided the clinical material for his first published paper, reprinted here. In it he makes a careful statistical analysis of this group of patients. He thoroughly examines the hundred patients for common features in their illnesses. His early scientific education at the feet of his father buttressed by his premedical and medical scientific training is evident as he methodically examines, describes, compares, and classifies the mental disturbances associated with influenza.

Thus in his first published scientific paper he evidences an interest in a subject that was to become a preoccupation with him—psychiatric nosology, the classification of mental illnesses. Throughout the paper he uses "dementia praecox" and "schizophrenia" interchangeably with no evident preference for one term over the other. He brands the attempts of German writers to classify deliriums as "bewildering." In another part of the paper he comments on "the picture *denoted* dementia praecox." Perhaps his elder colleagues at the time thought him presumptuous for the implied disparagement of the then current terminology. But for Karl Menninger it was the first sign of a ferment of dissatisfaction with "denoting" people with clinical labels. This dissatisfaction was

* Gay, Frederick P. *The Open Mind.* New York: Normandie House, 1938.

to grow and to lead him later to make a bold disavowal of all such labeling as unscientific and cruel. His search for a better method for describing and classifying mental illnesses proved to have a curiously circuitous course, but the search continued. The story of the search and his findings and conclusions will soon be reported in a new book.

Between 1919 and 1930 Karl Menninger published a total of thirteen papers based largely upon the clinical material fortuitously provided him by the influenza pandemic. Those papers—important as they are as detailed studies of the mental reactions to influenza, and of the influence of influenza upon the psychoses, neurosyphilis, hypophrenia, and epilepsy— had a far greater and more lasting importance for their author. The subsequent development of Karl Menninger's theoretical thinking was decisively influenced by these early clinical studies, which, together with other concurrent developments in psychiatry at the time, encouraged the young psychiatrist to believe that the mentally ill can recover.

Emil Kraepelin had influenced psychiatry from the nineteenth century when he extended the use of the term "dementia praecox," which Morel coined earlier for one of the most common forms of mental illness. The term was supposed to describe the illness, namely, one which struck men and women during their youth and which led progressively to an ultimate dementia. The hopelessness implied by the term was further supported by the belief that this illness was the result of actual pathology in the brain. Distinguished neuropathologists, among them Adolf Meyer, spent much of their lives trying to find the organic brain pathology by studying autopsied brain specimens of patients who died with this disease. Eugen Bleuler, dissatisfied with the limitations of the term "dementia praecox," attempted to introduce a better one, "the schizophrenias." But even this term carried at the time a most unfavorable prognosis. Patients with these diseases were studied more from the standpoint of differentiating the detailed nature of their afflictions; little thought was given to their treatment because they were considered untreatable.

But Karl Menninger observed in his studies of the mental reactions to infectious diseases something which troubled him and made it difficult for him to accept the historical and pessimistic pronouncements about the prognoses for mental illnesses. He observed that patients in their reactions to a serious inflammatory disease of the central nervous system behaved very much like patients who were commonly labeled "dementia praecox" or "schizophrenia." He observed that as the inflammatory disease subsided, many of these patients recovered from their psychoses. Their re-actions were therefore temporary, and this implied to Karl Menninger that the more serious syndromes of mental illness were reversible.

He stumbles in these early papers as he attempts to pin down the meaning of this observation, but the important effect of this experience was not in what he wrote about it but in the effect that it had upon the way that he began to think about the mentally ill. It is doubtful that even he realized the historical significance of the title that he used in 1922 for one of his papers, "Reversible Schizophrenia." This title, more than the paper, represents an early break through the therapeutic nihilism that had shackled psychiatry for centuries. It heralded the appearance of dramatic changes in the psychiatric attitude toward, and the treatment of, the mentally ill.

The significance of this group of early papers therefore lies in the fact that they were the springboard for Karl Menninger's future thinking as a psychiatrist. These studies left a lasting imprint upon him. He has been dissatisfied ever since with the complacent labeling of patients, and this dissatisfaction had led him to dramatic actions. These early studies also provided him with a beginning scientific basis for a belief about which he would later become militant—that there is hope for the mentally ill.

—B. H. H.

I. Psychoses Associated with Influenza

I. GENERAL DATA:
STATISTICAL ANALYSIS*

Sir William Osler[1] succinctly remarks that apparently "almost every form of disease of the nervous system may follow influenza." This postulate is seemingly quite justified by the accretion of neuropsychiatric data from cases in the recent pandemic. The frequency of mental disturbances accompanying the acute illness in the epidemic has been the subject of frequent comment, and the wave of psychiatric material that followed in its wake was unexpectedly large and correspondingly interesting.

The literature on the mental diseases associated with influenza is remarkable for its paucity and the inadequacy of the communications, and this well applies to toxic psychoses in general. Bonhoeffer,[2] considered authoritative on the subject, ascribed this in a measure to the fact that "for the most part communications concerning the psychoses accompanying or following infectious disease proceed from the pens of others than psychiatrists. . . . A practical knowledge of the frequency and nature of the [mental] diseases encountered can only be learned from material that includes both internal and mental diseases."

Precisely because of the latter point, the Psychopathic Hospital affords unusual and highly desirable opportunities for the study

This study was published in two parts. Only Part I appears in this collection. Reprinted from the *Journal of the American Medical Association*, 72:235–241, January 25, 1919.

* I would express my indebtedness to Dr. E. E. Southard, director, and Dr. L. G. Lowrey, chief medical officer, for invaluable suggestions and help. [K.M.]

and evaluation of data concerning the influenzal psychoses. Not only are many cases sent to the Psychopathic Hospital seen early in the course of the mental disease, but in all instances careful collateral study is made from the physical, serologic, and social standpoints. The average influenza patient cared for at home is not seen by a psychiatrist; the average institutional patient is usually seen late in the course of the mental disease, long after aid from the physical side is practicable.

For these reasons the series of cases observed at the Boston Psychopathic Hospital during the recent epidemic are of particular importance. This institution serves a varied function in the community, but primarily it is a clearing house for cases of mental disease, and above all for the study of incipient (or borderline) mental cases. All the cases here presented were regularly admitted patients, affording a certain definite uniformity of methods of study of the clinical material.

DIAGNOSTIC METHODS

A word is in place as to the methods used in the diagnosis of the "influenza" and of the "psychosis." As to the former, the statement of the attending physician, substantiated by the descriptions offered by the family or friends, was in most cases the chief evidence. In a considerable number we were able to make or confirm the diagnosis intramurally. In a few instances we have only the patient's word. For the accuracy of these we have no criterion or proof. On the other hand, the ubiquity of the disease, the singularity of its symptoms and course, and the absence of intercurrent epidemics in Boston at that time make the diagnosis of an acute febrile illness of short duration with respiratory tract symptoms and disproportionate prostration comparatively simple. Finally, it is certain that the percentage of error in the diagnosis is under the circumstances probably less than the average error in diagnosis of acute illness of all kinds, at all times, by all physicians.[3]

The psychiatric diagnoses in the Psychopathic Hospital are arrived at after this fashion. On the fifth day of the patient's stay, the case is presented to the entire staff by one of its members with the complete data of outside history, mental, physical, and serologic examinations, and the special examinations, such as spinal fluid, roentgenographic, clinical chemistry, ophthalmoscopic, and psychometric. At this time a preliminary diagnosis is made by vote. In a few cases this diagnosis is changed by or after the tenth day when the reconsideration of doubtful cases is made, usually at staff conference.

I hold no brief for the diagnostic ability of the staff of this hospital. I am glad to be able to refer to the statistical investigations of Lowrey,[4] the well-substantiated conclusion of which is that the diagnoses made here are in some 85 per cent correct (as measured by longer observation in other institutions).

STATISTICAL DATA

The epidemic appeared in Boston about September 15, 1918. From that time until December 15, a period of three months, 100 cases of mental disturbance associated with influenza were admitted here. Of these 100, data are complete on only 80, and except for some general statistics it is the latter number which is considered.

Diagnostic groups. For the sake of statistical convenience and clarity it is desirable to introduce here a diagnostic grouping which will be elaborated on later in the paper. The psychiatric diagnoses in this series of cases vary, of course, within wide limits, including nine of Southard's eleven major groups of mental disease.[5] On the basis of numerical preponderance, however, they are readily classifiable into four groups:

Group I comprises those cases generally agreed to be states of delirium, dependent on the acute infection. "Infection-toxin delirium" seems to me better than the recognized reversal of the phrase, namely, "toxic-infections," since from the name the latter may legitimately be interpreted to include incidents of delirium tremens superimposed on pneumonia.

Group II comprises the cases of frank dementia praecox.

Group III comprises the other forms of psychoses encountered which were thought to fit more or less precisely the generally recognized entities.

Group IV comprises the cases in which there was enough doubt or difference in opinion on the part of the staff to justify leaving the case unclassified. That is to say, this is a group in which we did not feel certain of any one diagnosis.

On the basis of this grouping, the numerical incidence of the cases was as shown in Table 1.

TABLE 1. NUMERICAL SUMMARY OF EIGHTY CASES

Group I, delirium 16
Group II, dementia praecox 25
Group III, other psychoses 23
Group IV, unclassified 16

The large size of Group IV will be remarked. It is here appropriate to point out that in many of these cases time will be the great diagnostician. Already one of the patients included in that group has returned to the hospital with this time a clear picture of dementia praecox. A forecast of probabilities, to be accepted only at its face value, is chiefly interesting in its confirmation of the results in the established groups. In other words, the indications from the unclassified group would seem only to augment in numbers the tendencies pointed to by the data of Groups I, II, and III. Thus of that group, at the present time, three patients seem most likely to have been forms of delirium and three of dementia praecox; six cases are between those two diagnoses, and the remaining four cases are of other types. On a basis of probabilities, the totals of the 80 cases, plus the probabilities in the remaining 20 cases of the hundred, are presented in Table 2.

TABLE 2. NUMERICAL SUMMARY OF 100 CASES
ON BASIS OF PROBABILITIES

Group I, delirium 26
Group II, dementia praecox 35
Group III, other psychoses 30
Group IV, unclassified 9

From Tables 1 and 2 there appears at once the most conspicuous and remarkable fact of the present data. This is the unexpected frequency of dementia praecox as a postinfluenzal psychosis. It occurred more frequently in this hospital than all other psychotic forms combined, delirium excluded, and even more frequently than the delirium which should be the most common. In the latter cases, however, the fallacy is quite obvious, since the great majority of deliria are never sent to a hospital for mental diseases. In fact, it may be parenthetically remarked that some authors do not recognize delirious states as psychoses, the chief reason being, however, that there is no established definition of psychosis, rather than that the nature of delirium is not appreciated. However, the strength of the first comparison is undiminished, and becomes more remarkable on further consideration. This is, of course, necessary, since not all the cases of dementia praecox were storms from a clear sky. The matter will be considered in detail below.

Sex. The 100 cases comprise 43 males and 57 females. The 80 cases more extensively studied comprise 34 males and 46 females. In both groups the proportions are the same, the females proponderating by 57 per cent to 43 per cent.

On the basis of the tentative groupings detailed above, the sexual distribution appears as in Table 3. The chief deduction from this table is the predominance of the female sex in the patients presenting the picture of dementia praecox. Relative equality obtains elsewhere despite the influence of alcohol in augmenting the proportion of males in Group III (e.g., acute alcoholic psychoses).

TABLE 3. SEXUAL DISTRIBUTION ACCORDING TO PSYCHIATRIC DIAGNOSES

	80 CASES ESTABLISHED DIAGNOSES		100 CASES PROBABLE DIAGNOSES	
	MALES	FEMALES	MALES	FEMALES
Group I, delirium	9	7	14	12
Group II, dementia praecox	4	21	8	27
Group III, other psychoses	15	8	16	14
Group IV, unclassified	6	10	5	4

Age. The age range was from 16 to 69, the youngest patient being a male, the oldest a female. The youngest woman was 18, the oldest man 61. The average of all was 31.7 years, without marked differences in the sexes (e.g., for Group I, males, thirty-three; females, thirty-one).

The average ages of patients in the diagnostic groups appear in Table 4. There is a statistical suggestion from this table of the bizarre hypothesis that the age is a factor in the determination of the form of resultant psychosis. Thus below, say, 18, no serious mental complication is common. In the succeeding decade the tendency is toward the development of dementia praecox; in the next decade, toward some other psychotic entity. It is not pretended that this theory is to be taken entire, but neither is it wholly to be ignored. Nothing that contributes to the further elucidation of the question, "Why does a specific individual develop dementia praecox?" should fail to receive consideration.

Time factors. The two principal considerations concerning temporal factors are the duration of the influenza, particularly in relation to the psychoses engendered, and the chronology of the influenza and respective psychoses.

TABLE 4. AVERAGE AGE OF PATIENTS ACCORDING TO
DIAGNOSTIC GROUPS

Group I, delirium 32
Group II, dementia praecox 23
Group III, other psychoses 40
Group IV, unclassified 34

Taking up first the matter of the duration of the influenza, we at once encounter a large factor of unreliability. In the first place, there might be some theoretical objections to the designation of any particular moment as the terminal moment of a specific attack of influenza. This can be pragmatically circumvented by assuming that the influenza terminates when the fever abates, that is, when the temperature returns to normal and there remains. Not only, however, are many of the patients not informed by their physicians of the precise date of this termination, but in not a few cases the physicians themselves evidently did or do not know. However, the difficulty was actually more apparent than real, because in most cases in which it was not known it could be estimated from the relative time spent in bed, the subjective symptoms, etc.

TABLE 5. DURATION OF ATTACKS OF INFLUENZA:
DATA FROM HISTORIES

Uncomplicated Influenza:
    Range of duration .... From 2 to 17 days
    Average duration (49 cases averaged) .... 6 days

Influenza with known Pneumonia:
    Range of duration .... From 3 to 25 days
    Average duration (19 cases averaged) .... 13 days

On this working basis the facts presented in Table 5 were obtainable. The reputed duration of the acute illness was, as may be observed, quite variable; but the listed cases fall into four rather clearly defined groups: those of a duration of less than 5 days, those of from 5 days to a week in duration, those lasting from 8 days to 2 weeks, and those exceeding that length of time. Thirty-six per cent of all the cases fall into the second group. On this basis, Table 6 is presented to show the relative frequency of each, and of the development of dementia praecox as the specific psychosis.

The conclusions justifiable from these statistics are, first, that the duration of the influenza or influenza and pneumonia precipitating mental diseases is probably not appreciably greater than that of the average attacks of influenza or influenza and pneumonia in the present epidemic. The frequency of pneumonia (about 25 per cent) is certainly larger than that obtaining generally, but this may in part be due to the fact that at least two thirds of our "pneumonia" patients were brought here, more or less moribund, because of the deliria of profound toxemia.

The second conclusion concerns the tendency of dementia praecox to show no constant relation to the duration of the influenzal attack precipitating it. As large a percentage of cases of dementia praecox followed the briefer attacks as followed the most prolonged and presumably more severe.

TABLE 6. INCIDENCE OF PSYCHOSES AND PARTICULARLY
OF DEMENTIA PRAECOX ACCORDING TO
DURATION OF INFLUENZA

Duration of Influenza	NUMBER OF CASES, ALL FORMS	CASES OF DEMENTIA PRAECOX	
		NUMBER	PER CENT
From 1 to 4 days	18	6	33
From 5 to 7 days	29	10	32
From 8 to 14 days	18	5	28
From 15 to 25 days	12	4	33

SYMPTOMATOLOGY

A representative but synthesized case history reads as follows:
During the convalescence from influenza, Miss X suddenly became excited and rushed from her bed into the street, screaming.
She was recaptured and confined in bed, but seemed to be bewildered, deluded, and hallucinated. The motor excitement faded;
the perverted ideation became augmented, and the family physician
advised the Psychopathic Hospital. At about this stage the diagnosis
is always in more or less doubt between various obvious possibilities.
Subsequently the symptoms follow in most cases a more or less
stereotyped course and the diagnosis becomes clear; that is, one
case will progressively clear up and the patient be sent home recovered, with a diagnosis of postinfluenzal delirium; another will
manifest more and more evidences of schizophrenia and be committed with a diagnosis of dementia praecox, etc.

Depression is traditionally the postinfluenzal symptom par excellence. Osler comments on it; most writers in psychiatry as well
as general medicine follow suit. But depression as an emotional
state of the psychoses following influenza is not strictly comparable with the depression which presumably is common after the
disease in nonpsychotic subjects. (I am aware of one instance in
which a mild tendency toward hypomania rather than the reverse
was observed in a normal young man, and so recognized by himself.) Aside from a few cases of postinfluenzal depression in which
the diagnosis was in doubt between the normal and the psychotic,

depression was in this series distinctly uncommon. Only three cases of the depressed phase of manic-depressive psychosis were encountered. Only about a fourth of all the cases showed any depression at any time, and it was rarely constant when present.

The heterogeny of symptoms is manifest from the divers forms of psychoses presented. Certainly the most common two are delusions and hallucinations. The delusions are of all sorts: somatic, referred, paranoid, transformation, grandeur, etc. One sort or another were present in 70 of 80 cases. Hallucinations in one or more fields occurred in all the cases diagnosed dementia praecox, and in all the cases of delirium, and in two-thirds of the remaining cases. The constancy of hallucinations in delirium as here seen might arouse curiosity as to why Regis and others have specified a particular "hallucinatory" type of delirium (*confusion mentale aigue*), as if hallucinations were not generally present.

No cases were monosymptomatic. In the first two groups, however, there were characteristic symptoms. In the deliria, it is amnesia. This was present in all cases, either as an amnesia during the acute psychotic period for past events (including the paramnesia of the Korsakow syndrome) or an amnesia after the acute psychosis for events transpiring during it, or, as not infrequently occurred, both. The second form is an integral symptom of delirium, but it is not an absolute differential point, as it occasionally occurs in dementia praecox and some other forms.

In the dementia praecox cases the characteristic and omnipresent symptom was schizophrenia, used in the symptomatic sense. As this is, in fact, the criterion of the diagnosis of dementia praecox, the foregoing statement is axiomatic. A more remarkable fact is the occurrence of distinctly schizophrenic symptoms in cases in which the patients quickly recover and which are necessarily diagnosed delirium. Six cases were left in doubt because of this fact, and one-third of the cases diagnosed delirium showed at one time or another frankly schizophrenic symptoms.

Group III is too heterogeneous to allow of any such representation. The specific psychoses were so far as diagnosed more or less true in type, and this is not the place to review the symptoms of the recognized psychoses.

Motor excitement and emotional acceleration were not conspicuous except in Group III. Here both the alcoholic psychoses and the cyclothymoses (especially manias) showed the characteristic hyperkinesis and hyperthymia.

DIAGNOSTIC GROUPS

The four groups used throughout this paper are, of course, by no means as homogeneous as their captions might suggest, and it is proposed to analyze, in a degree, their componency. The lack of space prohibits illustration by means of case histories or even abstracts, so only the structural framework of the series is presented here.

Group I. The cases diagnosed "toxic-infectious delirium" or "delirium with infectious disease" (American Medico-Psychological Association nomenclature) embrace three forms of delirium. These forms are not based, as by Kraepelin,[6] on ambiguities, such as "confusion" and "exhaustion," or, as by Bonhoeffer,[7] on the predominant symptom. They are based on the most simple and the only uniform factor, namely, time. It is in our experience here quite impossible to follow either Kraepelin or Bonhoeffer in distinguishing types of delirium. On the other hand, the deliria are in all cases of one of three types: prefebrile delirium, (cum-) febrile delirium, or postfebrile delirium. Either of the first two may be prolonged over into the subsequent period. This classification is so pre-eminently valuable from a pragmatic standpoint, and the subdivisions of the German writers so bewildering and so conducive to ambiguous descriptions, that for the present I feel that no further justification is required.

Statistically, there were in the present series one, possibly two, cases of prodromal delirium type.

Of the typical delirium concomitant with fever, the present series includes twelve. Of these patients, seven died. In one instance the fever abated two weeks before death.

Of the postfebrile deliria there were three, one of which was fatal. In one of the other two the delirium lasted two weeks.

Any general hospital could probably furnish more examples of all of these types than a psychopathic hospital. These cases are in a sense representative of the more severe forms of delirium.

Neurologic signs were not infrequently present. I am elsewhere reporting with Myerson an instance of severe bilateral optic neuritis which occurred in but one case, although all eye grounds were examined as a routine. One woman, aged 40, with typical delirium, presented absent pupillary and patellar reflexes, with muscular fibrillation. Several cases were noted with transient Argyll-Robertson pupils. Convulsions were rare, occurring in only one case, and incidently in one fatal case in one of our nurses, not included in this series.

The spinal fluids were examined in most cases, and in only one instance was there any inexplicable change. This was a case of postfebrile delirium, with slight increase of albumin and globulin, and a mild midzone gold reading; Wassermann tests were negative. These negative findings do not coincide with the post-mortem findings on spinal and cerebral fluids of patients dying of influenza, in which Southard and Canavan have found marked changes.

Group II. The patients who developed dementia praecox during or soon after an attack of influenza may be differentiated into three important groups. These are: (1) those with pre-existent indications, (2) those with morbid family history, without previous tendency, and (3) those with neither. Of the first class there were, of course, two varieties: those with previous attacks of acute psychosis, dementia praecox episodes, and those who, without previous episodes, manifested a tendency to the seclusive, egocentricity, etc. In both of these types the acute psychotic episode seems to have been precipitated by the influenza, a process frequently mentioned in the literature, but by no means understood.

The patients in whose family history there appear pathologic elements—a psychotic father, a feeble-minded brother, etc.—are separately grouped because of the possible contribution of these elements.

The group in which there was no previous indication, no evinced tendency, and no morbid family history is certainly the most momentous group of this series. It is subdivided into those complicated by parturition, and those due solely to the influenza. In this group the influenza (and parturition) seemed to act by directly inducing a process for which there were no previous indications. There are as yet insufficient data to conclude that the infectious process may be the direct etiologic factor (perhaps via some such mechanism as Bonhoeffer proposes) of dementia praecox. Nevertheless the evidence which these cases constitute for the organic view of dementia praecox, as held by Alzheimer, Dide, Deny, Southard, Regis, Rosanoff, and others, is of considerable weight. What effect it will have on the view of "curable dementia praecox," of which only rumors have thus far reached us *ex bello,* no one can say.

TABLE 7. SUBDIVISIONS OF THE DEMENTIA PRAECOX GROUPS

With pre-existent indications 9
   Definite episodes 3
   Disposition only (including 1 parturient) 6
With morbid family history (including 1 parturient) 4
With neither personal nor familial predilection 13
   Influenza plus parturition 2
   Influenza (or pneumonia) alone 11

The numerical frequency of the foregoing subdivisions of Group II appears in Table 7.

Group III. This heterogeneous group includes cases of the usual psychoses which were precipitated in acute form by the influenza. This does not relate to their permanence, since forms of manic-depressive psychosis will likely all prove transient; of neurosyphilis, presumably permanent. All began during the defervescence of, or convalescence from, the influenza. The cases of neurosyphilis are included, as the others, because although it is indisputable that the neurosyphilitic process precedes the influenza, the symptoms were so exaggerated or the process so accelerated that for the first time the conduct of these patients became such that institutional care was considered necessary.

An outline with the numerical frequency of each group appears in Table 8.

Group IV. This group of cases of dubious diagnosis consists of sixteen cases. Of these, three were most likely postfebrile deliria; six were indistinguishable between postfebrile delirium and episodic dementia praecox; three, in my opinion, will likely prove to be dementia praecox, and five remain undiagnosed because of unusual combinations of symptoms, insufficient data, etc.

TABLE 8. STATISTICAL ANALYSIS OF GROUP III

So-called "functional psychoses"		11
Cyclothymias		9
Manic phase	5	
Depressed phase	3	
Mixed phase	1	
Psychoneurosis		1
Paranoia (Kraepelinian)		1
Recognized organic psychoses		12
Alcoholic psychoses		5
Neurosyphilitic psychoses		5
General paresis	4	
Diffuse form	1	
Arteriosclerotic psychoses		2

The striking point in this group is the frequency of difficulty in distinguishing between postfebrile delirium and dementia praecox. There is not time here to dilate on this theme, or to recall the references to this difficulty made by the French authors who regard dementia praecox as essentially a toxic psychosis. It is sufficient to indicate that this fact, and the presence of schizophrenic symptoms in one-third of the cases diagnosed delirium, add considerable force to the suggestion made above from the statistics in Group II, concerning infectious processes as the possible etiology in some cases of dementia praecox.

Another classification of the diagnostic groups is suggested by the facts presented. The influenza acts in two ways: as an inciting factor for a process not previously manifest, and as an exciting factor for rendering visible a previously latent or semilatent process.

Thus the cases of manic-depressive psychosis with first attack following influenza illustrate well the first tenet, and the augmentation of neurosyphilitic processes the second. Our knowledge concerning both methods is at present in a clouded state, and only much careful study of series of cases such as the present will elucidate the matter.

From such a point of view the cases of this series may be presented numerically as in Table 9.

TABLE 9. NUMERICAL SUMMARY ACCORDING TO WAY
INFLUENZA ACTED

Latent Processes Activated:

Dementia praecox	8	
Manic-depressive psychosis	6	
Neurosyphilis	5	Total 32
Alcoholic psychoses	4	
Other psychoses	5	
Unclassified	4	

Processes Instigated:

Delirium	16	
Dementia praecox	17	
Manic-depressive psychosis	3	Total 48
Other psychoses	0	
Unclassified	12	

COURSE

The course of the psychoses has in general been indicated in connection with the individual groups. The delirious patients either recover mentally and physically or die. Those diagnosed as having dementia praecox are all alive at the present time except two, who died within the month. There have been no deaths in Groups III and IV. Necropsy results will appear later.

Statistically the present status and probable prognosis is represented in Table 10.

TABLE 10. COURSE OF THE PSYCHOSES

Groups	I	II	III	IV
Transient	10	0	14	6
Interrupted by death	6	2	2	3
Permanent	0	23	7	7

SUMMARY AND CONCLUSIONS

1. One hundred cases of mental disease associated with influenza in the recent pandemic have been studied at the Boston Psychopathic Hospital. Eighty of these have been intensively analyzed.

2. The variety of mental disturbance manifested is wide, embracing in this series nine of Southard's eleven groups of mental disease. For convenience they are readily classifiable into four groups: delirium, dementia praecox, other psychoses, and unclassified. Of these the second (dementia praecox) is the largest group numerically.

3. That age may be a factor in determining the form of psychosis evolved is suggested by an analysis of the average ages of the groups.

4. Analysis of the time relations proves that the duration of the influenzal attacks in the patients developing psychoses is not appreciably greater than the average as reported in the present epidemic, nor does the duration modify the form of psychosis developed.

5. There is in most instances an interval between the termination of the influenza and the first manifestation of symptoms of psychosis, the averages varying from two to eight days in all save the febrile deliria. Herein, Bonhoeffer's principle of the relation of interval and complexity of the psychoses is supported.

6. The symptomatology is as complex as the nosology. Delusions and hallucinations are the most common symptoms, and depression is relatively infrequent, contrary to the case in mentally normal subjects.

7. The states of delirium encountered are best classified as of three forms, on a temporal basis: prefebrile delirium (prodromes), (cum-) febrile delirium, and postfebrile delirium (collapse delirium, exhaustion delirium, confusion, etc.). This accounts for all cases and avoids ambiguity.

8. Neurologic signs were few; ophthalmoscopic examination negative, save for one instance of bilateral neuritis, and spinal fluid examination negative save for one instance of modified colloidal gold reaction.

9. An organic basis for some instances of the picture denoted dementia praecox is supported by the pre-eminent frequency of its occurrence in this series (31 per cent), the age factor above mentioned, the frequency of schizophrenic symptoms in otherwise typical cases of delirium, and the occurrence of several (six or more) cases in which a diagnosis could not be made between delirium and dementia praecox, despite the presence of all diagnostic aids.

10. The psychiatric prognosis in influenza justifiable on the basis of the present series may be expressed in general as delirium (with recovery), death, or dementia praecox. This excludes cases of previous psychotic basis, such as alcohol and neurosyphilis.

2. Reversible Schizophrenia

A STUDY OF THE IMPLICATIONS OF DELIRIUM SCHIZOPHRENOIDES AND OTHER POSTINFLUENZAL SYNDROMES

Dementia praecox is apparently sometimes *a chronic delirium* (schizophrenia deliriosa). Delirium is apparently sometimes *an acute dementia praecox* (delirium schizophrenoides). Both forms are (sometimes) reversible. These two forms may represent an identical process manifested by varying degrees of reversibility of the schizophrenia. The concept "reversible schizophrenia" (cf. the term "delirium schizophrenoides") is not a mere nosological quibble, since it may affect our conception of the nature of dementia praecox. It implies *conditions* of reversibility which we may discover to be under our control!

Delirium and dementia praecox have many points of contrast. Delirium is certainly the oldest psychiatric entity, dementia praecox the newest. Delirium is short, schizophrenia is long. Of dementia praecox books are filled with minute descriptions; of delirium there is scarcely a single satisfactory description extant. Of delirium we possess not even an adequate definition, yet agree unanimously upon its autonomy; of dementia praecox we possess precise definition, and still doubt its existence as an entity.

For all this contrast, we recognize their essential similarity. Thus ever the paradox. They are alike, as I shall endeavor to emphasize,

Abstract of a paper read at the seventy-seventh annual meeting of the American Medico-Psychological Association, now The American Psychiatric Association, Boston, Massachusetts, May 31, June 1, 2, 3, 1921. Reprinted from the *American Journal of Psychiatry*, 1:573–588, April 1922.

in incidence, in appearance, in nature; and, as I do not need to demonstrate, they are alike in that of these two the psychiatric world possesses less real knowledge than any other of the twelve great orders of mental disease.

HISTORY OF DELIRIUM

Our ignorance of the real nature of delirium is the more strange because of the hoariness of the conception. Perhaps because in its classical form it is of all mental disease pictures the most evanescent, the shortest lived, there is, as I have said, now no adequate definition or description of it. "What is delirium?" asks Hoch, and he remains unanswered.*

From the time *de* and *lira* were combined to mean literally "wandering from the furrow," this generic meaning has clung to the word. Through various stages it has passed, such as that now represented by the French word *délire,* meaning delusional state, and many other prostituted uses, to this present moment of ambiguity and uncertainty. It appears that today everyone takes it for granted that everyone else knows precisely what delirium is, or at least what he means by "delirium"—so no one defines it, and it remains vague in meaning and indefinite in conception. One recalls the day of Esquirol, Martini, Georget, and Burrows, who, as Bonhoeffer points out, were unwilling to regard delirium as within the range of psychiatry.

Let us set down here that we will for the present regard "delirium" as a certain mental disease picture concomitant with and directly dependent upon a more general somatic disease, the psychological features being an irregular dissociated disturbance in all mental spheres—perceptual, ideational, emotional, volitional. The pathologists may insist that an encephalitis is inferred.

DEMENTIA PRAECOX AS A DELIRIUM

Now of course it is not a new thought that dementia praecox may be a chronic delirium—the psychic manifestations of an enceph-

---

* The statistical manual prepared by the committee of this Association defines many syndromes, many pictures, many terms, but nowhere does it define or delimit "delirium," although the word is used on almost every page.

alitis. Southard, Alzheimer, and all the organicists in the dementia praecox controversy have held that general view unframed perhaps and not always so expressed. But here we are considering clinical aspects, and there have been clinicians of ability who insisted upon the relationship.

It was none other than the great French psychiatrist Regis, to whom I think it is not inappropriate to here render particular homage, who developed the conception of dementia praecox as toxic or infectious in origin, from a study of its clinical features. He said they were essentially similar processes—"with the same fundamental symptoms of obtusion, torpor, psychic inhibition, confused and senseless delusions, alternating agitation and stupor. . . ." In his second edition he defines dementia praecox categorically as "the phase of chronicity of all mental confusion not recovering, particularly of those arising in puberty." In his edition of 1909 he flat-footedly asserts that "dementia praecox is essentially a toxic psychosis" and classifies it as a species of "mental confusion," a descriptive denominator of the aberrant mental states accompanying or following acute somatic disease. In this edition he confesses the essential inseparability of dementia praecox and "chronic" (i.e., prolonged) mental confusion. He circumvents the difficulty of pronounced predisposition in dementia praecox by allowing two forms, the *constitutionnelle* and the *accidentelle*.

Following essentially the ideas of Regis were Dupré, Deny, and others of the French school, but the idea was perhaps most ardently advanced by Dide, who proposed *"to give to the different states [of dementia praecox] the name toxic-infectious psychoses,* subacute and chronic, primary (hebephreno-catatonic) and secondary (paranoid)." Deny was more conservative, but freely conceded that "it is certain there exist very great analogies between the clinical picture of dementia praecox and the states of confusion, of torpor and dream-states which characterize the toxic-infectious psychoses, and the autotoxic origin of that affection is rendered very possible by this fact."

It is possible that had Regis adopted Dide's excellent suggestions instead of cumbering his ideas with unwieldy names of cumulative adjectives, the idea would have been projected farther and its impression made more lasting. For the fact remains that for all its apparent plausibility the theory of Regis was left decidedly in the background. True, no less a man than Bonhoeffer [1] concedes that "severe cases of catatonia not infrequently begin with the alterations wrought by a fever," and points out that many symptoms are held in common by dementia praecox and acute toxic psychoses. "Of the infection psychoses and catatonia, it may be said that any and all symptoms of the one may occur in the other." But he does not admit of this etiology for catatonia, for dementia praecox, and he is in this negation distinctly in the majority.

In fact, little has been written in support of this work except by the French. Kraepelinian domination more or less eclipses the French psychiatric products, with the result that an infection toxemia etiology of schizophrenia has been little considered. In more recent times we have been too much concerned with mental catharsis and Salvarsan to give the cause of schizophrenia its due in consideration or research. Thus it was, at least, until the very present. But note the sudden change in conception implied by the program of this very meeting. Of nine speakers scheduled for this date, dealing with the nature of dementia praecox, six are frankly taking the position that we speak only of a syndrome, and that this syndrome may be the manifestation of numerous somatic ills and exogenous toxins, as well as of an idiopathic endogenous psychosis of the familiar stamp. It is as if we had all been simultaneously converted from the conventional Germanic to the previously ignored French conception. Most striking is the fact that it would seem as if we were of a sudden all agreed in our revolt. Occasionally an isolated contribution on the matter has appeared, e.g., Cotton, Gosline, Knapp, Hoch. The only progressive work has been done in the field of neuropathology.

Thus dementia praecox in the role of a delirium has long been familiar to psychiatrists. Except by the French, however, there has been a tendency to dodge the issue of the phenomenon, by giving the syndrome a name neither delirium nor dementia praecox, to wit: amentia, confusional insanity, puerperal psychosis, acute confusion, acute hallucinatory confusion, acute dementia, etc. Of a sudden, we in America seemed to recognize these syndromes as schizophrenic, whether associated with hyperthyroidism, which I have recently seen illustrated very beautifully, the puerperium, in the too familiar forms with syphilis, with typhoid, alcholism, trauma, epilepsy, and psychic trauma. I say we have all of a sudden jumped to the admission that these syndromes are *schizophrenic,* and of very late we have many of us made bold to declare them identical with what we call dementia praecox. It is a salutary sign when we lay aside an assumed technique of discrimination and flatly declare that whether or not this or that picture *ends up* as our classical (Kraepelinian) dementia praecox is supposed to end up, it is nevertheless indistinguishable in cross-section from the picture which is schizophrenia.

A PROPOSED CLASSIFICATION BY PROGNOSIS

A very practical standpoint is, I suppose, concerned more with prognosis than with diagnosis. Even those who are not disposed to favor my conception of a reversible dementia praecox will not gainsay the fact that influenza, the war, and an increase in the analytical approach to psychiatry has made the old conception of eventual dementia for all cases of schizophrenia no longer tenable. We must grant in view of such studies as those of McPherson and Hohman,[2] Austregesilo and many others, that many of the cases we have called dementia praecox have not deteriorated and will not dement. I propose to these pragmatic persons for whom facts are of more interest than theories that we are at the present time wholly justified in recognizing for dementia praecox three prognoses, or, if you will, three types of dementia praecox based on the prognosis, viz.:

1. The type illustrating Kraepelin's original premise of ultimate irrevocable total dementia.

2. A group on which the acute manifestations of dementia praecox occur in waves or attacks clearing up in large part so that the patients are often discharged recovered, but return sooner or later

in one or many subsequent episodes much after the classical fashion of manic-depressive psychosis.

3. A group of cases presenting the syndrome of schizophrenia, but arising upon variously constructed soils and precipitated by a variety of incidents; clinically called dementia praecox, but making, after a relatively short time, what is apparently a complete and permanent recovery.

Obvious as this prognostic partition is, the fact remains that we persist in a grim determination to crowd our individual cases into a nosology of hebephrenic, catatonic, paranoid, and simplex pigeonholes regardless of the uselessness (to say nothing of the doubtfulness) of such classification. The pragmatic point to grasp is the existence of a phenomenon which I propose to ally to the chemical process known as *reversibility*. I contrast this chemical metaphor with the time-worn physical conception of organic and functional, the strictly clinical attitude of benign and malignant trend, and the futile fallaciousness of alleged cause and effect. It seems to me a grave question as to whether any of these have ever helped us very much. Abstractly, chemistry, in so far as it can be considered apart from physics, is the realm in which brain processes carry on and there is at least some logic in looking to it rather than to physics for an explanation of fundamental phenomena. From the philosophic standpoint there is the pragmatic justification that a recognition of the reversibility of the schizophrenic process may stimulate us to a further study of the conditions favoring this reversibility.

Influenza, like the other somatic ills discussed on this program, can apparently in some mysterious way so affect the brain, normal and predisposed, that the syndrome of dementia praecox unmistakably appears. That this psychosis is sometimes transient, sometimes permanent, will appear from further discussion. I submit that it appears in two (or more) guises, with a distinction but perhaps no difference. Sometimes we are faced by what seems to be a simple delirium, coming on with the somatic illness or directly after it, in the familiar, classical way. Delirious features, e.g., perceptual obnubilation and active visual hallucinosis, are conspicuous. But these symptoms persist, and there develop more and more the stigmata of dementia praecox, and of chronicity. Our usually too favorable prognosis is belied by this outcome. I have termed this form "schizophrenia deliriosa."

The foil thereto is the "delirium schizophrenoides" which others confirm having seen frequently in the recent epidemics. It is a psychosis arising in close association with the somatic illness, but so colored with the hues and tints of schizophrenia that one feels obliged to give a pessimistic prognosis which is usually belied by the further course of the disease, namely, its eventual disappearance.

I maintain that these two forms are not essentially different. It was our clinical experience that many of the acute post-influenzal psychoses [3] were seriously difficult problems in differential diagnosis, and still more difficult problems in point of prognosis, and that our mistakes seemed to be largely mistakes along the lines indicated by the above two groups. We shortly profited by this, however, but found ourselves in the dilemma of being unable to decide at all as to whether specific cases were delirious or schizophrenic (i.e., waiving the possibility of their being both, which of course was my ultimate conclusion).

Concisely, I may state my conclusion that between the mildest attack of simple delirium and the most profound dementia of late schizophrenia, there is a progressive gradation, not in the intensity of schizophrenic symptoms present (since these are variable products of little prognostic significance), but *in the degree of reversibility*. By the degree of reversibility I mean the potentiality for recovery. I am persuaded that dementia praecox (schizophrenia) is at least in most instances a somatopsychosis, *the psychic manifestations of an encephalitis*. This conception is receiving unexpected support from the epidemic of encephalitis. There has been in the literature repeated mention of the cases of encephalitis closely resembling in symptomatology acute schizophrenia.[4] The acuteness or chronicity, the benign or malignant nature of this encephalitis perhaps determines the degree of reversibility of the schizophrenia. In this it is allied to the clinical features of many other organic brain diseases, e.g., cerebral hemorrhage. Even these, indeed, might be conceived as having degrees of reversibility.

It is on this basis that the pragmatic classification of dementia praecox by prognosis as proposed above is theoretically supported. Diagnosis is chiefly useful for prognosis. Prognosis depends on reversibility. It remains then to determine the conditions of reversibility. They are the touchstones of treatment.

3. The Schizophrenic Syndrome
as a Product of Acute Infectious Disease

May schizophrenia result from acute infectious disease? If so, in what manner and with what frequency does this occur, and what is the relation of this psychotic product to the so-called symptomatic psychoses? To these problems the present study is addressed.

No one now doubts the exogenous origin of some cases of the schizophrenic syndrome, cases of what are in every other respect orthodox "dementia praecox"; Bleuler, Jaspers, Kretschmer, Birnbaum, and others have advanced this fact beyond dispute. Few writers, however, have been statistically precise. To these, Rosanoff [1] and Strecker [2] are exceptions; the former found somatic exciting causes in 26 of 202 cases of schizophrenia, and the latter found that in 17 of 100 cases there were serious or overwhelming physical diseases as precipitants and in 17 others there were somatic precipitants of doubtful (not insignificant) importance.

There is scarcely any literature regarding the percentage of schizophrenic patients in whom the psychosis was precipitated by acute somatic infections, and such statistics would probably be of little value because of the fluctuations in the prevalence and seriousness of infectious disease. More accessible are the casuistic data relative to the psychiatric products of the various somatic diseases, but these data are not abundant and much of the material is useless because of the irreconcilable discrepancies in terminology and nomenclature.

Reprinted from the *Archives of Neurology and Psychiatry,* 20:464–481, September 1928.

So far as is pertinent, the literature may be summarized as follows:

1. Schizophrenia, strictly regarded, occurs occasionally (frequently as compared to other types of psychoses) after any of the acute infectious diseases; it sometimes appears during the acute illness, more frequently during the defervescence and occasionally weeks, months, or years afterward. Kraepelin thought scarlet and typhoid fevers the most frequent precursors; in the more recent literature, influenza is far in the lead, but this is probably due largely to the enormously greater morbidity rate of influenza, with the consequent greater total quantity of psychiatric data.

2. The schizophrenic syndrome, usually not so labeled, but equivalently described and called dementia, acute confusional psychosis (or insanity), acute hallucinatory confusion, catatonia, oneirical delirium, frenosia sensoria, cataphrenia, and delirium schizophrenoides, is frequent following most of the acute somatic diseases, e.g., typhoid fever, scarlet fever, diphtheria, cholera, typhus fever, peritonitis, malaria, recurrent fever, and other diseases.

3. Other psychiatric pictures, e.g., the manic-depressive psychoses, appear in some instances after some, perhaps all, of these diseases, but much less frequently.

The most comprehensive recent study is that of Skliar,[3] whose statistics may be summarized as follows:

Typhus fever: One hundred and nine cases were followed by psychosis, of which only 35 were precipitated by the infectious disease; 9 of the 35 cases resulted in schizophrenia, 10 in manic-depressive psychoses and 6 in hysteria.

Recurrent fever: Forty-one cases of psychosis occurred, of which 9 were precipitated by the infectious disease; 4 of the 9 were cases of schizophrenia, 3 of manic-depressive psychoses and 2 of hysteria.

Typhoid fever: Seven cases were followed by psychosis, of which 5 were precipitated by typhoid fever; 3 of these 5 cases were schizophrenia.

Influenza: In 4 cases influenza was followed by psychosis, of which 2 were of the schizophrenic type.

Malaria: In 4 cases this was followed by psychosis, of which none was a case of schizophrenia.

Cholera: Psychosis occurred in 3 cases, 1 of which was of the schizophrenic type.

In many, but not all, of these cases there was an hereditary taint.

REVIEW OF THE LITERATURE

Tuberculosis. This relationship has been much discussed. Claude and Rose,[4] and Gosline[5] concluded, after a study of 17 cases of schizophrenia, that the mental and physical pictures are so nearly parallel that one must be taken for the cause of the other. Dide[6] gave a table showing that tuberculosis was found at 34 of 202 autopsies (16.83 per cent) in cases of mental diseases other than schizophrenia. Nineteen of these patients died from tuberculosis. Tuberculosis was found at 21 of 36 autopsies (50.75 per cent) in cases of schizophrenia; 14 of these patients died of tuberculosis. He believes that the frequency of tuberculosis in schizophrenic patients means that it plays a causal role. Dide believes that hebephreno-catatonia is a primary toxi-infectious psychosis. "Paranoia" (meaning thereby Kraepelin's paranoid type of schizophrenia) is only secondarily related to the infection, the infection having entered later. Intestinal toxemia is a primary cause, as is also tuberculosis.

Wolfer[7] calls schizophrenia a "metatuberculosis."

Meningitis. Lagriffe[8] reported a case of meningitis accompanied by "mental confusion" from both of which complaints the patient recovered; they were followed in seven years, however, by schizophrenia.

Sepsis. Focal sepsis: Trepsat evidently believes that gastrointestinal and hepatorenal intoxications are responsible for the schizophrenic syndrome; the work of Cotton[9] in this country points in the same direction.

General sepsis: Trepsat[10] quoted Aschaffenburg as reporting that of 132 patients with "puerperal insanity," hebephrenocatatonia developed in 56. Meyer reports 51 cases, with an unfavorable outcome in 10; these cases were designated by M. Claus, who cites Meyer, as catatonia. Trepsat discusses a case of dementia of his own in which gastro-intestinal fever played a part.

Syphilis. The theory of syphilitic schizophrenia persists. Urechia

and Rusdea,[11] for example, stated that the symptoms of schizophrenia may be observed in the course of syphilitic disease of the
brain, including general paralysis. These schizophrenoid symptoms
may be transient or lasting. In one case, the clinical picture was that
of schizophrenia through the entire six-year course from onset to
death. Cases of twenty years' duration have been reported, lumbar
puncture or necropsy finally establishing the diagnosis. These authors
conclude that catatonia is evidently the result of a certain injury to a
certain part of the brain, but the morbid agent causing the injury
need not always be the same. Gosline [12] described one case which was
definitely syphilitic, another which was alcoholic and possibly
syphilitic, and two others, all of which he thought represented instances of schizophrenia produced by the infectious or toxic process.
Ballet and Gallais [13] described a patient, aged 21, with a positive
Wassermann reaction of the blood, although the cerebrospinal fluid
gave a negative reaction; he showed mental confusion simulating
schizophrenia from which he recovered at the end of thirty months,
when the Wassermann test was faintly positive and Argyll-Robertson pupils were still present. Bahr found a positive Wassermann
test in 31 per cent of ninety-five schizophrenic patients. Southard
and Solomon [14] gave the case histories of four neurosyphilitic patients presenting schizophrenic syndromes. Kraepelin [15] mentioned
a schizophrenic form in discussing general paralysis, although he
declined to accept the view of Steiner and Poetzl that syphilis could
cause schizophrenia. Yet, a few others have contradicted these views
on statistical bases, e.g., Wassermann reports (Greene [16]).

Epidemic encephalitis. Typical schizophrenic pictures of various
types have been described in this disease.

M. Briand believes epidemic encephalitis enters into the etiology
of schizophrenia more often than is generally believed. Rogues de
Fursac is of the same opinion, and H. Claude, Conos, and Kahn
are quoted as supporting the view that the syndrome may reappear
in the chronic form and that some dementias, evidenced by fleeting
ocular symptoms and myoclonic contractions, can be referred back
to an epidemic encephalitis.

Babinski and Jargovski report a case of muscular rigidity with a catatonic state, but without other psychic symptoms, following epidemic encephalitis.

Briand and Rouquier mention postencephalitic hebephrenocatatonia; Harmand, pseudodementia praecox; Pierre Kahn, a syndrome of the form of dementia praecox (hebephrenocatatonic and chronic hallucinatory psychosis); Truelle and Petit de Bourges, catatonic syndrome, motor disturbance associated with psychic (hebephreno-catatonic) manifestations. Padeano's conclusions are that cases of pure catatonia are rare, that the pure psychic syndrome (mental confusion, melancholic ideas, hypochondriasis, persecutory states, mania, and catatonia) is equally rare, and that the mixture of organic and psychic symptoms is the most frequent.

Kinnier Wilson [17] reported two cases in which the patients had encephalitis and cerea flexibilitas; one of them was alternately apathetic and noisily excited; the other had hallucinations, and was denudative and "catatonic." Tilney and Riley [18] included a "cataleptic" type in their clinical classification of cases of epidemic encephalitis; this is illustrated by a patient whose relatives believed she had "gone insane." Sicard and Bollack [19] discussed at length the cataleptic picture in encephalitis.

Influenza. Influenza is the only acute febrile disease which occurs with sufficient ubiquity and morbidity to make possible any general statistical study of its psychic effects. The epidemic of 1918–1919 was intense, widespread, and apparently productive of much mental illness; for these reasons, the relation of schizophrenia to acute somatic infections may well be analyzed on the basis of the post-influenzal material.

A great variety of postinfluenzal psychotic pictures occur, the influenzal toxin apparently having unusual neurotoxicity. These pictures may be classified into: (1) the more or less simple deliria; (2) the schizophrenic syndrome sometimes called schizophrenoid delirium, sometimes toxic-infectious psychosis and amentia; and (3) other recognized psychotic entities or reaction types, e.g., general paralysis, manic-depressive psychoses, and psychoneuroses.

The literature is not in entire agreement concerning the statistical enumerations of the relative frequency of various syndromes and entities. Nearly all authors find the schizophrenic syndrome by far the most frequent, but not all are willing to call it schizophrenia. They agree as to the good prognosis. Nearly all consider also that the schizophrenic syndrome may appear both in predisposed (schizoid) and unpredisposed (syntonic) persons, and similarly in those of good as well as those of bad heredity.

The literature just summarized may be given in some detail, as follows:

Waterman and Folsom [20] studied 51 cases of psychosis associated with influenza at the Manhattan State Hospital in 1918 and 1919. Seventeen of 23 cases in males were diagnosed as belonging without doubt to well-recognized psychiatric groups. Of these, 4 were schizophrenia, all the patients being predisposed to this disturbance. Of the 28 cases in females, 3 were regarded as certain and 5 as probable schizophrenia.

Paton [21] remarked the occasional precipitation of schizophrenia by influenza, but ascribed to it only a minor role. Gosline [22] reported on histologic observations on the brain and pointed out the similarity of the observations in a case of influenza with delirium and in cases of schizophrenia; he concluded that "certain cases of dementia praecox are due to infectious or toxic processes."

In a study of 20 cases of postinfluenzal psychoses at the Walter Reed Hospital in 1919, Fell [23] reported schizophrenia as the diagnosis in 5 cases (25 per cent); he also said that "the occurrence of dementia praecox symptoms is not a sure indication of permanency, but such cases run a longer course and recovery is less likely." The same author, in another study,[24] again emphasized the mixture of delirium with schizophrenic symptoms for which he favors the designation "delirium schizophrenoides."

Sandy,[25] in a study of neuropsychiatric cases reported to the office of the surgeon general of the Army, remarked that from among over 70,000 neuropsychiatric cases only 73 could be ascribed to influenza; but of these 73, 7 were cases of schizophrenia (as compared with 32 cases of the infective-exhaustive type, and 4 of the manic-depressive type).

Jelliffe [26] discussed in some detail the mechanisms of the production of schizophrenic symptoms in postinfluenzal infections, but did not give any statistics.

Harris [27] studied 18 cases of postinfluenzal psychosis at the Worcester State Hospital, of which 8 were diagnosed schizophrenia. In 4 of them there was apparently no predisposition to the disturbance.

In a study of the delirium accompanying influenza, Schlessinger [28] described the varieties of delirium observed by him in Geneva, mentioning catatonic states, peculiar automatisms, and stereotypies.

Riese [29] described 6 postinfluenzal cases in detail, including one called "amentia," and two which were probably schizophrenic. Although holding to the usefulness of the amentia concept, he concedes that many cases so-called subsequent to influenza must today be classed as schizophrenia.

In sharp contrast with these observations are such studies as that of Harris and Corcoran [30] at the Brooklyn State Hospital, who did not find any cases of schizophrenia in 50 consecutive cases in which influenza or influenza with pneumonia precipitated a psychosis. Similarly, in an elaborate study of 160 pages, Walther [31] of the University of Berne described 60 cases of postinfluenzal psychoses from the canton of Berne, without anywhere in the book mentioning the words "schizophrenia" or "dementia praecox." The author made much of the old concept of amentia, which he divided into 4 types, comprising 16 cases. He seems to have been cut off entirely from the American and English literature.

Bleuler [32] was exceedingly ambiguous in reference to this subject. "Neither the grippe nor the war has added to the existence of schizophrenia." Elsewhere (p. 363) he says:

> Like Kraepelin I saw several influenza deliria . . . in which paresthesias were interpreted illusionally. In grippe psychoses it is chiefly a question of a schizophrenic sort of dissociation of the mental stream, which appears all the more similar to the schizophrenic because irritations of the nervous system readily give occasion to a kind of physical hallucinations; the affectivity invariably, however, continues to fluctuate. . . . Fever deliria, without a schizoid character . . . also occur at the same time as the infection.

In a printed discussion of the work of Waterman and Folsom, Kirby [33] stated that it seemed improbable in the light of their observations that schizophrenia is precipitated abruptly by influenza, although conceding that peculiar catatonic-like symptoms are frequently observed, and also conceding that "as soon as we get away from the ordinary febrile deliria we come immediately into a very obscure field and must recognize that mixed types occur . . . in very puzzling combinations."

PERSONAL STUDIES

My own study of the problem dealt with approximately 175 cases of acute mental disease admitted to the Boston Psychiatric Hospital in 1918 and 1919, in which influenza was regarded as having something to do with the outbreak of the mental illness. This series has been reported in whole and in part in previous communications.[34] The data relevant to the present discussion are as follows:

Sixty-seven of the total series were diagnosed "dementia praecox" according to the psychiatric standards of that period, and presented an acute syndrome which was convincingly schizophrenic to an unprejudiced staff. Of 50 patients who were followed up, 35 were found apparently to have recovered completely; 5 were improved, 5 were unimproved, and 5 were worse. The diagnosis was not always confirmed by subsequent examinations by the staff, the diagnosis being changed (frequently because of the tendency toward recovery) to manic-depressive or toxic-infectious psychoses. Whatever term the nosologic categories ultimately utilized, the acute picture presented the unmistakable schizophrenic stigmas, including intrapsychic ataxia, emotional-ideational splitting, incoherence, stereotypies, and other bizarre expressions, and were not conspicuously different from the usual types of schizophrenia.

SUMMARY OF THE MATERIAL ON INFLUENZA

From my observations, and from the literature in general, it would seem that the schizophrenic syndrome after influenza is characterized by three notable features: (1) it is relatively the most frequent psychotic disorder produced; (2) it occurs with and without predisposition or hereditary taint, and (3) in most cases, it terminates in complete recovery, in some cases promptly and in some after many months or even a year or more.

Implications of the data on influenza: If one retains the Kraepelinian conceptions of schizophrenia, one must think from this that influenza precipitated many cases which only seemed in the acute phase to be schizophrenia but which actually were somatic psychoses or cyclothymic psychoses of strongly schizophrenoid coloring.

For those, including myself, who reject Kraepelin's conception of schizophrenia in favor of the conception of a schizophrenic syndrome of varied and cooperative etiologies, including the toxemia of infections, representing certain phases of psychic disintegration with varied courses and varied degrees of reversibility, the conclusions are that many cases of true schizophrenia occurred subsequent to influenza, most of which ended in recovery, indicating a benign or reversible process.

IMPLICATIONS OF THE DATA ON INFLUENZA AS RELATING TO THE PSYCHIATRIC THEORY

One may judge from case histories and inferences from the older nosologic designations that these same conclusions and implications apply to the psychiatric results of other acute somatic diseases, although probably to a lesser degree, owing to the alleged greater neurotoxicity of influenza. The differential diagnosis problem centers about the "amentiafrage," i.e., as to whether there is any intrinsic psychopathologic difference between delirium and schizophrenia, aside from chronicity. Between them, for a long time a borderline group, best described by Meynert as "amentia," was postulated. Subsequently it was given up by most psychiatrists; the Kraepelinian school abandoned it because of the doctrine of the specific entity conception of schizophrenia; the French and some Italian psychiatrists abandoned it for precisely the opposite reason, namely, because they placed it with delirium and schizophrenia in a confusional syndrome group. Regis,[35] for example, wrote of the schizophrenic and of the obviously somatogenic pictures that they were essentially similar processes, and in 1909 he asserted that "dementia praecox is essentially a toxic psychosis" and classified it as a species of "mental confusion," a descriptive denominator of the aberrant mental states accompanying or following acute somatic disease. He insisted on the essential inseparability of schizophrenia and "chronic" mental confusion. He circumvented the difficulty of pronounced predisposition in schizophrenia by allowing two forms, the *"constitutionelle"* and the *"accidentelle."*

Dupré, Deny, and others of the French school followed essentially the ideas of Regis, but the idea was perhaps most ardently advanced by Dide,[36] who proposed "to give to the different states [of dementia praecox] the name toxic-infectious psychoses, subacute and chronic, primary [hebephrenocatatonic] and secondary [paranoid]." Deny was more conservative, but freely conceded that "it is certain there exist very great analogies between the clinical picture of dementia praecox and the states of confusion, of torpor and dream-states which characterize the toxic-infectious psychoses, and the autotoxic origin of that affection is rendered very possible by this fact."

LITERATURE PERTAINING TO THE THEORY

Bleuler regarded the schizophrenic syndrome as capable of varied pathogenesis. He conceded the indefiniteness of the definitions, the difficulties of diagnostic differentiation, and the probable relationships of even the most typical deliria and schizophrenia. Some of his characteristic passages should be cited:

There remains the relationship between schizophrenia and infectious diseases. Schizophrenia often begins with a febrile disease and in some cases there seems to have been nothing abnormal prior to the febrile illness. This could be a coincidence but one often sees how a fever is followed by some improvement; if it thus influences a psychosis, one must also assume that there is some relationship between the fever and the aggravation of mental symptoms. This may be accomplished by physical or psychic influence. It must further be remembered that many cases, which were formerly placed in the amentia group, really belong to our schizophrenia and that a weak physique plus a febrile illness constitute the etiology.[37]

Most difficult is the differentiation of schizophrenia from the forms designated acute confusion. A useful diagnostic description of these does not yet exist.

In these forms, with which I may here consider the fever psychoses, I know of absolutely no symptom which may not also occur in schizophrenia; in the foreground stands confusion, often with it hallucinosis. Both are very ambiguous symptoms; and no one has yet described anything characteristic of the confusion and of the hallucinosis of these psychoses. Thus nothing else remains than the diagnosis of schizophrenia in those cases of confusion showing schizophrenic symptoms; but where, despite a good examination, schizophrenic symptoms are not to be found, one must accept one of these other confusions. Outspoken catatonic symptoms, with the exception of flexibilitas cerea and especially command-automatism, speak against any such confusion and against Kraepelinian amentia. Frank negativism and impulsive verbigeration in such a condition always indicate schizophrenia, even if it is not at once possible to find the schizophrenic disturbances of association and affect.

I may add that we have done well with this method of diagnosis for years, in that it has not been necessary to revise our diagnosis in any case in which the examination justified us in making a diagnosis. And yet one cannot be satisfied with such a negative differentiation. Though one does not find schizophrenic signs in a particular case today, they may yet be seen tomorrow.[38]

Later he stated:

Many think they are turning against me when they say physical changes lie at the bottom of the group (dementia praecox). I myself have expressly emphasized this fact. One must acknowledge that at least the great majority of clinical pictures which are now collected under the name dementia praecox rests on some toxic action or anatomic process which arises independently of psychic influences. That such groups (those arising from psychic causes) exist is yet to be proved, while the principal group in my opinion is certainly caused by organic changes.[39]

This was definitely the view of Ernest Southard,[40] supported by his neuropathologic research observations and his ingenious correlations of these with clinical symptoms, a process which students of epidemic encephalitis syndromes are endeavoring to further. The work of Alzheimer and others of the "brain spot" theory (versus the "mind twist" theory—a figure of Dr. Southard's) need only be mentioned.

Kraepelin, under the title of "infectious imbecility," an expression certainly not generally used by American psychiatrists, describes "a temporary or permanent diminution of general mental ability after illness." Influenza, acute arthritis and, occasionally in children, pertussis bring about the milder forms running for from a few weeks to a month with or without delirium. More severe forms follow typhoid fever, erysipelas, cholera, variola, malaria, tuberculous peritonitis, and acute arthritis. They begin with delirium or confusion, depression, delusions of sinning and of persecution, mild hallucinosis, usually complete disorientation, and marked amnesia. Silliness, impulsive violence, insomnia, and anorexia are frequent. The prognosis is "gradual recovery in a few months in 50 per cent of the cases, the remainder proceeding to permanent imbecility." The impossibility of deciding whether such cases should be regarded as belonging to the hitherto delimited groups of toxic-infectious psychoses, epidemic encephalitis, or catatonic dementia praecox is obvious.

Bumke [41] has recently called attention to the similarity of certain types of schizophrenia to some other symptomatic psychoses, not only in symptomatology, but also in the conditions of onset, and that there frequently is no difference between the two except that one results in recovery and the other in dementia. This does not indicate that the two should be separated.

Bumke supports the view that schizophrenic and so-called symptomatic psychoses frequently differ only in outcome, and hence essentially not at all. In summarizing modern psychiatric trends, he points out again that while it has long been recognized that schizophrenia does not always lead to dementia, the question arises as to whether the end results of schizophrenia are really anything more than a form of unfavorable departure which different mental diseases may take. That catatonic syndromes in the narrower sense are not specific has been known for a long time; also that they are apt to follow any kind of injury, that qualitatively similar injuries would cause one brain to have a transitory psychosis and another to have a long-lasting and even incurable defect, and that the picture in both cases would remain the same for a long time. It is conceivable, he thinks, that these things resemble the schizophrenic process. Here also the course would not depend on this or that disease entity but, as in other pathologic processes, on the organism and the disease-producing causes.

Elsewhere Bumke [42] expressed the belief that the investigations of constitutional difference have led to an underestimation of exogenous factors in schizophrenic syndromes, and that the whole structure of the conception of schizophrenia is crumbling.

Hall and Neyman,[43] basing their studies on 50 cases selected on a basis of a recent onset and a definite clinical syndrome, in which the patients were subjected to a routine physical and mental examination in which all the modern laboratory methods were employed, including examination of the cerebrospinal fluid, the endocrine functions, basal metabolism, sugar tolerance tests, etc., concluded that there were definite toxic complications in some of the cases; that in other cases there were endocrine disturbances; and that the term "dementia praecox" represents not a disease entity but a clinical syndrome capable of subdivision into groups associated with (1) toxic conditions, (2) endocrine disturbances, and (3) psychogenic disturbances.

Hoch [44] wished to differentiate organic reactions, affective reactions, and trend reactions, applying this differentiation to delirium and other somatopsychoses. He regarded amentia as a transition state between the simple deliria and frank schizophrenia.

Austregesilo [45] called this syndrome cataphrenia, defining it as a state of mental debility of the dementia type, differing from dementia as ordinarily conceived, however, in that it may retrogress to complete recovery.

Stransky [46] expressed the belief that the "dementia accompanying amentia" is differentiated from that accompanying schizophrenia by the natural expression of affect. Since the schizophrenic alteration of facial expression in mild cases is not in every case recognizable, one cannot make a differential diagnosis by this sign alone. Consideration of etiology helps very little. There are many such confusions without weakened states and without fever; in two cases, Stransky could demonstrate at post-mortem examination only chronic nephritis. On the other hand, schizophrenia so often becomes manifest on the occasion of febrile illness that this criterion is utterly useless. Much more certain is the anamnesis, but unfortunately only in the direction of a schizophrenia which has already given sufficient indications in the symptomatology.

Bonhoeffer [47] thinks that organic deliria of the type described by Hoch were rarely seen during the period of defervescence, but that the pictures seen then in various types of amentia differed from organic deliria in that the patients were apt to be less accessible, less disoriented, less variable in their level of consciousness, nearly or entirely free from speech defect and more severely and permanently incoherent; that they were apt to manifest more complicated thought content, a wider flight of ideas and other manic symptoms; and also that they were apt to act more like catatonic patients and to show negativism, stereotypies, and verbigeration, "so much so that no symptom that occurs in dementia praecox cannot be seen here also . . . and the differential diagnosis may be very difficult . . . or only possible on the ground of etiology and onset or outcome . . . but these cases usually get well." (These, as will be recalled, are almost Bleuler's words.)

Numerous neuropathologists have pointed out that the psychologic changes and histologic observations described in schizophrenia are similar to those found in toxic deliria in cases complicated by severe visceral disease. Of these investigators, Southard [48] is the best known, but Rosanoff,[49] Sioli,[50] Alzheimer, and many writers quoted by Gosline [51] could be mentioned.

No one has put the whole question better than has Phillip Coombs Knapp [52] in a paper read before the American Neurological Association twenty years ago, the substance of which is incorporated in the first few and in the last paragraphs, which are worthy of nearly full quotation:

The history of the differentiation of acute confusional insanity from other forms of mental disease follows the ordinary course. First established as an independent affection by Delasiauve and Westphal, it might fairly have been supposed to have won definite recognition with the appearance of Meynert's masterly essay in 1889 and Chaslin's monograph a few years later, even though English and American writers, always slow at that time in assimilating the psychiatric work done upon the Continent, made little mention of it.

The subsequent history of confusional insanity, however, has been peculiar. With a number of writers *amentia,* the term suggested by Meynert, was substituted for confusional insanity, but the development of Kraepelin's doctrine has forced amentia decidedly into the background and established dementia praecox as the chief mental disease. Amentia, according to Kraepelin, occurs in only one-half of 1 per cent of admissions to his clinic, while dementia praecox occurs in about 15 per cent and forms the great bulk of the permanent chronic inmates of the asylums. Stransky reports cases of amentia as a rarity and Jahrmarker believes that many cases of this rare disease are really dementia praecox or maniacal-depressive insanity. There has been a tendency, however, to include amentia with the toxic and infectious psychoses and to admit some connection if not an actual identity of the affections.

In the differentiation between the two affections, Kraepelin, as is well known, stated that in dementia praecox the onset is gradual and there is not a previous history of exhausting influences. Among the characteristic symptoms are negativism, verbigeration, mutism, stereotyped attitudes, and catatonic states. The patient is not influenced by emotions, and his attention is defective, but he has good perception and orientation. He has a fair memory for recent events, understands his environment, has correct ideas of time, and recognizes persons. Hallucinations and delusions are less frequent. In amentia, on the other hand, consciousness and memory are more impaired, perception and orientation are much affected, the patient has no knowledge of persons or of recent events and he is often emotional and has hallucinations and delusions. Negativism, verbigeration, and stereotyped attitudes are rare. Amentia is of sudden onset, and often follows some exhaustion. Recovery is not uncommon, while in dementia praecox the tendency is to mental deterioration and recovery is rare and apt to be incomplete or followed by a recurrence of the disease with increasing dementia.

Many of the symptoms which Kraepelin attributes to dementia praecox, however, were described by Meynert as characteristic of amentia. The confusion of amentia, for example, is regarded as due to a disturbance of association, the projection system being unaffected. Perception is, therefore, not disturbed, but when the process advances further the projection system also becomes involved, and a state of stupor develops in which perception is also affected. Confusion and stupor, with Meynert, are thus different states of the disease, the disturbance of perception marking a greater involvement of the brain. Kraepelin, however, assumes that the disturbance of perception is one of several symptoms which serve to differentiate amentia from dementia praecox. There can be no doubt that the cases reported by Meynert and his description of amentia correspond very closely to the cases and descriptions given by Kraepelin and his followers of dementia praecox. The distinction between the two is admittedly difficult at times (Paton). It is therefore not surprising that Bianchi frankly admits that amentia, acute dementia, dementia praecox catatonia, stupor, and mental confusion are merely syndromes representing certain phases of a complex psychosis, to which he gives the name of sensory phrenosis, or that Regis and many other French writers regard dementia praecox simply as a more advanced stage of acute confusion. . . .

The fact that a term is inappropriate or etymologically incorrect is not a sufficient reason for discarding it, if, like hysteria, it has the sanction of long usage. Dementia praecox has not that sanction, and, what is still worse, it is a term prejudicial from the start. It emphasizes the feature of dementia as the inevitable outcome of the disease, which to ordinary minds, in spite of the term "acute curable dementia," only too often connotes an incurable terminal state. The teaching of Kraepelin emphasizes the element of mental deterioration if not of actual dementia, which is not an inevitable result even if we accept the extreme doctrines of the Heidelberg school. Bianchi's term of sensory phrenosis is not open to this objection, and, if we accept with him the probable identity of confusional insanity (amentia) and dementia praecox, we can extend a larger hope to the patient and his friends by recognizing that complete recovery is often possible and that the patient is not inevitably doomed to "dementia praecox."

In brief, the manifestations of certain kinds of deliria and certain kinds of schizophrenia look exactly alike and these conditions are differentiated only by the onset and the termination, a differentiation which in this stage of knowledge is begging the question. This business of diagnosis by outcome instead of by psychologic analysis is an illusory self-deception resulting logically enough from the psychiatric fundamentalism accompanying the introduction of Kraepelin's useful but acknowledged premature groupings to a practical and suggestible American medical profession. It has required two decades for an attitude of pluralism in psychiatric diagnosis, such as that of the French, to make perceptible alterations in our technic in spite of the insistence of such leaders as Adolf Meyer, with his "reaction types," Ernest Southard with his syndrome and major group conceptions, and Jelliffe and White with their emphasis on analysis.

After all, the delimitation and designation of the syndrome type is a matter of descriptive partitioning which does not of itself contribute to one's understanding of the patient or the disease process. Much more important is an analysis of the psychic architecture of the particular case and the kinds of damage done to it by certain accidents (e.g., somatic infections) and its reactions thereto.

That in some cases this damage is a stripping-off of superficial elaborations of consciousness or a breaking of surface tension relationships, in such a way as to reveal an underlying skeleton of the configuration known as "schizophrenic" is a theory not difficult to apply to the known facts, and supported by much of the clinical data. The particular kind of psychotic picture revealed by the toxic attack on the encephalon and its consciousness-fabrications probably depends on the kind of mental substructure pre-existing, to speak in static terms, or on the type of habitual conflict solution, to speak in dynamic terms. That these pre-existing substructures may be correlated with certain characterologic aspects known as "temperament," or with certain anatomic aspects known as "Körperbau" is without the province of this discussion, except so far as in future studies they may appear to be correlated with features of the clinical picture revealed by the toxic disintegration.

Representing the analytic point of view in the study of the psychic products of infection, Jelliffe,[53] in a combined descriptive and analytic study of postinfluenzal conditions, says of the psychotic conditions:

> By almost insensible gradations, mild or profound depressed states develop on a basis of the toxic condition plus a greater individual unconscious conflict. The flight into the psychosis may become an overcompensatory one in those by no means rare cases, in which suicide is affected or attempted. Less severe depressions are the rule and are very frequent. . . . At times the depression may be accompanied by delusional ideas. These are not specific. They have no relation to the influenza per se but are the symbolized products of the individual's own conditioned reflexes or complexes, using a physiological (Bechterew, Pavlow) or a psychoanalytic term (Freud, Jung). They tell of the patient's conflicts which existed long before the influenza came along, but which by reason of what for lack of a better concept we call the "reduction in resistance" or "lowering of the psychological level" because of the toxemia and the attending worries, financial or in the love life, permit the conflict to break through under various camouflaged forms.

Hollos and Ferenczi,[54] after an illuminating exposition of the psychic significance and interpretation of certain symptoms and trends in cases of general paralysis, added that "of course, one should seek to explain in a similar manner the non-paretic cases of anoia (amentia) and the symptoms of most toxic deliria. . . . Through these patterns of the individual soul the way would be pointed out for the explanation of psychical tendencies toward unification hitherto unexplained, even of the basic facts of thought association."

CONCLUSIONS

Studies reported by me and by others justify the following conclusions relative to the schizophrenic syndrome and infectious diseases:

Infectious disease, not to mention other exogenous agents, in certain persons breaks the integrative fabric of consciousness and releases a psychologic regression of various degrees and types. These regressive pictures include all of the recognized "reaction types," but apparently most frequently the delirious and the schizophrenic. The syndromes formerly designated "dementia praecox," "toxic-infectious psychosis," "amentia," and "confusional psychosis," are all included, the differentiation being in many cases neither possible nor useful. The particular type of psychotic picture revealed in a particular case by a toxic attack on the encephalon probably depends on the kind of mental substructure pre-existing, and not demonstrably on the kind of toxin (or infection). Evidences of the nature of this substructure may or may not be previously apparent in the ordinary descriptive observation of the patient; similarly, the hereditary record may or may not contain outspoken evidences of psychopathy. The schizophrenic types of regressions are relatively frequent, but, although ordinarily ominously regarded, they are, when of this somatogenic precipitation, usually reversible; i.e., the splitting (or stripping or breaking of surface tension relationships, or whatever may be the best figure of speech) tends to be benign rather than malignant.

DISCUSSION

[The following questions submitted to Dr. Menninger before the Commission, together with the answers to them, are here reported verbatim.]

DR. WHITE: I shall repeat a question which I asked this morning and which apparently was misunderstood. Here are thirty-five of fifty patients who get well, and I am wondering whether the cross-section of the psychosis, when it is in full bloom, would not show the presence of certain constructive, conative tendencies. I should like to know whether you have discovered any evidences of rehabilitating, reconstituting factors at work in the direction of recovery, and if so, what they are.

DR. MENNINGER: I do not know what they are. I do not even know whether they are there. I infer that they must be, and that it would be interesting and valuable to know what they are. Further analysis of the clinical material, some of which was recorded stenographically as produced by the patients, may provide a basis for conclusions on this important point.

DR. KIRBY: I should like to ask whether in Dr. Menninger's series it was possible to distinguish any predominating clinical types. It would be important to know whether the usual paranoid, catatonic, or hebephrenic clinical pictures were represented, or were his cases essentially all deliria which presented certain features which he thought indicated a relationship to the schizophrenic reaction type?

DR. MENNINGER: We were not very much interested in the Kraepelinian type at the time and did not always classify our cases according to them. I have only an impressionistic recollection as to how they would be tabulated. I think the excited types of catatonic reaction were the most frequent. (Reference to the case histories indicates the correctness of this impression—of thirty-three cases in which a typing was attempted, fourteen were listed as catatonic, eight as hebephrenic, and eleven as paranoid. Some of the latter were labeled "paranoid or hebephrenic.")

DR. BASSOE: Did I understand that you meant to include under schizophrenia the types that we used to call confusional insanity and amentia, or, if not, what is the relative proportion of cases to which these old terms would apply?

DR. MENNINGER: I think that it is impossible to contradict Bleuler, who says that a useful distinction between those pictures and the schizophrenia picture does not exist. It is of course impossible to say what these would have been called ten or fifteen years ago. I have been of the impression, from reading, that the same pictures of "acute confusional psychoses" that occurred after influenza in 1889–1892 would have been called acute schizophrenia by us. We were often aware that the somatogenic factors were important, and of course we saw many cases in which we thought them chiefly responsible, and diagnosed such cases according to the current nomenclature for somatogenic psychoses ("toxic-infectious psychosis," etc.). Those that we diagnosed as schizophrenia, however, possessed definitely and abundantly the earmarks, as it were, of orthodox schizophrenia.

DR. JELLIFFE: Dr. Menninger has very nicely delimited a problem, in so far as he has spoken only of possible relationships following such types of acute infectious disease which of themselves are more or less limited. He has spoken of typhoid fever, measles, scarlet fever, influenza, etc., those types of infectious disease which, by reason of the transitory nature of the stress put on the organism, might in a sense be excluded, as he has more or less excluded them, as occasioning factors. Now I should like to ask him if he were to consider some of the more chronic infectious types of disease, what would the nature of his response be?

Thus, for instance, shall we say, tuberculosis? Would he say a word about the anomalous situations that arise in syphilis and the pictures that look like schizophrenia? Might he say a word about the as yet unrecognized so-called focal infections, and of course leave out the subject of encephalitis, which I wish to talk about.

DR. MENNINGER: Tuberculosis, syphilis, focal infections, and encephalitis are dealt with in the body of my presentation but were omitted from the abstract as presented to the association. It is my personal conviction that these chronic infections are of even more practical importance in the precipitation of psychotic picture, including the schizophrenic syndrome, than is influenza. They are somewhat less dramatic, however, and because of their continued prevalence are somewhat less accessible to a statistical study of the type undertaken by us with influenza. Some writers have felt very definitely that all the chronic infections mentioned by Dr. Jelliffe are frequently responsible for the calling forth of the schizophrenic syndrome. Of course, we all know that they frequently, in fact usually, occur without severe psychopathologic accompaniments, and it is likely that we should consider the existence of a conflict between the degree to which "somatic compliance" (Freud) affords a gratification for libidinous tension and the degree to which the life adjustment already engineered by the cerebrum is impaired by an injury from these exogenous toxins. Concerning these intricate problems, no one is better fitted to speak than Dr. Jelliffe.

DR. ADOLF MEYER: I should like to ask a question which in years past was occasionally raised by critics of my dynamogenetic conception. In your experience, how frequent are those cases that present a definitely destructive development, and to what extent were you able to convince yourself that a constitutional study and a previous history of the case had been made, so that one would be able to say that the condition was definitely a deterioration produced by the infectious disease itself? Is there, in the deterioration that is produced by the infectious processes, adequate evidence that we might be dealing with fever damage, or things of that sort, or do we have to admit that perhaps the literature in that direction is, and will be, thoroughly deficient, until the importance and difficulty of the constitutional problem is fully realized by the investigators?

DR. MENNINGER: The degree of visibility of the underlying substructure before being exposed by the scraping-off process or what you may call it, varied considerably. In some instances, it was conspicuous that a case was (shall I say) predisposed; that it took only a little pull on the trigger to fire the gun. In other cases, however, there was no apparent predisposition and no hereditary taint; and, while there is no way of saying that more investigations might not have found it, certainly the routine investigations did not find it. This was similarly reported by a number of authors, some of whom were not sympathetic with our point of view that the syndrome was a frequent one.

However, Dr. Meyer, I certainly should not want to give the impression of being unitarian enough to suppose that any one thing has any one cause. I am pluralistic enough to insist that there could be no one cause for schizophrenia. Influenza or other somatic infection is not a cause, but it may be one of the factors involved in the debacle. I think I said seven years ago that influenza caused psychosis. I have grown older since and I hope, wiser. I have certainly changed my mind.

4. The Amelioration of Mental
Disease by Influenza

That any somatic disease may influence any mental disease favorably is a matter of great theoretical and practical importance. The malarial treatment of paresis is a concrete example of its clinical utilization.[1] But its theoretical implications extend far into the complicated questions of the interrelations of psychic and somatic disease and touch intimately on the important problem of reversibility.

That it is a fact of repeated observation that somatic disease may favorably affect pre-existing psychotic manifestations should not require much evidence here. Pinel[2] enumerates various disorders "operating to produce a permanency of recovery." Jacobi[3] mentioned it in 1844. Koster[4] wrote an inaugural dissertation on it in 1848 at Bonn; and the literature contains fully two score contributions, case reports, and discussions. Back of all this, of course, is the theory, presumably based on many observations, of traumatic or shock treatment.

But the precise delimitation of the observed "fact" and the present status of the data relative to the problem merit recapitulation.

DELIMITATION

Symptom manifestations of mental illness, i.e., "attacks of mental disease," are sometimes (1) precipitated by somatic infectious disease, (2) aggravated by somatic infectious disease, or (3) amel-

Read before the New York Neurological Society, March 5, 1929. Reprinted from the *Journal of the American Medical Association*, 94:630–634, March 1, 1930.

iorated by somatic infectious disease. As far as 1 and 2 are concerned, all types of mental disease and all types of infections are included. For example, it is known that influenza may precipitate or aggravate all known types of mental disease pictures.

$$\text{Individual} + \text{Influenza} \rightarrow \begin{cases} \text{Schizophrenia} \\ \text{Deliria} \\ \text{Mania} \\ \text{Melancholia} \\ \quad \text{etc.} \end{cases}$$

It is also known that schizophrenia, for example, may be provoked into external expression by many agents including any and all infectious diseases.

$$\text{Individual} + \begin{cases} \text{Influenza} \\ \text{Typhoid} \\ \text{Trauma} \\ \text{Disappointment} \\ \quad \text{etc.} \end{cases} \rightarrow \text{Schizophrenia}$$

In regard to the ameliorative process, there is evidence in the literature [5] that various of these mental disease pictures—melancholia, mania, confusional psychosis, hebephrenia, catatonia, paranoia, epilepsy, idiocy, paresis—may be favorably affected by one of these infections: typhoid,[6] typhus fever,[7] recurrent fever,[8] scarlet fever,[9] rheumatic fever,[10] smallpox,[11] angina,[12] pneumonia,[13] pleurisy,[14] abscesses,[15] erysipelas,[16] diphtheria,[17] measles,[18] cholera,[19] malaria,[20] osteomyelitis,[21] and influenza.

My own particular interest in this field has been influenza, and this study deals particularly with specific instances of its ameliorative effects on mental diseases. Its deleterious effects are so many and so well known that this should make more interesting its function in the opposite direction. I shall present briefly: (1) a review of the literature on influenzal amelioration of mental disease; (2) reports of cases of my own observation; (3) an analysis of the cases; and (4) the theoretical implications of the phenomenon of amelioration *ex nocentibus.*

REVIEW OF THE LITERATURE

The 1889–1891 epidemic of influenza brought forth a great number of contributions dealing with its psychiatric aspects. Only five of these, so far as I could find, present actual case reports of amelioration, although it is occasionally mentioned as occurring by several others.

1. Gauster,[22] an asylum superintendent in Vienna, in the course of a general report describes two cases: one a recovery, one a remission. He says:

> A severe melancholia completely recovered under the influence of severe influenza; the patient was transferred—mentally restored—to a general hospital for treatment of a pleurisy which developed.
>
> A case of chronic delusional psychosis showed a tendency toward improvement during an influenzal attack, and recovery seemed hopeful, but a severe relapse occurred shortly.

2. Helweg,[23] a Danish observer, reported two cases of long-standing "puerperal psychosis," one cured, one improved by attacks of influenza. One woman was thirty-two; her psychosis had begun three years previously, after a delivery, and had progressed through delusional and hallucinatory stages into "dementia"; but after an attack of influenza in February 1889, complicated by pneumonia, she improved and was discharged well.

The other patient was twenty-eight and had been ill four years with a postpuerperal psychosis; she, too, had influenza and pneumonia and was mentally improved afterward to the point of being capable of some work in the institution, although still "slightly idiotic."

3. Metz [24] describes in detail a dramatic case in which a bricklayer, aged thirty-two, of negative family history but typical schizoid makeup ("reserved," "touchy"), became increasingly restless, suspicious, deluded, and excited, accusing his wife and others, arming himself, and threatening to shoot various persons. After eight months this led to his commitment, February 21, 1889. In the institution he became increasingly disturbed, suspicious, deluded, hallucinated, and

aggressive, attacking another patient and requiring restraint (a typical picture of excited schizophrenia).

January 13, he developed typical influenza, and was ill for four days, his temperature never exceeding 39.4 C. (102.9 F.). January 17, he wrote an exceedingly sensible letter to his wife acknowledging his illness and his delusions, and agreeing to stay longer for observation. Thereafter he appeared to be perfectly well mentally—free from delusions, hallucinations, and emotional disturbances—and was dismissed entirely well on February 8, 1890.

4. From the epidemic in Greece in 1898 comes the remarkable case reported by Coveos.[25] A Greek boy, aged ten, had so-called epilepsy, which had begun when he was three, and was having two attacks every other day. The convulsions had been limited to spasm of the face and neck muscles with drooling followed by severe headaches. He also had a speech defect. The family and past history were negative. The "signs of idiocy were clear from the sixth year on," and increased so that he was completely idiotic at eight, and "so demented that he ate the dung of man and animals."

He had a severe attack of influenza, lasting thirty days. The author remarks that the parents hoped he would die. He began to recover from the influenza and simultaneously from his idiocy and epilepsy. He returned to school and made better grades than his healthy brother and even than many others of his age.

This case gave rise to considerable discussion at one time and Jean Foustenaous, editor of *Grèce médicale,* discussed it in his journal.[26] He considers it a case of gross brain disease, possibly hydrocephalic encephalitic, hemorrhagic, or neoplastic. He favors the first, but he does not make it clear wherein this favors the improvement.

5. The pandemic of 1918 brought forth a few additional and better recorded instances. Damaye,[27] for example, reported three cases. In a woman, aged twenty-eight, the schizophrenic[28] picture developed after her husband's death in the war and lasted a year prior to an attack of influenza in September 1918 of ten days' duration. As the influenza subsided, her excitement did likewise, and she was discharged cured October 30, 1918.

Another woman, aged twenty-seven, had a manic-depressive psychosis and a depressed phase with agitation, anxiety, and ideas of persecution and suicide. Exactly one year after admission, i.e., in September 1918, she had influenza and bronchopneumonia, her temperature reaching 40 C. (104 F.). In the course of this illness her delusional ideas faded and disappeared, and she recovered completely (in about two weeks).

Damaye's third patient was a youth, aged twenty, who presented a schizophrenic picture [29] without much question, unchanged after eighteen months. During the epidemic in the fall he contracted influenza (October 10) of the gastro-intestinal type, with a fever of 37.5 to 38 C. (99.5 to 100.4 F.); the duration of the illness was not stated. Following this disturbance, however, his mental state improved rapidly, the delirium disappeared, and by November 1 he was entirely well.[30]

6. Latapie [31] also reported two cases, one cured, one only provoked to remission. The cure occurred in a married woman, aged thirty, admitted to the asylum in January 1918, in maniacal excitement with incoherence, confusion, and delusions of persecution, which continued fairly constantly until November, when these symptoms disappeared entirely during an attack of influenza. During December she assisted in the care of other influenza patients and was dismissed in January 1919, well.

The remission occurred in a married woman, aged thirty-five, who entered the asylum in August 1917, presenting such schizophrenic stigmas as hallucinations, and delusions of having two stomachs, of being controlled by electricity, and of being forced to talk against her will. During an attack of influenza in November 1918, she appeared transformed, relinquished her delusions and hallucinations, and seemed normal only until the influenza abated, when the former picture reappeared.

7. Moreira [32] observed "ameliorations of mental disease both temporary and permanent after influenza but no complete cures." One case is cited, briefly, of a man, aged thirty-three, with a manic picture of seven months' duration, who improved after an influenzal attack.

8. Numerous writers have cited instances of the improvement or cure of epileptic manifestations by influenza specifically, e.g., Maillard and Brune [33] and Damaye,[34] and a case is included in a report by Ebaugh [35] of a white child, aged nine, ill-nourished, listless, and stupid, who had had convulsions since the age of two, and numerous acute infections and diseases. The convulsions stopped after an attack of influenza.

Dr. David F. Weeks of the New Jersey hospital, Dr. W. T. Shanahan of the New York Hospital, Dr. A. S. Hubbard of the Kansas Hospital, and Dr. H. B. Carriel of the Illinois Hospital for Epileptics observed numerous instances of the remission of attacks during the acute influenzal illness, as indicated by personal communications to me, reported elsewhere.[36]

Two cases were discovered and noted by Leledy,[37] the details of which I have been unable to secure. One was a personal observation (case LXXXIII), the other a report of Jouriac [38] from the Blois (insane) Hospital (observation XCIX).

REPORT OF AUTHOR'S CASES

The following cases have come under my own observation:

Case 1. *Epilepsy, cure.*[39] A school boy, aged fourteen, white, with a father subject to temper tantrums and a mother to chronic headaches, began to have epileptiform seizures at the rate of about one a month in August 1916. In September 1918 he contracted severe influenza, in the course of which he had three or four more seizures, and thereafter none. He was lost sight of, however, within the year.

Case 2. *Epileptic psychosis, remission.*[40] A woman, aged thirty, confined to an institution for epilepsy, with much pointless logorrhea and superficial hyperactivity, was severely ill with influenza for most of two weeks, recovering gradually. During the period of high fever she seemed entirely altered in personality— quiet, intelligent, and emotionally responsive. This gave way to her former state as the physical illness declined.

Case 3. *Epilepsy, improvement and remission.* Six patients at Craig Colony had fewer seizures during the influenza month (six weeks) than their usual wont; seven patients had fewer attacks a month for the following nine months. These cases were reported to me personally by Dr. Shanahan.

Case 4. *Chronic mania, remission.* A very disturbed old offender at the Kansas State Hospital for the Criminal Insane, seen with Dr. Sherman Axford, had been in practically the same condition of excitement and destructive hyperactivity for eight years. He talked incessantly, until voiceless in fact, tore up his bedding, and kept constantly on the move. During an attack of influenza in 1918, during which he was severely ill, his excitement completely subsided, and he conversed quietly and sensibly with the physician and nurse, and manifested none of his antics. On recovery from the infection, however, he resumed his former mental status. Six months later a similar remission occurred during a streptococcic infection of his hand. Since then he has slowly and very slightly improved.

Case 5. *Migraine, cured.* H. W., a graduate male nurse, aged thirty-five, had suffered from severe migraine attacks every two to six weeks since his earliest recollection, and had missed much school on account of them. He had no visual symptoms, but typical nausea, prostration, vomiting, and cessation were present. His mother and only sister were similarly affected. He had no children. In 1918, during the pandemic, he had a moderately severe attack of influenza. Thereafter he never had another headache (ten years). Once only he had a gastrointestinal upset with headache, at Thanksgiving time, but not typical migraine. He does not know of any other changes in himself.

Case 6. *Idiocy, improvement.* This remarkable case was the occasion of my first interest in this subject, ten years ago. A child, aged six, the daughter of college-bred parents of bad heredity from the psychopathic standpoint, was admitted to a state school for the feeble-minded at the age of four, physically normal but in point of intelligence an idiot, with a mental age of ten months. Many details of her birth history and early infancy are recorded in a previous report of the case, together with psychiatric and psychologic examination data which will be passed over here.[41] Fourteen months after admission, at the age of five, she had severe influenza plus bronchopneumonia, plus empyema, with a long convalescence. During this convalescence she manifested marked evidences of mental awakening (detailed in the previous report). Her automatic purposeless movements disappeared, she took an interest in things, became tidy, learned to dress and feed herself, and learned kindergarten participation. In six months her intelligence quotient had gone from 27 to 40; a year later it was 52, two years later 68. Her mental age, in other words, developed more rapidly than her chronological age—and at eight years (1922) she had reached a mental age of nearly six and was doing first grade work.[42]

A report of her development since 1922 is not available.

I myself have not observed improvement in any cases of schizophrenia or psychoneurosis or melancholia after influenzal attacks.

An analysis of the foregoing series of cases is presented in the accompanying tabulation.

ANALYSIS OF CASES OF POSTINFLUENZAL AMELIORATION

Sex:
  Males 9
  Females 7
  Unknown 2

Duration of psychosis:
  1–1½ years 7
  2–4 years 3
  5–15 years 6
  Unknown 2

Result:
  Cured 11
  Improved 3
  Remission 4

Presumptive or stated diagnoses:
  Mania 3
  Melancholia 2
  Probably schizophrenia 7
  Organic brain disease 2
  Epilepsy 3
  Migraine 1

Presumptive or stated diagnoses
  of cases reported "cured":
  Mania 1
  Melancholia 2
  Schizophrenia 4
  Organic brain disease 1
  Epilepsy 2
  Migraine 1

From so small a series it would be unsafe to draw any statistical conclusions. It is apparent, however, that both sexes, various syndromes, and illness of variable duration are included.

THEORETICAL IMPLICATIONS

Of the many intriguing speculations which the establishment of this phenomenon makes possible, I would address myself to three:

1. What are the mechanisms of the process?

(*a*) Chemical theory. The chemical theory, as it might be called, holds that the result is achieved by the neutralization of primary toxins by the antibodies of secondary toxins. Marinesco, Latapie, Alfred Gordon, and others take this view.

(*b*) Physical theory. Another explanation, on an anatomic basis, is advanced by Courbon.[43] In a discussion none too clear he conceives of healthy "psychic" neurons existing beside diseased neurons and inhibited by the latter, and suggests that these inhibitions may be removed through a further injury to the diseased neurons, which paralyzes them and permits the healthy neurons once more to act normally.

(*c*) Humoral theory. A so-called humoral theory has been advanced by Leroy, but I can't understand it. Various suggestions of metabolic changes have been made, without clear evidence of value.

(*d*) Catalytic theory. From the purely mechanistic standpoint, I venture to suggest that the process closely parallels the phenomenon of catalysis. An enzyme or other catalytic agent, it will be recalled, acts to accelerate certain reactions in a direction in which they were already slowly moving. No change in energy relations takes place, and the catalytic agent does not enter into the reaction. (The influenza, for example, comes and goes—leaving or taking nothing.) Furthermore, the same catalytic agent which promotes a reaction in a certain direction may effect the reversibility of that reaction, i.e., may promote it in exactly the opposite direction, under certain environmental conditions. Ptyalin, for example, which induces starch rapidly to become sugar, may convert sugar into starch under certain circumstances of temperature.

Now this is precisely what seems to occur in the problem under consideration. Infectious disease is known to hasten the disintegrative processes and tendencies of certain personalities, occasionally to the point of breaking, i.e., of breaking out, as it were. Just how it accomplishes this we really do not know. It is inadequate to refer to "toxic effects on the cerebrum" because in the first place we don't know exactly how the cerebrum is affected by these toxins, and, secondly, we don't know exactly what is meant by "toxic effects."

What we do know is that a certain mass reaction occasionally follows, and much less frequently precisely the opposition reaction takes place. This, I submit, is exactly parallel to catalysis.

2. What are the psychodynamics involved?

The psychologic factors are probably identical with those which are operative in the post-traumatic cures with which we are familiar under various guises. Recoveries following accidents, hemorrhages, parturition, suicidal attempts, legal crises, surgical operations, spinal serum injections,[44] Kaufmann's *ueberrumpelung* cure, and so on, are probably all to be regarded as accomplishing a reconciliation of the distraught and warring processes of the unconscious with a declaration of peace. The gratification of Freud's recently postulated death instinct, the assuaging of the demand for propitiatory suffering from an unconscious sense of guilt, the threat to the extinction of the ego—these and many other possibilities appear which could be chosen between only by individual and penetrative case study.

In general, what must occur is a redistribution of libidinous streams, some of which are released from investment in unpropitious directions.

A corollary problem is raised, however, which may throw light on the general principles involved. Not infrequently this phenomenon is observed: a patient with a chronic or recurrent physical ailment, but free from psychic distress, presents himself at a medical or surgical clinic for treatment of his condition. Successful removal of the disorder is then promptly followed by acute mental illness. A patient of mine recently submitted himself to an operation for a duodenal ulcer of ten years' standing. It had pained him constantly, but not seriously enough to prevent his success in a business career. Promptly after the operation he developed a melancholia which has now persisted two years, with complete incapacitation.

In these cases the removal of the pain—the punishment, the attrition—results in the appearance of a previously restrained flood of self-attacks of another sort. This is precisely the reverse of the phenomenon of amelioration of mental disease by infectious somatic disease.

3. Finally, I would mention the implications of these data as to the essential nature of schizophrenia, and particularly as to its reversibility. Apparently the plurality of reported cases presented schizophrenic pictures, but even if only one did so, and clearly, the contention that the schizophrenic process is a reversible one would receive valuable support.[45] The theory of catalytic action proposed bears especially on this hypothesis. All of the pragmatic consequences depend on it. What are the real conditions of reversible action in schizophrenia? To date I think we know none of them definitely.

NEUROLOGICAL STUDIES

The term "neuropsychiatrist" is not used as much now as when Karl Menninger started private practice. The basic relationship between neurology and psychiatry remains, but neurology's younger sister has grown up. Few men feel any more that they are sufficient masters of or can give the required dedication to both of these specialties and they choose to limit their practice to one or the other.

When Karl Menninger and others referred to themselves as "neuropsychiatrists" early in their careers, they were being practical—they had to make a living. More patients with neurological diseases than psychiatric illnesses sought their ministrations. The medical concept and therefore the lay concept of what constituted psychiatric illness was then an extremely narrow one.

Karl Menninger wrote seventeen papers dealing with neurology, most of which have to do with that notorious chameleon of the diseases, syphilis. Particularly in its later stages, it affects the central nervous system and thereby becomes a neurological disease. This disease was once very common. The entire scene of medical practice changed, however, when Wagner-Jauregg introduced his now famous malarial treatment for paresis, one type of syphilis of the central nervous system. He later was honored with a Nobel prize for his discovery. The scene of medicine was again changed with the dramatic introduction of the antibiotics which made it possible to halt syphilis in its early forms. Young physicians studying psychiatry now usually learn about Wagner-Jauregg and his historical achievement in medicine by reading about it; few of them have ever seen a patient suffering with paresis.

Karl Menninger's neurological studies included, in addition to those papers reprinted here, studies of epilepsy, poliomyelitis, pernicious anemia, skull fractures, and the use of several diagnostic and treatment methods for different neurological conditions. He and his brother, William C. Menninger, studied syphilis of the central nervous system for many years and the latter published a medical classic on juvenile paresis.*

—B. H. H.

* *Juvenile Paresis.* Baltimore: Williams and Wilkins, 1936.

5. Symptom Analysis in Paretic Neurosyphilis

A STUDY OF 166 COMPARABLE
CONSECUTIVE CASES

This paper presents a study of 166 consecutive cases of paretic neurosyphilis, with particular reference to the first symptoms of the disease and the symptoms precipitating hospitalization. These cases were taken from the records of the Boston Psychopathic Hospital in 1919 with the permission of the Director, the late E. E. Southard; some, but not all, of the patients were personally seen and examined by one of us (K.M.).

The object of the paper was to determine statistically why cases of paresis are brought to the hospital, and what such cases are remembered to have shown as the first evidences of their illness.

Accordingly, the histories of these 166 established cases of paresis were carefully scrutinized, and the first symptom of the illness noted, in the words of the hospital record. In the same way, the symptoms provoking the bringing of the patient to the psychopathic hospital, or to the doctor or police who referred him to the hospital, were noted. Then these symptoms, and signs, were classified, as appears in the following tables.

In general, the manifestations of disease may be grouped as mental or neurologic, i.e., psychic or sensorimotor. Subdivisions into disturbances of perception, intellection, emotion, and volition on the one hand, and cranial nerve, motor function, and sensory function

Written in collaboration with William C. Menninger, M.D. Reprinted from the *American Journal of Syphilis*, 9:104–112, January 1925.

disorders on the other are obvious enough, although sometimes difficult. Where several symptoms appeared simultaneously, they have been listed in multiple.

Twenty-seven of these cases were women, 137 men. The age range of the former was 26 to 69, the average 41.5 years. Of the latter, the age range was 25 to 70, the average 43.1. Only 25 cases gave a history of a primary lesion. No mention is made in this paper of the duration of the symptoms, since in many instances this was not stated or was given with such indefiniteness as to be of little value.

I. FREQUENCY OF SYMPTOMS AND SIGNS

In order to compare the frequency of the two groups of symptoms, initial and presenting, we have arranged the individual symptoms

TABLE 1. ARRANGED IN THE ORDER OF FREQUENCY

SYMPTOM	NUMBER OF CASES	SYMPTOM	NUMBER OF CASES
1. Memory loss	35	26. Weakness	6
2. Irritability	28	27. Aphasia	6
3. Depression	28	28. Fainting	5
4. Speech defect	28	29. Efficiency loss	5
5. Delusions	23	30. Tremor	5
6. Hallucinations	20	31. Disorientation	5
7. Conduct disorders	20	32. Paresthesia	4
8. Excited state	18	33. Fatigability	4
9. Grandiosity	16	34. Gait disturbance	4
10. Convulsions	15	35. Mania	4
11. Headache	15	36. Indifference	3
12. Confusion	14	37. Untidiness	3
13. Paranoid ideas	12	38. Unconsciousness	2
14. Eye symptom	11	39. Dullness	2
15. Paralysis	11	40. Sphincter-control loss	2
16. Insomnia	11	41. Religiosity	2
17. Expansiveness	11	42. Apprehension	2
18. Nervousness	10	43. Ambition loss	2
19. Threatening	9	44. Solitary habits	2
20. Loquaciousness	9	45. Childishness	1
21. Euphoria	8	46. Vertigo	1
22. Disposition change	7	47. Destructiveness	1
23. Ataxia	7	48. Tinnitus	1
24. Resistance	7	49. Negativism	1
25. Queerness	6		

TABLE 2. ARRANGED IN THE ORDER OF FREQUENCY OF INITIAL SYMPTOMS

	NUMBER OF CASES	
SYMPTOM	INITIAL SYMPTOM	HOSPITALIZING SYMPTOM
1. Memory loss	17	18
2. Irritability	15	13
3. Depression	11	17
4. Speech defect	11	17
5. Headache	8	7
6. Eye symptoms	7	4
7. Paralysis	7	4
8. Insomnia	7	4
9. Nervousness	7	3
10. Convulsions	6	9
11. Disposition change	6	1
12. Fainting	5	0
13. Conduct disorder	4	16
14. Weakness	4	2
15. Fatigability	4	0
16. Excited state	3	15
17. Euphoria	3	5
18. Aphasia	3	3
19. Indifference	3	0
20. Loquaciousness	3	6
21. Delusions	2	21
22. Confusion	2	12
23. Ataxia	2	5
24. Gait disturbance	2	2
25. Sphincter-control loss	2	0
26. Apprehension	2	0
27. Ambition loss	2	0
28. Solitary habits	2	0
29. Hallucinations	1	19
30. Paranoid ideas	1	11
31. Expansiveness	1	10
32. Tremor	1	4
33. Paresthesia	1	3
34. Vertigo	1	0

in the order of frequency in each group, appearing in Tables 2 and 3.

From Table 1 it is evident that the three most common initial symptoms are mental (in the ordinary sense), while the next seven are neurologic.

TABLE 3. ARRANGED IN THE ORDER OF FREQUENCY OF
HOSPITALIZING SYMPTOMS

SYMPTOM	NUMBER OF CASES	
	HOSPITALIZING SYMPTOM	INITIAL SYMPTOM
1. Delusions	21	2
2. Hallucinations	19	1
3. Memory loss	18	17
4. Speech defect	17	11
5. Depression	17	11
6. Grandiosity	16	0
7. Conduct disorder	16	4
8. Excited state	15	3
9. Irritability	13	15
10. Confusion	12	2
11. Paranoid ideas	11	1
12. Expansiveness	10	1
13. Convulsions	9	6
14. Threatening	9	0
15. Headache	7	8
16. Resistance	7	0
17. Loquaciousness	6	3
18. Queerness	6	0
19. Ataxia	5	2
20. Disorientation	5	0
21. Efficiency loss	5	0
22. Eye symptom	4	7
23. Paralysis	4	7
24. Insomnia	4	7
25. Tremor	4	1
26. Nervousness	3	7
27. Aphasia	3	3
28. Paresthesia	3	1
29. Weakness	2	4
30. Gait disturbance	2	2
31. Unconsciousness	2	0
32. Disposition change	1	6
33. Tinnitus	1	0

Thus in the twenty most common symptoms which are present
or may enforce hospitalization (Table 3), only four are neurologic,
i.e., speech defect, convulsions, headache, and ataxia, which occur
fourth, thirteenth, fifteenth, and nineteenth in frequency. Mental
symptoms, then, not only are the most frequent initial symptoms
(Table 2) but also greatly predominate as the immediate cause

of bringing the paretic to the hospital, and in a large proportion of the cases they form the most constant and conspicuous clinical features.

There appears to be some pragmatic advantage in analyzing the symptoms as to their general type, i.e., mental or psychic disturbances in the ordinary sense, and neurologic or neuropathologic. A further advantage is gained by grouping the symptoms according to the major psychologic (Table 4) and neurologic (Table 7) categories. The order of frequency of the individual mental symptoms is presented in Tables 5 and 6, the neurologic symptoms in Tables 8 and 9.

II. ANALYSIS OF MENTAL SYMPTOMS

From this analysis (Table 4), it may be noted that emotional disorders constitute much the most common initial symptom, with disorders of intellection occurring about half as frequently. Conduct disorders are still less frequent (contrary to prevailing popular opinion) and perceptual disorders are rarely the initial symptom. On the other hand, disorders of intellection most frequently bring the patient to the hospital; conduct disorders and emotional disorders somewhat less frequently, and perceptual disorders again least frequently.

Memory loss and depression are included in the first five of both groups. Irritability, disposition change, and conduct disorder occur in the first five most frequent initial symptoms and occur eighth, twenty-third, and sixth respectively in their frequency as hospitalizing symptoms. Delusions, hallucinations, and grandiosity occur among the most common presenting symptoms, yet as the initial symptom of paresis, the first two named occur eleventh and fifteenth respectively in frequency, while the last named does not occur at all in this series.

In other words, the first mental symptoms of paresis are not those which ultimately bring the patient to the hospital, loss of memory and depression being the exceptions. Irritability, dispositional change, and minor conduct disorder are more apt to be overlooked or at least tolerated; whereas delusions and hallucinations are conspicuous enough to enforce hospitalization, although they are rarely the "first symptom" of the disease.

Table 4. Partitional Analysis of Mental Symptoms

SYMPTOM	NUMBER OF CASES	
	INITIAL SYMPTOM	HOSPITALIZING SYMPTOM
I. Perceptual disorders	3	36
Confusion	2	12
Disorientation	0	5
Hallucinations	1	19
II. Intellectual disorders	22	80
Delusions	2	21
Dullness	0	2
Expansiveness	1	10
Grandiosity	0	16
Inaccuracy	1	0
Memory loss	17	18
Paranoid ideas	1	11
Religiosity	0	2
III. Emotional disorders	43	51
Apprehension	2	0
Depression	11	17
Disposition change	6	1
Excited state	3	15
Euphoria	3	5
Irritability	15	13
Indifference	3	0
IV. Conduct disorders	11	59
Ambition loss	2	0
Conduct disorder (not specified)	4	16
Childishness	0	1
Destructiveness	0	1
Efficiency loss	0	5
Loquaciousness	3	6
Mania	0	4
Negativism	0	1
Queerness	0	6
Resistance	0	7
Solitary habits	2	0
Threatening	0	9
Untidiness	0	3

TABLE 5. MENTAL SYMPTOMS ARRANGED IN THE ORDER OF FREQUENCY
OF THE INITIAL SYMPTOM AS GIVEN IN THE HISTORY

	NUMBER OF CASES	
SYMPTOM	INITIAL SYMPTOM	HOSPITALIZING SYMPTOM
1. Memory loss	17	18
2. Irritability	15	13
3. Depression	11	17
4. Disposition change	6	1
5. Conduct disorder	4	16
6. Excited state	3	15
7. Euphoria	3	5
8. Indifference	3	0
9. Loquaciousness	3	6
10. Confusion	2	12
11. Delusions	2	21
12. Apprehension	2	0
13. Ambition loss	2	0
14. Solitary habits	2	0
15. Hallucinations	1	19
16. Expansiveness	1	10
17. Paranoid ideas	1	11
18. Inaccuracy	1	0

TABLE 6. MENTAL SYMPTOMS ARRANGED IN THE ORDER OF FREQUENCY
OF HOSPITALIZING SYMPTOMS

	NUMBER OF CASES	
SYMPTOM	HOSPITALIZING SYMPTOM	INITIAL SYMPTOM
1. Delusions	21	2
2. Hallucinations	19	1
3. Memory loss	18	17
4. Depression	17	11
5. Grandiosity	16	0
6. Conduct disorder	16	4
7. Excited state	15	3
8. Irritability	13	15
9. Confusion	12	2
10. Paranoid ideas	11	1
11. Expansiveness	10	1
12. Threatening	9	0
13. Resistance	7	0
14. Loquaciousness	6	3
15. Queerness	6	0
16. Disorientation	5	0

SYMPTOM	NUMBER OF CASES	
	HOSPITALIZING SYMPTOM	INITIAL SYMPTOM
17. Efficiency loss	5	0
18. Euphoria	5	3
19. Mania	4	0
20. Untidiness	3	0
21. Dullness	2	0
22. Religiosity	2	0
23. Disposition change	1	6
24. Childishness	1	0
25. Destructiveness	1	0
26. Negativism	1	0

III. ANALYSIS OF NEUROLOGIC SYMPTOMS

TABLE 7. PARTITIONAL ANALYSIS OF NEUROLOGIC SYMPTOMS

SYMPTOM	NUMBER OF CASES	
	INITIAL SYMPTOM	HOSPITALIZING SYMPTOM
I. Cranial nerve disorders	18	22
Eye symptoms	7	4
Speech defect	11	17
Tinnitus	0	1
II. Motor-function disorders	25	24
Aphasia	3	3
Convulsions	6	9
Gait disturbances	2	2
Paralysis	2	0
Sphincter-control loss	2	0
Tremor	1	4
Weakness	4	2
III. Sensory-function disorders	35	24
Ataxia	2	5
Fainting	5	0
Fatigability	4	0
Headache	8	7
Insomnia	7	4
Nervousness	7	3
Unconsciousness	0	2
Vertigo	1	0

TABLE 8. NEUROLOGIC SYMPTOMS ARRANGED IN THE ORDER OF
FREQUENCY OF INITIAL SYMPTOMS

	NUMBER OF CASES	
SYMPTOM	INITIAL SYMPTOM	HOSPITALIZING SYMPTOM
1. Speech defect	11	17
2. Headache	8	7
3. Eye symptoms	7	4
4. Nervousness	7	3
5. Paralysis	7	4
6. Insomnia	7	4
7. Convulsions	6	9
8. Fainting	5	0
9. Weakness	4	2
10. Fatigability	4	0
11. Aphasia	3	3
12. Gait disturbance	2	2
13. Sphincter-control loss	2	0
14. Ataxia	2	5
15. Tremor	1	4
16. Paresthesia	1	3
17. Vertigo	1	0

TABLE 9. NEUROLOGIC SYMPTOMS ARRANGED IN THE ORDER OF
FREQUENCY OF HOSPITALIZING SYMPTOMS

	NUMBER OF CASES	
SYMPTOM	HOSPITALIZING SYMPTOM	INITIAL SYMPTOM
1. Speech defect	17	11
2. Convulsions	9	6
3. Headache	7	8
4. Ataxia	5	2
5. Eye symptom	4	7
6. Paralysis	4	7
7. Insomnia	4	7
8. Tremor	4	1
9. Nervousness	3	7
10. Aphasia	3	3
11. Paresthesia	3	1
12. Weakness	2	4
13. Gait disturbance	2	2
14. Unconsciousness	2	0
15. Tinnitus	1	0

From Table 7, it is noted that sensory-function disorder was the most frequent group of initial symptoms, with motor-function disturbances somewhat less frequent, and cranial nerve disturbances least frequent. As symptoms enforcing hospitalization, all three groups are about equal in frequency.

Speech defect occurs first in each group (Tables 8 and 9) while headache is the second most common initial symptom and third most common hospitalizing symptom. Eye symptoms occur third in the first group and fifth in the second. The indefinite symptom of nervousness occurs fourth as initial and ninth as admitting symptom, while ataxia occurs fourth as an admitting symptom and fourteenth as an initial symptom.

In other words, with the exception of speech defect and headache, the more severe neurologic conditions result in hospitalization (convulsions and ataxia) and do not occur frequently as initial symptoms.

CONCLUSIONS

An analysis of initial and presenting symptoms in 166 consecutive cases of paretic neurosyphilis yielded the following generalizations:

1. Mental disturbances more frequently than neurologic disturbances are the initial symptoms of paretic neurosyphilis, and very much more frequently the immediate cause for bringing the patient to the hospital.

2. With the exception of memory loss and depression, the first mental symptoms in paresis are usually not those which ultimately bring the patient to the hospital. Irritability, disposition change, and minor conduct disorders are more apt to be disregarded or tolerated outside the hospital.

3. Of the mental symptoms, emotional disorders are much the most frequent initial symptoms and intellectual disorders the most frequent hospitalizing symptoms.

4. Of the neurologic symptoms, sensory-function disturbances are the most frequent initial symptoms; as symptoms presenting upon

hospitalization, cranial nerve disorders, sensory-function disorders, and motor-function disorders are all nearly equal in frequency.

5. The more severe neurologic symptoms (convulsions and ataxia) which bring the patient to the hospital occur infrequently as initial symptoms.

6. Encephalomalacia with Marked Reactive Gliosis of an Entire Hemisphere

A married woman, aged 44, had always been well, as had also her family, until eight months before her death. Six months before the clinical examination she had a "stroke" partially paralyzing the left side. This cleared up promptly.

Three months later, under the duress of much financial difficulty and social unhappiness, the same syndrome reappeared. This time there was also some paralysis of the right side. The latter cleared up, however, but a hemiplegia remained on the left side until her death.

It was afterwards recalled rather indefinitely that several times at intervals of from three to ten days she had noticed upon arising in the morning that her left arm and leg seemed numb, but this sensation had worn off during the day. The relatives also recalled a slight head injury incurred in an automobile while going over a bump in the road at some indefinitely stated time prior to the first attack of paralysis.

After the second hemiplegia she was more or less constantly bedridden and a week or so before the examination recorded below she had become increasingly stuporous until she could scarcely be roused at all. She ran a fluctuating temperature from 98 to 103,

Reprinted from the *Journal of Nervous and Mental Disease*, 84:146–151, August 1936.

typically hectic and usually up rather than down. Her pulse averaged less than 60, often went as low as 50, and rarely above 65. Blood pressure was normal prior to and during her illness. The laboratory examination had been negative with the exception of a leucocyte count of over 14,000 and a spinal fluid which although under no marked pressure showed a slight amount of globulin and a slight increase in the amount of total protein and 100 cells per millimeter, all of the lymphocytic type. Wassermann tests of the blood and spinal fluid were negative.

Neurological examination was made August 23, 1922, which was six months after the first hemiplegic attack. At that time she showed the following neurological condition:

Cranial nerves. The eyes showed a conjugate deviation to the right which was constant although it was possible to get her to follow the finger through an arc of about 60 degrees. At this point nystagmus would appear with a slow component to the left and the eyes would then fly back to the position of extreme dextro-deviation. The physician in charge said that the nystagmus had formerly been marked; when I saw her it was only occasional. Ophthalmoscopic examination showed normal retinae and discs. The pupils were also within normal limits as to reaction.

There was a frank left supranuclear facial paresis.

Hearing could not be tested, which is regrettable in view of the fact that there was a definite history of frequent right-sided earaches. The drum, however, was examined and found normal. Singultus was frequent, stertor occasional. The tongue showed distinct deviation to the left.

Motor functions. There was a complete left-sided flaccid hemiplegia. As indicated above, this involved the cranial nerves.

Sensory functions. This could be tested only very roughly because of her stupor but apparently there was a generalized hypalgesia over the entire left side. This was determined by the pin-prick test. Finer tests could not, of course, be applied. The nurse stated that she had shown a very noticeable dysmetria in grasping a glass of water a week or so previously while still conscious.

Reflexes. In spite of the flaccid hemiplegia there was a distinct bilateral hyperreflexia, the right side slightly less marked than the left; there was a very strongly positive Kernig on the left (the paralyzed side) with a weakly positive Kernig on the right; a frank Babinski sign on the left with a questionable result on the right; flexion of the neck showed no stiffness but there was a Brudzinski response on the right.

The MacEwen sign was very marked; over the entire right side of the skull the percussion note was loudly tympanitic, audible across the room.

Diagnosis. The patient was of necessity examined hastily and, of course, with no cooperation. In view of the history of ear trouble, the hemiplegia, the rapid progress, the hectic fever, the bradycardia, the leucocytosis, the neurological findings and the positive Mac-Ewen, a tentative diagnosis of a right parietal subcortical abscess was made. A right subtemporal decompression and deep exploration were recommended.

She was seen two weeks later by another neurologist who made a preliminary diagnosis of tuberculous meningitis but changed it subsequently to cerebral abscess, in which, therefore, we concurred.

One month later the patient died without marked clinical change.

Autopsy. Post-mortem examination was limited to the brain which was described as follows: In size and external appearance it was quite normal. The dura was not at all adherent and there were no external evidences of inflammatory reaction, softening, bulging, etc. There was a suggestion of slight enlargement of the right half of the brain.

The brain was sectioned transversely, at intervals of 1 to 2 cm.

The very large increase of white matter of the right side as compared with the left was conspicuous. The first impression was of a diffuse gliosis of neoplastic origin (i.e., a diffuse infiltrating glioma).

Deep in the temporoparietal region a focus of softening not greater than 5 x 4 x 3 cm. was discovered. There was no fluid; the substance of the hardened brain was about the consistency of unfixed gray matter. More posteriorly the homogeneous solidity characteristic of formalized white matter, present throughout the anterior portion of the hemisphere, was resumed. In the occipital pole there was a cyst, about 1½ cm. in diameter, filled with a thin yellow fluid. The probability that this was an inclusion within the distended hemisphere of the tip of the posterior horn of the ventricle was inconclusively considered. The right lateral ventricle was compressed throughout its extent.

The entire right hemisphere, then, showed a fairly uniform expansion of the white matter, without conspicuous distinguishing features except a small cyst and a small central area of necrosis. The entire left hemisphere was negative. No disease of the vessels was found except the microscopic changes in the affected hemisphere.

Microscopically the suggestion of glioma was immediately dispelled by the discovery of normal glial overgrowth only, with other exudative elements in abundance. In fact, the perivascular rims revealed in toluidin blue, Van Gieson, and hematoxylineosin stained specimens look exactly like the generally accepted picture of epidemic encephalitis although this is largely an illusion as the cells composing these perivascular halos were more predominantly compound granular corpuscles and fat granules than lymphocytes (although both were present).

Much of the normal tissue was displaced, or at least rendered invisible by diffuse glial overgrowth (Mallory connective tissue stain). Distended meshes of glial fibers and swollen endothelium were everywhere dominant. The glia cell nuclei were very numerous and surrounded with narrow rims of protoplasm ("cytoplasmic" glia). Compounded granular corpuscles were abundant in the perivascular areas.

SUMMARY

A case of encephalomalacia is presented in its clinical and pathological aspects.

Clinically it is remarkable for the fact that the signs were so inconclusive; by retrospect the history should have led to a correct presumptive diagnosis, multiple vascular insults.

Pathologically the case is remarkable for the fact that an entire hemisphere of the brain was involved in the softening; this is apparently a rare occurrence.* Histologically the picture is characteristically that of encephalomalacia, with reactive phagocytosis and secondary glial response. Microscopically, the sections look as if infiltrated with a large glioma; this is, of course, an illusion, but it recalls the disagreement in regard to the exact differentiation of primary and reactive gliosis, the latter so frequently resembling the former (cf. Pines, J. L., "Concerning Diffuse Glial Reactions," *Schweiz. Arch. Neurol. v. Psychiat., 10:* 289, 1922, to which my attention was kindly called by Dr. Henry Woltman, of Rochester, Minnesota).

No definite conclusion can be reached as to the etiology. There is every reason to believe that the primary disease was vascular and produced the central area of softening in the temporoparietal region. Why the response to this insult did not remain confined to the area of the infarct but should have led to glial reaction throughout the hemisphere is not clear. If this were due to the glial response to vascular disease throughout the hemisphere (Globus, J. H., *Arch. Neurol. & Psychiat., 20:* 14, 1928) it does not answer the question why the disease should have involved only the one hemisphere and that in its entirety.

---

* Oppenheim wrote, "The size of the areas of softening varies from that of a pinhead . . . to that of a fist. It may occupy the greater part of a hemisphere. . . . I have found *in one case* the whole hemisphere transformed into an area of softening." *Textbook of Nervous Diseases,* 5th ed., English translation, 2:817.

STUDIES OF
CLINICAL SYNDROMES

The papers included in this section are the freshman exercises of a student. From the clinical experiences described in the studies of psychological reactions to infectious diseases, Karl Menninger's attention was drawn to various syndromes of symptoms and signs of mental illness. These exercises are important more from their historical position in his development of a unitary concept of illness than as contributions to medical knowledge.

In the first paper, "Paranoid Psychoses," his devotion to Southard is particularly evident. Southard was one of the sources of Karl Menninger's lifelong preoccupation with psychiatric nosology. In this first paper he laboriously attempts to elaborate one group of psychotic illnesses and fit them into Southard's rather clumsy nosological system. The reader will note that Freud's famous study of paranoia is not included in the bibliography for this paper. The paper had been published but Karl Menninger had not read it. When he discovered Freud's writings and became imbued with psychoanalytic theories, he followed Freud's general tendency to be uninterested in diagnostic terms.

In the last two papers in this section a refreshing new interest in the dynamics of the illnesses appears. He seems weary with the confusion of nosological terms, and concerned because physicians not only use different words for the same thing but use the same words for different things. The intellectual unrest which would lead him to a unitary theory of illness and health is already in evidence.   —B. H. H.

7. Paranoid Psychoses

A PROPOSED ADDITION TO SOUTHARD'S MAJOR PSYCHOTIC GROUPS

The grouping of the mental disease entities into eleven primary categories, as proposed by Southard,[1] is highly satisfactory from a pragmatic standpoint. It is very palpably superior to any more detailed subdivision, from the viewpoint of both student and teacher—easier for the one to present and define, easier for the other to grasp and correlate. It serves, moreover, as a neat and facile diagnostic index in which practically every psychiatric entity may be quickly placed.

From the standpoint of the practical psychiatrist, however, one possible alteration may be suggested which would, without altering the principle of major categories, or that of diagnosis by orderly exclusion, materially augment the practical value of the Southard nosology. This is the insertion of a twelfth group, to be number IX, embracing paranoid psychoses, and possibly labeled paranoicopsychoses, or paranoidoses, which should include all idiopathic psychoses characterized by paranoid symptoms, including "paranoid dementia praecox."

That such a group is amply justified by clinical findings, in both a quantitative and qualitative sense, is not difficult to demonstrate.

First of all it should be pointed out that in all of the eleven major groups of Southard's classification there occur paranoid forms, or

Reprinted from the *Journal of Nervous and Mental Disease*, 51:35–40, January 1920.

paranoid colorings. With these we are here not at all concerned. Thus we may exclude, a priori, such representative examples as the following:

In Group I, the neurosyphilis group, syphilitic paranoia should certainly remain. In Group II, the hypophrenias, the paranoid state dependent upon hypophrenic judgment defect are certainly properly retained. Similarly in Group III, the epileptics, with their proverbial egocentricity and frequent paranoicism. Group IV, the drug psychoses, contains the beautiful examples of drug paranoias, e.g., alcoholic *Eifersuchtswahn,* to mention only the most conspicuous.

The psychoses with focal brain disease (Group V) may be accompanied by striking paranoid symptoms, as was shown in a case reported by the writer,[2] and Schuster has demonstrated the association of paranoid symptoms with variously situated brain tumors. Similarly, paranoid delusions with psychoses associated with somatic disease (Group VI) are frequently seen, and were conspicuous in the recent influenza epidemic.[3] Of the geriopsychoses (Group VII), senile paranoia or paranoid senile dementia is common enough. Group VIII, paranoid forms of the schizophrenias, are discussed below. The cyclothymic psychoses (Group IX) are frequently strongly colored by paranoid trends, as are also the psychoneuroses (Group X). The paranoid constituents of Group XI, the psychopathies, etc., are discussed below.

But with all these we have here nothing to do. There remain yet many forms in which the elaboration of paranoid elements forms the characteristic and determining feature, and for which we have no satisfactory explanation.

In the first place, those two psychiatric cousins, paranoia (Kraepelin) and paraphrenia, are at present completely divorced in Southard's scheme, and the one added to the schizophrenic group, while the other is relegated of necessity to the group (XI) of psychopathies and miscellaneous psychoses. Waiving for the present the question as to the deserts of these diseases from the standpoint of basal symptoms in abnormal psychology, and as to the justifiability of losing so frequent and so characteristic a psychosis as paranoia in a group of miscellanies, or so dubiously schizophrenic a disease as paraphrenia in a group characterized by that phenomenon, we pass on to other closely allied forms.

Above all stand a group of "Unclassified paranoid psychoses" or "Unclassified paranoic states." The great frequency with which this diagnosis is made in a rapidly turning psychiatric clinic is surely a most striking fact. To those whose associations are stimulated by statistics, it will emphasize this fact to know that according to Pollock's census of the New York state hospitals in July 1917, there were therein:

Psychoneurosis   150
General Paresis   1325
Manic depressive insanity   2408
Paranoic conditions and paranoias ....   1642 (or 4.7 per cent
                                    of the total number of insane, 35,000+)

Add to this, possibly,

Allied to dementia praecox, 1,233.

These cases, as they are seen at the Boston Psychopathic Hospital, for example, Dr. Southard's own institution, do not correspond to classical paranoia, neither to paraphrenia, nor by any means to paranoid schizophrenia (dementia praecox). Indeed, a certain large proportion of them fall in a group which surely merits special study. I refer to those cases of psychosis developing in the later years, often soon after the menopause, and characterized by persecutory delusions or persecutory (*sic!*) phonemata, or both—but always without demonstrable damage to the personality, or evident schizophrenia.

The writer falls in strongly with the view of Seelert,[4] who in a study of "paranoid psychoses in advanced years" concludes that these more or less uniform cases probably comprise a distinct and unnamed syndrome, which is "probably an individual reaction of an endogenous sort to a chronic, slowly progressive, organic cerebral process."

Perhaps they should even be considered in the light of a new entity—but be that as it may, it is without the province of this paper. That they exist is not to be doubted, and as demonstrated they occur in surprising numbers. And as the Southard grouping now stands, these more or less uniform cases of committable psychoses of striking stamp must be crushed into the composite group of psychopathies, with committable and noncommittable entities of divers sorts.

Add to this list, then, those quasinormal persons of paranoid personality—the querulants, litigants, cranks, et al. These persons, as borderline cases, might be grouped with great pragmatic advantage in an order of paranoid psychoses, and regarded as definitely psychotic, rather than merely (!) psychopathic—even though they be not committable.

Again, one recalls those rather hazy and infrequent entities, insisted upon by one or another European psychiatrist, and clung to tenaciously by this or that American devotee. Here, to list but a few, one would include: Wernicke's[5] *Hallucinoze,* Kraepelin's[6] *Eifersuchtswahn* (non-alcoholic), Kraepelin's[7] *Beeintraechtigungswahn,* Ziehen's[8] hallucinatory paranoia, French writers'[9] *délire paranoiaque* and *délire systématisé,* Sander's[10] original paranoia, Kleist's[11] involutional paranoia, Westphal's[12] acute paranoia, periodic paranoia, Lasèque's[13] *folie de persécuteurs persécutés,* Falret's[14] *folie lucide, raisonmante,* Magnan's[15] *délire chronique à évolution systématique,* Regis'[16] *psychose systématisée progressive,* Serieux's[17] *délire d'interprétation, délire de revendication,* Dupré's[18] *délire d'imagination,* Neisser's[19] confabulatory paranoia. (Among these, of course, one must allow for many synonyms.)

Finally, I propose the possible advantage of a separation of the so-called "paranoid form of dementia praecox," or "dementia paranoides" or "schizophrenia paranoides" from the main group representing schistic psychoses, and its identification with this new group of paranoid psychoses.

I shall not recall here the historical development of the presently composed dementia praecox, nor more than mention the doubts expressed by Seglas,[20] Serieux, Bleuler,[21] and even Kraepelin, as to whether this form would eventually stand affirmed as identical in essential nature with hebephrenia and catatonia.

The word "paranoid" seems to have been coined by Kraepelin to describe cases resembling but distinct from paranoia. This term, in turn, was introduced by Snell[22] and Griesinger,[23] and originally meant merely "delusions." Kraepelin gives Kahlbaum,[24] and then Krafft-Ebing and Mendel the credit for substituting the word for the older conception of *Verruechtheit*. Later, under the influence of Ziehen[25] et al., it came to include hallucinations and was finally whipped into the stereotyped, standardized form now recognized by Kraepelin.

The derivative word "paranoid" has never been rigidly enough delimited. Following Kraepelin, because of his influence in promulgating the term, it probably should be restricted to symptoms of the nature of "delusions and hallucinations of a persecutory bearing, and rapid development, be they changing, dissociated, or fully developed."[26]

The writer would propose a more generic definition for the reason that the above does not sufficiently succinctly include the very closely allied symptoms of delusions of reference, delusions of influence, etc.

Southard[27] has divided delusions into two classes—those expressing a degenerate wish and those expressing a degenerate hypothesis. I have elsewhere[28] proposed that the idea is perhaps more readily grasped if the conception of direction is introduced, and the delusions termed afferent and efferent, with respect to the ego and its environment, or egocentripetal and egocentrifugal. Thus, the egocentripetal delusions, or erroneous ideas conceived as originating from without the limits of reasonable possibilities, represent delusions of persecution, influence, reference, molestation, etc.—or expressions of degenerate hypotheses. I have also suggested that hallucinations might be similarly regarded. Now it appears that this type of delusion and hallucination is precisely what is intimated in general in the current use of the word "paranoid." At any rate it would be of immense pragmatic value in the teaching of psychiatry, and hence in mental hygiene, if we would make some such specific definition of so important a term. The proposed limitation of "paranoid" symptoms to afferent or egocentripetal delusions or hallucinations (or both) and with or without systematization, grandiosity, etc., has certain inherent commendations.

Accepting, however, for the present, Kraepelin's ill-defined conception of paranoid, it appears that his "paranoid dementia praecox" is precisely this symptomatology plus the factor of progress to a terminal dementia. As a matter of fact, however, we do not know that any considerable proportion of what we are calling paranoid dementia praecox actually does progress to a terminal dementia. This is a matter which will soon be conclusively demonstrated either in the affirmative or negative, now that the Kraepelin conception is growing to an age beyond that of the average state hospital case.

We do know, even at present, that at least some of these cases show no demonstrable evidence of dementia even after years of observation. Southard's insistence on the extirpation of the term "dementia praecox" as of pragmatic value in mental hygiene is then here directly to the point. It were better to give these cases the benefit of a doubt than to condemn them to a pessimistic diagnosis of implied hopelessness. Every psychiatrist must be occasionally overwhelmed with the utter lack of similarity in the cross-section view of cases of so-called "paranoid" and "catatonic" schizophrenia. If, then, the terminal and supposedly criterion state is in doubt we are the more justified in at least a tentative divorce. This is in addition to and without reference to the historical arguments in favor thereof.

CONCLUSION

But whether or not this group be included, perhaps now the point is self-supporting—that there are paranoid states, i.e., psychoses characterized by afferent type of delusions, which are not well placed in Southard's otherwise efficient and practical major group nosology. These, it is proposed, might be bunched as a twelfth group—the paranoicopsychoses, or paranoidoses, possibly to stand ninth in the list, and to include those mental disease forms, characterized by paranoid (i.e., afferent) delusions, with or without hallucinations, not otherwise provided for in this inclusive classification. Herein would fall such currently recognized entities as paranoia, paraphrenia (and Magnan's disease), paranoid personalities (to be considered before the more generic and more tenuous psychopathy group), together with the unclassified paranoid states, the unclassified paranoid psychoses, numerous entities described by various European psychiatrists listed above; and finally, with probable pragmatic benefit, the paranoid form of schizophrenia.

8. The Isolation Type of Personality

The "rube" of the stage is funny only to those who know nothing about him. They think that he does exist, just so, or else they think he doesn't exist at all. So they can laugh. Those of us who know the original can't laugh; to us the prototype of the caricature is a pitiful, deplorable spectacle—an enormous failure in social adaptation. He has been withheld from sufficient social contacts to humanize him. Of course, all farmers are not "rubes."

Among the personality types prone to failure in social adjustments, the seclusive, withdrawn, queer, eccentric, grotesque, odd, unsociable types are both conspicuous and numerous. Psychological analysis discovers that these are really of two sorts. Some are "constitutionally" unsocial and really prefer to be left out of it, although they may possess graceful social technique; the other group is made up of wistful derelicts who long to dive into the swim and either don't know how or are held back by restraining fears.

The former are called "schizoids." More of them anon. The latter ought to be christened something; "isolated personalities" will do as well as anything. They are those who have been artificially withheld from human contact to the point of developing curious deficiencies, mannerisms, attitudes, oddnesses, which serve to preclude their absorption or amalgamation into the group when, later, opportunities do develop.

Reprinted from the *United States Naval Medical Bulletin*, 27:609–620, July–October 1929.

The "rube" sometimes comes to college, as some of us know. Sometimes he leaves college only a little less rubish than he entered. It is a task, indeed, to alter a mold that has been setting for eighteen years. But it can be done, and it is one of the unwitting functions performed by some of our large state universities and by our Army and Navy.

The farms of the West and the great cities of the East develop two different types of provincialism, or "isolation," equally extreme. It is in the towns and small cities that socialization reaches its height. But geography and transportation facilities are by no means the sole determinants of breaking the shell. Isolation may result from many other things. We shall illustrate, for example,

1. Isolation by reason of geographic factors.
2. Isolation by reason of being an only child.
3. Isolation by reason of esoteric home training.
4. Isolation by reason of poverty and (again) wealth.
5. Isolation by reason of pathological parents.
6. Isolation by reason of physical defect.

ISOLATION BY REASON OF GEOGRAPHY

"Two sisters from a family home none too comfortably situated left a small mountain state to attend a very fashionable university, noted for its social functions. Their attendance was made possible by the fact that an uncle who was very fond of their mother resided in the university town.

"The high-school career of these sisters had been in no way out of the ordinary. They had manifested the usual amount of indifference to their studies and to their teachers and had attended all the simple but enjoyable parties that were given by the students.

"In the university, however, they found themselves left out of social functions that play so important a part in the student life, and after two years of unhappy struggle they returned home. The plain, simple Swedish girls who had left two summers before returned intellectual snobs. Education and learning, so they thought, were the most important things in existence. The simple frankness of the two high-school graduates of two years before had been supplanted by a snobbishness, a sourness, and a bitterness that ill disguised their frustration." [1]

ISOLATION BY REASON OF BEING AN ONLY CHILD

At the age of 2, Irene was the center of the concentrated interest and acclaim of two parents, four grandparents, two great grandparents, and sixteen uncles and aunts.

At the age of 4, Irene was the single engrossing object of her mother's time, interest, attention, and love.

At the age of 6, Irene was a lonely child, peering wistfully out the window at neighborhood children, envying them their brothers and sisters. Her mother's exhortations pushed her into the play occasionally, but she was shy and diffident; a few minutes found her standing on the sidelines unnoticed and unmissed, and after a session of silent and envious observation she would slip away to play by herself in her playroom of dolls and fancies. She gave trees and pieces of furniture the names of fancied children playmates and talked to them, scolded them, entreated them.

At 10 she was more socialized, thanks to the public school, but she was a grade ahead of her age and far more worldly-wise and versed in the ways of adults than her schoolmates. A suggestion of disdain covered up (?) the traces of her loneliness. She found a chum whom she could dominate, and until they grew tired of each other she made the most of the opportunity.

At 16 she was through high school, but considered too young for college and kept at home a year by her parents. "We just can't bear to give her up to go away from home to school; you know she's our only child and she's such a companion to us. Why, I really just take her with me like I would another woman of my own age and talk to her just the same. . . . She's so mature, and yet she's still my baby girl!"

In college she was a cold, disdainful, self-centered little snob. She was elected to a sorority of social pretensions and made a very representative member in that she held her head high, purred softly upon occasion, and kept up the proper front. She utterly disregarded all of the rules and regulations of the chapter, however, and managed to do so with impunity by a haughty, unquestioning assumption of prerogative which her sisters feared to challenge. She considered her own comfort and profit first and last.

She graduated with few acquaintances and fewer friends and a reputation for belonging to the upper crust. She married a man who threw himself at her violently and swore to be her slave as long as he lived.

She is busy keeping him to this vow. They have no children. She is too busy.

ISOLATION BY REASON OF HOME TRAINING

"A cadet at West Point complained of depression and a feeling of insecurity. He had been brought up in a home in which he had no companionship except that of his father and his father's friends. The other boys in the neighborhood were not considered suitable company for him; he knew no boys of his own age and did not play boys' games. One can imagine the adjustment difficulties with which he was confronted upon being thrust suddenly into an environment of twelve hundred youngsters of his own age. His colleagues considered him peculiar from the beginning, and this, of course, added to his difficulties. After a feeble effort to adjust, he gave the situation up as hopeless and sought the quietude of his room and his books. Without any attempt to go more deeply into the problem, he was told that his reaction was decidedly unwholesome and was urged to make more contacts. His progress was slow at first, but it was consistent. I had an opportunity to observe this cadet for three years, and I know of no case in which a more gratifying result was obtained. He did not become a class leader, but he was just around the corner from it when he graduated. There was one interesting sidelight on the situation. One day during his last year he came in quite enthusiastic about a man whom he had met in a nearby city who just couldn't do enough for him. 'Why, he knows lots of my boy friends and he takes us on joy rides, dinner parties, theater parties, and so forth, and he insists upon paying all the bills, even the hotel bills.' Upon careful questioning it was learned that girls never attended any of these parties; in fact, the friend did not care for girls. A few weeks later he informed me he had learned that the man not only was homosexual but was in love with him, and had attempted to kill him. Relations were broken off at once. This cadet is now engaged to be married." [2]

Alice is an only child, and the sole object of the adoration of her parents and grandparents. Her mother was also an only child.

From the very first, Alice has been trained to be "a little lady," that is, in everything but her temper, which was uncontrollable even before she could talk. As a baby, whenever Alice was refused anything she wanted she screamed and cried and then held her breath until her mother was frightened into giving her anything she wanted.

When she grew older the process of "breaking Alice's temper" began. It seemed to imply constant surveillance on the part of her mother and grandmother. The latter, who prided herself upon being a Southern gentlewoman, considered Alice too dainty a child to be allowed to soil her clothes and conversation by contacts with the common little neighborhood children. Alice mustn't play boisterous games with yelling and running in them. She played with dolls, but her dolls were little aristocrats, too, who didn't associate with other common dolls. Alice played alone usually, but most of her time was spent with her mother and grandmother.

When she started in school she was always detained by her mother until the other neighborhood children had gone on to school. When they had gone, she was told to hurry on to school and not to loiter on the way home, for she must practice right after school.

Alice's family was continually reminding her of her high scholastic achievements, so that she soon assumed a superior attitude toward the few other children she was allowed to associate with.

As soon as Alice began showing curiosity in regard to sex, her mother "told her everything." After this was accomplished Alice's mother was frantic every time Alice was out of sight.

Now that Alice is in junior high school, she is lonely and odd. She is not an unattractive girl, though instead of being dainty she is big and raw-boned. This, added to her awkwardness in meeting people of her own age, makes her predestined to social failure, which is for her parents the greatest of human calamities.

ISOLATION BY REASON OF PATHOLOGICAL PARENTS

"A boy about 10 years of age was at a summer camp and the question came up whether or not he should come back home. He had been there eight weeks and was unhappy. He spent a good deal of the time by himself and was looked upon by the other boys as queer, peculiar, eccentric. He had not participated in swimming, riding, and playing games; and, on the whole, he had been an undesirable comrade. When he first came, some of the other boys teased him, but soon he was passed by and ignored. The question was, Why should a boy 10 years of age be queer, peculiar, and eccentric, standing out alone among sixty other boys?

"In order to understand each type of individual, we must interpret conduct in terms of past experiences. Now, going into the past experiences of this boy, we find that the father is a professor who has a position of prominence. Five years ago the boy's mother died of an acute infection. The father was so emotionally upset that he developed an exaggerated and distorted condition of health. He got a nurse for the boy, and she was told that this child must be protected against every possibility of sickness. The boy was not allowed to go to the public school or the private school, but had tutors at home. He was not allowed to ride on public conveyances, and only occasionally permitted to play with other boys. So his whole life was built around the problem of ill health.

"The emotional reaction in this father was, of course, in response to a serious situation, but most individuals are able to recover and adjust themselves, even in the case of the loss of a person very near to them and much beloved, and to make the experience a part of their lives. It is a part of our plasticity in life to be able to do this, but here was a man, a professor, an intellectual man, who stands out as a leader in his particular field, whose emotional reaction was so intense that he could not do so, and he planned the life of this boy around his emotional reaction, with the result described." [3]

ISOLATION BY REASON OF POVERTY

Both wealth and poverty may bring about isolation, as every movie fan knows. (The "poor little rich girl" theme of Mary Pickford's proclivity and the all, all-alone horrors of Lillian Gish in *Squalor.*) College students and their advisors know it at first hand.

All through the grades Lucile had two anxieties—the anxiety of keeping up in her studies and the anxiety of poverty. These were the two topics which she heard discussed in her home. Her parents were poor and hard-pressed, and her mother was a woman of high idealism who expected Lucile to make up in intellectual brilliancy what she lacked in glad raiment and finery.

Unfortunately Lucile was a normal child and hence couldn't make this extraordinary compensation. The constant reminders of her poverty which she received from her mother's tears, her father's complaints, and the obvious comparison of her clothing with that of her schoolmates combined to produce in her a marked sense of inferiority. In order to avoid the unpleasantness of comparisons, she quietly withdrew from situations in which such opportunities were afforded. In high school, when the students' social life began to develop, she voluntarily excluded herself by declining invitations and avoiding opportunities. Because of her pretty face and sweet manner, she was in a way to be very popular, but she would decline dates and resort to various subterfuges and circumlocutions to avoid the humiliation of having her friends see the shabbiness of her home.

During her senior year in high school a relative died, leaving her mother considerable money. It was decided that she should go to college. She outfitted herself prettily and her mother bought her a Ford for her own private use, so that she entered college with considerably more than the average personal comfort. The old habits, however, were hard to break. She was shy, diffident, retiring, and self-distrustful. These traits, together with her evidences of prosperity, stimulated the enviousness and dislike of her companions who had formerly loved her for her very meekness. Her life was lonelier than before. She left college in her sophmore year.

An example will show us the effect of the opposite type of home atmosphere on a girl who was fundamentally normal. In this case, as so often, the person developed an inability to make friends and lacked self-confidence. She is always inconspicuous in a group, in spite of attractive dress, pleasant face, and kindly disposition. The girl is longing for friends and companionship, but as no one goes out of his or her way to talk to her she simply goes more into the background. At times she has developed a really dangerous despondency as a result.

The fact is that the parents laid emphasis on the material side of life and built their home atmosphere on it. None of the three children were anxious to remain at home, though they loved their parents and the parents provided liberally for them. There was no friction between father and mother.

What was the matter? The atmosphere was simply the atmosphere of a fine store or hotel. The furnishings were tasteful, rich, and beautiful. The children grew up in it and were taught to think that if they looked and behaved well they would grow up to marry and live happily ever after. From the start the girl was known at school as the most spick-and-span child in the class. Her dresses were always white and starched. She learned her lessons with the same mechanical precision and could rattle them off faster than anyone else.

To her parents dirty clothes meant inferior people not fit to play with. Consequently she, like her older sister, lost her childhood companionship. They could not play with or know the children at school or in a large part of their neighborhood. The parents were unaware of the spiritual malnutrition of their children, and did not even attempt to make up for the lack of playmates by themselves playing with the children. And if quarreling and harsh words were unknown in the household, so were noise and laughter.

The girl fortunately possessed a good physical, emotional, and in-

tellectual makeup, which has helped pull her through a very difficult period. Now, at 28 years of age, still unmarried, she has become
aware of the deficiencies of her early life, and with unusual intelligence she has changed her business life to one of work with children, which is helping greatly to satisfy her lonely longings and
giving her greater ease with people of her own age. She is practically free from her previous spells of depression.[4]

ISOLATION BY REASON OF REAL OR FANCIED PHYSICAL DEFECT

The isolation of the deafened or crippled child is an obvious
tragedy, to avert which systematic efforts are now made in most
civilized communities.

Far more frequent, more devastating, and more inaccessible are
the isolation and suffering caused by the famous sense of inferiority
based (usually) upon fancied defects or upon the emotional reactions to defects which of themselves are not isolating.

"A sense of inferiority" is a phrase so aptly describing a painful
emotional experience common to all mankind that when coined
by the psychiatrists it was immediately appreciated and pressed into
use by the laity as well as the medical profession.

What is it, and why? The sense of inferiority is a complex, painful, emotional state characterized by feelings of disadvantageous
comparison, of incompetence, inadequacy, and depression. With it
go certain typical traits or tendencies, particularly:

1. Self-consciousness or self-preoccupation; shown by blushing,
embarrassment, delusions of reference, a tendency to be concerned
with one's feelings, thoughts, plans, motives.

2. Self-criticism and self-dissatisfaction; a tendency to feel that
one is not appearing to good advantage, to be critical and worried
about what one is doing or has done, to reflect on possible mistakes
and blunders.

3. Touchiness and oversensitiveness; a tendency to make exaggerated responses to praise, blame, defeat, and disappointment, to
care intensely about what other people think of one.

4. General emotional and nervous instability; unresolved emo-

tional complexities and antagonistic trends, fits of despondency, depression, apathy.

5. Persecutory trends of a more or less definite sort; the feeling that one is unappreciated, unjustly treated, that the world in general fails to appreciate and reward merit, and to recognize wrong-doing.

6. Unwillingness to put one's self to the test because of fear of an unfavorable outcome, which would be intolerable.

7. Lack of ability in certain lines of overt behavior which demand a fair degree of self-assurance; lack of social poise; inability to carry on enterprises such as selling and executive work.

8. Perfectionist tendencies; an attempt to compensate for felt inferiorities by exaggerated conscientiousness, meticulousness, fastidiousness.[5]

What causes it? Real disadvantages of physique or talents or race or appearance; these, to be sure. But many persons quite overcome these handicaps—they may or may not achieve greatness, but they do achieve happiness.

The sense of inferiority depends not upon actual comparisons, but upon certain emotional predilections, and prejudices based upon fear. These date back to earliest childhood and are added to or subtracted from thereafter according to the mental healthiness of the parents and home environment.

Basically, feelings of inferiority depend upon comparisons of the subject with other individuals, and these comparisons are originally of tangible, visible things, i.e., physique and physical accomplishments.

The child early compares himself, his little body, his physical equipment, with that of his omnipresent and omnipotent parents; later, also, with siblings and playmates. Necessarily he is constantly aware of discrepancies in size, in height and weight, in strength. His obvious inferiorities are associated with his obvious dependency and subservience. Since what father and mother say "goes," he is early taught without words that "might makes right." This may as well be written "height makes right."

The child's first reactions to the constant reminder of his littleness take many forms. There comes to be a resentment of being called "little." There is much talk of "when I grow up"; mama-and-papa games are indulged in; long dresses and trousers are donned, and various types of rebellion and insubordination are indulged in, in spite of foregone conclusions of ultimate defeat.

These compensations, which the child makes gradually, become less necessary as the child becomes aware of his growth. Soon I will be as big as they, he thinks—and so he is often told.

There are certain other comparisons which the small child makes which leave most stubborn resistance. These relate to comparisons which, from the covert or coy behavior of his parents, he infers should not be made. They relate to the tabooed areas of the body. The axillary and pubic hair, for example, are never-failing sources of mystery and humiliation. It is so definitely there on his parents and so definitely not there upon his own little person. What is wrong that he is thus minus this attribute of the big and powerful folks? *

Not only the hair but the primary and secondary sexual organs are noticed by every child. The little boy compares his small genitalia with those of his father and suffers more acutely in his perplexity than most of us stop to consider. He wonders what is wrong that he is so incomparably less developed in this not-to-be-discussed part of his body. Later he becomes conscious of pleasurable genital sensations and a sense of guilt develops with the theory that his underdevelopment is a punishment. Similarly, the little girl is not only chagrined to discover the equipment of the males of her family, but distressed at her lack of breasts such as her mother has. Psychoanalysis of many patients has revealed that the child spins theses to account for these lacks and develops innumerable compensatory defense mechanisms to save himself the pain of an inferiority realization.

Now such inferiority feelings are common to nearly all children. They are based, to be sure, on misconceptions and ignorance, but the emotional response is there, and it has to be expressed. It may be

---

* Readers will be reminded that hair as the symbol of power runs through all history and legend—Samson, for a classical example; Dempsey, for a more modern one; "The Hairy Ape," for an O'Neill elaboration of the theme.

handled very easily—a harmless discharge, as it were, especially where proper educational methods and manners are used by the parents.

These primary inferiority feelings are ordinarily submerged into oblivion in the majority of persons. But nothing in human life is ever really forgotten. The memories only sleep. Hence it is easy to revive these childish anxieties and add to their intensity a few years later by unfavorable comparisons made by someone in authority, e.g.: "Sam is not as bright as his sister," says mother to a visitor. "George is unusually awkward and clumsy for his age." "Daughter, it's a good thing you are smart in your studies, because you certainly are the homeliest child on earth." "John's teeth are so ugly, they make him look just terrible." "There's no use in paying out any more for your music lessons—you haven't the voice." * (This girl later became a professional musician and concert singer.)

Such comments are deadly. They often crush the child's hopes and efforts and self-respect completely. They rarely stimulate, because the authority of their source makes them incontrovertible.

Then there are other less obvious ways in which parents stimulate and build up inferiority feelings in their children. One is by manifesting their own inferiority feelings. Some parents are incessantly complaining of their misfortunes, comparing their acquisitions and opportunities with those of their neighbors, voicing their enviousness and unhappiness and disappointments. They may go farther and berate themselves, or they may scowl and sneer at their envied friends. In either case, the effect on the child is the same—"My folks lost out; they're licked. They aren't as good as . . ."

The social organization of most American cities is built up upon the existence of this sensitiveness. Many exclusive clubs keep their dues unjustifiably high and their membership dismally lonely in order that the members may gain consolation for their inferiority feelings by the realization that many envy them in their exclusiveness who can't afford to join.

Still other parents excite inferiority in their children by their delinquencies. The child feels much more keenly than his parents the

---

* These are all true quotations.

social disapprobation which they incur. An alcoholic father or a divorced mother may serve as a burden of bitterness to the children throughout their lives. This we see frequently appearing in college students, whose sense of inferiority crops out conspicuously under the stress of readjusting themselves to the new requirements of college life. "I have always felt as if I must apologize for my father," one remarked in discussing his self-consciousness. "I always have in the back of my mind, 'What if they knew!'"

Many children early develop certain types of reaction to these inferiority feelings—patterns which continue to dominate their behavior long after the original cause is extinct. Others develop them later. Enviousness, aggressiveness, penuriousness, acquisitiveness, flight reactions, anxiety states, bluffing, stealing, and all sorts of adventitious behavior may result—does result. The roots of many neuroses of later life are to be found here. "Neurasthenia," in which a patient is sure that his or her eyes are weak, stomach ailing, legs impaired, etc., are states in which unconsciously these organs are used as substitutes for others concerning which, as a child, the sufferer had grave and painful misgiving.*

Alfred Adler's theory is that the child who actually does have a lack, an organic inferiority, may become aware of it without becoming conscious of it—i.e., he may react to it without knowing to what he is reacting. The weak-eyed become artists, the poorly endowed gastrointestinal tracts drive their owners to become cooks, the possessors of poor ears turn to music as a career. Beethoven, Demosthenes, Whistler, and many others are cited to prove this.

---

* The following example cited by Doctor Kerns, mental hygiene counsellor at West Point, is typical: "Cadet G. came to the hospital complaining that he felt weak and insecure. He was afraid of everything, afraid that something was going to happen. He could get interest in nothing but his own thoughts. He worried constantly and had even thought he was going insane. This lad was seen for an hour on each of three successive days. He was markedly introverted, self-conscious, and deplorably lacking in aggressiveness. He displayed all the earmarks of an inferiority mechanism, based, it appeared, among other things, upon a diminutive stature. This mechanism, along with certain other contributory ones, was gone into quite carefully and explained to him. He was given Hart's Psychology of Insanity to read and told to return in one week. A month later he appeared and said that he was getting along finely and saw no reason why he should not continue to do so. The book, apparently, had mirrored and explained away many of his own problems. I can almost recall his words: "I think a book of that sort should be placed in the public schools, for I know that lots of people have grown up in the dark, so to speak, just as I have." [6]

But there are certain conditions of which no one needs to speak, and yet the organic inferiority cannot remain unknown to the subject. He knows because he can see himself in the eyes of strangers; he knows because the cruel taunts of the little animals about him, glad to find someone their inferior and some one to torture, won't let him forget.

This group includes speech defects, birthmarks on the face, dental deformities, crippled limbs, deformed bodies, and above all, cleft palate and harelip. So obvious are these things and so disfiguring that they permit of little real protection from exceedingly great mental pain.

A patient of ours, a woman of 52, lived as a recluse on a large ranch in Kansas, one-half of which she owned, but which she rarely ever left. She had a curious speech defect which immediately attracted attention wherever she went, whenever she spoke. She felt her immolation keenly; she went through phases of bitter resentment, cynicism, sad resignation, hopeless despondency. All her life it was her chief concern. "I've never been able to forget it long enough to get interested in the real things of life," she said. We tried to help her find a happier viewpoint, but one day she was found dead across her bed, and an empty cyanide bottle on the floor.

One of our senior students at Washburn College a few years ago was among the brightest girls we have ever had. She came of a good and respected family and she was not unlovely to look upon. But from infancy she had been obliged to wear very heavy lenses for her near-sightedness. They were, to be sure, rather conspicuous. But they were nothing in comparison to the conspicuousness she had come to think they had. She felt that everyone who looked at her saw the glasses rather than the girl; she was so self-conscious that she became seclusive, and her seclusiveness made her odd, and her oddities made her more uncomfortable and conspicuous. Her life, full of opportunities by reason of her superior intellectual gifts, was nearly ruined by her emotional distortion.

One of my friends had a child with harelip who was so tortured by his schoolmates, who reviled and jeered him, that his parents moved from place to place seeking to find more tolerable conditions.

In this instance, of course, not he alone but his whole family suffered untold agony.

The wounds of the soul resulting from these disfigurements are made very early in life. Entirely aside from surgical considerations, these blemishes should be eliminated just as early as possible in the life of the child, from the standpoint of mental hygiene. Five, six, or seven years of age is much too late. The prevention of mental illness in these instances is early surgical treatment of the physical defect.

For the others, preventive treatment consists in better mental hygiene instruction for the parents. Lacking this prevention, we must resort to psychotherapy. This is one of the functions of the psychiatrist in practice, but nowhere with more satisfaction than in the treatment of inferiority reactions developing in college students.

The dentists have done much with orthodontia in the direction of mental hygiene. Many such cases as the following are reported in the dental literature. "A stenographer, aged 24, had been under treatment for two years for a very bad disfigurement of the face caused by dental deformities. The mental effects were particularly marked. She had always taken a position in the back office where it would not be necessary for her to meet the public. Two years later she was working in the front office and wearing an engagement ring." [7]

9. Recognizing and Renaming "Psychopathic Personalities"

Pinel described a "mania without delusions" which subsequent writers have regarded as being equivalent to what has in more recent times been designated "psychopathic personality." [1] It was mentioned earlier (1775) by Ettmuller, but Pinel's description is better. In 1837 Prichard [2] introduced the term "moral insanity" which dominated clinical discussions of this condition for the next sixty years. There were more arguments as to whether there could be such a thing as "moral insanity" than there were accurate descriptions of the clinical picture.

Early in the twentieth century Kraepelin, [3] Bleuler, [4] Adolf Meyer, [5] and Kurt Schneider [6] described the condition according to various classifications. The most important element in all of these was the elimination of the concept and implications of "moral insanity" and the introduction of more accurate delimitations of the symptom complex. There was a great lack of uniformity and unanimity in these descriptions. Meyer wisely excluded the neurotic syndromes which had been included by others but twenty-five years later (1931) Kahn [7] reintroduced them as forms of "psychopathic personality."

All of the earlier authors assumed the etiology to be primarily constitutional. Psychoanalytic and psychodynamic concepts, emphasizing psychological factors in the etiology, were introduced by Reich [8] ("instinct ridden character"), Alexander [9] ("neurotic character"),

Reprinted from the *Bulletin of the Menninger Clinic*, 5:150–156, September 1941.

Karpman [10] ("antisocial character"), Wittels [11] ("phallic character"), and the present writer [12] ("perverse personality"). (See also Bartemeier [13] and Levine. [14])

For more details in regard to the history, the reader is referred to excellent summaries by Partridge [15] and by Sydney Maughs. [16]

CLASSIFICATIONS

In order to give some idea of the vagueness and polymorphous nature of the concept, the following classifications are worth a glance:

Kraepelin [17]
Excitable
Unstable
Impulsive
Eccentric
Liars and swindlers
Antisocial
Quarrelsome

Schneider [18]
Hyperthymic
Depressive
Insecure
Fanatic
Self-seeking
Emotionally unstable
Explosive
Affectless
Weak-willed
Asthenic

Partridge [19]
1. Inadequate
   a. insecure
   b. depressive
   c. weak-willed
   d. asthenic
2. Egocentric
   a. contentious
   b. paranoid
   c. explosive
   d. excitable
   e. aggressive
3. Criminal
   a. liars

b. swindlers
c. vagabonds
d. sexual perverts

Kahn [20]
Nervous
Anxious
Sensitive
Compulsive
Excitable
Hyperthymic
Depressive
Moody
Affectively cold
Weak-willed
Impulsive
Sexually perverse
Hysterical
Fantastic
Cranks
Eccentric

The U.S. Surgeon General [21]
Inadequate
Paranoid
Emotionally unstable
Criminalistic
Pathological liars
Nomads

World War [22]
Inadequate
Egocentric
Emotionally unstable
Sexual

British [23] (One of the most practical)
1. Contentious (grievances, threats, abusiveness)
2. Mendacious (lie or steal without apparent forethought)
3. Sexual (uncontrolled, often perverse)
4. Skulking (malingerers, work evaders, tramps, beggars)

SYMPTOMATOLOGY

Under an ambiguous title an excellent book has appeared recently by Cleckley [24] in which a list of essential symptoms is given which, modified somewhat by myself, is as follows:

1. Superficial attractiveness, cleverness, facility in talking, and often (not always) apparent intelligence.
2. Freedom from classical psychotic symptoms.
3. Complete unreliability and irresponsibility.
4. Total disregard for the truth, honesty, fairness, and justice.
5. Continual projection of blame.
6. Absence of a sincere sense of shame.
7. Cruelty, cheating, bullying, etc., often apparent in childhood.
8. Impulsive, unwise, unpredictable generosity.
9. Bad judgment and inability to profit by experience.
10. Tremendous egocentricity with practically no capacity for object love.
11. General poverty of affect, including little if any sense of humor.
12. Little or perverse responsiveness to special consideration or kindness.
13. Very frequent prominence of excessive drinking, associated with shocking and fantastic behavior with little or no alcohol.
14. Utterly bizarre and preposterous conduct when drinking heavily.
15. Infrequent sincere suicidal attempts.
16. Striking peculiarities of sexual behavior—ostentatiousness, sordid surroundings, degraded and perverse objects, no restraint or taste, excesses, often impotence or frigidity or defeat of aim by drunkenness, aggressiveness, etc.
17. "Bad" companions elected consistently.
18. Playing off of one "friend" against the other, "double crossing" both.

(Cleckley includes, "Greater lack of insight than of any other psychiatric disorder." In my experience some have very keen insight; some have insight but cover it up; others have no insight.)

DETECTION

Diagnosis is usually based on the history of self-destructive perverseness along the lines indicated by the above symptoms, without organic brain disease, classical signs of psychosis, psychological tests indicating feeble-minded or outstanding neurotic syndrome. Hence detection must be based chiefly upon the source of data not available to medical examining boards, the history. Detection in the course of examination may occasionally be possible from observing the registrant's reaction to the total situation (challenging, indifference, smugness, evasion, lying, etc.) and his reaction to examinations (arrogance, malingering, impudence, disobedience, truculency, excitement, terror). Since deception is one of the essential features of the syndrome, these are the most difficult cases to detect, and the more difficult any particular case is to detect, the more important it is to detect it.

SPECIAL MORALE PROBLEMS INVOLVED

In the army these cases disturb morale in many ways: when dismissed and returned to civilian life, they continue to disturb morale, and most European countries tend to detain them under military control because of the latter fact. Military experience with psychopaths has been very bad for several reasons: (1) They give a false impression of superficial brilliance, and are later very disappointing; (2) they are essentially disloyal, if not actively mutinous; (3) they are a constant source of annoyance and trouble to officers, trying to evade assignments, provoking anger, stirring up trouble, etc.; their equipment is never in good order, they get into a lot of difficulty— petty thefts, etc.; they are easy tools of propagandists. A few military psychiatrists feel that if they are predominantly cheerful some types may be useful in war under skillful leadership as shock troops and raid troops.

Psychopaths are so provocative that they excite revenge attitudes on the part of draft boards, officers, other soldiers, and the public generally with the result that there is a tendency to mistreat them, and thus give them occasion to justify their aggressiveness. There is a tendency against rejecting or dismissing certain of them from the army for the same reason, yet it is generally agreed that they are a heavy liability. (See excellent articles by Dunn [25] and Hall.[26])

A NEW NAME AND A NEW DEFINITION

What is now called "psychopathic personality," as I indicated above, has been called by at least a score of other titles, none of which is satisfactory, some because they are moralistic, some because they are meaningless, some because they imply dubious etiological factors, etc. I regard the term "psychopathic personality" as particularly bad since, logically, the schizoid or cycloid personality is also a "psychopathic" personality.

Alexander and some of the psychoanalysts tried to get away from the term by using "neurotic character" and this practice we formerly followed at the Menninger Clinic. I do not approve of it now for three reasons: (1) It introduces the term "character" as something vaguely differentiated from personality; (2) the condition is closer to a psychosis than to a neurosis and the term neurotic is, therefore, misleading; (3) Alexander's emphasis was upon the unconscious sense of guilt and the resulting self-punishment, which I do not think are the most important elements in the condition.

What uniquely characterizes the syndrome we are describing? If one looks over the classifications and the symptoms, one gets certain very definite impressions, namely: (1) The patient of this type puts up a front or façade for the benefit of the person he desires to impress or exploit; usually he is hyperagreeable, sometimes the reverse; (2) he irritates, disappoints, and distresses the doctor (and everyone else); (3) he does this by dissembling, lying, play-acting, pretending, etc., to cover up all sorts of aggressive self-exploiting behavior—in short, fraudulency and insincerity; (4) he breaks the rules as if he had a presumed impunity from the consequences which affect other people; (5) he maintains no consistent fealty.

All this can be interpreted to mean that these individuals are nearly overwhelmed by their hate and aggressive impulses and control them only by a continuous pretense which fools even themselves. They seem to live only for the moment, and that moment is filled with a grand show of intention contrary to the patient's deeper intentions. Hence they seem incapable of any sustained loyalties to anyone. Their need for signs of approval to prove that their aggressiveness remains unrecognized or unresponded to is so great that they dare to take chances and run risks that the normal person would not. They feel that they have everything to gain and nothing to lose, right now; the future is a vague uncertainty.

In coining a new word to describe this personality type, it is important that we eliminate words having confused historical meanings, like "psychopathic personality," and words arising from the physician's sense of disapproval, resentment and annoyance, etc., such as "moral imbecile," "fraudulent personality," "insincere personality," etc. The following have occurred to me:

1. *Predatory personality.* (This describes without emotion or moralizing the essentially aggressive, interpersonal relationships which these patients regularly establish with all other people.)

2. *Sycophantic personality.* (This refers to the attaching of oneself to a person and getting passive satisfaction paid for by flattery. It is essentially the same as parasitic and it may be somewhat moralistic.)

3. *Histrionic personality.* (This implies that the patient is acting out something never genuine, never himself, only pretending to be somebody who he thinks the other person wants him to be.)

4. *Façade personality* (because they put up a better front than even most normal people).

5. *Transilient personality.* (The adjective is described in Webster as "passing as by a leap from one thing to another; marked by breaches of continuity or abrupt transitions or variations." It seems to me the most accurately descriptive.)

The author believes that a new classification of personality types is needed, based on our new concepts of personality structure.

PSYCHOSOMATIC STUDIES

Another of Southard's students, Myrtelle M. Canavan, has expressed the following tribute to Southard: "He bestowed on us the benediction of the open mind, a golden treasure if we can but preserve it." * Most of Southard's students have preserved this benediction. In commenting about their debt to Southard, Karl Menninger has said, "I think all of us . . . have in the heat of battle tried to do the best that we could with Southard's image in our hearts rather than by invoking his name or referring to him as the original authority as we probably should have done more often." *

Many students never outgrow their teachers. Many who have been influenced by a great teacher remain thereafter harnessed by a kind of hero worship that is evident more often as adulation than as approbation. In the spirit of the open mind, Southard's students would have discredited him if they had not departed from his teachings when their experience so dictated.

Karl Menninger made a departure from the influence of Southard when he embraced psychoanalysis. Perhaps Southard also would have changed in his attitude toward psychoanalysis if he had lived longer, but during his lifetime he remained hostile to it. When Karl Menninger began to write papers such as those included in this section he was already markedly influenced by what Freud and other psychoanalysts were teaching him. He had outgrown some of Southard's influence on him.

It is noteworthy that, although he has written many psychoanalytic papers, a large percentage of them have to do with psychoanalytic studies of illnesses commonly considered to be physical illnesses and not psychiatric illnesses. Karl Menninger is proud to be a physician. When he became a psychoanalyst he experienced a loss of prestige in the eyes of many of his colleagues who thought him not only young but foolish. These papers are significant clinical psychoanalytic studies and are as useful now for study by the young psychiatrist as they were when they were written.

But for Karl Menninger there was an additional purpose in writing them—to justify to himself and to others what appeared to be a departure

---

* Gay, Frederick P. *The Open Mind.*

from medicine. He, more than many of his colleagues, came to recognize that many of the repeated observations about patients made by physicians for centuries could be understood more clearly by the application of psychoanalytic knowledge. For example, physicians have long known that the right treatment method used at the right time with the right patient resulted in a cure. Such recoveries could not always be explained on the basis of the nature of the pathology or of the nature of the treatment used. Suggestion has been invoked as that powerful healer that explained all treatment outcomes that could not otherwise be understood. But what is suggestion and what makes it work or fail to work? He attempts to extend medical understanding by exploring the psychological meaning to the patient of the process induced.

Karl Menninger is a supremely able clinical observer and this clinical skill is evident in the papers in this section. He respects this skill in other physicians, as is shown by the way he was particularly impressed with the psychiatric acumen of many physicians who did not consider themselves psychiatrists. He was amazed at the dispatch with which dermatologists could draw certain inferences about their patients, and he credits these physicians for their help in his attempts to sharpen his own powers of clinical observation.   —B. H. H.

10. Psychoanalytic Study of a Case of Organic Epilepsy

The work of Jelliffe and White in this country and of Groddeck, Ferenczi and Hollos, and others in Europe has recently directed our attention to the psychoanalytic mechanisms observed in certain psychiatric syndromes undoubtedly based upon structural disease. I have elsewhere presented a psychoanalytic study of some symptoms observed in a case of uremic delirium.[1] The following is a very incomplete study of certain aspects of a case of epilepsy which seemed to have arisen upon the basis of congenital syphilis. My brother and I are making a study of thirty-five cases of congenital syphilitic epilepsy, and this is the only one in which the psychodynamic factors were easily accessible.*

Family history. The patient was the only progeny of her parents, both of whom were entirely free from epilepsy. One other pregnancy resulted in a child which died in two weeks. Miscarriages were

Read at the eighty-first annual meeting of the American Psychoanalytic Association, Richmond, Virginia, May 12, 1925. Reprinted from the *Psychoanalytic Review*, 13:187–199, April 1926.

* In one case, however, there were interesting psychoanalytic data as follows: Mary, aged eight, had involuntarily and apparently unconsciously urinated in her clothes three or four times in the three months prior to her first convulsion. The second convulsion occurred a month later at five o'clock in the morning. She awoke her sister saying that she had had a bad dream and was afraid she had wet the bed. This in fact she had done slightly. She arose, went to the toilet and urinated, and then climbed into bed with her mother. Her mother described her as feeling cold as ice, and she huddled up against her mother and quivered and gurgled. This gave place to more queer noises and she became tonically stiff, then clonic, and then flaccid.

denied but not convincingly. The father was generally considered to be syphilitic. He had lost all his hair early in life, was regarded by the neighbors as being fast and promiscuous. His Wassermann was always negative, however, in our laboratory. His eyes were strikingly pathological and the opinion of the oculist was that there were distinct corneal scars and other evidence that he himself had congenital syphilis. His pupils were irregular, unequal, and almost fixed; he had a scrotal tongue and his epitrochlear lymph nodes were much enlarged.

Past history. The patient was perfectly well, according to the history, until the present illness, having graduated from high school at the age of 17, one of the best in a class of twenty.

Present illness. She came to our attention at the age of 19 on account of a typical attack of status epilepticus in which she had a total of several hundred attacks of very severe tonic and clonic convulsions in the course of ten days. In such attacks she would stop breathing, champ her jaws, contract the muscles of her face, bite her lower lip almost to shreds, and then extend her arms and legs in rigid, rather bizarre attitudes, with the elbows bent, the wrists slightly flexed, the fingers and thumbs hyperextended.

The history was that she had had such convulsions for nearly two years, usually nocturnal, accompanied by bed-wetting and followed by amnesia. She had been advised by physicians, who evidently thought that she had hysteria, that to get married would cure the convulsions. Instead, it had apparently made them much worse. Tonsillectomy, dilation, and various other procedures were indulged in without avail, including eight months of osteopathy. The doctors were alleged to have advised that having a baby would help the convulsions, and at the time of her status epilepticus she was three months pregnant.

Examination. Very careful examinations were made of this patient during and subsequent to the attack of status epilepticus, including spinal fluid examination and other tests of an extra-routine sort, most of which were negative or inconclusive. She was a well-nourished girl of rather small stature, with plump face and hands, and typical infantile facies and manner. Physical and laboratory findings were never absolutely conclusive of syphilis but there were numerous stigmata. There was a notable difference in the tendon reflexes on the two different sides, the left knee-jerk being totally absent and the left ankle reflex very faint, but otherwise not much evident neuropathology.

She was given a great deal of antisyphilitic treatment before and after the birth of her child and has shown considerable improvement. She was also given small doses of luminal.

The next year she was seen by us occasionally, chiefly for the administration of antisyphilitic treatment. During this time the husband and mother frequently mentioned certain rather unusual symptoms in her convulsions. She had relatively few attacks of *grand mal* and rather frequent attacks of *petit mal* which she would describe as little flashes. In some of these she would exclaim "Oh!" and raise her hand and fall back, limp, in her chair. Upon one occasion she seemed to be unconscious for about ten minutes, sat up and asked, "Where am I?" and fell back into a deep sleep for an hour.

Another feature was the fact that she kept mentioning a visual aura which seemed to be very persistent, in the nature of a group of people, the identity or number or occupation of which she could never remember. She would simply say, "I saw those people again," or "It was those same old people," or something of this kind.

One day she complained that while she had had no convulsions she had felt flashes all day and there had been the scene of the people about her constantly to the extent that she couldn't sleep. "I wasn't in this world at all, all day." Later in 1922, for a month or so she would have no attacks and then she would have a series of this sort: flashes for four days, nothing for two days, a severe convulsion, dizzy spells for three days, another convulsion, waves of nausea and dizziness, remission, occipital pain for one day, no symptoms at all for a few weeks.

She seemed then to be getting nowhere with the antisyphilitic treatment and the psychic factors were rather numerous. In talking over the matter with a consultant, who is not a psychoanalyst, it was suggested that I try the experiment of a formal psychoanalytic treatment, which I did, with these results:

First session, about thirty minutes (my notes on her free associations):

"Those people."

"Room with table in it."

(Numerous attacks of *petit mal.*)

"I see round black tanks."

(Divers reflections in regard to their present homelessness—the baby troubling people—whether husband wants to go home for his folks' sakes or his own.)

Second session, about forty minutes: (She staggered as she entered the room and was tremulous and anxious.)

"So weak—statue out in water—comes toward me—divides at my face. His brows go across my eyes.

"Specks like the sea is pictured—going.

"Those people keep coming every day—different ones at different times but all the same. . . . In another land—there is a suppressed feeling with them. One is a little boy standing by a fence—just see him for an instant and he's gone—seems like I'm way up in the air [dizzy spell].

"Eyes looking on both sides of my face. Kind of a window—the light jerking and [her baby cries without] I saw kind of a light—couldn't tell what it was. Big kind of a white post of something—white. Bunch of chorus girls, now, I see—see a man—hat and coat on—couldn't see his face. Seems to be another one—his hat is off—speaking to somebody, gun or something.

"Darkey girls, then a wave.

"Water again with white triangles on it—kind of in front of it. Race horses—riders suited as in races. Birds flying—wings outspread."

(The varied array of apparently disconnected but obvious symbols is notable.)

The patient then disappeared and I saw nothing of her for four months. (Resistance.) Then she came in and said that she had had no convulsions for over a month and she felt the best she ever had in her life; she had no flashes and no depression, and aside from actual attacks of lightheadedness was in perfect health. (Transference improvement.)

Again she disappeared and I saw her no more for another period of four months, when she came in to tell me she had had attacks about once a week for several weeks. Her attacks came at night. A new type of *petit mal* had appeared, a sudden feeling as if something were going around and around and "couldn't get together in my head."

Having described one, she proceeded to have one. She breathed rapidly and deeply, fixed her gaze straight ahead, exhibited an anxiety facies, and trembled conspicuously; in about forty-five seconds she was perfectly normal again. During the attack I asked her casually if she was raising any chickens this summer, and after the attack she remembered the question and answered it.

Again she disappeared and I saw her no more for five months, when a second attempt at psychoanalysis was begun and proceeded irregularly for six months with a total of twenty-three sessions, from which the following material is derived:

The first session was on January 19, 1924, at which time she came in with her mother, having a continuous series of attacks of gasping, staring, fixing her eyes as if frightened, trembling, holding herself rigid, etc. It seemed to me that these were precipitated by coming into my presence, and her mother said she had been wanting to come and see me all week. The phenomena looked hysterical to me and the mother said she was sure they were perfectly voluntary.

Her first free associations were the phrase, "Out of a deep hole." Then came numerous pictures, especially of a woman and a child, neither of whom could she identify or discuss. (Certainly these were herself and her mother, the deep-hole reference to birth being clear enough, and confirmatory.)

For the next hour she sprang up several times gasping and shaking; she said she felt "as if my head flew away; no mind at all— nothing left in there to think with. Feel as if my neck were grasped by fingers and they were shutting off my breathing; makes my neck rigid and tense."

Subsequent to the visit to me she was very much better for a week and agreed to make an attempt to come every four or five days for an hour. She lived some fifty miles from my office and felt that was as often as they could bring her in.

At the next session she had a dream of being in a little house in the woods, sick abed, nursed by a boy, and then that the house was filled with water. A second dream was recalled in which she was at a neighbor's and her mother sat down and ate but wouldn't permit her to do so. "In all my dreams I seem to be sick. I don't feel so or seem to feel so, but I can tell by the way they treat me and do for me that I am sick."

(This invalidism and infantilism and desire to be waited upon appears throughout the series.)

Third session: She first had a series of fits (which she said were the first for some time) with much blocking. When the hour was half over she began to talk about her husband and how unhappy they were together in many regards, and how distressing it was that her husband and her parents disliked each other so much.

I asked then about her sex life, and she related that she had masturbated considerably since marriage, chiefly because of a lack of sufficient gratification.

Fourth session (February 19): She reported only two flashes in spite of the fact that she had had a bad cold. She had had a dream of a fire in a bank, or at least so she surmised from the fact that smoke issued from the safes. There was a woman who elbowed her aside—and cautioned her against withdrawing her money from the bank.

(It was my impression from the associations, notes on which I have not saved, that the dream probably related directly to the treatment—to the money that goes like smoke. The banker was obviously the analyst and the lady who was ahead of her and elbowed her aside probably relates to her favorite aunt, who was a psychoanalytic patient of mine who frequently came the same day and who sometimes preceded this patient.)

At the *fifth session* she was blocked for practically a full hour.

Sixth session (February 26): Her husband came with her and sat outside. She had left her parents' home and had gone to stay with him for a time. I asked how she had been doing down there, to which she responded with an attack of gasping, staring, and head clutching, and finally with an apologetic laugh said, "I can't get settled down," to which I made no reply. She went on as follows: "The closer I get to there, I mean to my husband's house, the worse I hate to go. I told him I guess he could see I wasn't very responsive to his welcome. [Tears.] The farther I get away from him the better I feel."

This was followed with a discussion of the disagreeableness of her husband's parents. She insisted that it was because of them and not because of him that she disliked his home. Her sex ardor she claimed to be undiminished. She was sure she loved him but was much distressed by the fact that he lived so near his undesirable parents. Her last remark was, "I can't remember when we were married or anything about it. Today I feel that I just want to go home to mama."

Three days later she came back saying that she had gone home with her mother and had been "just feeling fine." She announced that she had decided to return no more to her husband; she had been wakened up to the fact that she no longer loved him and gave a long list of reasons why she didn't love him and why she knew she didn't love him, including considerable quotations from her mother.

I made no comment but advised her to make no announcement of the final decision at this time. A few days later she came in again with two dreams.

First dream: Her husband was forcing her to pull a wagon over plowed ground, with the greatest difficulty. When the wagon got stuck he whipped her. From this dream she awoke, screaming.

Associations promptly brought out the obvious interpretation that in addition to the heavy burdens of life which were entailed by the necessity of living with him and doing the necessary work for him which she described in some detail, he added the torture of coitus (whip symbolizing penis). From this it developed that she had never really enjoyed intercourse, that she was disgusted at the way he referred to it and demanded it; that it was impossible for her to get any pleasure out of it except by more or less violent exertion which exhausted her completely. It was because of this that she masturbated.

(It would be seen from this dream that a single theme is coming more and more into prominence, namely, that heterosexual pleasures and obligations were distasteful and horrible to her and that she wanted to go back to mama, and anything else was torture [to which her reaction is convulsive].)

Second dream: She was between two faces; on one side of her was a hideous face and on the other a pleasant man.

This is so obviously the husband and the analyst that the patient herself pointed it out within a few minutes after she had related the dream, with appropriate discussion of her emotional sets toward us both.

At the next (*ninth*) session, however (of course!), the resistance seemed much more marked. She said that she had had no dreams. I insisted, however, and she did recall that she had had one in which the pleasant man (analyst) was a guest at the same dinner party. "I enjoyed myself and he took me home. He never makes any advances; it is just pure friendship."

(Enjoying herself at a dinner party with the analyst is obviously enough significant of coitus which the rest of the dream attempts to smother with the essence of platonic innocence which also refers to the passivity of the analyst with [probably] a little smack of resentment.)

At the *tenth session* I asked her why she had ever married. Her first reply was that "it certainly wasn't sex urge." She went on to decry "sex urge" and to tell me that she couldn't remember her wedding at all or her wedding night, but that her husband had frequently told me that she cried when he insisted upon intercourse and made so much fuss about it that he deferred it. While describing this, she had a light "head-pain" attack. She could recall nothing further.

She had been so much better that I thought we could decrease the luminal from grains 3 to grains 1½ daily. However, a few days later she came in to say that her husband and baby had arrived by train and that she had several attacks which began immediately after phoning him. She had an attack at the depot when he came in.

"But today I feel again a little as if I belonged to him." With this she began to cry and then had a severe gasping attack, fell off the couch onto the floor and lay there, and then jumped up suddenly and said, "Where is he? Where is he?"

She recovered herself and went on with the free associations. She said she was conscious but couldn't help herself, and apologized. "I just wanted to relax. I couldn't hold on any more. I couldn't keep holding back my thoughts. There was a man coming toward me—makes me shudder—I couldn't see his face—surely I don't love him or I wouldn't feel that way."

Then she had a series of flashes and saw a "covered wagon, a man and a woman [slaps the air in front of her face], a woman and a little boy and a cup." "It isn't seeing them that hurts me—I feel it—pushing down on me, my chest."

(My interpretation of this session was that it represented an hysterical projection of her coitus aversion coupled with a breaking through of the poorly repressed conflicts of a type to be elaborated later.)

On *March* 27 she spent an hour saying that she couldn't recall anything; she was trying to, but nothing came, and she couldn't quite catch them, etc.

Thirteenth session (April 4): She came in looking very well indeed. "Everybody says I am better than I ever was in my life. I have had no attacks whatever and aside from getting dizzy at my menstrual period I feel perfectly well."

From this she went on to a pro-and-con discussion of the benefits of leaving her husband, and the following significant facts resulted from her conversation:

(1) *"He always treated me as a child and so does everyone else."*

(2) "The dizziness comes *only when I think of my husband."*

(3) *Her convulsions began at the time she began to go with her future husband!* (Strangely enough, although it had been carefully inquired into, this point had never been developed previously.)

(4) Her husband made sex advances before they were married, which were offensive and repulsive to her. "I don't see how some

girls can do such things; they just defile their womanhood." (The patient went on to some length about the wickedness of this.)

(5) *"I would always tell mother* when I would go into the house; I told her everything; I never kept anything from her; I just told her everything. I am surprised she didn't throw him out of the house."

Fourteenth session: She reported that she still had no convulsions and no dizziness, and went on berating her husband, his ignorance, his uncouthness, his vulgarity, his offenses, etc. She was distressed, however, by having waves of the opposite feeling, and this ambivalence distressed her mother, who, the patient says, "throws up her arms in frenzy."

"I don't know what love is; I don't know what the feeling is to be in love with somebody. I know what love for my parents is, but have always wondered what real love for a man would be. I asked mother. I think I liked John but I always wondered what love really was. I was never very passionate and now I am not at all, and I got less passionate every time I was with him. Intercourse was always hard for me. I would never feel him in intercourse. I'd have to work up myself and didn't feel him at all. When I think of this side of my life with him I think more and more that I am through with him forever. He is ten years older than I. Anyway, I'm glad that I'm free; that's the way I feel today."

(These sessions reveal more clearly than ever her psychosexual infantilism and her incapacity for heterosexual life. She is obviously building up a resolution to desert her husband and return to her mother, substituting this resolution for the convulsions which have previously settled the conflict. Her heterosexuality was the more painful for her because of the infantilistic transparency of her object choice, i.e., her "husband" was too obviously her father image.)

Fifteenth session (April 18): "Feeling fine." Was advised to cut down the luminal because she had no convulsions or other attacks. Dreamed of her husband begging her to return. Says her mother puts on the same clutching, agonizing scenes when she mentions the possibility of returning to her husband that she herself has in her spells. "Mother says she will just die whenever I mention it." I point out that this was a protest of her mother against her leaving home for John just as she herself in this same way made the same protest, to which she added significantly, "Mother's was conscious; mine was unconscious."

She came next complaining of feeling dizzy and nervous. Her husband, she related, always said she was so youthful and babyish and he wanted her to be more dignified and older; anything but youthful, like herself. He wanted her to be like older people, practical, quiet. Then she spent forty minutes in deep, rapid breathing as if about to break into sobs, which, however, did not occur. (Abreaction?)

Her free associations to this dyspnea were "pressure in the chest; her husband's weight lying upon her, especially in intercourse."

May 17: She came in very tremulous and quavery, with a dream of climbing a ladder (which is obvious enough); also a dream of going from flat-boat to flat-boat with imminent danger of falling into the water (returning to mother). Free associations were not forthcoming; she would ramble along about how fleeting and fleeing her ideas were and then keep still for a while.

May 24: She came in with a dream of having been sick; free associations to this led to a discussion of her menstruation which she said had occurred after her last visit here and made her feel better, and also the first marriage night, for which she insisted she was totally amnesic. "The only thing I can recall is that I cried and wanted to go home to mother." She is amnesic for most of the next year, i.e., for the entire period of her marriage prior to her attack of status epilepticus.

June 3: More dreams of being sick, and almost dead. No free associations.

I did not see the patient again for several weeks, at which time she and her mother came in to tell me that they had sued her husband for divorce, charging him with cruelty, perversion, and being the cause of her epilepsy. I reproved them for charging things which they knew were not true.

The patient was feeling fine; said it was a great load off of her and that "I at last feel like myself." When I told her I thought the divorce matter was somewhat muddled she cried and said, "Must I go back to him?"

She did not go back to him and did not come back to me for two months, when she came in to ask if she should come back for more treatment. *She had had no more convulsions!*

Two weeks later she came in again. When she entered the door she fell at me, almost on me, as if in a sleep, and then fell on down to the floor with a look of anguish and with shuddering. I immediately called the office nurse and the patient arose at once. I noticed then that if I helped her she tottered and seemed about to fall, but when I let her go she managed to get about fairly well and go to the couch successfully. Then she began to explain that the walk upstairs had tired her and she could have held on to herself but wanted to let go now that she had the chance.

She lay on the couch jerking her right arm, her eyes filling with tears, her head shaking. She remained silent. I finally asked her what occurred to her. She made no reply at first but at length smiled and said she was thinking of taking hold of herself again and that she recalled trembling at the door. "When I got here and came in and saw you I just thought I could relax. I just wasn't holding on to myself then." (Transference sustenance.)

"The back of my head aches. I can't recall having had any fits at home but Mother says that I have. I don't recall asking the questions that Mother says I did (Where is John? Is John here? Is he down to his home? Do I have to go back to him? Our boy—where is he? Where is our boy? Am I divorced from John? Is someone in bed with me? Am I going to have to go back to John?)."

I asked for her associations to the idea of someone in bed with her and she began upon a denunciation of her husband. When I insisted upon her feeling particularly in regard to him she suddenly stared, appeared frightened, seized my hand, rose up in the chair, stared at the bookcase, cried, and exclaimed, "Oh, my head!" I insisted that she lie down, which she then did, and she said she felt as if an iron band were clamped about her head and that the book she was staring at was the Kingdom of Evils (Southard and Jarrett). She said her husband had always accused her of masturbating but that she didn't do it, although she was occasionally passionate even now and went so far as to clench her thighs together, which she demonstrated. As a child she masturbated with her hands but she always told her mother, who didn't scold her or scare her about it. "But there is no connection between it [eroticism] and my spells. Why, they are the farthest removed." She left much relieved.

I saw her no more until I wrote to her just prior to making this report, nearly a year later. In the meantime she had secured her divorce and was living with her parents. Her husband came occasionally to see the baby but no longer provoked any manifest interest in the patient, either of attraction or aversion. She was looking and feeling very well and had had relatively few convulsions in the past year, certainly less than one a month. (Her total inability to remember how frequently they had occurred contrasts with the meticulous care with which she formerly reported the date and hour of each attack.) "I'm as happy as I can be. Of course I wish I had a home for my little fellow, but all my aunts just worship him and I couldn't have a better place than I am.

"Mother is doing pretty well, too, but sometimes when we have an argument she clenches her fist and makes a scene, and I find the easiest way to do is just to relax and drop. I drop to the floor, but I'm not unconscious and get right up, and by relaxing the tension is gone. I feel all right."

(This is clearly her characteristic solution for unpleasantness. Formerly the attacks were of the organic *grand mal* type; then, as described, they took on more and more hysterical stigmata; here they are frankly conscious, deliberate, histrionic stunts.)

(Do you ever see "those people" any more?)

"No, nothing like that, and I don't dream any more, and I sleep well and eat well."

(What helped you the most?)

"Getting free from John. But I never would have done it; I never would have found out what I wanted, that I wanted to be free, if it hadn't been for psychoanalysis." (Which may or may not have been a correct opinion; probably not.)

SUMMARY

A case is presented of a typical epileptic syndrome arising upon a basis of definite structural cerebropathy, presumably syphilitic, which was studied by the psychoanalytic method. Although thorough systematic psychoanalytic investigation was impracticable, the dreams, free associations, and clinical developments made it seem clear that the occurrence of convulsions was in part psychogenically determined. Intolerable pressure from unconscious conflicts set up by the attempts of a girl of manifestly infantile psyche to fit herself (or be fitted) into an adult heterosexual relationship, and relief was accomplished by the epileptic flight, a reaction type characteristic of her (brain). Her convulsions began in association with her engagement; they became aggravated by her marriage and most severe during her pregnancy; they decreased rapidly when she lived apart from her husband, were intensified again by his revisits, and decreased markedly after her separation and divorce, with a concomitant improvement in her general physical health.

Dreams and free associations indicated a persistent back-to-mother trend throughout, and the transference to the analyst was clearly of the mother-libido variety.

The improvement was probably due to a combination of (1) transference, (2) catharsis (the emergence into consciousness of repressed and suppressed material), and (3) environmental alterations. The motive for this report was not the presentation of the therapeutic result or technique, however, but the wish to report certain psychoanalytic trends observed in a case of organic "epilepsy."

CONCLUSIONS

The author believes that this study adds confirmatory evidence to the thesis that the manifestations of structural ("organic") pathology are associated with if not determined by psychic mechanisms which are accessible to study by the psychoanalytic method with, in some cases, objective clinical improvement.

11. Some Unconscious Psychological Factors Associated with the Common Cold

Every clinician knows that organic diseases often occur under circumstances that make it seem as if the disease served some psychological purposes for the patient. I do not refer to the secondary capitalization of the illness by the patient, with which we are all familiar, seen particularly in the neuroses. Rather I refer to those cases where the illness seems to be, in part, a reaction to a certain event even though the nature of the illness precludes the possibility that such an event alone could have brought on the illness. We know that sore throat is caused by an irritation, usually bacterial; but when a woman who is not subject to them develops a severe sore throat immediately after an episode in which she has maligned the character of a friend, or immediately after a relative has swallowed carbolic acid, or immediately after a fellatio experience, we have reason to suspect a connection which psychoanalytic research may substantiate.

Much work has already been done in this field through the pioneering courage of Smith Ely Jelliffe in this country, and by Felix Deutsch, Georg Groddeck, and others in Europe. In this brief communication I shall not attempt to review the literature. I shall only mention Groddeck's hypothesis, which is that the libido in some way or other pervades the entire body so that the body may accept or reject an infection in accordance with some instinctive

Reprinted from the *Psychoanalytic Review*, 21:201–207, April 1934.

demand. Even though this is not entirely scientific it is, at least, stimulating and fruitful because it reconciles the bacteriological theories of resistance and immunity with the psychological theories of self-protection and self-destruction.

Where should one expect to find more abundant evidence concerning the nature of these unconscious factors in physical disease than in that most prevalent of all infections, the common cold? We do not know how it is caused, how it is communicated, or how it can be cured. We all know its symptoms very well, both subjectively and objectively, but what are the psychological factors that accompany it? Beyond the well-known descriptive aspects of irritability, sluggishness, etc., I think almost nothing has been recorded.

Yet every psychoanalyst in the course of his clinical work with neurotic patients has the experience time after time of observing the inception, development, flourishing, and decline of a "cold," and in these cases he is able to learn rather completely what the psychological configuration of his patient's unconscious is, both before and during the cold.

Perhaps the reason more has not been written about the subject is that the psychological material does not appear to be entirely constant or identical in all patients, or because the common cold is so ubiquitous that it is often exceedingly difficult to be sure how much the cold is a specific result of particular psychological tendencies and how much it is simply a general and habitual "invalid" reaction to the unpleasant.

I recently had the opportunity to observe the development of a very severe cold of a typical sort in a woman who is not at all subject to colds. This occurred when there was no general epidemic of such infections. It was a matter of common knowledge and remark in her family that she never suffered from colds as other members of the family did. In her entire life of forty years she had not had more than three or four colds. Therefore, it could not be charged that this was simply an habitual response on her part or an incidental event. Nor could it be charged that she was only one of many who were affected by a prevalent epidemic. As will be shown, the cold occurred in such a way as to represent dramatically, in organic terms, certain very pronounced psychological tendencies of hers.

Just prior to the development of her cold she had recognized quite definitely in her analytic work her aggressive tendencies against men in general and her husband in particular, and had had a dream in which she was once more at the deathbed of her younger brother. Her husband was also there dripping something all over the floor which she interpreted to be menstrual blood.

With her associations which dealt with the fact that her brother died of a bladder affliction and that her husband was actually present at his death, I was able to make the interpretation to her that the wish to humiliate me, of which she was quite conscious, was also present in her attitude toward her husband, whom she represented in this dream to be menstruating, and that this wish to have her husband castrated was also present toward the brother by whose death she had been so profoundly moved. She had already recognized before this that her marriage to a man she regarded as cruel had been influenced by the death of her brother since it was a fact that she had fallen in love with her husband at the deathbed of her brother. I asked if it might not be possible that her submitting herself to her husband in marriage had been an attempt to propitiate for wishing to castrate her brother.

Following this session she returned to her home for the week end and I did not see her until Monday, when she reported that there was a marked change in her marital relationship, that her husband had seemed unusually loving for the first time in over a year, and that she had mentioned it to him and he had assured her that it was she that had changed and not he.

"But," she said, "*I have a terrible cold.* I noticed as I was leaving here last Friday that my eyes were watering so that I could not see clearly. Now I am having the worst cold I ever had in my life. It was always a proverb when I was a child that I never took colds and I have never had but three or four in my life and this is certainly the worst ever. There must be some psychological cause for it."

After a short digression she returned to the theme and asked me if I had noticed that she had used the expression "took cold." She

went on to remind me that I had told her a week or so previously
that she had a great wish to take things from people (she was actually taking some money from her brother at the moment and she
also referred by this to her wish to take the penis from her other
brother and from her husband) and that she had denied this by
saying that all her life she had tried not to take anything from
anyone and was very proud.

"Perhaps," she said, "you were right after all, that I do want to
take things, so intensely that I lean over backward and try to persuade myself that I don't want to accept anything from anybody.
But now this cold comes along and I speak of 'taking' a cold and
my use of that expression catches my own attention which makes
me think that perhaps I have decided I *would* take things from
now on."

"And not pretend that you don't want to," I said.*

"Yes," she said. "Perhaps this had something to do with my
better relations with my husband over the week end."

"That you were able to be more feminine and take the love he
had to offer?" I asked.

She didn't know about that but she did know that she was dis-
pleased with this miserable cold, she didn't want to take colds, whatever she took. If psychoanalysis was going to mean that she would
lose this immunity to colds which had distinguished her formerly,
she didn't like it at all and she didn't want to find out what caused
her to have it. But upon second thought, since it looked as if she
had already lost this immunity, she might as well face it; something
in her must have changed already.

Here the analyst explained that if the cold represented a greater
acceptance on her part, she must observe that she was still able to
take only something that gave her distress, i.e., she *took,* but she
punished herself for taking. She made no comment upon this and
the hour was up.

The following day she announced first of all that her cold was

---

* A more appropriate comment might have come from the analyst at this point.
From the patient's next remark it is strongly suggested that her use of the expression "taking it" had also the connotation of taking her punishment; cf. the expression
"take it on the chin."

much worse. Also, she wanted to tell me that she had concealed from me the fact that she was expecting her husband and that he would be here on this day, the very day on which her cold seemed to be at its height. She had been planning for his visit for some time.

"It looks as if I felt guilty about having him come and was trying to spoil it," she said. "I am sure that isn't true, however."

She went on to remark that the most conspicuous thing about her cold seemed to be her nose, that it was so red and raw, twice its natural size and running profusely. As she described her nose she suddenly stopped and after a pause remarked that it came to her mind that something which got red and enlarged and discharged mucus made her think of a penis, for which her nose might be a substitute. Now she was reminded again that the way in which the cold began was in connection with her dream about her brother's death and her wish to castrate him. But what connection could that have with the coming of her husband? Maybe it was to show him that she was a man and could exert a masculine and controlling influence over him (which, as a matter of fact, she did).

The following day she developed more fully the idea that her red and running nose represented the penis that she had taken from her brother and asked if I thought it possible that that was why she was punishing herself for having it. I agreed, whereupon she immediately returned to the theme that she did not want to lose her immunity. (The foregoing and subsequent material will show that "immunity" is in her unconscious synonymous with virility.) Then she spontaneously recalled something from her childhood which was too terrible to mention. After considerable stalling she said she would spell it. It was the appellation "snot nose." I asked her why this term seemed so objectionable to her. She remembered that certain unkempt, neglected, unloved children whose nasal discharges streamed down their faces were disparagingly referred to by her mother as "snot-nosed children." As she reflected upon the matter she recalled that all these were little girls and realized that it had to do with the extreme disparagement with which she felt that she and other little girls were held by her mother and by society in general. (Back of the feeling that these children were rejected because of their noses was the earlier idea that they were rejected because they were girls and had no penises.)

The following day she began as follows: "What on earth do you think happened yesterday after I left here? I had a terrible hemorrhage from my nose! It bled all over my handkerchief and down on my dress so that I had to change my clothes. I never have nosebleeds and I asked myself, What does all this mean? Then it came to my mind that it was a reaction to what you said about the nose being the equivalent of a penis. 'He says my nose is a penis. Penis, the devil! I have no penis. Look, I *menstruate* from my nose! That shows I am feminine.'"

She wanted to know if people ever did such things as this, that is, reacting with physical symptoms to psychological concepts. Bleeding from her nose that way and getting blood on her clothes reminded her so vividly of menstruation it couldn't be anything else, but she had never heard of it.

Furthermore, there was another development about her cold. She had a cold sore on her lip. It was a large, swollen one. It seemed to be full of a liquor. She had known for a long time that she got cold sores on her lip after drinking liquor. There must be some significance to this, something about taking liquor into her mouth. Could it relate to kissing? Actually it prevented her from kissing her husband. Maybe that was its purpose.

The analyst remarked that the kiss is often only a disguised bite and that biting was a violent way of taking things.

"You know," she said, "when I was a child my father used to make wine and my mother objected strongly and sometimes would go down in the cellar and pour it all out angrily. Very early in my life I got the idea that alcohol was masculine, that liquor was for men, and perhaps that has something to do with my always getting cold sores when I drink, because naturally semen is also the fluid that belongs to men and as a little girl I thought that women got pregnant by taking semen into their mouths. I spoke to you about taking something into my mouth, didn't I, and a cold sore is a little bag full of liquor, isn't it? Now I must confess to you that until I was married I didn't know for sure that semen was a fluid." (I pointed out that this contradicted what she had just said.) "Well, I know it does, but I thought that all the liquid connected with intercourse was feminine and that the only liquid that men could supply came from their mouths. It isn't clear, but I had some notion about men having a liquid they put in a girl's mouth and it made her pregnant, but I didn't know it came from the penis."

The following day the cold was much better. There was no more coryza, the cold sore had receded *—"But now it is all down in my chest," she said, "and I keep coughing. I believe the chest must represent the uterus and that my cough is something like the cramps a woman has when she menstruates or bears a child. It is just more of what I said yesterday. The analyst is mistaken about my having a penis. I am feminine and my cold is in my chest, I am pregnant.

"Perhaps the cough is rejection of masculinity and perhaps it is a rejection of my femininity also, because I seem to be both a man and a woman. I make myself pregnant by getting my own cold down in my own chest. You know I have often spoken about how masculine I am in so many ways but at heart I am really feminine."

Here she gave me details as to her masculine and feminine tendencies and finally came back to mention of her brother. She wanted to know how her discovery of her castration wishes toward her brother was connected with her cold. I asked her what she thought. She replied by giving details of the last hours of her brother's life. She sat beside him as he hiccuped and belched out bloody fluid which she kept wiping away. Immediately after his death she fainted. She remembers that she was menstruating at the time.

"I believe it means that I had to accept my femininity and be a girl because I had these castration wishes toward my brother, so I have to give up my nose as a penis and get a cold in the chest."

Her cold thus would seem to be a re-enactment of her wish to castrate her brother and acquire his penis, the acquisition of a sym-

---

* A clinician who read the history pointed out that for a cold sore to heal in one day is very unusual. I can only say that the cold sore as I saw it and the cold as I observed it were quite typical of such affections.

bolic penis in the form of a conversion symptom, combined with punishment at the same site and finally the renunciation of this wish in favor of the feminine receptive attitude, masochistically symbolized, the whole drama being transposed from the genital region to the respiratory tract and represented somatically. Most of the symptoms could be traced to childhood experiences. We did not discover why her cold first affected her eyes but one assumption might be that this was related to some sense of guilt about seeing her brother's penis or some parental activities.

I do not mean to suggest that such re-enactments of castration wishes are back of all colds. My purpose is only to show that when the habitual gratifications are disturbed by an analysis, it is possible to see how psychological necessities find what Freud calls "somatic compliance," in such a way that the bodily organs and the sympathetic nervous system carry out what the striated musculature and voluntary nervous system are not permitted to do.

P.S. This case was presented at the Chicago Psychoanalytic Society. Numerous confirmatory reports were contributed by various members. One in particular was contributed by Dr. George Wilson, whose case showed an amazing identity of symptoms and mechanisms, even to the cold sore and the cold on the chest.

12. Impotence and Frigidity from the Standpoint of Psychoanalysis

Those physicians who have made the genitourinary system their chief field of interest have recognized more clearly than the members of almost any other specialty the interrelation between the organic lesions treated by them and the emotional conflicts of their patients. In spite of this, however, they not infrequently seem to the psychiatrist to put the cart before the horse, perhaps for purely pragmatic reasons. For example, sexual impotence associated with anxiety and depression, which psychoanalytic study has shown to be a protective device stimulated by unconscious or dimly conscious fears—this urologists often treat by instrumentation, rectal massage, drugs, etc., with this justification: "The patient thinks there is something wrong with his genitalia. We know that isn't true, or at least that the organ pathology is secondary to the psychopathology, but experience has taught us the curative value of treating the genitalia locally, and by its suggestive value reassuring the patient and relieving his anxiety and thereby his impotence." Of course, this very ingenious pragmatism must claim our support, if true; about its truth many urologists seem to have serious doubts.

Another instance of this relates to those adolescent and young adult males who consult urologists complaining of their addiction to irresistible masturbatory habits or of consequences ascribed thereto, such as spermatorrhoea. The urologists discover an enlarged hy-

Reprinted from the *Journal of Urology*, 34:166–183, August, 1935.

peraemic verumontanum, which they (quite often) treat by cauterization. Now I think no urologist actually believes that masturbation is caused by this local lesion; they cannot escape, however,
from the logic that medical recovery follows such treatment, and
so they have elaborated the theory as follows: Masturbation too
often indulged in causes this lesion, this lesion causes irritation,
congestion, local stimulation, and predisposition to repeated masturbation, and so a vicious circle is established, which must be
interrupted in some way; this we can do by a painful local treatment.

From the psychoanalytic standpoint, we are able to see why such
treatment occasionally succeeds for purely psychological reasons.
Masturbation is indulged in by every child as a normal phase of his
sexual development. Because it is a transitory stage, however, normally superseded by normal forms of sexual gratification and because it is accompanied by phantasies of highly forbidden acts, and
implies violent aggression against its original forbidders, it is always
accompanied by a sense of guilt which in most instances is greatly
augmented by the attitude of the outside world. These feelings of
guilt about masturbation intensify its erotic value; but they also
involve the necessity of some kind of propitiation. So long as he is
under the dominion of parents and can interpret some of their
conduct toward him as punitive or restrictive, he considers the
account squared. But when the process of emotional development
becomes to some degree blocked and masturbation is persistent and
the infantilism is continued into late adolescence and no external
punishment is forthcoming, the anxiety and fear dependent upon
the unatoned sin becomes unbearable. If now he meets with a
urologist who will punish him (by local treatments), he thereby
is relieved of his anxiety. Herein is the weakness of this practical
urological measure, as well as its reasons for success. The patient's
anxiety it does indeed relieve; and in so far as it acts as a threat (a
threat of castration as the psychoanalysts call it) it may act also as
a temporary deterrent of the immediate cause of the anxiety, i.e.,
the masturbation. But it acts also to permit the re-establishment of
the infantile sexual propensities on cleared decks, i.e., on an anxiety-
free basis, instead of eliminating or diverting them. The patient often

unconsciously feels that he has overpaid and is therefore justified in returning to his indulgence. Furthermore, it has the fault of concentrating attention and treatment on a single organ exponent of the narcissism of which masturbation is only one manifestation. The total personality remains unchanged.

We have digressed somewhat from the main thesis. It is not our function to analyze the technique of the urologists, but rather to discover the mechanisms whereby certain urological pathology is brought about. We see, however, in what has just been said, that the psychological needs of the sexually immature person can be doubly gratified, especially through the intervention of the urologist, by the development of local pathology, whereby the anxiety connected with the sexual habit can be projected or corporealized in the sexual organ.

This leads logically to a consideration of impotence and of its corresponding female syndrome, frigidity. While not in the vast majority of cases primarily organic, these conditions are frequently so regarded and treated by urologists, and undoubtedly become so quite often.

One of the functions of human life, the impairment of which provokes extremely serious consequences, is that of the physical union of the sexes. It is a testimony to the curious prudishness of even scientific men that this subject is so generally slighted even in medical treatises. A standard textbook of medicine like Osler's, for example, refers to impotence in only three places and to frigidity nowhere; references to the function of the impairment of walking, on the other hand, occupy in the same book more than a full page of the *index*.

The topic has not been entirely ignored, however. Psychiatrists, urologists, gynecologists, and general practitioners meet the problem constantly in clinical practice and from time to time representatives of these groups contribute to the medical literature discussions of the symptoms or treatment of sexual incompetence.

The theories regarding impotence and frigidity which are most prevalent do not give an adequate explanation of them or indicate a rational technique for treatment of them.

One of these is that disorder of sexual functioning is a constitutional pathology or abnormality—something to be regarded as we regard the early loss of hair—unpredictable, uncomfortable, incurable, but not very serious. Logically, if it is a constitutional deformity it is incurable and the best technique of handling it would be to sympathetically minimize its importance.

A second assumption which is commonly made is that interference in sexual functioning is the result of some organic disease, either local or general, usually the former, and that if the infection in the prostate or the retroversion of the uterus is corrected, normal sexual feeling and capability will return.

Thirdly, it is frequently assumed that frigidity in women and impotence in men are the consequences of bad sexual technique, that human beings in contrast to animals don't exactly know how to cohabit without instruction, or that their prudishness, selfishness, and clumsiness prevent them from doing naturally what more primitive persons or animals accomplish easily. On the basis of this assumption sexual disability can be corrected by the simple matter of a little psychological re-education, instruction, and advice.

It would be unscientific to dismiss these three theories without giving them the credit they deserve. That there may be a constitutional incapacity to feel sexual pleasure is theoretically just as possible as the existence of congenital absence of hunger (or pain sensation). But there is no reason to assume that congenital sexual incapacity should be any more frequent than these. All of them represent the instinctive physical activities which make life possible, and if there were any general prevalence of the congenital absence of either one of them, life would have long since disappeared from the planet.*

As to the second common assumption: it is just as logical to believe that the loss of sexual appetite can be ascribed to an infected prostate or retroverted uterus as to believe that the loss of appetite for food can be caused by enlarged tonsils or a ptotic stomach—

---

* That there are those whose sexual propensities are diverted in abnormal directions on what may be described as a constitutional basis, I cannot deny, but I think it is self-evident that such cases are exceptional, that they are clinical freaks so to speak, and in no sense helpful in the understanding of so general a phenomenon as that which we are considering.

just as logical, but no more so. There simply is no connection between these accessory organs of reproduction and the psychophysical
nexus which is represented by coitus. Appetite does not originate in
the stomach, although hunger is felt there, nor in the tonsils, and
sexual desire does not come from the uterus or from the prostate.
People lacking these organs frequently lead normal sexual lives.*

This attempt to explain psychological experience and behavior on
the basis of physics, chemistry, and organic reactions is, as Alexander [1] has pointed out, a vestige of the Elizabethan era of medical
science when doctors felt constrained to disbelieve everything they
could not see with their eyes or touch with their hands lest they be
confused with the philosophers and magicians with whom the
medical men were so closely identified only a few decades previously.

The third assumption that prudery and clumsiness are responsible
for sexual disability and that it can be overcome by instruction and
education, is true sometimes. There is no doubt that the unfortunate
consequences of a prudish upbringing or a selfish obliquity on the
part of men which makes them inconsiderate of the psychological
nature of women can be combated to some extent by education and
advice. For the general practitioner this is by all means the most important weapon. Many couples who simply do not know how to
have sexual intercourse consult physicians. The act of coitus has
assumed for them an exaggerated, distorted, detached significance.
Instead of the periodic culmination of a strong love linkage, coming
about automatically but with active preparation of the partner, it is
a nervous occasion of clumsily managed intravaginal masturbation
about which both parties feel embarrassment, shame, and misgivings.

For a few cases, then, helpful instruction is sufficient. But it is a
great mistake to assume that by this method we could eliminate all
cases of impotence and frigidity. Most of them depend upon far
more subtle and complicated factors.

---

* Even the testicles are not essential to coitus. I know of two cases where both
testicles were long ago removed and the men still have normal sexual desire and
sexual power, and every surgeon knows many women who have been castrated
without change in their sexual feeling.

VARIETIES OF IMPOTENCE

Let us first define the phenomenon more carefully. In men one observes impotence in the following forms:

No interest. A total or almost total disinclination for sexual intercourse is not rare. This does not preclude a considerable interest in women, nor a tender solicitous attitude toward them. Such men do not necessarily evade marriage. Indeed, the doctor's attention is more often brought to such cases through the wife than through the patient himself.

No erection. This form of impotence in men is common; and indeed it is pathological only when habitual or frequently repeated. The paradox of it is well known—there is a strong desire, there is often well-demonstrated evidence of great sexual capacity; erection is vigorous at some time before as well as after the attempt. Yet in spite of this, it cannot be effected at the moment needed.

No endurance. Premature ejaculation, i.e., orgasm, either before or very soon after intromission is another very widespread form of impotence, which is frequently not recognized as such. Obviously the purpose and result of *ejaculatio praecox* is to defeat the ends of coitus—both the pleasurable and (in the extreme form) the reproductive. Both parties are thwarted. It is true the ego is somewhat less offended than in that form of impotence in which erection fails entirely, but the genuine satisfaction of normally aroused, sustained, and finally relieved sexual feeling is completely routed in an abrupt and baffling way which only substitutes one kind of disappointment for another. Indeed, the physical consequences to both parties (malaise, irritability, etc.) are perhaps more noticeable after sexual episodes of this sort.

No orgasm. Just the opposite of premature ejaculation may occur —an inability to achieve orgasm. This may occur with priapism *— i.e., erection is maintained and coitus is indefinitely prolonged but results only in exhaustion. It may also take the form of a loss of

---

* A urologist friend, Dr. Arthur D. Gray, states that "this is actually *very rare*. I canvassed 52 urologists a few days ago and did not find 20 cases in their combined experience. When found it may be from drugs, excesses, and splenic disease; true priapism is usually surgical (drainage of cavernous bodies)."

erection after a few minutes of what starts out as if to be quite normal intercourse. It is as if the semen must not, could not be expended.

No pleasure. It may be surprising, even to physicians, that many men who believe themselves to be potent and who perform the sexual act in a mechanically correct way, often to the complete satisfaction of their wives, obtain from it only a minimum of pleasure. Indeed for some the orgasm is actually painful, and the whole act something of a bore. This absence of pleasure is a common form of impotence. Another manifestation of this same kind of psychic impotence is frequently observed (again, often in men who regard themselves as normally or abnormally potent)—as a feeling of regret and loss after the completion of the act. I recall one patient, for example, who having insisted upon intercourse would, upon its completion, reproach his wife bitterly for having permitted him to perform it, declaring that now he would be nervous and below par all day, might catch cold, and might be weakened mentally.

Associated perversions and fetishisms. Finally, there are those forms of impotence which are relative, i.e., sexual satisfaction is obtained in a fairly complete degree, but only by means of special devices and conditions. One man can cohabit only if his wife wears gloves and stockings, another can function only in the inverted posture, another only if fellatio precedes the act, another only if the woman first spanks him or vice versa. Those associated fetishisms and perversions are not uncommon, but they constitute something of a special case, in which the impotence has been spontaneously or automatically remedied by an unconscious psychological device—like the attempts at surgical healing represented by proud flesh.*

IMPOTENCE IN WOMEN

It may not be self-evident that frigidity in women is identical psychologically with impotence in men. Certainly the popular view of it is scarcely that. Numerous statistical investigations as to the

---

* Strictly speaking, it is incorrect to describe any physical activities which culminate in normal genital union and orgasm as perversions. Perversions are aberrant forms of satisfaction complete in themselves and not used merely as preliminary contributions to forepleasure.

frequency of frigidity in women have been made, but no one thinks of making such an inquiry among men. This is partly due to the more subtle forms which male impotence so often takes, but even more, I think, to the prevalence and strength of sexual repression in women. There are actually people of both sexes who do not know that conscious sexual feeling is ever experienced by women. One of the ablest general practitioners I have ever known once amazed me by a casual remark which I cite only to show how mistaken even a man of wisdom and long experience may be. "You know," he said, "women never enjoy intercourse."

On the other hand, another very intelligent professional man of my acquaintance whose married daughter had consulted me for relief from sexual anesthesia which she knew to be pathological, declared in amazement that he had never realized that there could be such a thing as a woman devoid of sexual feelings. He could scarcely be convinced that his daughter was not a very exceptional and freakish case.

With such a wide range of ignorance, even among the professional men, it is not surprising that the scientific understanding of frigidity and impotence is so far behind that of much less widespread and less devastating afflictions.

The forms of sexual incompetence manifested by women correspond only very roughly to those described by men. They are:

Great aversion. There is, for example, no syndrome in men comparable to the great fear, aversion, and horror which some women have for the sex act, or, in some cases, anything which suggests the sex act, e.g., the sight of the male genitals. In such women, attempts at intercourse produce local spasm and pain, the symptom of vaginismus, as well as great psychic distress.

Painful submission. Less extreme in degree but essentially similar in nature is the exceedingly frequent form in which the woman submits to intercourse as a necessary evil, a form of legalized torture to which marriage has made her a martyr. For such women the act is genuinely although variably painful—the vaginal mucosa remains dry, rough, and unreceptive. These women are very apt to exhibit conspicuously other indications of the spirit of submissive martyrdom in which they conceive themselves to be obliged to live.

Passive indifference. A total disinterest in genital sexuality, a tolerance of intercourse "for my husband's sake"—a complete lack of feeling, either painful or pleasurable—likewise characterize a very large number of women, if clinical experience and statistical inquiries are to be given any reliance. This form of frigidity corresponds most closely to the impotence of the male manifested by lack of interest. Women so afflicted frequently show some intellectual interest in sex, may even read books on the subject, but as a rule, like their male counterparts, do not consult physicians, do not discuss it with friends or neighbors. The whole subject is a closed book, to be mentioned as little as possible.

Genital anesthesia. In sharp contrast to the preceding group in this respect are those women who have faint or inconstant feelings of pleasure connected with intercourse and even—at long intervals— an occasional orgasm. These women are, as a rule, genuinely concerned over their affliction and make energetic efforts to become normal. They read books on the subject in great number, they consult friends, neighbors, doctors, and quacks; they try all sorts of experiments. I recall a man and wife who consulted me once who had been so distressed over the wife's lack of pleasure in intercourse that they had even tried the experiment of having a friend of the husband cohabit with the wife to see if this might make a difference. Indeed, many instances of marital unfaithfulness in women depend in part upon this motive.

Nymphomania. Not a few women experience an intense desire which cannot be satisfied. They never, or rarely, achieve an orgasm in spite of repeated and prolonged attempts. That this is really a form of impotence comparable to priapism in the male, is obvious.

Associated perversions and fetishisms. With women no less than with men, the satisfaction of sexual desire may be conditioned upon certain fetishes or modes, i.e., perversions.

THE MOTIVES BEHIND IMPOTENCE AND FRIGIDITY

If we say that a symptom is psychological in its origin, what we mean is that the symptom carries out some wish or intention of the personality and is not merely the consequence of accidental, malevolent factors in the environment. We know that all functions of the organism strive to carry out the wishes, the instinctive cravings, of the individual in the face of a hostile or indifferent environment. The physiologists have demonstrated that when danger threatens and we wish to fight, the body automatically prepares itself. Blood rushes from the skin and to the muscles, glycogen is mobilized in large quantities, adrenalin and prothrombin are poured out. All this is accomplished automatically by the body to make possible the fulfillment of pugnacious wishes, which may be scarcely conscious.

We know from clinical experience that these defense reactions may involve more complex units. For example, a man in the trenches is "shell-shocked." Paralyzed with fright, his legs conveniently refuse to carry him into the field of greater danger. These extended defense reactions are not discriminatory and not so automatically self-regulating as the older and simpler ones, and so such a man's legs also refuse to carry him anywhere else, even to a place of greater safety. Thus we recognize that such defenses, although carrying out the purposes of one wish, violate other wishes of the personality—and hence we call them *symptoms*. Their development may be facilitated by factors in the environment, e.g., the paralyzed soldier may actually have received a blow on the legs, but the determining factor is the unconscious wish of the organism for self-preservation.

The fact that such a wish is unconscious is intrinsic in the explanation. A conscious wish can be dealt with rationally—either gratified or denied and the solution accepted. But unconscious wishes (including fears from which we wish to escape) are dealt with in unconscious automatic ways, often exceedingly irrational and unpropitious for the personality, by symptoms and inhibitions. Back of these is always an unconscious wish and a conflict.

Let us ask ourselves now what it may be that lies back of the automatic inability of a man or woman to complete satisfactorily a function as universal and natural as that of the reproductive act. What great and irrational fear can be harbored in the unconscious to make this automatic defense reaction in the face of such powerful conscious wishes to the contrary? We must expect great difficulty in ascertaining this because the functions of the sexual organs excite the highest degree of pride and shame; they are, therefore, veiled most obscurely.

The practicing physician's first thought may be what some of his women patients have told him who have come complaining that intercourse was painful, terrifying, or at least disagreeable. "I want very much to let myself go," one says, "but I'm so *afraid* of pregnancy." Or perhaps she says, because she is so *afraid* of being hurt by her husband, that his penis is too large or that he is too rough, etc., and one will recall also men patients who have declared that they could not be potent with their wives for *fear* they might hurt them and were too much *afraid* of venereal disease to be potent with anyone else. Another common fear inhibition is that which follows veneral disease contracted through illicit intercourse.

Fear, then, appears to be a conspicuous factor of deterrence. But we are apt to take these *conscious* fears too literally. Of course they may be partly justified by reality; but only partly so. There are ways of circumventing pain, there are ways of avoiding venereal disease, there are ways of precluding pregnancy. We know from experience that such conscious fears always mask much more powerful unconscious fears; they are really only "alibis." One need only compare these with the feelings of the normal man and the normal woman at the time of her defloration, when, if both are psychologically prepared, she is gratified in spite of her pain and he is not deterred although he knows he is hurting one whom he loves.

UNCONSCIOUS FEARS

The clinical experience of psychoanalysis has shown exactly what the unconscious fears are that make people impotent. Of course they vary from case to case but there are some general principles which are applicable. From the clinical investigations of many analysts we can summarize some of these.

The fear of punishment. One of the most powerful fears is the fear of punishment. In normal adults a distinction is made between things which society really does punish and acts for which one expects punishment only because of a childhood misapprehension. For many people sex is still a kind of evil-doing, hence punishable.

Let us look at some clinical material:

A patient is under psychoanalytic treatment. In the course of the conversation he relates that frequently he cannot have intercourse successfully with his wife; so frequently has this occurred that lately he has given up entirely. He loves his wife very much. She is a strong, capable woman and a good mother to their children. In the course of the analysis we discover that he thinks so much of his wife because she is so much like his own mother, who was also a strong, capable woman. Then he begins to recall that although he loved his mother he was also very much afraid of her. She was rather severe to him, especially on those occasions when he disobeyed her. She was fair but strict, and never a woman to turn over the chastisement of her children to her husband.

For many days the patient relates details of his mother's kindness and also of her punishments. Suddenly one day during the treatment hour he recalls a particularly terrible incident. He had been playing with a neighbor girl in the back yard. She had suggested that they inspect one another. Just then his mother appeared. She seemed to be horrified. She sent the little girl home and whipped her son severely and told him he must never do that again. He did not know just why, because it was really very interesting and he was much surprised to see that the little girl was made differently from himself. Perhaps she had done this before, he thought. Perhaps she had been punished too and that is why she is different "there." This gave him grave anxiety. He wondered if he too might have something happen to his penis. He felt of it several times a day and worried about it a great deal.

One day as he was reassuring himself in this way by examining his penis he discovered it gave him a great deal of pleasure to do so. This led to masturbation, which continued for a short time. Then one day his mother, thinking to forestall masturbation, told him in vague terms that one must not do certain things with his penis, that to do so was very serious and might cause disease and even insanity. This frightened him terribly for "Of course," he thought, "she doesn't know what I have been doing. Perhaps now I shall lose my penis and become like that little girl, or perhaps I will lose my mind." It worried him so much that he could not sleep, he could not study. He lost weight. He was examined for tuberculosis and worried over by the family physician who could find no pathology.

Gradually he forgot this secret fear and all went well for a few years, until one day he overheard his father and mother talking about the neighbor boy who had done something to a girl which seemed to be very serious. The boy was to be sent away. He could not learn what it was; he asked a playmate. The playmate laughed, pointed to his penis, and said, "Oh, you know, don't you? He did something to the girl with that and the girl told on him." My patient was too humiliated by his ignorance to ask more questions. Meantime his desire to masturbate had come back with renewed vigor. He learned that other boys sometimes masturbated and they did not seem to be suffering evil consequences but apparently evil consequences might follow any kind of sexual pleasure. It was too great a risk. Other boys might get by with it but he would take no chances. It was too terrible to think what might happen if mother found out, or even if she didn't.

We could go further with this patient's sexual experience but I think it is clear from this how such a man married to a woman who unconsciously represents to him a new edition of the mother whom he so much loved and feared, of the mother who so successfully inhibited his sexual activities during boyhood, could not possibly overcome this fear sufficiently to permit his body to act out his instinctive desires. The Hindu who sits on one foot for twenty years because he believes it to be his religious duty could not possibly leap to his feet and begin to run, even if he were threatened by a fire or coaxed by a great reward.

The case I have cited is typical of what happens in one kind of impotence. The child may learn in later life that discriminations may be made between various kinds of sexual activities and that some are now permitted him under certain circumstances, but although his intelligence is now able to make such discriminations in the depths of his soul he cannot change the attitude which was early inculcated in him, namely, that which is pleasurable is sexual, that which is sexual is bad, and that which is bad is punished.

One is unconsciously dominated by childhood attitudes throughout life. In the normal person, the unfortunate misunderstandings of childhood are corrected by later experience but it implies no weakness of intelligence that some persons cannot overcome them. The reactions of conscience are determined in early life and change but little as a result of experience. Accordingly, with or without the presence of conscious fears and quite independent of them, there exists in the unconscious of many people a compelling fear of punishment which is excited to great activity at the very moment when the ego believes itself threatened with an alluring temptation of a nature once associated with punitive pain.

We can scarcely overestimate the extent or the power of this unconscious fear of punishment, a fear which arises in earliest childhood from external sources—the parents, teachers, nurses—but later comes from an internally established source, the "conscious." It is quite sufficient to prevent any conscious sexual satisfaction in many people. All manner of devices are utilized by the unconscious to circumvent it and to permit the forbidden sexual indulgences to be psychologically acceptable. For example, I recall a woman who very much desired intercourse with her husband but could not enjoy it because during the act a picture of her father with a stern disapproving expression on his face would always appear before her. Now there was a curious circumstance connected with this which will further explain this fear of and need for punishment. This woman and her husband had themselves discovered that if her husband would first strike her as if in anger she could then enjoy sexual intercourse normally. It is quite clear, I think, that this woman had the feeling so many children do that punishment squares everything. Therefore she could dispel this frowning face of her father by carrying out the punishment which she felt she deserved for indulging in an act of sex which he disapproved. But, like the little girl who first slapped her own hands and then stole a piece of candy, she insisted upon having her punishment first so that she could enjoy the forbidden act without the fear of punishment or inhibiting any more satisfaction.

Precisely the same thing holds true of men. Indeed it is this need for punishment that explains the favorable results sometimes obtained by painful treatment administered to the genital organs by urologists and gynecologists.

Other fears. Impotence and frigidity are also often associated with other childhood fears originating in the misconceptions of the child about the mysteries of the world about him, particularly the sexual world. One such fear, common to both men and women, is that they will be injured by the sexual partner. There are many forms of this —women have fantasies of being split asunder by men, and men have fears that women will in some way or other injure the penis. Space prevents going into much detail about this except to say that children frequently have such sadistic and violent conceptions of sexuality which their later intelligence may correct but which remain operative though buried in the unconscious.

CONFLICTING LOVES

Parental fixations. Fear is not the only thing which produces impotence and frigidity. The desire may be inhibited instead by conflicting wishes. In other words, a man may be impotent with a woman because he loves someone else and doesn't know it. The same is true of a woman. We all know men who have failed at being doctors because they wanted to be musicians and vice versa. In the sexual life, half of this conflict is usually unknown to the individual. The person loved may have lived long ago, may have been a childhood ideal as in the case of the boy who is prevented from loving his wife because he is "tied to his mother's apron strings" and cannot love any other woman. Many men who marry are nevertheless so attached to their own mothers deep in their unconscious that they cannot give to their wives anything but the childlike love which a boy gives to his mother. In the sense that she is a wife, a sexual partner, such men cannot really accept her or treat her as she craves to be treated, providing of course that she herself is normal. Frequently one sees such mother-attached men falling in love with women who want to be mothers. Such unions may be fairly satisfactory; they cannot, however, be regarded as normal sexual unions, and many of them go upon the rocks.

Precisely the same sort of fixation occurs in the lives of many women. A girl may be so much in love with her own father that she cannot possibly accept a husband sexually. She may go through the motions of living with him, of loving him, and of cohabiting with him, but however well she may fool him—indeed, however well she may fool herself—she cannot enlist the services of her unconscious in this deception. The body cannot respond to a love situation which all her repressed feelings regard as disloyal to her first and real love.

Homosexual conflicts. Secondly, there is a kind of conflicting love which is not so easily recognized as the fixation on the parents or a brother or a sister but which is almost as frequent. We know that in the process of transferring the affection which he first concentrated upon the father and mother to other persons outside the family the child goes through a stage in which he prefers persons of the same sex as himself. This *homosexual phase* in the course of the individual's development is ultimately repressed and represented only in the sublimated form in normal persons as the basis of much of the friendly intercourse of later life. In many individuals, however, either because it is excessive in quantity or because it has been favored or nurtured in some way, this homosexual element does not disappear. Such persons remain strongly but unconsciously attached to homosexual love objects, even though consciously they think they are normal heterosexual individuals. In fact it is just these unconsciously homosexual people who go about the world proving how heterosexually potent they are, as if to deny the secret which their unconscious whispers to them. Two kinds of people brag about their sexual exploits—the adolescent, who is surprised that he can have any at all, and the unconscious homosexual, who wants to convince others as well as himself that he is not homosexual.

Narcissism. Finally, there is a conflicting love which is more powerful than any of these and also more prevalent. This is the love of the self. We should not forget that all our love for husband or wife, friends, neighbors, brothers and sisters and even parents is only the overflow of self-love. We all love ourselves first and last and most. In the normal person, however, experience enables one to see the advantage of drawing upon the treasury of self-love and investing some of it in the love of others; in a vast number of individuals, however, this process is inhibited. For various reasons—sometimes a lack of self-confidence, sometimes a fear of deprecation by others, sometimes because of painful experiences, sometimes because of faulty training—this cannot be done. For such people a true and deep relationship with another person is impossible except on such a basis as feeds this self-love instead of detracting from it. Such persons may fall in love but they fall in love with people who are like themselves, with people who flatter them, who feed their vanity and build up their self-confidence by a constant process of emotional nourishment. If one is so much in love with himself, then one cannot accept the role in which he must give love; he can accept only the role in which he is always the recipient of love, like a little child whose self-love is fanned and fed by the attentions of his mother.

In the sexual act, such persons may be at times very potent, particularly if the circumstances of the act are such that their vanity is flattered, their feeling of omnipotence encouraged. This is not real sexual potency, however, and such individuals sooner or later are apt to meet with disaster. They are very proud of their sexual organs and, indeed, it is not inaccurate to say that such persons prefer masturbation to sexual intercourse. Such intercourse as they perform is frequently only a kind of intravaginal masturbation and as such is really a kind of impotency which sooner or later becomes manifest.

CONFLICTING HATES

We have seen thus far that conscious intention (for intercourse) may be inhibited by fear, or by conflicting love. But it may also be inhibited by a third thing—aversion or actual hate for the very thing or person consciously desired. In other words, a man may be impotent with a woman because he is afraid of her, because he loves someone else, or because he hates her—in each case, of course, without knowing it.

But why should a man hate a woman whom he thinks he loves? There are four common reasons for this:

1. The first is that we hate anything we fear. Many times it is the hate rather than the fear that we show evidences of. We have already discussed impotence from fear.

2. Another common reason for unconscious hate is revenge. This may be revenge for something that has recently happened or something that has happened long ago at the hands of an entirely different person. Many people go through life trying to take out on someone feelings that were generated within them as children. You will recall that Don Juan, the world's greatest cad, was deserted by his mother in early childhood; he spent his entire life treating other women in exactly the way that his mother treated him, first making them love him and then leaving them.

A male patient, a very successful man, was under psychoanalytic treatment on account of periodic depressions. In the course of treatment it developed that he manifested a certain kind of impotence with his wife. His sexual overtures were accompanied by tenderness and love which would greatly arouse his wife, whereupon he would either lose all interest or have *ejaculatio praecox*. In his analysis it became quite clear that the purpose of this was to thwart his wife, and in this it was indeed very successful. Intuitively she perceived the hostile nature of this abortive treatment and would become hysterically nervous and so distressed that she would cry and strike him with her fists. This would cause him to be remorseful and depressed. As a child this man had been raised in a family presided over by a very capable, energetic mother who was much more interested in her clubs and social activities than in her children. The patient had been the firstborn and was probably unplanned for because he interrupted a project which his mother had gotten under way and to which she devoted herself for a number of years after his birth, leaving him largely in the hands of a governess. During the analysis he remembered with great emotion how bitterly he had resented his mother's frequent desertion of him which even as a child he had protested against by fierce crying and what were called temper tantrums. When he was punished for these he only grew more resentful. He was thwarted by his mother and the wish to thwart her back he had carried throughout his life.

3. A third reason for unconscious hate, especially on the part of women, is a wish not so much to get revenge for themselves as to avenge their mothers. They think as children that their mothers are suffering at the hands of their fathers and when they learn something of sexual intercourse they interpret it as a violent act of cruelty. Of course many women actually favor this impression on the part of their children, setting them against their own fathers and warning them that all men are to be feared. Such mothers think they are safeguarding their daughters, but we know they are also revenging themselves on their husbands. For these various reasons the daughter grows up determined to pay back this old grudge against the male. She masks this spirit of vengeance with love but sooner or later her husband feels the consequences.

4. The fourth reason for hate is envy. Unconsciously men envy women and women envy men to an extent far beyond ordinary recognition. The old saw about the better grass in the other pasture is very true here. Women are frequently conscious of it and protest bitterly against the superarrogation of males. To play the normal passive feminine role seems to them a kind of humiliation which they cannot bear. They envy all the male prerogatives, they envy man his physique, his strength, even his sexual organs. They sometimes show this by ostentatious demonstrations of their own abilities. "Look, I am just as capable as any man," some of them like to say. Of course, such women are very neurotic; they do not realize that they are renouncing their biological superiority over men in exchange for play-acting which is dictated by childish enviousness. It would probably surprise them very much to know that many psychiatrists are consulted by men whose greatest secret pleasure is to put on their wives' underclothing and play at having a baby. Of course, the normal man brings forth children in the form of ideas and inven-

tions and books and hard work. But, unconsciously, some men envy women just as some women envy men. In the presence of the hate dictated by such envy a woman cannot be other than frigid.

INSTINCTUAL CONFLICTS

A final reason for the inhibition of the sexual function is dependent upon the unconscious rejection by the individual of his biological role. By this we mean that however brave an effort a man may seem to be making to live up to his masculine responsibilities and aspirations he may be doing so at (for him) an enormous psychological cost, i.e., it really may not be in him, so to speak, to be as much of a man as he thinks he ought to be. Precisely the same is true of some women. Of course, this rejection of the appropriate biological role is often determined to a considerable degree by the child's early experiences, e.g., the boy may covet the greater protection and love bestowed on his sisters and envy their role or the girl may envy the greater freedom and strength of the boy, the more so because of some disappointment in her own love expectations in the home. But these factors are what Alexander calls structural rather than instinctual conflicts and I have in mind now those individuals who seem to be almost constitutionally less masculine or less feminine than the ideal or norm. I have in mind a patient, a successful, popular, and apparently very normal man who underwent a long treatment at the hands of several competent physicians on account of one symptom, namely, the development of terrific anxiety under certain circumstances when in his home certain additional responsibilities devolved upon him. Chief among these was the wish of his wife for more children. Intellectually he concurred in her wish but the contemplation of such a plan threw him into such distress that he had to resign his position and seemed to some of his physicians to be on the verge of a complete mental collapse. In another similar instance a man who incidentally was a national figure at one time was in his own home a pitiful object; his wife begged him to give her a child, but so frightened would this person become at such a prospect that in spite of intense sexual desire he would discontinue all sexual intercourse for months on end rather than run the risk. The situation became so acute that his wife divorced him. He married another woman who became pregnant by him, but before this child was born the man died. I do not say that his death was the result of this morbid fear; I am only stating the facts as I know them to have been.

SUMMARY

To summarize, then, psychoanalytic study confirms the impression held by many urologists on the basis of intuition and experience, namely, that unconscious emotions often (always?) determine the inhibition of sexual pleasure known as impotence in the male and frigidity in the female. The specific nature of these unconscious emotions has been determined in many instances to consist of fears, especially of punishment or of injury; hostilities toward the love object; conflicting loves, particularly parental and homosexual fixations; and rejection of or incapacity for the full assumption of the appropriate biological role and its responsibilities.

The inference is and the psychoanalytic experience also is that some of these cases can be successfully treated by psychoanalysis by bringing the unconscious conflicts to consciousness in such a way that their irrational nature can be dealt with in the light of experience and reality. In practice these cases are usually treated by urological techniques for which a psychological explanation is offered above which might theoretically account for their success, entirely apart from physical effects.

13. Psychological Factors in Urological Disease

This paper is an attempt to investigate the contribution of emotional factors to pathological tissue alterations in the genital apparatus, particularly the prostate.

Urological afflictions are, of course, seen more frequently by urologists than by psychiatrists and psychoanalysts, and investigation of the psychological factors in these conditions is therefore, for practical reasons, rare. A man suffering with suppurative prostatitis, for example, is naturally impelled toward direct mechanical or chemical relief and neither he nor his urologist is likely to have much patience with the proposal that psychological factors are involved in the illness. Their existence might even be conceded but their practical importance would certainly be discounted.

Our knowledge of anatomy, bacteriology, and immunology is so much more complete than our knowledge of psychology that even this theoretical invasion of the urologists' field seems presumptuous, especially while thousands of urologically afflicted patients are being successfully treated every day without any particular consideration of psychological factors.

Notwithstanding this fact, the occasional glimpses obtained by the psychiatrist into the emotional factors pertaining to a specific instance of urological disease cannot but lead to conclusions, and

Read at the midwinter meeting of the American Psychoanalytic Association, Chicago, Dec. 22, 1934. Reprinted from the *Psychoanalytic Quarterly,* 5:488–512, October 1936.

tempt one to further speculations in the interests of furthering our understanding of this acknowledgedly undeveloped field. In this we are met with encouragement by many urologists and clinicians whose intuitive skill in therapeutic work is by their own admission and conviction due to a hazy but highly capitalized recognition of the contribution of the emotional factors to the development of the pathological condition.

Such urologists speak and work from intuition, however, rather than from definite knowledge and certainly without any authoritative help from the generally accepted body of medical knowledge and theory. This is particularly striking with respect to the symptom of sexual impotence for which practically all prescribed treatment is mechanical and chemical, even by those authorities who suggest that some cases are psychogenic in origin. Yet impotence is a symptom which brings some patients to the psychiatrists as well as to the urologists and it is interesting to observe the radical differences in their respective attitudes toward this condition.

These differences in attitude must be ascribed primarily to the illusion of partial examination. The urologists examine the patient's genitalia and the psychiatrists examine the patient's emotions and they come to conclusions from these respectively local examinations which are comparable in their incorrectness to the conclusions of the celebrated blind men who palpated different parts of a passing elephant and argued for days thereafter about their contradictory impressions. Few psychiatrists are competent to make urological examinations; few urologists are interested in making psychological examinations. It is seldom, therefore, that a patient with urological pathology is studied simultaneously from both standpoints. Were this more frequently possible a quite different total conception than those generally held might be arrived at, one relating not only to this symptom (impotence) but to more complicated conditions.

Let us, for example, examine more minutely the respective findings and theories of the urologists and the psychiatrists with respect to the symptom of impotence.

The urologists have made certain observations concerning the organs involved in impotence which cannot be disputed. They find, with some degree of regularity, that many patients complaining of impotence show definite congestion and inflammation of the posterior urethra, especially of the verumontanum, and tenderness, enlargement, and congestion of the prostate, with or without definite evidence of infection and suppuration. The interpretation generally given these data by the urologists is something as follows. The prostate becomes the site of local infection owing to a concatenation of factors—for example masturbatory congestion plus influenza, or local injury plus streptococcus localization of a bacteremia. The resulting inflammatory reaction impairs functional activity (impotence). The impotence causes the patient mortification and anxiety—he is driven by this distress to seek medical advice and treatment and comes to the urologist. The urologist treats the local condition (by massage, irrigation, endoscopy, chemotherapy, and so on) and it shows improvement. The impotence then (sometimes) disappears, and the theory is substantiated. If, however, both inflammation and impotence persist, this may be regarded as evidence for the theory of an organic lesion which resists efforts toward removal.

In justice to the urologists it must be stated that not all of them subscribe to this theory, even though they may carry out this routine. The treatment is sometimes successful out of all proportion to the amount of treatment administered, just as the symptoms are sometimes out of all proportion to the degree of pathological alteration discovered. Hence a vague generalization about "psychological factors" is frequently invoked to bolster up the theory of etiology and the old illusion of "suggestion" is brought in to explain the success of treatment.

So much for the findings and theories of the urologists. Psychiatrists, on the other hand, using the psychoanalytic technique, have also made some findings with a fair degree of regularity in cases of impotence which should be taken into account. Just as the urologists make vague and inexact references to psychological factors, so the psychoanalysts are apt to make vague and inexact references to the organic status. But the data resulting from psychoanalytic investigations must be accepted—as are the special findings of the urologists—in good faith.

Psychoanalysts find that patients suffering from impotence prove upon examination to have a definite psychological need for this inhibition, in spite of their distress about it. In other words, they have unconsciously wanted or needed to be impotent to satisfy certain unconscious emotional tensions. It will not lead us too far afield to list some of the specific emotions which, though they exist only in the unconscious, exert a contrary and prohibiting effect upon the sexual function. These consist in one or more of the following: first, fears, especially of punishment or of injury; second, hostilities toward the love object; third, conflicting loves, particularly parental and homosexual fixations; and fourth, rejection of the masculine (or feminine) role with its responsibilities.

Associated with and dependent upon these emotions is a great sense of guilt, and experience has shown that the relief of this sense of guilt by any one of several devices will frequently serve to free the patient from his fears and thus from his inhibitions. The psychoanalysts therefore are quite ready to believe that urological treatment frequently cures patients but they ascribe it not to the structural changes effected by the treatment but to the gratification of the need for suffering always associated with the sense of guilt—for example, guilt over masturbation. In support of this, they point to the fact that devices for relieving anxiety which do not involve any tissue manipulation are also used successfully as treatment, and to the fact, well known to urologists themselves, that some patients seem to erotize and enjoy urological treatments, even though painful. Wälder [1] reports the case of a man in whom this erotization of urological treatment went so far that he could even produce an orgasm by passing a sound into the posterior urethra. Dr. Walter Brunet, a prominent Chicago urologist, told me of a case he had seen in which urethral catheterization had been necessary for examination some five years previously; the patient had been so relieved of nervous tension by the process that once a month since that time he had insisted upon a repetition of the procedure to combat insomnia!

I have already passed from the findings of the psychoanalysts which we must accept at their face value to some of their theories. We do not absolutely know that the explanation just offered accounts for the manipulative cure of some cases of impotence. In general the psychoanalytic theory is that fear and the other emotions mentioned above develop a high degree of effectiveness in certain individuals on account of sensitizing childhood experiences and are then activated by events in the patient's contemporary life resulting in the necessity for inhibitions. Here psychoanalysts generally stop, ignoring or disregarding the structural factors which the urologists have shown to exist. If they take cognizance of them, as of course some do, they are apt to depart from the logic of their own experience and, reverting to their medical-school traditions, ascribe the infection to accidental or at least extraneous factors. Nor is this altogether erroneous in some instances. For example, what we frequently see is that the patient suffering from impotence feels impelled to relieve his anxiety by demonstrating that he is not impotent, and in such compulsive overcompensations, which are probably also motivated by a sense of guilt, he indulges in indiscretions which his conscious intelligence would ordinarily prohibit in the interests of safety. By such a technique such individuals frequently succeed in infecting themselves with gonorrhea in spite of their impotence.

However, it is not to such adventitious infections resulting from conscious activities that I refer, but rather to the nonspecific infections and the inflammatory processes without infection which, as we have said, while not demonstrably the cause of impotence, frequently accompany it and, of course, occur in many instances not accompanied by impotence. The logical extension of the psychoanalytic theory would be that the results of such inhibition of a strong instinctual tendency must tend to appear in a concrete form. Some of the energy is of course dissipated in the form of anxiety, but every clinician knows that anxiety can be focused upon certain organs and it was long ago suggested by Ferenczi that the anxiety actually becomes, as it were, *invested* in an organ so that the patient, instead of a vague, generalized sense of uneasiness and distress is aware only of local distress. The conservative, shall we say orthodox, psycho-analytic view is that this is in the nature of an illusion, depending upon purely symbolic and ideational connection of the organ with the anxiety. But there is nothing in the known facts about the automatic defenses of the body which would contradict a more literal and specific operation of this principle. It might be assumed, for ex-ample, that the results of psychic inhibition would be physical in-hibition (impotence), the unconscious fear being relieved by this symptom, the conflicting impulses being transferred, as it were, from the psychic sphere to the physical sphere, in such a way as to produce vascular dilatation, congestion, and perhaps some unknown changes in the humoral efficiency or consistency such that infection is invited even to the point of suppuration. This symptom then brings the patient to the doctor. Later we shall examine in more detail the structure and plausibility of this theory.

It certainly does not seem possible to resolve the matter into such naïve conclusions as (1) that impotence may result from prostatitis, or (2) that prostatitis may result from impotence, because neither proposition would be unequivocally supported by the data of either the urologists or the psychiatrists. But both groups would (probably) agree (3) that impotence and prostatitis are frequently found in con-junction.

At this point there comes real divergence in opinion. Most urolo-gists share the prevalent conception of infection—that it is entirely determined by relatively accidental factors which substantially defy analysis. This view concedes the descriptive data of the serologists—namely, that the humoral and tissue defenses of the body fluctuate and may be taken advantage of by a particularly virulent or per-sistent strain of bacterial invaders. It concedes, or at least some of its defenders do, the concepts of organ inferiority and of *locus minoris resistentiae*. But that processes connected with the thought, feeling and behavior of the subject have anything to do with these defenses is almost totally foreign to most medical thinking.

Not entirely, however; the current literature contains an increas-ing number of clinical contributions in which the psychological factors relating to the acquiring or retaining of the infection are acknowledged. Leshnew,[2] for example, reports several cases of which the following is typical:

> A young mechanic was being treated for urethritis and prostatitis. At the close of the treatment the urologist told the patient that he was well but that he really should have had one more treatment; this, however, was impossible since the urologist was leaving the city. The patient returned home happy over his recovery but with the notion of the incompleteness of the treatment firmly fixed in his mind. For six months he went from one specialist to another attempting to find one who would perform the cauterization which he assumed to be necessary. [The author implies that a slight discharge persisted.] Finally he came to the author, who found him in good condition so far as the local findings were concerned. *For purposes of psychotherapy* [italics mine] urethroscopy was done and the patient's symptoms disappeared.

Another prostatic case but without the factor of infection is reported by Dr. Frank J. Clancy[3] of Seattle, Washington, who comments that physicians "who are most meticulous in regard to diagnosis and treatment of organic pathology are apparently satisfied with the most unscientific information in regard to psychopathology." He writes:

> A man 65 years of age from a neighboring city presented himself for urologic study. Chief complaints: frequent and painful urination, pain in the region of the prostate, intermittent in character, day urination every hour, night four or five times, duration several weeks. He had been seen by his personal physician who advised prostatectomy and suggested the possibility of malignancy. He was also seen by a urologist who was for immediate operation. The patient by this time was in a highly agitated state, and if the diagnosis was substantiated was to go to an eastern clinic for operation. Examination: rectal palpation, prostate only moderately enlarged, residual urine 60 c.c., clear, containing a few pus cells. Cystoscopic examination of the bladder neck failed to show any pathology.
>
> A man of 65 does not come in complaining of urologic symptoms, even willing to submit to a serious major operation, unless there is a real condition. The patient was questioned carefully again regarding his symptoms, and a casual inquiry made if he was worried over any particular thing before the symptoms came. This key opened the lock.

The man, a highly respectable and retired business man, married and with married children, had had an extramarital experience. This had preyed on his mind until he had worked himself into a hysterical state, but to all outward appearances he covered up his mental turmoil.

One is led to suspect that many of the urethral strictures so promptly relieved by the passing of a single catheter are of a psychogenic rather than an organic nature.*

Such cases, however, leave us in doubt as to the precise way in which the susceptibility to infection was increased psychologically. This is, in part, a problem for the physiologists. It is for them to tell us just how certain *wishes* (to use the accepted psychoanalytic term) can be expressed through the autonomic nervous system and the organs and tissues innervated by it. The task of the psychiatrists is to indicate as specifically as possible just what these "wishes" are, why and how they arose, and in what discoverable way they are gratified by the organic changes effected.† That such investigations and the accompanying emotional alterations may benefit the patient is of clinical interest, but a step removed from our immediate research problem.

Our theme is that it is conceivable that in some instances the emotional factors so alter the physiological processes of a part of the body that a train of pathological results ensues. Sometimes this seems

---

* This opinion is confirmed by a urological colleague, Dr. Arthur Gray, who in a personal communication told me of a patient who takes a periodical "grand fling" at the end of which he comes to his urologist, Dr. Gray, demanding that a series of sounds be passed, for which he refuses to have a local anaesthetic. He insists that the drinking and sexual activity bring back the "old stricture." He leaves thoroughly relieved in mind and body and has done so now for six years. "But," Dr. Gray drily comments, "he has no stricture"!

In further substantiation of the value of the illness as a form of suffering to gratify the sense of guilt, Dr. Gray also related a case of a college student with an acute gonorrhea who quit school until he should be well because "although it was very hard to do" he felt he "had no right to mingle with 'clean' people." He told every member of his family, in compliance with his confession ritual, so that they might know, as he put it, what sort of a fellow he was and protect themselves against him. This patient had left another physician and stopped an entirely satisfactory course of treatment because he was getting well faster than he thought desirable, as he "figured it would be better if it ran awhile."

† It is surprising how seldom this has been done, or at least how scanty are the reports in the psychoanalytic literature. There are numerous brief references but almost no full accounts of the development of uropathological lesions. Perhaps some have eluded my search.

to be accomplished without the aid of any extraneous factors and a spontaneous pain * or hemorrhage, for example, occurs. In others an infection appears to be invited and (as we have put it) *accepted* by the local tissues to develop and wreak havoc in the well-known ways characteristic of different infections. In still other instances there is less evidence that the receptivity to the infection was greater than average, but the external behavior of the patient makes up for any "reluctance" on the part of the tissues, and he, so to speak, forces an infection upon himself with purposive indiscretion and then appears to capitalize and keep it in defiance of all ordinary efficacious therapeutic attacks. I cite examples of each of these:

Spontaneous lesions. A spontaneous organic urological lesion manifested by the symptom of hematuria was reported by Dr. Alan Finlayson of Cleveland before the Chicago Psychoanalytic Society in 1933. This incident was so closely related to the patient's material and characterology that Finlayson seems entirely justified in having regarded it as "psychogenic hematuria." The patient was a professional man of thirty-three whose presenting symptoms had centered about an extreme phobia lest anyone see him urinate, with a resulting inability to urinate when anyone was present. So great was this phobia that it affected practical arrangements with respect to every department of his life; he was unable, for example, to take an automobile ride of any length lest, as he assumed, he would be unable to retire to the toilet unaccompanied. This symptom had been present since the age of five. It developed that during his early manhood the reciprocal tendency of voyeurism was manifested so that he would spend much of his time visiting men's toilets for the purpose of watching them urinate. This excessive interest in the process of urination had been a marked characteristic during most of his life.

The hematuria occurred at a time when he was frankly avowing his wish to be a woman, a tendency which, as one might expect, was very strongly developed and was related to his masturbation anxieties

---

* Dr. Paul Schilder, in the discussion of this paper before the Psychoanalytic Association, referred to a patient seen by him who developed spontaneous attacks of severe pain in the perineum later traced to early childhood experiences.

and his urination phobia. As a child he had been called a sissy and was fond of dressing in his mother's clothes. With his wife, and in fact with all women, he was for the most part impotent.

He had complained one day of a pain in his right flank which he ascribed to gas. That night he dreamed that he was looking for a place to urinate, saw a boy sitting on the toilet masturbating, marveled at the boy's audacity, and began immediately himself to have an orgasm, the semen being bloody. He awoke with a start and went to the toilet, urinating with some pain (but no blood at this time). After returning to bed he did not go to sleep for some time, as he was disturbed by the dream. About two hours later he awoke with a terrific pain in the right side. A physician was called and morphine ⅓ gr. was given by hypodermic, but as this failed to relieve the pain more morphine was given four hours later. A specimen of urine voided at this time showed microscopic blood. The patient was admitted to the hospital and a tentative diagnosis of renal or urethral calculi was made. An attempt to take X-ray plates was made but without avail because of intestinal gas. Enemas were given, each one setting up violent vomiting. When the analyst visited the hospital the afternoon of the first day the patient looked very sick and was vomiting. He greeted the analyst with the remark, "I thought you would come around to see if the pain was a fake."

He remained in the hospital several days and during this time several specimens of urine showed microscopic blood. The X-rays were negative for calculi and the vomiting ceased with the suspension of the enemas. On one occasion after returning home the blood appeared again in the urine after a repetition of the first dream; this time the blood was macroscopic. The pain reappeared three other times, two of the attacks occurring during the psychoanalytic treatment hour.

The subsequent associations of the patient to the incident and to the dream and his previously clearly defined tendency would strongly suggest that the hematuria incident was superficially the symbolic enactment of his conflicting wishes to masturbate and the fear that if he did so he would be castrated and made into a wounded and menstruating woman, a role which he unconsciously accepted and sought for as the price of his irresistible and illogical instinctual impulses.

But such symbolic gratifications as these episodes of hematuria could not have been possible had there not been deeper determinants and a long period of organic preparation. In this case, however, the lifelong gratification afforded by urination, i.e., the increased erotic value, is presumptive in the light of the history. To put it more simply, if one has concentrated his sexual life on the urinary process for twenty-five years it is not inconceivable that the urinary apparatus has been modified in some minor way to afford a maximum organic adaptation to this perverted psychological demand. Whether this modification is in the form of greater vascular supply, more fragile endothelium, a change in the arrangement or sensivity in the nerve endings or some other device must, of course, be left entirely open; even speculations concerning it would take us too far beyond the known facts.

Spontaneous infection. I myself studied a case in which hematuria occurred, apparently as the result of emotional conflicts, although its origin was prostatic rather than renal. This case will illustrate a second form in which the unconscious wish is carried out organically. In this form it is accomplished with the cooperation of bacterial invasion, which seems to be invited not through behavior but through compliance on the part of the local resistance.

This patient was a man of thirty-five whose previous life had been uneventful from the psychiatric standpoint. He had been sent to a distant city as a temporary representative of the firm which employed him and took this occasion to enter into a liaison with the wife of an acquaintance with whom he was thrown into contact in his new location and who had shown him some business favors. The affair began upon a platonic basis, but when sexual relations were attempted later he was entirely impotent. He was so disturbed by the experience that he left his post of duty and returned home to his wife, with whom he found himself to be quite potent, thus relieving his anxiety temporarily.

Later, however, he returned to the city in which he had been stationed and resumed his friendship with the woman he had disappointed. A tentative engagement was made for another night together, but forty-eight hours prior to the appointment he developed a urethral discharge. He went immediately to a competent urologist, who made a diagnosis of nonspecific (staphylococcus) infection of the urethra and prostate and prescribed the customary treatment—irrigation, instillation, prostatic massage.

The patient persisted in this treatment faithfully for six months but the symptoms showed no improvement. There was at times a profuse discharge, at other times almost none. Ulcers and small abscesses formed in the prostate, so that there was for a time bloody urination and a bloody discharge. The symptoms did not show any tendency to subside until after instrumentation by the urologist, who found that some adhesions and pus pockets had been formed in the prostatic structure.

Meanwhile the patient was greatly disturbed emotionally, ostensibly because of his impotence. However, the urologist ascribed this to the local pathological condition and urged the patient to disregard it. He consulted another urologist, who concurred in this opinion and also in the diagnosis, but recommended psychotherapy and referred him to me. I proposed psychoanalytic treatment, which the patient accepted and carried through successfully.

I shall bring out only such of the psychoanalytic material as is pertinent to the prostatic infection. It was clear that the illness was precipitated by the abortive episode with the woman. The fact of the matter was that the affair was entirely compulsive, that is, it was an activity into which he entered not so much for conscious and intelligent reasons as for some unconscious reasons which he later came to recognize. In the first place, the woman was the wife of a man to whom he had become very much attracted (homosexually), a fact which he kept deeply concealed even from himself. His relations with her thus represented a means of homosexual gratification in a heterosexual disguise, which explains the extraordinarily severe conscience prohibition. In the second place, the affair was intended unconsciously as an aggression against his wife, to whom he had been nominally faithful but only through fear of detection and because of a feeling of inferiority to her. In the third place, as we learned only after a very deep analysis, the woman unconsciously represented his mother (not only resembled her in some respects but treated him in the manner of his mother, whose pet he had been). Thus the act was in several senses a repetition of the "Oedipus crime": he took the woman away from a man toward whom he had mixed feelings of love and fear, and secondly, he attempted relations with this woman which in his unconscious were incestuous.

This enables us to see certain purposes in his illness, and where purposes exist there must be unconscious striving toward that end. Whether this purpose and striving are participated in and realized biologically is, of course, begging the question; let us see just what usefulness and therefore what purpose this illness subserved. It was, as we have indicated, a solution for the impasse into which he was forced by the irresistible strength of his instincts and his sense of inferiority on the one hand, and his conscience and reason on the other hand. The first solution for this was impotence, which not only eliminated the hazard of the temptation but punished him for having so much as entertained the wish for the incest crime.

But the sexual impotence was not a satisfactory solution, because of the terrific blow to his narcissism which it entailed. It was not only a deep humiliation in the eyes of the woman whose esteem he sought, but it was equivalent to a castration and feminine identification for him which must have aroused strong instinctual conflict-tension. He had good reasons, therefore, for "accepting" the infection and the related structural pathology in place of the functional inhibition. The narcissistic injury was thereby salved, since we do not hold a person responsible for his physical illnesses. *The narcissistic injury was, so to speak, transferred from a general to a local focus; only the narcissism of the prostate now suffered.* The narcissistic injury was also replaced by physical suffering—pain, hemorrhage, anxiety. It more than balanced the sense of guilt created by the original episode. The economic consequences of such a circumstance are that an individual not only makes atonement for past sins but feels that he has bought indulgences for the future as well. From this we can understand why this patient subsequently regained his potency and with the additional punishment of the urological treatment even gave up the organic penalty.

But there is a third element of purpose in the illness which cannot have escaped the sharp eyes of the reader. This relates to the capitalization of the displeasure, first masochistically in the enjoyment and exhibition of the suffering, and secondly in the gratification of the feminine components of the personality which were in such a fair position to be gratified by an illness which simulated feminine identification, even to the extent of supplying a genital discharge, mucoid, purulent, and hemorrhagic. This patient once showed me how the blood oozing from his urethra had bespattered and stained his underclothing, an act of exhibition and feminine identification which even he himself promptly recognized and (indicating its erotic and aggressive significance) apologized for.

This phenomenon of a man wanting to be feminine seems so extraordinary and perverse to the average physician that a word might be said as to its great frequency as revealed by psychoanalytic study. Naturally it is usually a deeply repressed tendency, although I have occasionally been consulted by men who secretly confessed consciousness of such wishes. That some men surreptitiously enjoy putting on their wives' or sisters' clothing (so-called transvestitism) is better known. And I once had a married man, entirely "sane," referred by the Mayo Clinic, who seriously sought to have himself surgically altered so that he would be more nearly female. He was even willing to have an artificial vagina constructed if plastic surgeons would undertake it. In its repressed form these wishes more usually express themselves in an identification with the mother and the development of maternal attitudes toward other people. Vicarious menstruation as a kind of symbolic representation of it is occasionally seen—and various forms of submission of a symbolic character are familiar. The patient of Wälder cited above would plunge a sound into his own urethra and utriculus and produce an *orgasm* and a *bloody* discharge.

In this case we have illustrated the same mechanisms with which we have become familiar from the study of other types of self-destruction, namely, the original aggressive purposes, the inhibition of these aims and consequent direction of the destructive impulse upon the body, the augmentation of this reflected aggression from conscious elements, and the erotization of the whole process. Furthermore, just as we have seen in the study of self-mutilations [4] that there is a tendency to make successive bargains with the conscience so as to yield the maximum satisfaction at the minimum cost, so we see here that the organic illness succeeded the impotence because it more completely satisfied the psychological requirements. Whether this was done in this case through the lowering of local resistance or of general immunity so that an omnipresent bacterial infection could come to the assistance, so to speak, of the self-destructive needs, again we can only speculate.*

Capitalization of infection. That individuals with strong sexual needs and equally strong conscience denials will sometimes relieve the former at the expense of the latter is well known. It is perhaps less well known that they sometimes seem almost deliberately to involve themselves in difficulties over their sexual satisfactions as if to satisfy or appease these conscience demands. In fact, it is a familiar experience that it is the highly moral and rarely transgressing individuals who are most apt to do this—for example, to acquire venereal infection after a single isolated exposure. Psychoanalytic study of such individuals has led us to the conviction that this is unconsciously done for the very purpose of placating the conscience—a form of self-inflicted punishment to relieve the sense of guilt.

This much is well known to psychoanalysts. What is less well understood by them is how (or whether) some individuals can, through their bodily devices and physiological mechanisms, unconsciously control in some way and to some extent the retaining or re-

---

* The urological literature contains in recent years considerable emphasis upon the fact that nonspecific infections of the prostate are of very common occurrence. Following the influenza epidemic of 1918, many such were reported, and were first ascribed to influenza; later the opinion seemed to prevail that the influenza had weakened the resistances of the organism so that local prostatic infection could occur from the ordinary in-lying pathogenic bacteria. From this—and I think I present urological opinion correctly—the theory was extended to the view that nonspecific prostatic infections had always been more numerous than had been recognized, and that certain of the cases diagnosed as gonorrhea were not so at all. One authority goes so far as to say that 90 per cent of adult males have chronic prostatic infection.

jecting of such a deliberately acquired infection. Sometimes they seem to have an extraordinary ability to throw off the infection. Oberndorf has reported [5] two cases, in both of whom gonorrhea was acquired because of such guilt-reducing motives as I have indicated. One patient made a complete recovery in three weeks. The other dragged along in his treatment for months, then changed to another urologist who, however, administered the same treatment. Nevertheless, the patient recovered almost immediately. This strongly suggests some unconscious autonomic control over the processes of immunity and antisepsis. A more detailed study of the following two cases will perhaps make this more specific.

The first is a case which I studied over a period of two years, in which the infection of the prostate seemed definitely "retained" to satisfy certain emotional needs and relinquished when these needs no longer demanded such satisfaction, suggesting some operative relationship between the psyche and the local and generalized immunological defenses.

The patient was an intelligent but extremely neurotic young man who expressed his illness not so much in symptoms as in neurotic behavior, the net result of which was to cause him great embarrassment, humiliation, loss of friends, loss of money, and other "misfortunes." During his analysis this propensity for getting himself into trouble from which he was extricated only at great emotional and sometimes monetary expense was brought into sharp focus. He would act in defiance of the analyst in a direction which could easily be seen beforehand to be fraught with danger, and emerge displaying the scars of battle remorsefully but reproachfully. Among other things he acquired gonorrhea under circumstances so grotesque and externally senseless as to leave no doubt as to its compulsive motivation. He submitted himself for urological treatment to a very intuitive urologist, to whom I am indebted for urological data included in the study of the case.

It is unnecessary to include all the long history of subsequent events. The upshot of it was that he carried through the orthodox treatment for acute gonorrhea and up to a certain point made a prompt, positive therapeutic response. The discharge diminished almost to nonexistence. Pain ceased altogether and digital examination confirmed a recession of an inflammation which had originally extended to the prostate.

During this period the patient instituted for himself an exaggerated hygienic regime. Taking the urologist very literally he "rested" twenty-three hours out of the twenty-four by lying flat in bed. He would scarcely move about in the bed for fear of violating the injunction not to be too active. When it was pointed out that such extreme measures were defeating the purpose of the advice and that nourishing food was no less necessary during gonorrhea than at any other time, he permitted himself the indulgence of getting up for meals and for his psychoanalytic hour.

Gradually he relinquished his burlesque of the treatment and for a time acted in a more normal fashion. He grew interested in the unconscious material that was produced in his analytic session with reference to the motives for his becoming (and remaining) infected, the gist of which was his strong wish to sacrifice his own virility, i.e., self-castration. One root of this lay in his guilt feelings on account of the terrific aggressions constantly made toward all members of society with whom he came in contact, including the analyst and the man from whom he acquired the gonorrhea, both of whom represented a brother who had been the patient's bitterest childhood foe.

The other root lay in the erotic capitalization of this sacrifice of his virility, i.e., his unconscious passive homosexual wishes toward the analyst. He talked constantly of his homosexual feelings, which he declared were entirely conscious but which he always insisted were desires for playing the active, i.e., the masculine role. It was in the course of acting out his professed homosexual wish that he acquired the gonorrhea. Everything in his life, however, as well as in his dreams and free associations, showed that it was the passive feminine rather than the active homosexual role which he desired.

His violently aggressive behavior was actually a histrionic denial of these feminine wishes. While still denying them he began to act them out in so obvious a form that they ultimately became clear to him even in spite of his enormous resistance. For instance, with a rationalization that by cooking in his own room he could save himself the exertion of going out for his meals which might make his gonorrhea worse, he secured a set of cooking utensils and at enormous pains, with much blundering and the concoction of wretched food, he "kept house" for himself for some weeks, washing the dishes in the bathroom bowl, cooking over a gas stove designed for heating the room, and eating his meals from a board placed on the bed (his table was full of books and he could not permit himself the exertion of moving them). He tried draping clothes about himself to look like a woman and he bought a pair of women's stockings and wore them instead of socks. In his dreams he continued to portray himself as a girl, usually a girl who was being made to suffer by a cruel and relentless man.

As the patient realized more and more fully how much he wanted to be a woman, he began simultaneously to compare the way in which he reacted to his gonorrheal discharge with the way in which a woman reacts to her menstrual discharge. For example, he would comment upon the fact that it would be present for a few days and then gone for several weeks. When it reappeared he would be very depressed, a state which he compared with similar emotional reactions in women. To protect his clothes he would wear cloths similar to sanitary napkins. Most impressive of all to the patient was the fact that he could predict precisely when the discharge was about to reappear. This he did on several occasions which I knew of and can corroborate. Each time it would reappear he would return to the urologist for treatment. It would generally begin by his saying that he awoke in great fear from a dream which indicated that the discharge was about to return. He would examine himself carefully and find this to be untrue. This, however, he thought must mean that an unconscious wish for its reappearance was near the surface and that he could consistently expect it in a day or two. (How much this resembles the anticipation by a woman of her menstrual period is striking.) A day or two later the discharge would indeed reappear.

How he used this symptom to obtain attention and care from

the urologist of a sort he was unsuccessful in obtaining from the analyst became quite clear to him. To forestall a continuation of neurotic satisfaction in the illness, he decided not to return to the urologist for treatment. I felt some apprehension in not insisting that he do so, but thinking to make a trial of the matter I let him decide without interference. No sooner had he determined not to go back for physical treatment for a condition which he was convinced he was psychologically producing than the discharge ceased, and did not return!

After this had happened he relieved his sense of guilt for having "continued" his infection so long by projecting the blame upon the urologist, attempting to put him in the wrong and refusing to pay the last portion of his bill.

"That fellow didn't do me any good," he declared. "He knew this was psychogenic and he played into the hands of my neurosis not only by permitting me to keep coming but by advising me to. He gave me justification for continuing the illusion that I had no responsibility for the illness except to submit to his treatment, and of course that was exactly what the feminine elements in me wanted."

I reminded him that microscopic examination of the discharge had shown gonococci to be present even at the last emission, a fact which in reality considerably perplexed and disturbed my urological colleague. But this did not cause my patient the least discomfiture.

"Doctor," he said, "I don't believe that those bugs disappear merely because you put some chemicals in their vicinity. It may discourage them, but I think something in the individual himself helps to kill them. I don't know how it works, but time after time when I wanted that discharge to come back it came and as soon as I recognized my perverse wish and really renounced it the discharge went away."

One does see, as in the first case cited, that when psychic or behavioristic symptoms fail, that is, when they are insufficient to relieve the demands of the conflict or when they become too costly, organic symptoms on a structural basis supplant them and in such a manner as to make it seem probable that they occur by reason of some inner design or intent. The same pattern of focal self-destruction as was outlined in the preceding case is again visible in this case.

Dr. George Wilson, of Chicago, very courteously put at my disposal the details of another psychoanalytically studied case much like the preceding, but with certain details which make my patient's extravagant convictions about the psychogenesis of gonorrhea seem less absurd.

This was a twenty-six-year-old man who came for psychoanalytic treatment because of impotence. He had never had successful intercourse in spite of repeated attempts. He had always lived with his mother and for four years had been entirely supported by the mother and younger sister. After approximately seven months of analysis he decided to attempt intercourse with a prostitute whom he had known for some time. She often came in to buy cigarettes in the store where he clerked. In some unknown manner this woman sensed his psychic impotence and made the suggestion that he come to see her, that she understood and would assist him.

He was not encouraged in this project by the analyst but cautioned that if he pursued it he should use a condom and a prophylactic. He disregarded all advice, attempted—and at the third attempt was successful in having—intercourse, but used neither condom nor tube. (In this he clearly demonstrated by his *actions* that he wished to invite infection.)

A few days later he developed undoubted symptoms of gonorrhea, to the consternation of the patient but no less so of the woman, who had assumed a maternal attitude toward him. She protested stoutly that she had recently undergone examination and was positive that she did not have a gonorrheal infection. She was quite willing to have an examination at the same place as the patient *and did so.* Surprising as it may seem, both vaginal and cervical smears were entirely negative for gonorrhea.* Furthermore, several acquaintances

---

* The urologists inform me that this is less of a paradox than it seems, since smear detection can sometimes be evaded by a skillful woman by thorough douching; also from the statistical fact that seven out of ten exposures to known sources of gonorrheal infection escape it.

of the patient claimed to have had intercourse with her without infection (and presumably without prophylaxis).*

The patient's gonorrheal infection persisted for approximately six months, during which time he was seen three times a week at the Chicago Public Health Institute. He became somewhat of a curiosity at the clinic and at one time the urologist suggested that he see my brother, Dr. William Menninger, because of the unusual persistency of the symptoms, "as if he wanted to hang on to his infection." The infection would clear up and they would begin to pass sounds, beginning with smaller calibers and increasing in size, only to have the infection recur.

A dream that he reported during this process was significant as to the value of the illness and treatment.

Dream 1: He is walking down the street behind a man whom he knows, with his penis in this man's rectum.

Dream 2: He has no penis. He feels a peculiar "sound" in his throat with genital sensations referred to the perineum and has an orgasm.

The *associations* to these dreams confirmed the almost transparent interpretation, namely, that he has sacrificed his penis and become

---

* In the discussion of this presentation at the American Psychoanalytic Association meeting in Chicago, Dec. 22, 1934, the President, Dr. A. A. Brill, reported two similar cases—one of which he kindly wrote out for me to include here:

"The patient, a man of thirty, is now a very talented and well-known artist. An only son, his father always objected to his art, and wanted him to be a businessman. He had already achieved eminence as an artist, but his father still disapproved of it. The patient suffered from anxiety, in addition to definite manic attacks (both depressions and elations). His mother was of the same type, and killed herself.

"One day he came to me and complained of an irritation in his left eye. The eye looked very ugly to me, so I advised him to see one of our leading ophthalmologists. The doctor made the diagnosis of gonorrhea after microscopic examination of the secretion. The patient remained in the hospital for a few weeks, and fortunately his eye was not damaged. On investigating how he contracted this disease, I found that about thirty-six hours before the symptoms appeared, he had had relations with a married woman, who was highly indignant when it was suggested that she might have gonorrhea. She insisted on an examination, and was examined by the same physician who made the diagnosis of the eye condition, but no gonococci were found. I concluded that the eye infection was determined by the conflict—to be or not to be an artist—which was very marked for many years (in fact, until after the completion of the analysis), and secondly, castration for an incestuous act with a mother substitute. The patient was very suicidal, so that soon thereafter I had to send him to a sanitarium for a few months. I have no doubt at all that the eye infection was a partial suicide, although at the time, I did not think of it."

a woman to pay the penalty for his aggressive sexual (oral and anal) wishes toward men.

This interpretation was fully borne out by the patient's outside life. As already indicated, he lived a parasitic existence with his mother and sister. Later he moved away from home and lived with a married man whose wife was away on a visit, playing the housewife to this man, including the duties of cooking and housekeeping. Similar to my own case also is the fact that for several weeks during his infection he remained constantly in bed, waited upon slavishly by his mother.

The details of this case material are insufficient to indicate all the reasons for the election of this affliction, but—in all the cases cited—we have the phenomenon of a man whose emotional conflicts could tolerate neither a normal sexual life nor abstinence, and whose attempts at sexuality seem to have masked destructive impulses which were then reflected back upon him, first in the form of impotence (i.e., functional inhibition) and then, as if by replacement, with a more focal and autonomous self-destruction in the form of urethral and prostatic infection. If we may judge from these few cases, either staphylococci or gonococci may be utilized in the production of the lesions. For without invoking mystery or theories of bacterial transmutation, we can probably assume with justification that a man who acquires gonorrhea from his first and only contact with a woman, a woman whose supply of gonococci is so slight or nonvirulent as to give no clinical evidence, must have had a biological susceptibility (if not an actual chemotaxis) far beyond the ordinary or average. This corresponds precisely with the demonstrated psychological needs of the same individual which may, of course, have been merely a coincidence.

That bugbear, coincidence, hangs over our head constantly in psychoanalytic observations, because our material is, after all, so scanty in comparison to the millions of cases seen and treated by the urologists. We cannot *prove* that these two factors have a causal connection—we can only indicate that they *appear* to have, and that

this apparent relationship occurs in repeated—albeit numerically few
—instances.

Coincidence is probably less serious an objection than one which
arises upon a purely deductive basis. It may be, specifically, that these
few cases come about as we have proposed, through some expression of unconscious intent, but only through an unusual and irregular
psychosomatic structure. They may, in other words, be simply exceptions like those rare individuals who retain the ability to accelerate or retard the heart voluntarily, or possess other manifestations of conscious control of autonomic functions. But this, too, is
only a hypothesis.

Again, there is the fact that of thousands of patients undergoing
psychoanalysis, these mechanisms and results have been observed
(at least *reported*) in but few—which lends support to the previous
objections.

Finally, there is still the possibility—I submit it only as a possibility
—that these cases, whether exceptional or not, are fortunate illustrations of a phenomenon about which we are as yet too ill-informed
to be dogmatic but too oft-reminded to be completely skeptical.

It is a phenomenon which falls in direct line with a more general
hypothesis, so that in conjunction with this hypothesis we may perhaps venture a prediction without the fullness of conviction of the
astronomer predicting a planet, but with the same technique. The
hypothesis is that there is a self-destructive impulse in every individual which, hindered or fortified by other elements in the personality, achieves its purpose to varying degrees and in various ways.
Its conflict with the life instinct, with the demands of reality and
with the exigencies of the conscience result in compromises which
may be regarded as *partial suicides* or *focal self-destruction* (bearing in mind that this partial suicide is for the sake of personality
preservation). These focal suicides may be carried out in a conscious
deliberate way, as in self-mutilation, or in ways which seem accidental or extrinsically necessary, as in certain accidents and operations. There is nothing in the theory to make us doubt that these self-
destructive tendencies, lying, as they do, deep within the fabric of the
instinctual life, may also express themselves without the assistance of

the voluntary nervous system and the striated musculature, and are to be seen as well in the death or injury of organs not directly connected with consciousness. The physiologists have supported such a hypothesis from experimental work to the extent that we know that nervous pathways for the effecting of these purposes exist. Clinicians from their side offer the evidence that emotional factors seem to affect physical illness, although in just what way they cannot be sure.

The step that remains is to indicate that the self-destructive purposes for which we are able to find these clinical examples, on the one hand, and these psychological trends, on the other, are in some intimate and purposive way related. This we have pitifully small data to support but, such as it is, we have submitted it. It would seem as if the self-destructive tendency were such that it thrusts one arm into consciousness, and one arm into the somatic structure of the body, with sometimes the one, sometimes the other, more active. It is only occasionally and with difficulty that we are able to let "the right hand know what the left hand doeth." *Practically,* in the majority of cases, it probably does not matter, but *theoretically* this remains the task and the opportunity of psychoanalysis: to identify and relate specifically the emotional factors contributing to somatic disease.

14. Somatic Correlations with the Unconscious Repudiation of Femininity in Women

When Dr. Brill, whose generous spirit gave birth to the idea of this memorable occasion, invited me to participate in the program, he suggested that I present some aspect of the problem of psychosomatic relationships. Difficult as I felt this assignment to be, it seemed to me particularly fitting in view of the major life work of the man whom we have gathered to honor.

More than anyone else in this country, more extensively perhaps than any living man, Dr. Jelliffe has studied the psychological determinants of somatic symptomatology. Over twenty years ago he reported a case of skin disease associated with emotional conflict, and since then he has consistently sought to elucidate this aspect of disease and, in the face of ridicule, skepticism, and contradiction, he has given to the scientific world detailed studies of the contribution of emotional factors to asthma, bronchitis, tuberculosis, hypertension, postencephalitic syndromes, arthritis, bone and joint disease, spinal cord infections, thyroid imbalance, and eye disorders. That the energy which the human being turns to various tasks, pleasures, and defenses of his life may likewise be directed to and against his own body seemed so obvious to Dr. Jelliffe that the problem of tracing the devices of its accomplishment seemed to him to be the immediate task, and to it he applied himself with characteristic energy and fruitfulness.

Given at the celebration in honor of Smith Ely Jelliffe, M.D., at the New York Academy of Medicine, April 22, 1938, and published in the *Journal of Nervous and Mental Disease*, 89:514–527, April 1939.

Trailing many years behind him, there comes now an increasing flood of reported clinical observations to support the view he so long ago espoused. The vast accumulation of evidence in this direction is added to at every annual meeting of the American Psychiatric, the American Psychoanalytic, and the American Neurological Associations. What is to follow is but a small fragment in the rising edifice of the modern conception of psychosomatic relationships.

There are at least two conceivable ways in which to proceed with research in this field. One could select a physical symptom or syndrome in which structural and functional pathology is well known, hyperthyroidism for example, and from the psychological examination of numerous patients presenting this disease draw some conclusions about the psychological factors that contribute to it, and those which are evoked by it. This has been the more usual method. But one could also begin at the other end, as it were. He could select some recognized psychopathological constellation and ascertain the nature of the physical changes that take place in connection with it. This, too, has been done to some extent, for example by those psychiatrists who have so painstakingly investigated the blood chemistry, the cardiac function, the condition of the reflexes, and other such somatic features of the depressions, for example, or of schizophrenia.

The latter method has been far less fruitful than the former and there has been a tendency to depreciate it on this account. Indeed, the results obtained by this method have been used by some to prove the apparent lack of interdependence of psychological and physical factors. This, I think, is a false interpretation of conclusions based upon an inaccurate or at least incomplete use of the method. Depression and schizophrenia are not primary psychological processes but end results, and there are very good reasons, I believe (as I have outlined in considerable detail elsewhere),[1] why those who suffer from depression have less necessity for physical and chemical pathology. By the time the depression appears the somatic symptoms connected with the original psychological factors have often disappeared. (Parenthetically, by the time a patient has developed a contracted kidney, the psychological factors associated with the original hypertension and nephritis may have also disappeared from view.)

I should like to illustrate the application of this somewhat discredited but still logically justified method of procedure. And in casting about for a suitable psychopathological nidus from which to start, I thought of that well known and widely prevalent phenomenon which goes by different names and is viewed in somewhat different lights but which in essence consists in a partial repudiation of one's appropriate biological role. The wish of the little girl to be a boy and to some extent the contrary wish are so widespread that we can scarcely call them pathological. Even those who cannot subscribe to the theory of bisexuality would agree that it is a part of so-called human nature to wish to have all the advantages in sight; the grass in the other field always looks greener. But in some individuals, as we know, this wish to have the advantages of the other sex is accompanied by a wish to repudiate, reject, or deny one's own sex.

For present purposes let us confine ourselves to the problem as it appears in women. The repudiation of femininity just referred to may be quite conscious; it is well known that some women openly despise all women and despise their own femaleness. They dress, talk, act, and behave as much like men as possible. These conscious avowals of masculinity we should not expect to be accompanied by corresponding physical changes. But when the same tendency arising on the same basis cannot be satisfactorily expressed directly because of internal or external pressure, we should expect that somatic methods might be among those utilized. We know that this is theoretically possible. The vegetative and nervous regulation of glandular and smooth muscle activity is constantly recording our moods, wishes, fears, and hates. The cardiac response to emotion, the respiratory, perspirational, and other similar examples of the somatic expressions of emotion, circulatory changes, and endocrine changes which are, at first, only so-called functional responses, in time modify structure—and the structures so modified may be any part of the human body.

Before we look for some of the somatic correlations, if any may be found to exist, with the unconscious repudiation of femininity in women, let us review briefly the theoretical origin of this complex.

The envy of the opposite sex which is so clearly reflected in the conscious wishes of the little girl to be a boy (and the less easily acknowledged but equally important wishes of the little boy to be a girl) is derived not so much from the physical and social advantages accruing to the opposite sex as upon a feeling of frustration in the competition to obtain love from the parents. For if we define envy as the emotional consequence of comparing the gratifications one is *not* getting with the gratifications someone else *is* getting (or seems to be getting), we may safely infer that envy is the inevitable burden of every child. For every child must endure increasing disappointment, frustration, postponement, and displacement in the gratifications of his need for love.

In the case of the little girl, and particularly those little girls whose thwartings are especially great on account of behavior or attitudes of the parents, the flame of envy may reach a terrific heat. This heat must express itself largely in feeling, because the child has so slight a capacity for changing his environment, or for effective external aggression. In this respect her brother is often apparently more fortunate. Thus some of her hostility is directed toward him, as well as toward the frustrating parents.

Under ideal circumstances, the little girl is able to renounce her aspirations to be like her brother, and to repress her envy. She finds some compensations in aspects of the female role that she had previously underestimated. But in those little girls whose vision of these compensations is clouded or her way to the obtaining of them blocked, the envy cannot be repressed, and serves to direct her hostility in two directions: she resents the more favored and envied males, while secretly striving to emulate them, and at the same time she hates and would fain deny her own femaleness. In the latter process it is not difficult to see that she turns a portion of her hate inward upon her own femininity, a partial self-destruction aimed at the hated quality by reason of which she stands in such odious disadvantage with the envied and hated males.

The consequences of the hatred of the opposite sex (in this instance, the hatred of men) scarcely needs expansion here. It has been thoroughly treated not only in psychoanalytic and other scientific articles and books but in philosophical systems, in novels, in poetry, and in history. One could begin with the Amazons * and end with a certain type of ambitious, aggressive American woman, who attains her greatest satisfaction in attempting to destroy the masculinity of men by mastering, controlling, defeating, rivaling, or merely depreciating and ridiculing men. Such women are unfortunately too familiar not only to physicians but to every observing person.

But what are the consequences within the physical being of the individual? Or are there any consequences? Is she able to say with her body what she is unable to say with her lips, or her behavior—that she would like to be a man—and discard her badges of femininity?

If we were to take as our examples women of overt homosexual tendencies we should have plenty of evidence for our thesis. The homosexual female as we all know and as Henry and Galbraith [2] observed statistically is characterized by firm muscular and adipose tissue, excess of hair on the chest, back, and legs, a small uterus, a contracted pelvis, underdeveloped breasts, facial hirsutism, a low-pitched voice, and either undersized or overdeveloped labia and clitoris. Personally I should be quite willing to accept these data and these women as additional sources of substantiation for the theory, but I shall assume that some would be unwilling to do so for they would maintain with a great deal of historical justification that these women might be considered as having become masculine through no wish of their own, but by the will of God, as it were, or, more soberly, as the result of fortuitous germinal changes with which the unconscious psychological connections are very remote indeed. They would point to the clinical evidences that some of these changes are similar in parent and child and that some of them may be demonstrated to follow the development of tumors in certain endocrine glands.

There is no discounting this explanation but there is another inter-

* As a concept, not as a historical fact.

pretation of the facts. No one, certainly not the speaker, denies that the energy distributions of the human personality can be altered by chemical manipulations; but they can also be affected by psychological manipulations and if this is true then psychological factors must also have entered into their genesis. Goiter can be cured by iodine, but it can also be cured by psychotherapy. Homosexuality, also, has been cured by psychotherapy, and this is a fact regardless of whether one believes in the constitutional theory of the oak-tree-in-the-acorn, or whether one believes in psychological dominance. These are not antithetical but merely different points of view, hands on the elephant. Back of them both are the primary regnant processes of which the psychological aspects are just as valid and just as worthy of scientific consideration as the physical aspects or the chemical aspects. If we know quite definitely the chemical factors in a given condition and know very little of the psychological factors of that condition, it is easy to assume that none of the latter exist. To do so, however, is to commit a crime against logic unless one takes the position, as I trust no one in this audience does, that psychological factors are an illusion or a negligible concomitant of occasional syndromes, a concept which is comparable to assuming that chemical processes take place in some patients but not in others.

But rather than to labor the point in the case of women whose repudiation of femininity takes the form of overt homosexuality, let us return to women ostensibly normal in behavior, normal in conscious sexual interest, but manifesting neurotic symptoms and syndromes leading to a psychological exploration of their deeper motives and feelings, some of which prove to be in the nature of feminine repudiation. What do we find in these?

To begin with the item of body structure—here the answer is not difficult to supply. For who is not familiar with the unattractive angularity characteristic of certain spinsters—the thin, flat-chested, narrow-hipped, neurotic woman? There is little in the scientific literature, if we exclude the statistical typologies of Kretschmer and his followers, which would attempt to correlate this masculine body build, this absence of feminine plumpness and body beauty with this widespread masculine envy which we have been discussing. But

popular literature and lay opinion are not so silent about it. Some
would say promptly that such women are unmarried because they
are unattractive, but it would be equally convincing to others that
they are unattractive because they are unmarried. And are they unmarried because they are neurotic or neurotic because they are unmarried? It is certainly insufficient to assume that they are all neurotic because they are unattractive.

How much more satisfactory than any of these causal couplets is
the hypothesis that a deep unconscious rejection of femininity is reflected simultaneously in the appearance, the celibacy, and the neuroticism of these women, that these are three aspects of an inability
to adjust themselves in a rational way to their early masculine envy.

It is not difficult to conceive how such emotional trends as I have
described could be reflected in certain gestures, attitudes, gaits, and
pursuits which would to some extent determine the distribution of
muscle development and fat deposits. But it is unnecessary to speculate: every psychiatrist has seen in his practice many examples of this
in which it was possible to ascertain that the entire life was determined by a conscious effort to imitate as much as possible all the
characteristics of the masculine members of the family and to reject
as much as possible all of those things which were characteristic of
the females in the family. And if such definite trends can be recognized consciously, we may safely assume that far more extensive, far
more powerful trends exist unconsciously in the same direction.

To be more specific in respect to body structure, I have noted
masculine legs, thighs, and hips in several women patients in whom
it was possible to demonstrate that they had, since childhood, unconsciously or consciously imitated their father's gait or their
brother's athleticism. Many patients whom I have studied psychoanalytically recalled without difficulty the mortification and resentment with which they observed the development of their breasts.
Some of them long before the introduction of brassieres were accustomed to tying bands of tape tightly about them in order to keep
their breasts from developing any further. Indeed for a time this
was a universal fashion.[3] In the recent play, *The Women,* it will be

recalled that the daughter comes to her mother in tears because her brother has ridiculed her "bumps."

Of course it proves nothing to say that some girls do not want their breasts to grow and that these same girls later show a deplorable underdevelopment of mammary tissue. But it could be explained if we assume that those instinctual energies or drives or "regnant processes" (Murray) of which our conscious wishes are only subjective aspects, are capable of influencing within limits the degree of structural development of parts of the body.

Can there be facial evidence of the wish to reject femininity in favor of masculinity? It is well known that neurotic women frequently have hard, tense faces, often possessing a querulous, bitter, pained expression. But we cannot be certain that such women are attempting thereby to look like men. However, it is significant that an actual change often takes place in the facial appearance of some of these women in the course of psychoanalysis in which these masculine ambitions are renounced. This has been demonstrated to my own satisfaction in several instances on the basis of objective and not subjective evidence. I recall, in particular, one spinster of thirty-five who remained away from home the better part of two years undergoing analysis. The change in her facial appearance was so striking that it was a matter of general comment among various of my clerical assistants, upon whose judgment I have learned that I can rely heavily in such matters. Furthermore, when this woman went home, she was passed unrecognized by numerous lifelong friends. In another instance a girl whose face was unattractive, not only because of her unconscious wish to repudiate feminine beauty as completely as possible but also because smallpox had assisted her materially in this direction, changed in appearance so much in the course of analysis that she was sought out by a portrait painter as a special object for posing. But, as further evidence, she began to attract male attention and within a year was married. (The smallpox residua were, I must admit, uninfluenced.)

I do not know why we psychoanalysts should feel apologetic about announcing as a scientific fact that some of our patients grow prettier as a result of treatment. Certainly the surgeons and dermatologists have no such inhibitions. But to relate this change in facial appearance to instinctual rearrangements related to what we call a wish for or a renunciation of male identification is, to be sure, still upon shaky and unconfirmed ground.

We should not minimize the extent to which external manipulations—a great interest in trying to look feminine, a more skillful use of cosmetics—influence the result. However, no one will deny that the facial muscles express emotion and, if emotion, then tension and desire, and there is nothing illogical in assuming that if a woman unconsciously wants to look like a man she will to some extent accomplish this; if, on the other hand, she is willing to look like a woman she will do so.

We should logically expect that the most significant alterations in function or structure related to the repudiation of femininity would be in connection with the reproductive organs.

That frigidity and vaginismus may represent physiological rejections of the feminine role in intercourse is now fairly generally accepted by most of us and I should not mention them were it not for the ineradicable conviction of so many gynecologists that these conditions have a physical basis. While I have always doubted this, feeling that the symptoms could be explained entirely upon the assumption of psychological inhibition, a degenitalization of the genitals, as it were, I am prepared to concede that the gynecologists may be partly correct, for I cannot imagine that a long-continued frigidity or vaginismus could exist without some corresponding structural changes, or at least the atrophy of tissues and glands, characteristic of any unused part of the body.

Sterility is somewhat comparable to frigidity; * it represents the failure of normal biological functioning. That it occurs far more

* Whether sterile women are more likely to be frigid than nonsterile women is difficult to prove, since the actual incidence of frigidity is unknown. It is my impression, however, from clinical experience, that the association of sterility and frigidity is of frequent occurrence. One patient, for example, illustrated almost every proposition in this paper: she was completely frigid, suffered from dysmenorrhea, was sterile, resented all her feminine activities and obligations and had both breasts amputated, one after the other, on the pretext that she might be developing a cancer in them.

frequently in civilized men than in savage men and far more frequently in men than among animals should have suggested before now that something in the spirit of our civilization interferes with a process generally regarded as beyond psychological control.

That the emotional life has some relation to this phenomenon would appear to be demonstrated by those numerous reported cases in which a reorganization of the psychic life results in pregnancies ten, fifteen, and twenty years after marriage. I myself am familiar with an instance of this. Some gynecologists have gone so far as to postulate the details of the physiological mechanisms of this phenomenon. For example, Sellheim [4] assumes that the emotional factors are reflected in an over-action of the ovaries resulting in a premature maturation of the follicles such that ova are discharged which are not yet ready for fertilization. He believes that in some cases this is cured by psychotherapy, in others by a gradual reconciliation of the woman to her sterility, this reconciliation serving to decrease the pathological (emotional) stimulation of the ovary and hence allowing it to discharge normal ova and to terminate the sterility, as when a child is born after a couple has adopted one.[5]

Other physical manifestations of the repudiation of femininity are apparent when pregnancy ensues. *Hyperemesis gravidarum* is such a symptom, and is so recognized by many obstetricians. And to revert, in this connection, to the theme of frigidity, some women vomit after every act of coitus. I can say from personal experience that in some women the degree of discomfort, both in pregnancy and in parturition, is directly proportional to the intensity of the resentment at the femaleness thus expressed. To say that it represents normal feminine masochism is, to my notion, but playing with words. The very fact that parturition is so much more difficult and painful in civilized women than in the uncivilized is a substantiation of the theory invoked at the beginning of this paper, a theory not original with the speaker, namely, that civilization robs our normal sexuality.

In connection with the pains of pregnancy, I am reminded of a case which I saw recently in which the pregnancy was complicated by sudden, inexplicable abdominal pain of such severity that an exploratory laparotomy was performed. The operation revealed nothing, but the pains disappeared for a while, only to reappear with great violence as the date of delivery approached. It was as if the girl were obliged to inflict upon herself great punishment for the sin of being pregnant. Time precludes my relating the innumerable devices used by her to forestall this self-punishment and divert it to her sympathetic relatives. Among other things she had had five operations.

It is true that other drives than those connected with the repudiation of femininity may determine hyperemesis, for example, the wish to reject the child. But merely to be pregnant is a great trauma to the women afflicted as we have described, and many difficulties develop with it, which are, in essence, protests.

Coming at last to the uterus itself, in its nongravid form and functions, we think first of all of those disturbances of menstruation which have been traced to a direct connection with the unconscious repudiation of femininity. Of these, of course, amenorrhea is the most logical, dysmenorrhea probably the most frequent. But menorrhagia, metrorrhagia and even leucorrhea have also been identified as psychologically determined and, by removal or correction of the psychopathology, cured.

Several authorities have reported evidence that uterine prolapse, cystocele, and even fibromyomata are physical consequences of a disturbed psychosexuality—by which is implied, although not always stated, a rejection of femininity. That fibroids and sterility are associated is well known, and sometimes one, sometimes the other is made responsible. That both may be coordinate sequelae of the same fundamental condition—disturbed psychosexual adjustment—is the contention of some who claim to have seen them disappear when psychological reorganization was accomplished. The writer can speak only for the so-called infantile uterus. In two cases, so diagnosed, he has seen a sufficient metamorphosis occur as the result of psychological treatment to lead to amended diagnoses, and in one of them to pregnancy. In both cases the wish to deny and discard the uterus as a badge of femaleness was strongly active.

However skeptical we may feel in regard to these extraordinary findings, we must realize that as yet there has been little cooperation in the researches of psychiatrists and gynecologists. Indeed the attitude of modern medicine is not so very different toward these patients from that described in 1884 by Clifford Allbutt,[6] who said in speaking of the visceral neuroses:

> A neuralgic woman seems thus to be peculiarly unfortunate. However bitter and repeated may be her visceral neuralgias, she is either told she is hysterical or that it is all uterus. In the first place she is comparatively fortunate, for she is only slighted; in the second case she is entangled in the net of the gynecologist, who finds her uterus, like her nose, is a little on one side, or again, like that organ, is running a little, or it is as flabby as her biceps, so that the unhappy viscus is impaled upon a stem, or perched upon a prop, or is painted with carbolic acid every week in the year except during the long vacation when the gynecologist is grouse-shooting, or salmon catching, or leading the fashion in the Upper Engadine. Her mind thus fastened to a more or less nasty mystery becomes newly apprehensive and physically introspective and the morbid chains are riveted more strongly than ever. Arraign the uterus, and you fix in the woman the arrow of hypochondria, it may be for life.

If anyone thinks that attitude has changed, let him be disillusioned. I should say that the majority of the psychoneurotic invalids by whom we are consulted have had gynecological treatment, if not gynecological surgery. If anyone thinks this is limited to our own country, let him read the announcement made with pride in an English journal:

> The appointment, believed to be the first of its kind in this country of a whole-time gynecologist to a mental hospital . . . is a big step forward in the care of the mentally afflicted [!] . . . The treatment is usually as follows: First a series of glycerin irrigations of the uterus (as laid down by Remington Hobbs), then the pelvic diathermy treatment of Cumberbatch and Robinson, with vaginal bi-polar faradism, monopolar high frequency, and special levator ani and other exercises as indicated, together with colonic and vaginal lavage with sulphur waters. "Monsol" or "Iodex" pessaries are used when the discharge is very objectionable. Further general Spa treatment according to the needs of the case as directed by the physician concerned.[7]

Rather than to cavil at such treatment it would be more in keeping with our psychoanalytic principles if we attempted to analyze the reasons for the persistence of such a myth as that of the floating uterus, the theory that all nervous diseases are caused by disorders or displacement of the womb. I think we must regard this as indicating an unconscious recognition on the part of the physicians that there *is* something wrong with the genitals of such patients, something functionally wrong, something structurally wrong. With this goes also an unconscious recognition on the part of the patient that this is true and a wish to submit to painful treatment directed there. The willingness with which some patients submit to such treatment is suggestive evidence to the psychiatrist that they suffer from a sense of guilt connected with the genital organs. This is precisely what has been reported by those who have studied the conditions above mentioned, and it conforms to our original premise that some women wish to destroy—or to have destroyed—the femaleness within them.

As I pointed out in my introduction, rejection of the feminine role is dependent upon deep-lying hostility, a hostility which is directed outwardly against men and inwardly against the feminine part of themselves by reason of which they feel so inferior. In connection with both of these hostilities, however, there arises a sense of guilt and a sense of guilt focused upon that part of the body where a repudiation of femininity has been made concrete. Thus the symptom of amenorrhea, dysmenorrhea, leucorrhea, or whatever, serves simultaneously as a rejection of the feminine role, an aggression against the male, and a local self-punishment.

The same thing is true to some extent when the menstrual flow appears unexpectedly upon the occasion of a sexual approach from a man (the appearance of menstruation on the wedding night is widely familiar; there are many instances reported in the literature in which the menstruation appeared out of season, as it were, when a sudden opportunity for intercourse occurred). In these cases it has been repeatedly demonstrated that the appearance of the menstruation serves as a defense against intercourse, a method of rejecting and disappointing the excited man and at the same time evading conscious responsibility for doing so. There is another side to this, as has been pointed out by Groddeck;[8] the appearance of the menstruation is also a test for the man and may have some of its prehistoric aphrodisiac functions. Thus it serves as a defense against a coitus which is half-desired and half-feared, an aggression against the man which at the same time necessitates a suppression of the woman's own desires and in this sense punishes and deprives her. Of course it has other values, also.

Until we have actually examined microscopically the exact character of the irregular and apparently psychologically stimulated menstrual period, it is, of course, unscientific to say that this proves that menstruation can unconsciously be brought about by a woman at any time of the month to gratify unconscious purposes. All we can say for certain is that *uterine bleeding* can be brought about in this way and for these reasons, that this uterine bleeding may in such instances replace the normal menstrual period for that month, and that the subject is from the character of the flow and her own sensations unable to distinguish this bleeding from normal menstruation.[9]

Psychoanalysts are so familiar with the fact that psychogenic symptoms are over-determined that I must anticipate the questions which I know will have arisen in their minds. Does the author mean to say that such symptoms as leucorrhea, dysmenorrhea, and the like represent *only* the repudiation of femininity? Has it not been demonstrated that such symptoms may include a wish to harm a man or to humiliate him or to defile him? May not amenorrhea be the expression of a pregnancy fantasy no less than of a rejection of the capacity to be fertilized?

Of course I am familiar with these things and I concede that the precise nature of the fantasies may differ greatly in different cases. One cannot look through a telescope and a microscope simultaneously and I am trying, now, to bring into general focus a wide variety of phenomena ranging from behavior reactions through functional aberrations to actual structural changes. All of them, I think, may be visualized as representations in different spheres of a profoundly influential drive, the subjective aspect of which is a wish to repudiate, or *destroy* one's own femininity, one's femaleness, ex-

pressing at the same time self-directed aggression and self-punishment. In my book [10] I have called this organic suicide—an idea
which I owe in part to Dr. Jelliffe. To the extent to which the
human being is able to accept and express his biological role in spite
of the difficulties imposed by reality, including the reality of the
existing cultural pattern, to that extent he is free from the compulsion to destroy anything within himself and consequently free from
the necessity of atoning for such destructiveness. That this ability to
accomplish partial self-destruction may express itself in behavior
goes without contradiction; that it may appear in the form of perverted symptoms has been known in some degree since the hysterical
syndrome was first recognized; that the functional aberration which
we call hysteria may become structuralized into various organic
changes is at least a logical hypothesis, but it is not yet proved.

Here I am not raising an issue. I confidently believe that we are
all essentially unanimous in our scientific convictions on this point.
Whenever scientists find themselves in polemical positions, emotionally defending one point of view against another, it is fairly
certain that both of them are incorrect. There is no such either-or,
right-and-left, north-and-south problem in science. This is especially
true of the psychosomatic problem. The time is past when we can
get into a wrangle over whether a condition is psychogenic, physiogenic, or chemogenic. We all agree, surely by now, that any symptom may be psychogenic or chemogenic or physiogenic and that any
disease must be considered as a combination of all three. Diseases
can never be psychogenic alone nor chemogenic nor physiogenic.
What I am talking about today is the extent to which we can interpret the psychological aspect of some conditions with the physics
and chemistry of which we are more familiar. And I am approaching it methodologically from the psychological, that is, the least-
known side, merely for the purpose of exposition.

Many years ago Dr. Jelliffe wrote me a letter which I have never
forgotten. I cannot find the original letter, but the substance was
this: In science one must choose between being absolutely safe but
entirely sterile, on the one hand, and, on the other, of having the
courage to think beyond one's facts. The conclusions of the latter

method may require revision—it will certainly entail some mistakes and it is bound to expose one to the ridicule and suspicion of those who would rather be safe than constructive. Nevertheless, most of the great discoveries of science have been made with the deductive rather than the inductive method.

There can be no doubt in our minds as to which way Dr. Jelliffe himself has taken. I, for one, am proud to follow his lead.

And so I have mentioned some of the ways in which a certain aspect of self-destructiveness, the repudiation of feminity, might be expected to appear in bodily function and structure, and I have referred to ways in which some have felt that it does appear. Only a vast amount of patient research will substantiate these deductions. As I have said in the book referred to, I am fully aware of the unevenness of the evidence submitted and the speculative nature of some of the theory, but I cling to the belief that to have a theory, even though it proves to be a false one, is better than to attribute events to pure chance. A theory has the virtue of leading either to confirmation or rejection, thus clearing the way for the slow progress of science. This, I assume, is our common aim. This has surely been the aim of the great man who sits at my left; this man with his great mind, his great knowledge of neurology, of psychiatry, of medicine, of *life*, and above all his great and indefatigable spirit. Dr. Jelliffe, we whom you have inspired salute you!

15. Psychogenic Influences on the Appearance of the Menstrual Period

In his engaging *Book of the It,* Georg Groddeck remarked the frequently observed phenomenon that "many women who have been parted from their husbands for a long time start their period on the day they are united." He put forward the explanation *first,* that the menstrual flow is aphrodisiac to the man, *secondly,* that it is an attestation on the part of the wife of her faithfulness—"See," she says, "if I now have a baby it must be from you, for I was menstruating when you came and hence could not have been pregnant"—and *thirdly,* it is a hostage against rejection, i.e., if the man fails to be as sexually attracted to her as she hopes and wishes, she has the best of excuses to offer her offended vanity. "If the embrace is tempestuous all is well, the more so because the prohibition of custom is defied, and if it is not then that is because custom forbids."

Clinical psychoanalysts, who have such frequent occasion for observing this phenomenon, would wish to add to its determining factors (1) the hostility on the part of the woman towards the husband, (2) her wish to prevent or avoid coitus, and (3) the punitive symbolic self-infliction of her unconscious wish to castrate her husband. These functions support and are often supported by the phantasies that it is he who has castrated her (instead of vice versa) and that the act of cohabitation is a bloody and pseudo-sadistic performance.

Reprinted from the *International Journal of Psychoanalysis,* 22:60–64, 1941.

These latter psychoanalytic observations are so well known that I have nothing to add regarding them, but some recent observations of my own so sharply recalled the intuitive interpretation of Groddeck that I thought it worthwhile to set down the details. It will be recalled that Groddeck expanded his idea at some length to the effect that eczema about the face, cold sores on the lips, halitosis, clammy hands, and other repellent aspects of the points of contact serve the purpose of testing out the lover and at the same time guarantee against the trauma of disappointment. "If he loves me in spite of this then he loves me indeed; if he doesn't love me it is because of this."

The following pertinent observations were made on a patient who had not seen her husband for more than a year. The analysis was close to its end. The date of the husband's arrival was not determined by the patient although acquiesced in by her. Just prior to her husband's coming, the patient's resistances against the termination of the analysis had been under scrutiny and it had been recalled by her that the fear of being injured by the great penis of her father, which she had felt as a child when he held her close to him, was not alone a fear of what the penis might do to her but of the fact that he showed no external emotion or evidence of his desire for her: i.e., she felt she had failed to arouse him. This gave rise to an enormous fear that she could not or would not be appreciated as a woman by her husband just as she had not been by her father. She too, therefore, must conceal her real feelings, which in real life she accomplished by the assumption of a superficial urbanity; in other words, there was on the one hand the fear, "I shall be hurt, therefore I must hurt him first," and secondly, "He will not show his love for me, therefore I must not show my love or my disappointment either."

The day her husband arrived was apparently one of great joy for both of them. They had very satisfactory intercourse. But some time that night she dreamed that she *"so delayed the elevator in a store or office building by talking to the elevator boy that a man passenger on the elevator wet his pants."*

She awoke and prepared to come for her analytical hour, which was early in the morning, only to discover that she had begun to menstruate, although it was several days ahead of her usually regular period time. She was greatly distressed at this because her husband was to remain with her for only a few days and both of them thought immediately that this premature menstruation of hers was an (unconsciously effected) aggressive device to thwart one of the purposes of his visit.

The dream, I think, in connection with the analytic situation shows this element of testing to be much more important, in this instance, than the aggressive element. The *elevator boy* represented, almost indubitably, the analyst; *talking* to him symbolized the analysis; and the *passenger* who wet his pants because he could not wait any longer was her husband. From the standpoint of aggressive tendencies, it is true in the dream as in reality that she is treating her husband as she was once treated, i.e., kept waiting, excited sexually and left ungratified. On the other hand the more powerful motive seems to have been: "I dare not end my analysis until I am sure that my husband loves me, until he cannot hold in any longer. I want to see emotional expression come from *him*. Therefore I stall in my analysis, keep 'talking.' "

In view of this I asked if she thought it might be that the premature appearance of the menstruation was similarly a test of her wish to see if he would love her in spite of it.

The following day she reported that she had left the hour much heartened and very much surprised to discover that her menstruation, which had been excessive, gradually ceased and was entirely absent by evening. (Her normal period lasts five days and she flows profusely.)

The following night she had a dream to the effect that she could now dispense with her parents and the analyst, the "reason" being (in the dream) that her husband had had an erection! This I take as a further confirmation of the interpretation. The next day, which was the normal date for her menstrual flow to begin, it did begin.

The question immediately arises whether or not the first flow of blood which my patient experienced and which she assumed to be normal menstruation was actually that or whether it was a nonmenstrual flow of blood containing no deciduous cells or other normal menstrual content. This, of course, I was unable to determine. In this particular case I think it is not so difficult to believe that it was actually a prematurely induced menstrual period which was in turn inhibited through psychological influences. The physiological mechanisms can certainly be conjectured with greater ease in such a case as this than in those cases in which the woman appears to bring about menstruation several weeks away from the date of its normal appearance. If, in the menstrual cycle, the uterine mucosa is prepared for a menstrual period, let us say, on the 23rd, it is not difficult to conceive of an acceleration of this process under the influence of psychic factors such that the actual discharge of blood and tissue begins a few days earlier, e.g., on the 20th.

If there are two kinds of uterine bleeding, one a normal menstrual bleeding brought about in part through the well-known endocrine mechanisms and perhaps in part also by psychological stimuli and, on the other hand, another type comparable to hysterical epistaxis, which is also well authenticated,* then it would seem more likely that it is the second type of uterine bleeding which one sees in such cases as those reported by Freud, Abraham, and others in which the flow of blood occurs under what appear to be chiefly psychological influences at a time considerably removed from that of the normal ovulation period.

One of my patients, for example, who was always quite regular in her menstrual periods, managed upon two occasions to "menstruate" irregularly a week earlier than the normal time, on the day that her husband arrived after an absence of three years.

Another patient undergoing analysis was visited by her husband several times at intervals of three to six weeks. She insisted to me each time that she was highly pleased at the prospect of his coming,

---

* Vicarious menstruation in both men and women has long been a matter of record, baffling physiological explanation. If we look beneath the surface of consciousness, however, we see in the light of certain examples exactly why, if not exactly how, it happens. Bryan (1926),[1] for example, cites the case of a man who, during a certain period of his analysis, identified himself strongly with a woman, indeed, with a menstruating woman, and exemplified this during one analytic hour by developing a profuse nose bleeding which occupied his interest and attention markedly. When its significance was pointed out to him the nose bleeding promptly ceased. I myself (1934)[2] reported a similar episode in a female, which had similar psychological content.

because she so much desired intercourse with him. Each time, however, upon his arrival, which was never unexpected, she was menstruating profusely. She rather reluctantly recognized the obvious implication of this serviceable irregularity on her part. In discussing the matter, I told her of the case reported by Freud, in which an otherwise very regular woman suddenly began to menstruate every *two* weeks when her husband, whom she very much disliked, took to coming home every two weeks to see her. Some time after this, my patient remarked that she was a week overdue with her menstrual period, and reminded me of this case of Freud's, laughingly protesting that it was scarcely likely that she would unconsciously postpone her period until the sixth or seventh week just in order to thwart her husband again. Ten days later, i.e. six weeks "late," on the eve of another visit from her husband, her catamenia reappeared! *

We know definitely that the psychological factors can with a high degree of specificity increase the blood supply to certain parts of the body. Blushing is a familiar example of this phenomenon, and Ferenczi expanded it in his theory of the genitalization of the various organs other than the genitals themselves which accomplish their function through a temporary turgescence. It is certainly not difficult to conceive of a *psychologically* induced congestion of the uterine mucosa. We already know that such a congestion can be *endocrinologically* produced. It is theoretically possible that either one of these stimuli might bring about congestion to the point of hemorrhage without the assistance of the other. It is also theoretically possible and empirically very probable that the two factors combine

---

* In those cases in which there is only a slight delay or slight acceleration in the appearance of the period upon the occasion of the visit of the husband, there is an additional possibility in the way of explanation which should be mentioned. I have the definite impression that in such cases—for example, in the first one cited—the husband sometimes keeps accurate tab unconsciously upon his wife's menstrual cycle so that he too may avail himself of this protection against the chagrin of impotence. It is as if he said to himself, "I will go and see her; about such and such a date she will be menstruating. If I do not feel aroused by her—am not potent with her—and disappoint her, I can blame it on her menstruation." This, again, would follow in spirit the suggestion of Groddeck, namely, that of testing out the loved object, a motive which it is my impression has been rather understressed in psychoanalytic literature.

in varying proportions. It is well known by every woman that anxiety, fear, physical accidents, depressions, and other emotional causes can hasten the onset or entirely inhibit the flow of menstruation: this would indicate the cooperative function of psychological and endocrine stimuli in the induction of catamenia.

Until we have actually examined microscopically the exact character of the irregularly and apparently psychologically stimulated menstrual period it is probably unscientific to say that menstruation can be unconsciously brought about by a woman at any time of the month to gratify unconscious purposes. All we can say is that *uterine bleeding* may be brought about in this way and for these reasons, that this uterine bleeding may in such instances replace the normal menstrual period for that month and that the subject of these uterine bleedings is unable from the character of the flow or her own sensations to distinguish them from normal menstruation.

It has been my purpose in this paper to indicate again some of those psychological stimuli, i.e. rejection of love object, evasion of coitus, punitive symbolic self-infliction of castration wishes and in particular the less well-recognized one of "testing out," a kind of love trial by ordeal.

16. Some Observations on the Psychological Factors in Urination and Genitourinary Afflictions

In the recent accent upon what has been rather unfortunately designated psychosomatic medicine, the afflictions of the urinary tract have received rather scant attention. *A priori* this might seem to be surprising in view of the close connections of the urinary and genital functions.

On the other hand, it has long been recognized not only by psychiatrists but by some pediatricians and others that functional disturbances of urination could be closely dependent upon emotional factors. From the physiological standpoint urination serves the simple purpose of periodically discharging accumulated urine. From the psychological standpoint, however, urination has many other meanings, conscious and unconscious. Space precludes any attempt to catalogue all of these, but, following a scheme proposed in my book, *Man Against Himself,* I think it is possible to point out certain erotic values and certain aggressive values in urination to which self-punitive values are added when pathological disturbances of function become evident.

The erotic component in urination. There can be little doubt that the act of urination is one of the child's early expressions of sexual excitement. For the child, as for the aged, the passing of urine is the closest physiological approximation to genital activity

Reprinted from the *Psychoanalytic Review*, 28:117–129, January 1941.

which is physically possible, and of itself this suggests a reason for the polyuria of childhood and old age ordinarily explained on purely anatomical grounds. That bed-wetting gives way to masturbation and nocturnal emissions, that pride and satisfaction in urinating become more maturely genital activities and satisfactions, that compliance with parental regulations in regard to urination are replaced with the regulation of sexual activity in deference to social attitudes, are matters of common knowledge. It is thus logical that in the neuroses, where infantile satisfactions are sought for and accomplished surreptitiously and distortedly by adults, urinary symptoms frequently represent and replace sexual activity.

An exaggerated pleasure in the act of urination often persists long beyond childhood, and in psychoanalytically treated patients where this occurs the fact is often stubbornly withheld by the patient from communication to his analyst. This is particularly apt to be true in those patients who tend to erotize the psychoanalytic treatment process in a high degree. Such patients are very apt to interrupt their analytic hours by imperative trips to the toilet. I remember one patient in this category who regularly, but somewhat surreptitiously, made for the toilet immediately at the conclusion of each hour. Frequently she would then return to her own apartment and masturbate. The peculiar thing was that she was much more reluctant to confess the urinating than to confess the masturbating.

I discovered that she had been in the habit of urinating from ten to fifteen times a day. When it was pointed out to her that this was done for some psychological reason, she responded by bringing a dream in which she *was hunting in the bottom of a wastebasket for something which, after long search, she found; it was a very much soiled pot holder.* The associations occurring to her in connection with the wastebasket were that in psychoanalysis one empties out a lot of refuse material which is better outside than in; one throws it away. Waste also made her think of urine. Her associations to pot holder were that a pot is what she called the vessel into which she urinated as a child and that the pot holder is something which one uses to keep from soiling one's hands or burning them in the kitchen. She thought the dream meant that she was hunting in the bottom of her mind for something which she hadn't confessed, evidently something to do with urine and the avoidance of soiling her hands. This latter phrase made her think of masturbation.

Since the dream suggested both masturbation and urination, one looks for some basis of identification of the two. I asked her outright at this point if it might refer to some pleasure associated with urination. She blushed and said, "Yes, that is actually true. You see my mother told me terrible things would happen if I masturbated but, on the other hand, she told me to dry myself after urination and she encouraged me to go to the toilet often. So it was as if I had a legitimate way in which I could rub my vulva by drawing the toilet paper across it. This way I could masturbate without soiling my hand—figuratively and actually. Perhaps this is the very reason I have always gone so often. It is associated, however, with other pleasures which I have never confessed to you. For one thing, there is a glorious feeling of relief after holding urine as long as I can. And then for another thing, you know when a woman urinates some of the urine flows over her vulva and this has always given me more or less of a thrill, not quite as much as masturbation but a lot more than I have ever admitted."

In this connection the case reported by Van Ophuijsen [1] a number of years ago is extremely pertinent and is here briefly abstracted:

At the central point of the childhood-reminiscences of one of my patients . . . there stands the following dream; it dates from about her fourth year when she still slept in her parents' bedroom. . . . She lay in bed and her mother stood near her. She had a surprisingly pleasant bodily sensation and her mother told her it was quite all right, there was no harm in it. Thereupon she experienced a kind of orgasm and awoke. To her astonishment and horror she found that she had soiled the bed. She called her mother, who came to her assistance without being angry. Thereafter the patient . . . remained shy, had anxiety during the night, suffered to an increasing extent from sleeplessness, and . . . gradually developed a neurosis, which grew very much worse at the age of thirteen, when she lost her mother, and again at nineteen, when she lost her brother. . . .

We may suppose that the sensations which the patient had in her dream were derived from her filled bladder, and that the emptying of it corresponds to the orgasm of the dream. Her feeling of shame and astonishment on waking prove to us that the girl must already have learned to control the bladder function. As a contrast there is in the dream a return to an earlier period before she had learned this control, associated with the idea of the methods of teaching her cleanliness; the mother near the bed, who tells her to let it happen, is obviously the mother who makes her use the chamber. Urinating into a chamber has had considerable significance to her; her father also helped her with this function later, and imitated the noise to her in order to make her urinate. And in addition, she had in her early youth heard the sound of her father urinating in the next room.

Every analyst could supply cases from his experience in the reminiscences of adult neurotics illustrating the erotic abuses of urination, and my only excuse for citing the following instance is the unusual clarity of the material:

This was a spinster of thirty undergoing analysis on account of numerous neurotic symptoms, chiefly related to social timidity. As a child she had been a bed-wetter. Until the age of four she had slept in the bedroom with her parents (she was an only child). Then she was moved to a bedroom of her own and after that (as she recalls it) she began to masturbate. The material came up for analysis in connection with her insistence that upon Sundays, Tuesdays, and Thursdays, regularly these three days each week, she had for many years awakened very early, about five-thirty, and had felt wretched all day. She had been led by physicians to believe that this was an endocrine cycle of some obscure type. To the idea of three times a week, she associated the fact that she had heard that this was the approximate frequency of sexual relations between married people; she could not recall where she had learned this. (She had previously told me that her father, who was an accountant, was an exceedingly systematic man who regulated all his activities.) However, she denied that this could be the explanation of her early awakening and her unpleasant feelings, because, she said, "I am sure my parents did not have intercourse after I was born; if they had I would not have been an only child. What I remember is that I would frequently awaken early in the morning, unpleasantly wet, and my mother would reach out and take me into bed beside her."

The patient then related the following dream: "I had gone with my father and mother to a party in Blanktown [a city which she associated with emancipation from childhood prohibitions]. The next thing I knew the party was over and we were going home and I had the dreadful sensation that I had been asleep at the party and missed all the fun, and besides that I had done something dreadful to disgrace myself. I asked them if I had actually gone to sleep during the party."

Her association to "party" was that several of her married friends refer to their sexual relations by that term. The dream could be interpreted then that she had been aware of the sexual relations of her parents in a half-waking state, had resented the fact that she was excluded from this pleasure, had urinated to relieve her own sexual excitement, and had then become fully awakened or at least had then allowed her parents to realize that she was awake so that she could be taken into bed with them. Being asleep, believing that she was asleep, or pretending that she was asleep was necessary in order to absolve herself from the guilt connected with overhearing and envying her parents, as well as that connected with bed-wetting, for which she was, of course, reproached.

In another patient there was a clear conscious memory of the fact that upon overhearing the parents having intercourse, she definitely wished that the father would desire her instead of her mother, and with this fantasy there would be conscious sexual excitement and involuntary enuresis.

It would be an interesting speculation to consider what becomes of the erotic pleasure in urination after genital supremacy has been achieved. It is probable that urination is never entirely de-erotized, but on the other hand it is also probable that the aggressive elements represented by urination become much more important than the erotic ones. One frequently sees urination used to oppose genital activity. In everyday life this occurs in men who ascribe their sexual desire and erections to a full bladder, and think they have proved this by the fact that their erection disappears after they have gone to urinate. Many women, on the other hand, spontaneously discover that they have greater pleasure in sexual relations if the bladder is at least partially distended. Patients frequently report dreams in which they are about to have sexual relations but are suddenly interrupted by the impulse to urinate and at this point they awaken or the dream terminates.

The aggressive component in urination. I have already implied that enuresis may be a substitute for masturbation but in doing so have emphasized the erotic rather than the aggressive element, which, of course, is always present in masturbation. The aggressive function of enuresis is tacitly recognized in the ease with which we recognize the resentment and annoyance which it causes in parents and others. In his book *All Quiet on the Western Front,* Remarque describes the punishment meted out to soldiers for bed-wetting: they were obliged to sleep in the bunk *below* another bed-wetter.

But even diurnal enuresis, or indeed the mere act of urination without special frequency, may be for the child or the adult, a method of expressing hostility. Decorticate cats often squirt urine when the rage reaction is stimulated. (Personal observation by courtesy of Dr. David McK. Rioch, Washington University Medical School.) The vocabulary of vituperation includes numerous expressions the gist of which is to cast urine and feces upon the hated person, and such expressions undoubtedly originate in the era of childhood when physical helplessness restricts the child to such a narrow range of weapons and missiles. Every psychoanalyst is so familiar with this concept that it is apt to be passed over as of common acceptance; the average medical man may realize it in common speech but usually excludes it from his clinical interpretations. He may laugh understandingly when a patient relates boyhood games of boys urinating on one another but forget completely to make any connection between this reminiscence (which is really a confession of intention) and the fact that the patient asks at the termination of the consultation to be directed to the toilet. He forgets also to connect this with the patient's symptoms, or in general to seek in his cases of polyuria and enuresis this same element of excretory aggression.

Even in those patients who consciously derive erotic pleasure from urinating and hence yield frequently to the impulse to go to the toilet there is a subtle defiance of the parents and all those who represent the parents. It is as if they said, "Oh, so you do not want me to wet my clothes! Very well, then, but in that case you must let me go to the toilet as often as I like." Every observing parent has seen precisely this phenomenon in his children during the training period.

The unconscious element of aggression (particularly of the impulsive, ambitious sort) in urination is one of the chief characteristics of the urethral personality type which was suggested by Sadger and Abraham, but which even to the present time has not been fully delimited. For our present purposes it is more to the point to illustrate how the aggressive significance of urination develops.

A patient of mine underwent psychoanalysis because of his persistently disastrous exploits in defiance of his father which were of such an extent that at the age of thirty he had squandered a small fortune and in a dozen ways had brought misery and sorrow to his family. He told me in the course of his treatment of many humiliations and thwartings of his childhood. Among these were the vigorous methods used by his mother to induce him to overcome enuresis, which persisted until he was seven years old, such as photographing him at that age clothed in a diaper, then showing the photograph to family friends in his presence. At the same time she exploited his childish beauty and his curly hair and in many ways tried to make him like a girl. In after years he would fight violently against the designation of "sissy" and in fact went to the opposite extreme and became a daredevil and bully, especially toward women. One day during the analysis he had a dream that as he was eating in a restaurant (such dreams often refer to the nursing era) he saw a stream of water burst from a hole in the wall and squirt directly into the lap of an older woman with whom he was acquainted who had waited upon him as a nurse. In the dream he was convulsed with amusement at her predicament, "at her having," in his words, "to sit there and take it." Her lap became soaked with water.

When disturbances develop in the expression of a physiological function we know empirically that we find a corresponding disturbance in the psychological factors determining that function. It has been proposed by myself and others that what happens when pathological symptoms appear is that the unconscious aggressive satisfactions derived from the act are increased and a corresponding development of self-punitive satisfactions occurs; these in turn frequently require an artificial enhancement of the erotic elements in the function, a secondary erotization of the symptom. This can be seen in numerous urological disorders.

The psychiatric literature contains numerous examples of clinical disturbances of urinary function in which psychological factors were discernible.[2]

Anderson [3] has collected an extensive bibliography.

A typical example of the way these cases have been interpreted may be abstracted from the report of Mayer.[4] This was a woman of thirty-two who suffered from severe symptoms of irritation of the bladder necessitating forty to sixty micturations per day. The family physician had treated her with lavage of the bladder and injections of xylotropin, but without success. The somatic findings did not offer sufficient explanation for the symptoms. For this reason the psychological history was carefully sought. The patient was found to be a "strongly amorous" individual with high moral standards and an intense desire for a home and baby of her own. She had had warm friendships with three different men but none of them had ripened into marriage as she had hoped. She came to avoid men because of her increasing eroticism growing out of unsatisfied sexual desire, and had decided to become a children's nurse as a substitute for the natural expression of her maternal yearnings. The bladder symptoms seemed to be related to this erotic foundation, micturition seeming to afford sexual relief. This was confirmed by dream material.

After making the above findings and explaining the situation to the patient Mayer discontinued all other therapy. During the first

night after the interview she slept undisturbed for four hours and
during the second night she enjoyed undisturbed sleep for seven
hours. The symptom remained in abeyance. In such cases as this,
one sees the formula of resentment, increased hostility, expressed in
urination balanced by the self-punitive function and hyper-erotization.
I do not think it is so clear why Mayer was able to relieve the patient
so expeditiously, but this is a question related to the more general
principles of therapy.

From the standpoint of general medicine, however, the important
question is to what extent these continued functional disorders (for
example, retention and frequency) may become structuralized and
appear as organic genitourinary pathology. I was able to get some
direct evidence on this point through a patient of mine who had had
an exaggerated polyuria for so many years that she did not regard
it as a symptom of illness. She would urinate on the average of
every one and a half to two hours during the daytime, although she
could usually get through the night without the necessity of rising.
When I learned of this I insisted that such frequency was pathological and must indicate either some disease of the urinary system or
else the establishment of a habit for some reasons of psychological
economy. She denied this vigorously at first but later supplied me
with full evidence to support such a hypothesis.

The origin of her urinary frequency seemed to relate back to the
age of six, when she had the following experience, which was a
culminating episode of her father's demonstrativeness toward her.
He was holding her on his lap, petting and kissing her. She became
aware of the fact that he (also) was sexually excited. He was quite
able to control himself, however, and the result was that she experienced a mixture of genital stimulation and resentment at being
thwarted. This culminated in her impulsively emptying her bladder
as she sat upon his lap, wetting him as well as herself. Her father, as
provoked as he was astonished, jumped up and ordered her to bed
and, to finish matters off, her mother gave her a spanking. This
marked the end of a period of physical affection between the father
and daughter, on the father's part because of his annoyance at having been wet upon and on the daughter's part because of her thwart-

ing and her sense of guilt at the sexual stimulation and the aggression of the wetting episode. With her mother's adjuration, however, that she should go to the toilet frequently she was able to obtain from the mere act of urinating in the toilet a degree of sexual satisfaction. However, this also permitted her to express aggressive tendencies, as will be apparent from another use to which she put her urinating.

All through school she used to go to the toilet many times a day. In junior high school she was one of a group who took an examination for admission to an eastern school which required very strictly supervised examinations. One of the rules of the examination was that no applicant could leave the room during these entrance examinations. They were given on four successive mornings from nine to twelve and on every one of the four mornings she was overwhelmed after the first thirty minutes of the examination with the necessity for going to the toilet, and since leaving the room invalidated the examination she made a complete failure in all four parts. As it later developed, this changed the entire course of her life. She never went any further in her formal education.

It also became clear during her analysis that this frequent urination was associated with masturbation and represented a kind of substitute for it. It was on the toilet or after urinating that she indulged in masturbation most frequently during the school period. When her polyuria was called to her attention she insisted that it was not abnormal, that every woman urinated every hour or two, and that this was the reason for the many pay toilets in the department stores; that her mother did it, and her mother and she herself, in turn, had reproached children for not going oftener lest they injure their health.* It becomes clear, therefore, that this was a hypocritical way of saying, "If you masturbate you injure your health, but you can urinate all you want to because that doesn't injure your health but just the reverse." In other words, she converted the prohibition against masturbation into the exhortation to

---

* I was not personally familiar with this superstition on the part of mothers that their children would be injured by long retention of urine. I conducted some investigations among patients and others and found that it was by no means an isolated delusion of this one neurotic mother but is a fairly widespread idea, based perhaps on some knowledge of the symptom of anuria—uremic or hysterical.

urinate, thus substituting urinating for sexuality, and also for analytic
endeavor, thus expressing unspoken hostilities against her analyst
on account of thwarting her, just as she had once expressed the
same feeling on her father's lap.

When this became clear to the patient she made a determined conscious effort to regulate her urinary routine in a more normal
fashion. When, however, she would attempt to limit her trips to the
toilet to four or five a day, the vesical tension would become so great
that she would be unable to maintain the sphincteric tone with the
result that urine would trickle down her thighs and she would soil
her garments repeatedly during the day. I reached the definite conclusion that this habit had been so long established that there was
an actual contracture of the bladder, which, in turn, anatomically
justified her polyuria.

I am informed that it is a well-established fact in urology that
both men and women who from habit, prostatic obstruction, or some
other cause practice frequent urination over many years, develop a
small contracted bladder with greatly reduced content and greatly
reduced elasticity such that even if the pathological condition is
removed the contraction cannot be entirely corrected; that is, the
elasticity of the bladder is regained slowly and incompletely.[5]

Reference should be made to the cases of definite psychogenic
urinary pathology reported by Dr. Smith Ely Jelliffe.[6] In the first
a woman of sixty-four was studied, who from childhood had suffered from frequent urination; she was obliged to retire every fifteen
or twenty minutes throughout the day. In spite of this, she had married and had a child, but naturally her life was greatly hampered.
She rarely went out at all, and when she did, she of necessity had to
choose certain routes where she knew she could find relief. She had
been to all manner of doctors and had had all methods of treatment.
Roentgenological study of the bladder showed that it was indeed
very much contracted.

Now the significant thing about the case was this: In her sixty-
fourth year, a urologist, recognizing to some extent the psychological elements but impelled by pragmatic considerations, decided
upon gradual dilation of the bladder, which he readily accomplished

in six or seven weeks. No sooner had this been done, however, than the patient began to be restless, sleepless, and to showing increasing signs of anxiety; shortly thereafter she attempted suicide, at which time she was brought to Dr. Jelliffe.

In Jelliffe's opinion, urinary hyperactivity was this woman's means of sexual gratification, but it required a certain degree of somatic compliance which also required that the erotic significance remain unconscious. When her physician destroyed one of these requisites, he quite unwittingly took from her *her* only outlet for erotic gratification, and as we know, the blocking of all erotic outlets usually results in anxiety, which may, as in this case, be unendurable.

The other case reported by Jelliffe [7] is even more dramatic. This was a woman of thirty-six who had complained of headache for four years, dyspnea, edema, marked constipation, and occasional lapses of consciousness. Examination showed blood pressure of 240/150, albuminuria, urea retention, and other indications of a typical cardio-renal decompensation. She was in the hospital when first seen and was regarded as moribund. She improved enough for some psychological investigations to be begun, with very fruitful results; the patient recovered a relative degree of health and lived a useful, busy life for an additional eight years.

Jelliffe presents the psychological architecture of this case rather briefly. It was another instance in which the early urinary gratification pattern of childhood had never been relinquished. In spite of having had four children, she had never achieved sexual maturity, had been totally frigid with her husband, was not even capable of masturbation. She derived all of her satisfactions urethrally. As Jelliffe puts it, to get complete satisfaction at this (urinary) level, "she urinated quarts to get it and drank gallons to get the quarts . . . and the kidney had to pass it along in double time and finally rebelled. . . . When we refuse to get in line with nature, as registered in the faulty purposes of life, i.e., our mental states, even the kidneys, the blood pressure, and the urea protein become involved. And this is but one formula for many diseases."

Renal Colic. The urological literature contains numerous references to cases in which a diagnosis of renal colic is made with a fair

degree of certainty but in which definite evidences of stones are lacking. The patient will have all the classical signs and symptoms—he
will be seen "to sweat with pain, to look pale and red, to tremble, to
vomit well nigh to blood, to suffer strange contortions and convulsions, by starts to let tears drop from the eyes, to urine thick,
black, and frightful water, or to have it suppressed by some sharp
and craggy stone that cruelly pricks and tears. . . ." (Montaigne's
Essays, Book III). Yet careful urological examination, including
cystoscopy, yields negative results.

In some instances the patient substantiates the diagnosis with a
pebble or stone which he claims to have passed, which examination
proves to be adventitious. Braasch [8] has discussed this syndrome
in several communications and in a letter to the writer, in which he
makes it clear that, however convincing the clinical picture, it is a
hysterical manifestation, and if any stone is produced it is by trickery.

Nine such cases had been seen at the Mayo Clinic prior to January
1930, eight of them women. One patient had actually had stones
removed from the kidney surgically in another hospital. (Not consistent, of course, with Braasch's theory.) Many of these cases had
attacks of pain so acute that morphine had been resorted to. Braasch
is somewhat contradictory because part of the time he calls the
picture "hysterical" and part of the time he calls it "simulated,"
supporting the latter interpretation by reporting the frequency with
which the patients actually introduced stones into the bladder. Of
course, if something is simulated it is not hysterical, and vice versa.
My impression is that probably both occur and that of the two the
hysterical type is probably the more frequent, since we know that
conscious malingering is very rare in all branches of medicine.

Schwarz [9] has described the same condition. He believes the pain
has its basis in a periodically acute hyperemia which through increasing the kidney volume leads to painful overdistention of the
capsule. He believes these attacks may be precipitated by many
factors including psychic influences. Klemperer,[10] on the other hand,
is convinced that nephrolithiasis should be considered among the
psychogenically determined diseases. He thinks that nervous factors
are responsible for the secretion of substances favoring stone forma-

tion and recommends specific mental hygiene therapy as a prophylaxis for patients with kidney stone diathesis. Groddeck [11] is convinced that the organism has some means of ridding itself of the
tendency to stone formation and believes like Klemperer that a
prophylactic psychotherapy is possible. He reported a case in which
he thought he succeeded in accomplishing this.

I have personally seen at least three of these cases with classical
symptoms of renal colic (and in this opinion several urologists concurred) in which it was necessary to conclude either that no stones
were present or else that they entirely escaped detection by competent examiners. It so happens that various factors make it impossible, from considerations of discretion, to give the details of these
cases. Furthermore, I was unable to convince myself as to the precise
nature or mechanisms in the colic-like attacks. In general, however,
the constellations of traits were what we should expect. One of
them was in a woman who was cystoscoped innumerable times in an
effort to locate the cause of these terrific attacks. Her entire life
history was obviously colored by the most intense neurotic tendencies, including sexual frigidity and a sadistic attitude toward her
gentle, affectionate, patient husband. Another case was an unmarried lawyer with various somatic symptoms, including these
attacks of pseudolithiasis or renal colic and a condition which, I
think, is psychologically closely related to it, namely, *ejaculatio
praecox*. This man was in everything too impulsive, but always his
apparent generosity, enthusiasm, affection, or whatever—so suddenly and strongly expressed—lacked the quality of genuineness
to make it effective. In reality he was a much-inhibited man, underdeveloped in every way as is suggested by his substitution of urinary
modalities (ejaculating without pulsation, *upon* rather than *within*
the female; the "renal" symptoms; preoccupation with fire fantasies)
for real genital satisfactions.

SUMMARY

A brief and very incomplete review of the psychological factors in urination and in some urinary disturbances is presented,
emphasizing and illustrating the component erotic, aggressive, and

self-punitive elements. The question of how functional deviations
lead to pathological structuralization is approached on the basis of
one case illustration. The occurrence of attacks simulating renal
colic in certain individuals of the "urethral personality type" is
mentioned as a problem for further special investigation.

17. Observations of a Psychiatrist in a Dermatology Clinic

As a psychiatrist I have spent many hours in listening—listening to subjective descriptions of internal, invisible "lesions." An opportunity for a different type of clinical experience came when I received from Dr. Paul O'Leary of the Mayo Clinic an invitation to spend six weeks in the Dermatology Section of that great medical center to which come so many patients who present their quite visible lesions in eloquent silence. My experiences there were in the nature of orientation rather than the pursuit of a definite research objective. My listening experience stood me in good stead, but I had much to see that was new to my eyes and much to learn about the emotional atmosphere of the dermatological clinic, quite apart from the psychological factors in specific cases.

When an observer enters such a clinic, he is almost immediately aware of a characteristic atmosphere. The patients awaiting help give evidence of a controlled but anxious desperation, quite different in its nature from the more dramatic depression and anxiety of the surgical clinic, or the more placid resignation of the medical clinic. These "skin patients" are for the most part not threatened with death, paralysis, loss of vision, or other such catastrophes. But

(I am indebted to Dr. Paul O'Leary and his first assistant, Dr. Louis Brunsting of Rochester, Minnesota, for the opportunity of making the following observations, for many painstaking demonstrations, explanations, and discussions, and for editorial review of this paper. [K.M.]) Reprinted from the *Bulletin of the Menninger Clinic,* 11:141–147, September 1947.

the limiting boundary of their personality, the skin, has become diseased; and something psychologically more important than loco- motion or digestion is affected—namely, appearance. Their afflic- tion is usually no secret. Its very obviousness is one of the chief sources of the patient's distress. To the sensory discomfort or pain which such patients suffer, there is added the mortification of ex- hibiting a more or less repulsive and suspicious lesion which marks and segregates them immediately. It subjects them to countless con- jectures as to cause, implications, consequences, and treatment by curious, meddlesome, or even well-intentioned acquaintances. Sym- pathy is apt to be only secondary to fear in the observer. The tacit assumption of filth, lice, syphilis, or contagion—regardless of its injustice—tends to seal the taboo on the dermatological sub- ject.

With such a predicament the psychiatrist, familiar with the mis- understandings which augment the sufferings of his own patients, can readily sympathize. Regarded frequently as malingerers, fakers, liars, and the like on the one hand, or as potential maniacs on the other, those troubled sufferers who have the intelligence and the opportunity to consult a psychiatrist are often rewarded by having the knowledge of this fact used by their friends as confirmation of a suspicion that they are of unsound mind and presumptively dan- gerous.

Dermatological and psychiatric patients have something else in common: their sufferings are vastly underestimated by those who have not experienced them. The torture to which some victims of eczema are subjected day after day and night after sleepless night for weeks, months, and even years is a species of pain transcending that of far more dramatic afflictions. Only one who has observed these sufferers tossing and writhing in frantic anguish, or exhausted and desperate after a prolonged paroxysm of itching, can realize how far this exceeds the notion ordinarily connoted by the simple description of "itching." We are all familiar with mosquito bites and other minor itching experiences; and, as applied to someone else's sensations, the word seems to imply something trivial or ludicrous. The gross untruth of this easy but common assumption was one of the first startling realizations that came to me as an observer in the dermatology clinic.

Apart from the suffering involved, some dermatological lesions are so hideous or so situated—or both—that they can neither be exhibited nor casually described. I recall a case in which a destructive process had gradually eroded and destroyed most of the vulva and a part of the soft palate of a young woman who had been under treatment for four years! Dr. O'Leary informed me that the pain of these lesions is scarcely exceeded by that of an eroding carcinoma. The fact that her life was not threatened was hardly a source of comfort. Yet she could not easily explain or describe her affliction to friends and acquaintances. This is similar to the plight of most psychiatric patients, in contrast to that of most dermatological patients. The mentally ill have nothing to show the world, nothing to tell of their sufferings, that may not be met with skepticism or bewilderment. In general, the dermatological patient, whose "troubles" are exposed to the world, tries to assure others that he is not as sick as he looks, while the psychiatric patient who "appears perfectly well" tries to convince them that he is much sicker than he looks.

The average physician may assume, as did the author at one time, that dermatological practice is composed chiefly of distinguishing between syphilitic, psoriatic, parasitic, infectious, or other variegated lesions; fulgurating or X-raying facial blemishes, epitheliomata, verrucae, and the like; and occasionally diagnosing a rare skin disease to which a long Latin designation has been attached which no one but dermatologists can remember. By way of treatment, in the careless thinking of too many of us, the dermatologist is busy excising warts and applying salves.

No one should be more ready to sympathize with such depreciatory misconceptions of dermatology than the psychiatrist, who is himself often conceived of as busily patting rich, hypochondriacal women on the back or fastening restraints about the wrists of violent psychotics. It is not my function to set the world straight on what the scientific dermatologist does and doesn't do. My present purpose is to present the concept of dermatological practice that I obtained in the course of my stay at Rochester, with particular reference to certain practical diagnostic and therapeutic problems in dermatology which seem to bear reference to psychiatry.

Patients come to the dermatologist with a great variety of lesions of the skin varying in size and number from one papule of pinpoint dimensions to a million papules, pustules, or blisters, or ten million itching, coalesced, scaling areas, anywhere on, or all over, the body. These lesions are occasionally painful; more frequently they cause itching; and still more frequently they are disturbing to the patient because they alter his appearance in a conspicuous and perplexing manner. The perplexity relates to the inexplicable origin of the lesions. Some patients elaborate fantastic reasons to account for their misfortune, but more commonly will say that they have simply "broken out." The mystery surrounding the origin of the lesions increases the patient's apprehensiveness in reference to the extent to which the lesion will enlarge or its possible malignancy. Added to this, as already mentioned, is the variable degree of subjective sensory discomfort.

Empirically these lesions have been classified and given names by many different observers, some on the basis of pathology, some on the basis of morphology, and some on the basis of demonstrated or suspected etiology. Dermatological nosology is almost as confused as psychiatric nosology. But out of it can be organized certain large categories.

First, there appear to be certain *dermatological expressions of systemic diseases* such as measles, syphilis, and diabetes. Second, there are *neoplastic and infectious diseases* of the skin itself, such as lupus vulgaris, epitheliomata, and ringworm. Third, there are many more or less common *idiopathic syndromes* of which the etiology is unknown but of which the manifestations and course are well known, such as psoriasis and mycosis fungoides. Finally, there are the *reactive disorders* of the skin. These are caused by exposure to irritants, external or internal, and are often indistinguishable morphologically from the "eczema" to be discussed later. The detection and elimination of specific irritants is one of the most interesting fields of industrial medicine.

But in addition the dermatologist sees many reactive skin disorders of more obscure nature. They are sometimes episodic, sometimes recurrent, and sometimes persistent. This group includes hives, diffuse urticarial rashes, and angioneurotic edema. The contribution of emotional factors to these conditions is a matter which the dermatologists have thought about from time to time, but from which they are constantly distracted by other theories of the moment. Skin tests, patch tests, passive transfer tests, and the like are evolved and seem, for a time, to throw some light on the etiology and effective treatment of these conditions, even though it is apparent to the most superficial observer (and to the patient) that in many instances the symptoms are directly related to certain experiences and emotions. These cases have been studied by both dermatological and psychiatric colleagues, and their findings in specific cases have appeared with increasing frequency in the literature.*

But the great "plague" of dermatological practice is made up of a still more obscure type of reactive disorder, the eczema neurodermatitis family. It would seem as if in each specialty of medicine there is a sizeable group of patients suffering from conditions which are etiologically so obscure and therapeutically so refractory as to make them relatively "unwelcome" patients. Though they tax the skill and patience of the doctor, the results satisfy neither the doctor nor the patient. In the dermatological field the eczema family constitutes this plague.

There are large numbers of them, actually and relatively. Dr. O'Leary estimates that about a third of his case material falls into this group, and I understand that some dermatologists estimate the

---

* I myself studied some of these cases at Rochester and I am somewhat conversant with the literature. I think it is conservative to say that the psychodynamics and personality characteristics of such cases are better understood than for any other type of dermatological lesion, but that the practical advantages of this information to the dermatologist are still rather slight. The more or less homespun psychotherapy of the dermatologist is often more efficacious than the more scientifically ordered psychotherapy of the psychiatrist for the simple reason that the latter is apt to conceive of a more radical and revolutionary change in the patient's personality structure. For a chronic, disfiguring psoriatic lesion, a patient may well consider a long-time psychotherapeutic program worth the sacrifice; for an occasional urticaria most patients would not. Techniques such as hypnosis or narcosynthesis have not been consistently tried under research conditions.

fraction even higher. These patients often suffer greatly, often find relief only after prolonged disability. At the Mayo Clinic they are frequently hospitalized, and their hospital care is more difficult and expensive than that of any other type of patient. The therapy applicable to them is far from standardized and often is ineffective. What relieves one patient makes another worse; sometimes a half dozen different treatment applications have to be tried successively. The intractability of these cases and their tendency to recur lead the patient from doctor to doctor and from patent medicine to patent medicine. One of the Mayo Clinic stenographers remarked to me once that half the letters she was writing that day seemed to be answers to complaints that so-and-so "is still itching" or "is itching again." The reaction of such patients to their illness is often an unhealthy one; they become obsessed with the fear of recurrence or with disfigurement or with the intractability or with the arduousness of the treatment regimen. Their skin affliction becomes the most important topic in the home. Persistence of symptoms and conflicting medical opinion lead them and their families to become discouraged and depressed. (Curiously enough, these patients rarely become suicidal or psychotic.) In short, many of these patients are destined to chronic, intermittent, lifelong suffering and have a physical handicap comparable to that of a man who has lost a leg or an arm—sometimes perhaps even greater.

For these reasons I was particularly interested in this eczematoid-atopic-neurodermatitic-lichen simplex group. Dermatologists have repeatedly called attention to the importance of the emotional factor in these cases, and some of them have gone to some pains to delineate the personality characteristics which seem to be common to many patients with these afflictions. (See especially Stokes, O'Leary, Becker.) A few psychiatrists—but very few—have written a little about it. The opportunity to see and talk with a good many of these patients in Rochester was an experience which had never come to me in my regular psychiatric practice, though I had seen many cases of urticaria, psoriasis, and factitious dermatitis.

The object of the present presentation is more general. I should like to go back to the comment with which I began this article.

Psychiatrists come to depend very largely upon their ears, dermatologists upon their eyes. Psychiatrists spend long hours listening to the description of symptoms which no one can see; dermatologists concentrate upon examining lesions about which the comments of the patient are often not very helpful, or actually misleading.*

It would seem clear that dermatologists and psychiatrists should pool their skills in a cooperative effort. The great dependence of the dermatologist upon the discriminating observation which he has brought to such a high degree of perfection, has to a certain extent proved his undoing. No one is more aware of this than the thoughtful dermatologists themselves, because, while it is true that correct diagnosis frequently leads with automatic celerity to proper treatment, it does not do so in the great burdensome eczematoid group. It is just here that the dermatologist becomes painfully aware of the fact that the diagnosis is the least of his troubles, and that an effort to understand more about the patient than is presented by the skin lesion is an essential to the proper management or cure or relief. The life history of the patient becomes more important than the lesion history. And this life history must be more than a series of dates and events; it must contain some indication of the patient's stresses and strains, his frustrations and fears, his anxieties and disappointments. Dermatologists are apt to feel insecure regarding their technique in obtaining such data; furthermore most of them

* One of my first impressions in Dr. O'Leary's clinic was the lightning speed with which a skillful dermatologist could arrive at a correct diagnosis by inspection. I recall a woman patient with a rapidly extending metastatic carcinoma of the skin of the chest. She also had a lump in the neck which she declared to be of ten years' duration, dating from a period of acute tuberculous illness. I was considering the possibility that this lump in the neck was an irrelevant tuberculous lesion, of minor importance compared to the breast carcinoma. The dermatologist took a brief look and promptly disabused me of this notion. "What you see," he said, "is far more important than what you hear. The lump in the breast is carcinoma; the lump in the neck is also carcinoma, and it is not ten years old; it is recent. I think the biopsy will confirm this." And it did. I remember several cases of the familiar dermatitis factitia type about which I have recorded some discussion elsewhere (*Man Against Himself*). What impressed me was the rapidity with which the dermatologist recognized the untruthfulness in the clinical history after he had taken one look at the lesion. To me these lesions were no more bizarre than numerous others which I saw. Particularly in one instance was I astounded at the courage of the dermatologist in promptly challenging the truth of the story given him by the patient. But he (the doctor) was entirely correct, and the patient admitted that the lesion was self-produced.

are too rushed with routine procedures to devote the necessary time to it. Consequently, while not a few dermatologists have been at some pains to point out that the problem exists, and even to offer thoughtful and documented discussions of their own observations and suggestions with reference to the problem, it remains for the most part a *terra incognita*. Certainly it has had the interest and attention of very few psychiatrists.

On the other hand, the psychiatrist who acts as a consultant or visitor in the dermatological clinic quickly learns that the techniques of his own routine practice are not capable of direct transfer to the dermatological problem. The patient with the skin lesion has oriented all his thinking about that lesion, and it is exceedingly difficult for him to depart from this preoccupation. Furthermore, one is constantly aware of difficulty in limiting the biographical study for the psychiatric interview. By taking a detailed, circumstantial history of the present illness, one indeed learns that many things have happened in the patient's life which might be considered unusual emotional stresses. The question always is what role these stresses actually played with reference to current or previous skin eruptions. It is usually possible to discover the main trends of personality distortion; but without the usual landmarks of psychiatric history taking and psychiatric personality description, it is difficult to interpret the findings in terms of the skin lesions. One feels sorely the need of those more objective devices for personality investigation, the projective tests of the clinical psychologist.

I came away from my visit to Rochester with a very strong feeling that a cooperative research program in this field should be set up along broad and at the same time intensive lines. It would seem to be desirable to congregate for cooperative effort a skilled dermatologist, a number of psychiatric history takers (who might well be recruited from highly trained social workers), a clinical psychologist trained in administering and interpreting psychological tests, and a psychiatrist capable of taking an over-all view of the data which would thus be obtained. The empirical findings of dermatologists in the *treatment* of the eczemas and the data of several psychoanalysts who by arrangement or by chance have had the opportunity of studying the unconscious psychological material of such cases, should also be studied.

From such a conjoint and cooperative research program the most valuable thing learned might not be the definition of certain peculiar dermatological personality types or even clues to the more efficacious treatment of these refractory cases. It might be the discovery of more basic information in regard to the function of the skin in the total personality structure. How basic and how important it is to understand this better may be inferred from the fact that the greatest sociological problem in the United States at this moment is one based on the single factor of skin pigmentation.

STUDIES OF SELF-DESTRUCTIVENESS

When Karl Menninger returned to the Midwest after completing medical school, he developed a friendship with that delightful physician variant of Mr. Pickwick, Logan Clendening. Not only did they enjoy Dickens together, they shared many of their ideas. But they differed in their individual conceptions of man, of health and disease, and even of death. Logan Clendening wrote that "strictly speaking, death is not a biological necessity," but he continued, "as I think it over, death seems to me one of the few evidences in nature of the operation of a creative intelligence: of an intelligence exhibiting qualities which I recognize as mind stuff. To have blundered on to the form of energy called life showed a sort of malignant power. After having blundered on life, to have conceived of death was a real stroke of genius." *

Karl Menninger is not such a fatalist, nor is he satisfied with such a glib dismissal of another important part of man's behavior, dying. He became a student of the psychology of dying. He became aware that man is not as passive an agent in this act as he would like to believe, in fact, that man destroys himself in one way or another.

The importance of Karl Menninger's contributions to the study of self-destruction is not reflected in this book. Pursuant to our plan not to reprint material from his books that are still in print, we can only refer the interested reader to his classical study of self-destruction reported in *Man Against Himself* (1938). It is dedicated "to those who would use intelligence in the battle against death—to strengthen the will to live against the wish to die, and to replace with love the blind compulsion to give hostages to hatred as the price of living."

He states his theoretical convictions about the life and death instincts in the preface which is also a statement of a kind of personal credo:

> It is nothing new that the world is full of hate, that men destroy one another, and that our civilization has arisen from the ashes of despoiled peoples and decimated natural resources. But to relate this destructiveness, this evidence of a spiritual malignancy within us, to

* *The Human Body.* 3rd ed. New York: Knopf, 1941.

an instinct, and to correlate this instinct with the beneficent and fruitful instinct associated with love, this was one of the later flowers of the genius of Freud. We have come to see that, just as the child must learn to love wisely, so he must learn to hate expeditiously, to turn destructive tendencies away from himself toward enemies that actually threaten him rather than toward the friendly and the defenseless, the more usual victims of destructive energy.

It is true, nevertheless, that in the end each man kills himself in his own selected way, fast or slow, soon or late. We all feel this, vaguely; there are so many occasions to witness it before our eyes. The methods are legion and it is these which attract our attention. Some of them interest surgeons, some of them interest lawyers and priests, some of them interest sociologists. All of them must interest the man who sees the personality as a totality and medicine as the healing of the nations.

I believe that our best defense against self-destructiveness lies in the courageous application of intelligence to human phenomenology. If such is our nature, it were better that we knew it and knew it in all its protean manifestations. To see all forms of self-destruction from the standpoint of their dominant principles would seem to be logical progress toward self-preservation and toward a unified view of medical science.   —B. H. H.

18. Psychoanalytic Aspects of Suicide

It is logical to expect that a better understanding of how and why man destroys himself would prove of the utmost practical importance. The facile explanations for suicide which are offered daily in the drama and in the newspaper may leave us with an easy satisfaction which of itself should make us suspicious. In real life there is no such evident justice or such naïve simplicity in the workings of fate and retribution. Scientific study of suicide generally falls back upon barren statistical analyses; the general medical literature ignores suicide as if it were scarcely entitled to recognition as a cause of death.

We have reason to expect a clarification of the motives for this phenomenon from an understanding of the unconscious motives, i.e., from psychoanalysis. Yet not since June 1910 has suicide been a prominent subject of discussion even before psychoanalytical bodies.

It is easy to jump to the generalization that suicide represents in simple form an expression of the instincts toward self-destruction which we now consider as standing opposed to the life instinct. To do so, however, would leave entirely unexplained the extraordinary circumstance that so powerful and universal a principle should come to complete fruition in such a relatively small number of instances. It would also leave unanswered the question of how far

Read *in absentia* before the Twelfth International Psycho-Analytical Congress, Wiesbaden, Sept. 7, 1932. Reprinted from the *International Journal of Psychoanalysis*, 14:376–390, July 1933.

external forces and events determine the suicide, a question which in the popular mind admits of answers implying the most astonishing naïveté. If one is to judge by the explanations to be read with monotonous invariability in daily newspaper accounts, life-insurance reports, death certificates, and statistical surveys, suicide is the logical consequence of circumstances, particularly ill-health, discouragement, financial reverses, humiliation, frustration, and unrequited love.

To the psychoanalyst, what is most significant is not that these simple explanations are continually offered in a world where science and everyday experience alike confirm the untrustworthiness of the obvious, but that they are so patiently and unquestioningly accepted. No such lack of curiosity exists, for example, with reference to the motives for murder. The contrast becomes striking if one contemplates the fact that in the mystery and detective stories which are being turned off by the thousand it is rarely the explanation of a *suicide* which is sought but of a murder. Professional indifference in the matter has been equally great. Surely no other mysterious phenomenon of human activity has excited so little scientific investigation.

The conception of self-destruction as a flight from reality, from ill-health, disgrace, poverty, and the like is seductive because of its simplicity. It lends itself to the drawing of parallels between suicide and other regressions such as the taking of vacations, celebrating of holidays, falling asleep, delirium, delusions, drunkenness. Its essential fallacy is one of incompleteness; it lies in the implied assumption that the forces impelling the regression come wholly from without. From the standpoint of analytical psychology the push is more important than the pull, i.e., the ego is driven by more powerful forces than external reality. The paramount factors in determining behavior are the impulses from within, the motives originating in the individual which express his attempt at adjustment to reality. Innumerable illustrations in history and science could be marshaled to show that for some persons *no* reality can prove unbearable.

For we know that the individual always, in a measure, creates his own environment, and thus the suicidal person must help to create the very thing from which, in suicide, he takes flight. If we are to explain the act dynamically, therefore, we are compelled to seek an explanation for the wish to put oneself in a predicament from which one cannot, except by suicide, escape. In other words if, for one's own unconscious purposes, one brings about an apparent justification in external reality for self-destruction, the unconscious purposes are of more significance in understanding suicide than the apparently simple, inevitable external realities.

This, of course, disposes of those naïve judgments of suicide as either "brave" (if it seems "justified" by external circumstances) or "irrational" (if it does not), and of all such causal explanations as appear in statistical summaries and the like. Psychologically suicide is a very complex act, and not a simple, incidental, isolated act of impulsion, either logical or inexplicable.

It is not difficult to discover in the act of suicide the existence of various elements. In the German language it is literally a murder of the self (*Selbstmord*). But it is also a murder *by* the self. It is a death in which are combined in one person the murderer and the murdered. We know that the motives for murder vary greatly—and no less the motives for wishing to be murdered, which is quite another matter. For since in suicide there is a self that submits to the murder and would appear to be desirous of doing so, we must seek the motives of this submission.

In many suicides it is quite apparent that one of these elements is stronger than the other. One sees people who want to die but cannot take the step against themselves; they fling themselves in front of trains, or, like King Saul and Brutus, they beseech armor bearers to slay them. Paradoxically, also, it would seem that many suicidal persons, in spite of the violence of the attack upon themselves, do not seem to be very eager to die.

We must think of suicide, then, as a peculiar kind of death which entails three elements: the element of dying, the element of killing, and the element of being killed. Each element requires separate analysis. Each is an act for which there exist motives, unconscious and conscious. The latter are usually evident enough; the unconscious motives are now our chief consideration.

I. THE WISH TO KILL

Throughout the universe, of which we are a part, there appear to exist in constant cojacent conflict and opposition the two forces of creation and destruction. Whether this universality of the principle is an inherent property of matter, a subtle adaptation of language, or a psychological-philosophical concept to which we are blindly chained by the curious astigmatic limitations of our human mind it is beyond our present powers and purposes to determine.

We can only point to the not unexpected parallel in the findings of depth psychology as to the purposes of the human unconscious. To create and to destroy, to build up and to tear down, these are the anabolism and catabolism of the psyche no less than of the cells and the corpuscles—the two directions in which the same energies exert themselves.

And just as in the sexual embrace we recognize the concurrence of physical, chemical, and psychological forces in the supreme act of creation, so we see in murder its direct antithesis, the supreme act of destruction. Psychoanalytic investigations have established beyond any question the murderous destructive wishes which arise in earliest infancy (Klein) and wax and wane repeatedly in the successive periods of childhood. In line with the theory of the death instinct, these destructive tendencies are turned outward from their original engagement or neutralization within the personality. They emerge from the ego and are directed toward an external object in response to stimuli of thwarting or a threat which arouses envy and fear and, therefore, hate.

We know also, however, the curious propensity of the erotic elements, the sexual element of the life instinct for making the best of a bad situation and of endowing every object relationship with some of its saving grace. Hence in any attack upon an enemy, however strong the wish to kill, we must expect to find in varying quantities an admixture of erotic satisfactions. These act in a dual and contradictory fashion, however; in the erotizing of the cruel sadistic elements they strengthen the murder motif, but at the same time, investing the object of the attack in the form of sympathy, pity, and more especially because of passive dependence upon the powerful rival, they mitigate the severity of the aggression. What the net effect of the erotic component will be varies according to circumstances, i.e., depending upon the relative degree to which the object excites sublimated or unsublimated sexuality in the aggressor.

Introjection. This component of destructive aggression may seem for the moment far afield from the topic of suicide. How is it that these drives in the interests of self-preservation can actually be turned upon the self? The answer is to be found in the phenomenon of *introjection with displacement,* i.e., identification. It is almost axiomatic in psychoanalysis that an object of love or hate which is lost or escapes beyond the reach of the ego can be regained and retained by the process of introjection with the displacement of the emotions appropriate to the original object on to the introjected object, that is, the person within the person. Hence a person unconsciously hated may be destroyed by identifying oneself with that person, or, more accurately, identifying that person with the self, and destroying the self.

We must now consider what happens when the attack made by the destructive impulses directed toward an external object are thwarted, and introjection and displacement become necessary. Thwarting may occur under several circumstances: (1) the resistance offered by reality may be too great (2) the object instead of being overwhelming may be merely elusive; (3) the attack may be inhibited by various internal circumstances, chiefly fear and the sense of guilt; (4) failure of the attack may occur through an undue weakening of its force by the admixture of adventitious erotic elements. This happens regularly in some neurotics, and derives from the failure to make a useful distinction between friend and foe. The result is that the hostility cannot be sublimated by the erotism. The ego consequently must take toward such individuals an oscillating or ambivalent attitude such that the love and hate have alternate expression, or else the hate must be displaced as in the first case.

(5) The exact opposite of (4) occurs when the erotic elements of object relationship are suddenly withdrawn, as, for example, by the death of the object. A de-fusion of the instincts takes place, the erotic components are dispersed and the hostile component, since it would otherwise have to be directed against the whole world, is turned inward upon the self.

It is this last-named mechanism which is most commonly observed in melancholia, the condition in which suicide most often happens. The mechanisms of melancholia have been fairly well worked out by Freud, Abraham, and others to be schematically as follows: Having lost the love object in one way or another, the patient is left with uninvested hostilities deeply covered and disguised by the love which is now also uninvested. The destructive or hostile elements acting as the pathfinder, as Freud has suggested, now turn back upon the ego where the beloved object becomes incorporated. The bitter reproaches and attacks unconsciously felt toward the former love object are now consciously directed toward this same object incorporated and disguised within the ego. But now the erotic elements formerly directed toward the love object follow the lead of the hostile tendencies, and one sees the great increase in narcissism which is characteristic of melancholia in paradoxical association with the most extreme self-condemnation. Appropriately, the patient loses all interest in the outside world and until the fires of simultaneous self-love and self-hate have subsided, transferences or any other form of object love are impossible. Were it not for the protection of the narcissism every melancholiac would be determined to commit suicide.

Psychoanalytical literature is replete with illustrations of the phenomena of oral incorporation, introjection, and displacement in melancholia, but the following case is so diagrammatic an instance that it may be inserted as a paradigm in this consideration of suicide motivation.

A woman of thirty-five, of unusual capabilities, had manifested all her life tendencies indicative of strong oral-erotic cravings. This cannot be better summarized than in the words of her own sister, who wrote her at one time during her analysis, "You must realize, my dear sister, that you frighten your lovers away by loving so much. Your love is simply engulfing, devouring. You cannot eat your lover like a cake, you know. At least, if you do, you can't expect to go on having him!"

As is so often the case with such individuals, the poor woman had a propensity for selecting lovers whom circumstances made it quite impossible for her ever to possess. One of these, with whom she was deeply in love during a portion of her analysis, had a surname something like Allendorf and was usually referred to as "Al." Shortly after her separation from him (at his instigation) this patient attempted suicide by taking an overdose of the drug allonal. As she later told me, just before the attempt she had had a dream in which she and a group of men which represented the analyst, the lover Allendorf, her father, her brother of whom she was very jealous, and some others were in a car which was wrecked, and all killed except her.

"Yes," she said, quite offhand, "they were killed, *Al and all.*" Spoken rapidly in English, "Al and all" sounds exactly like "allonal." It was immediately apparent that in attempting to kill herself with the drug allonal she was also carrying out the devouring of her lover and the other disappointing males, which was so apparent in all her actions that even her naïve sister had detected it. Thus she obtained Al, in spite of his flight, by oral incorporation and simultaneously destroyed him by the same method, and *pari passu* she attempted to destroy him in that she had made a destructive attack upon herself in whom Al had been (was being) incorporated.

Gratification of the hostile aggressive wish by introjection is made the more easy by the fact that it seems to the ego to be less dangerous to attack an object of fantasy than an object of reality. But when the object of fantasy is identified with the self, i.e., when the hated-loved person is identified with the ego, the aggression serves two ends, the primary purpose and the secondary one of atonement, to be discussed later. Hence this reflection of the (self-) destructive impulses back upon the self appears to be accomplished with an increase in strength, so that the life instincts can no longer hold them in check except by reaction formation (symptoms). If this cannot be accomplished, actual destruction of the self results.

Indirect aggression. The hostile or destructive aggression against the hated-loved person may be carried out, as is well known, in many ways other than by direct attack. A brief consideration should be given here to these indirect methods of aggression.

The attack upon the hated-loved object is sometimes made, for example, through the destruction of something held dear by the person who is the real object of the attack. It is the greatest torture to a mother to see her child being tortured or killed. In suicide such an aggression can be carried out against the parents by the simple process of self-attack; hence, the overwhelming power of the revenge taken by the child who, piqued at some reproach or denial, takes his own life, takes it as it were from his parents. He robs them of their dearest possession knowing that no other injury could possibly be so painful to them.

To a less intense degree the act of suicide is an aggression against those who may in some way be related to the life of the person who kills himself. It may be taken as a reproach against certain individuals or against society as a whole and actually does serve in many instances as an embarrassment or humiliation. Every experienced analyst has been able to observe in the suicidal threats of his patients an intention to alarm the analyst or discredit the analysis. This same motive is undoubtedly active in situations other than the analytic one.

This, then, is an analysis of the *aggressive* component of the suicidal impulse; *it originates in the ego and is reflected upon the ego.*

II. THE WISH TO BE KILLED

We come now to the second element in suicide, the obverse of the killing motive, namely, the wish to be killed. Why, indeed, does anyone wish, not to die or to kill, necessarily, but *to be killed?*

Obviously, being killed is the extreme form of submission, just as killing is the extreme form of aggression. And the enjoyment of submission, pain, defeat, and, in the end, death, is the essence of masochism. But it would be a misleading oversimplification to let it go at that. We must understand why satisfactions may be achieved by punishment, that extraordinary phenomenon which we see occurring on all sides, from the persons who enjoy ill-health to those who deliberately put themselves in predicaments in which they suffer.

The result of indulgence in acts of aggression (dictated, as we have seen, by hate inspired by fear, envy, and the desire for revenge) is to bring about a sense of guilt with a corresponding feeling of need for punishment.

It is scarcely necessary, except for purposes of completeness, to point out that a sense of guilt may arise from other than actual aggression; in the unconscious, a wish to destroy is quite equivalent to the actual destruction. One who nourishes murderous wishes must also feel a need for punishment for that sin of a similar sort. From this we see the truth of that statement made by Freud many years ago that *many suicides are disguised murders,* not only, therefore, because of the introjection, which we have discussed above, but for the reason that murder alone justifies in the unconscious the death penalty. Suicide is, therefore, *the death penalty self-inflicted.*

In the analysis of compulsion neurotics especially, the tyrannical primitive severity of the super-ego is made manifest. Every analyst could supply scores of illustrations of this phenomenon. One must always remember, however, how the compulsion neurotic disguises the import of his acts and thoughts by the formula of *reductio ad absurdum.* One of my patients, for example, would alternately amuse himself by torturing small animals and then—without any conscious connection—indulge in mutilating, humiliating, abasing, or reproaching himself. Sometimes the treatment of the animals and of himself was precisely the same; for example, he would scorch a cat with a burning match, and that afternoon would singe his own hair with a taper. Of course, this did not cause him immediate pain as it did the animals, and he rationalized it by saying that it was done in order to promote the growth of his hair, but as a matter of fact he scorched his hair so irregularly that he gave himself a ridiculous appearance which he knew brought upon him the contempt of his associates. All this takes on a different aspect if one knows that his dreams and associations made it unmistakable that the animals which he killed were symbolic representations of the analyst and also, of course, of his father. By cutting his hair he gave himself the appearance of a prison convict, as if to act out his fantasies of punishment for his murderous wishes toward me.

Another illustration which might be added is that of a thirty-five-year-old son of a traveling salesman, whose parents had taken him in early childhood on many railroad trips and permitted him to sleep with them in the berth. Riding on the train has always had for him a great fascination and no doubt gratified some incest fantasies in association with the above memories, and also the satisfaction of father identification, his father having made his living by traveling.

At a time when his analysis was in reality progressing very favorably, he one day had the feeling, suddenly, as he rode on the suburban train, that it was senseless, unnecessary, futile, and there came a strong impulse to kill himself, "because my unconscious plays such tricks on me; I just thought, 'Hell! I'll show it! I'll jump out of the train.'" The analytical material of the next few days became chiefly lament and self-reproach for the feeling "that I have so constantly— *of course* unintentionally—deceived the analyst and tried to fool him and play tricks upon him, all of which reacts only, of course, to my own harm."

One can see in this impulse to jump from the train, first of all a direct aggressive threat toward the analyst and toward the father whom the analyst represented. Jumping from the train meant the end of the analysis, not only symbolically but in reality. It was also casting the father out of the train, an obvious symbolic parricide.

The reasons alleged for his contemplated suicide are equally significant. His conscious thought was that his unconscious had played tricks upon him and he would take revenge on his unconscious. Obviously his "unconscious" was the analyst; he was justifying his attack upon the analyst by charging him with having played tricks. As a matter of fact, however, such an allegation had no basis in reality and was an inverted charge, a charge against himself that he had projected upon the analyst. He had indeed played tricks upon the analyst, as he well knew, and felt guilty about it. He was anxious to show that these tricks had harmed him and the need for punishment is also fulfilled in the jumping from the train. "Punishment of the unconscious" represented punishment of himself.

But one can also infer from this (as was clearly brought out in the patient's subsequent material) that he actually wanted the analyst to play these said tricks on him. By playing tricks on him he had unconscious reference, of course, to the erotic motive, i.e., the wish to be homosexually attacked. But against this wish by way of defence (dictated by the super-ego), and against the indignity of the attack (directed by the ego), there arose the outwardly directed destructive tendencies of projection. Thus, "It is not I who play tricks upon the analyst, it is he who plays tricks upon me. He attacks me. Therefore I hate him, I want to kill him, I do kill him. But for killing him I also feel guilty and must suffer a like fate myself." [1]

In other words, this man feels guilty for (1) this parricidal wish, (2) his hostile wishes against the analyst, (3) his deception or attempted deception of the analyst, and (4) his homosexual wishes. The guilt for all of these demands punishment of a similar sort, namely, an attack directed against himself. Hence the suicidal impulse.

The problem of heredity in suicide. The question of suicide in families is one which has received almost no competent scientific investigation. Newspaper accounts indicate that in the popular mind the suicidal tendency is hereditary. In my own studies I have come upon several families in which it would certainly appear to be so. For example, one patient came to us at sixty-one on account of strong suicidal propensities which she had several times attempted to gratify. Three of the patient's sisters had killed themselves in an identical manner; the patient's mother, and the patient's mother's mother had also killed themselves in the same way. Moreover, the patient's mother was a twin and the twin brother had also killed himself!

In another instance, a highly regarded family contained five sons and two daughters; the oldest son killed himself at thirty-five; the youngest developed a depression and attempted suicide several times, but finally died of other causes at thirty; a third brother killed himself in a manner similar to that of his oldest brother; still another brother shot himself to death; the oldest daughter took poison successfully at a party. Only two children remain living of the entire family.

I have also on file numerous instances where sisters or brothers have killed themselves. In one instance, three sisters killed themselves simultaneously.

Striking as these illustrations may be, there is no convincing scientific evidence that the suicidal impulse is hereditary, and there is much psychoanalytic evidence to show that these cases of numerous suicides in one family may be explained on a psychological basis. Superficially there is the element of suggestion, but deeper than this is the well-known fact that unconscious death wishes reach their highest development toward members of the family, and when a member of the family dies or kills himself these death wishes are unexpectedly gratified; this produces a sudden and overpoweringly strong wave of guilt feelings which replace the death wish which has been gratified. This wave may be so great and so overwhelming as to make it necessary for the culprit to be punished by death. Sometimes this is done, as every psychoanalyst knows, by dreams of being executed, hanged, killed in some other way, or sentenced to life imprisonment. In other instances, the element of suggestion points the way for the actual self-infliction of the death sentence.

Methods used in suicide. A psychoanalytic study of suicide would be incomplete were not some attention given to the unconscious significance of the particular technique selected for the act. That this is strongly determined and over-determined by the unconscious trends of the victim we have good reason to believe on two scores: first, by analogy with similar acts in other patients with less serious outcome—in other words, the established "general" significance of certain acts; secondly, the much more definite evidence in frustrated suicidal attempts in patients who then, or later, undergo psychoanalytic treatment and study.

A full exposition of this latter evidence would require the inclusion of many individual case studies which the limits both of space and of my experience prohibit. One example has been cited; others have appeared in the literature incidental to the discussion of more general themes.

More general inferences we may readily gain from reading even the daily press. It is well established statistically, for example, that men more frequently choose shooting and women drowning or the taking of poison or gas. These modes are obviously and clearly related to the masculine and feminine roles in sexual life.

Extremely suggestive also are such exceptional but authenticated cases as that of suicide by thrusting a red-hot poker down the throat (i.e., fellatio acted out violently and punished with corresponding violence); or that of suicide by lying down before trucks and steam rollers (passive erotic submission); or that of plunging into molten glass, vats of soap, the craters of volcanoes, tanks of blood in packing houses, etc. (the significance of drowning fantasies is one of the earliest of psychoanalytic discoveries); or that of self-crucifixion (Messianic identification). One of my own patients calmly drank raw hydrochloric acid; it was vomited, of course; he tried repeatedly thereafter to accomplish suicide with this agent, diluting it with ginger ale. Finally, after a long period of surgical treatment for esophageal stricture resulting from the acid burns, and much other treatment (he refused psychoanalysis), he re-established his home and business, and then, about a year later, committed suicide successfully by eating firecrackers.

Just what these methods may have meant in full detail to these individuals we shall never know, but their similarity to neurotic fantasies and dreams with which we are very familiar in analysis leaves little doubt as to their general significance and reinforces what we have said as to the motives of suicide, viz., that it represents in one act a murder and a propitiation, both of which are erotized. This erotization is conspicuous in the technique of the act.

III. THE WISH TO DIE

Anyone who has sat by the bedside of a patient dying from a self-inflicted wound and listened to pleadings that the physician save a life which only a few hours or minutes before had been attempted, must be impressed by the paradox that one who has wished to kill himself does not wish to die. The popular assumption is that, having yielded to a sudden impulse, the patient has changed his mind. It leaves unanswered why the act should have brought about this change. The pain is usually not great. The prospects of death are actually less than they were before the attempt since "where there is life there is hope." One gets the impression that for such people the suicidal act is sometimes a kind of insincere play-acting and that their capacity for dealing with reality is so poorly developed that they proceed as if they could actually kill themselves and not die. We have reason to believe that a child has some such conception of death: that it is a going away and that for such goings away there is often a returning. Indeed the concept of a future life which is so real to many people is probably based upon this identification of death and going away.

One must distinguish also between the conscious wish and the unconscious wish to die or not to die, the latter being, as we have seen, the resultant of cooperating and conflicting factors. One sees this unconscious wish not to die in the very frequent attempts at suicide which turn out unsuccessfully because of faulty technique. Many poets and philosophers, including all the pessimists from Schopenhauer down, have been convinced of the desirability of death, yet, being impelled by neither of the other two motives, cannot escape the necessity of living on.

This, to a considerable degree, is perhaps true of many intellectual patients. Oftentimes melancholiac patients of superior intelligence and milder grade of affliction, will marshal unanswerable arguments for the desirability of dying. They will point out with a passionate eloquence and with flawless logic that life is hard, bitter, futile, and hopeless; that it entails more pain than pleasure; that there is no profit or purpose in it for them and no conceivable justification for their living on. Of such patients Freud has said, ". . . he has a keener eye for the truth. . . . When in his exacerbation of self-criticism he describes himself as petty, egoistic, dishonest, lacking in independence, one whose sole aim has been to hide the weaknesses of his own nature, for all we know it may be that he has come very near to self-knowledge; we can only wonder why a man must become ill before he can discover truth of this kind." [2]

The question for us to consider here is to what extent we may associate this conscious wish for death with the death-instinct conception. Freud's postulate specifically states that the self-destruction instinct never appears undisguised. Yet, as Alexander points out, nothing else can so well explain the pleasure in exposing one's self unnecessarily to great dangers—as do the mountain climbers, automobile racers, building scalers, or the popular interest in the antics of such movie actors as Harold Lloyd on the sides and tops of skyscrapers, etc. "The narcissistic gratification derived from one's powers of achievement may indeed play a part here, but no one will fail to see the impulse, completely independent of this . . . to play with death, to expose one's life to serious risks . . . something like a forepleasure . . . to the [ultimate gratification of] the death instinct." [3]

It is my own view that we may also interpret as some evidence for the activity of the death instinct the observation that the physiological body processes appear to be capable of acting either for or against the personality as a whole. The phenomenon designated by Freud as somatic compliance we may think of as a kind of biological acceptance or rejection of the id tendencies as modified by the psyche. One frequently sees such a thing, as is well illustrated by a case studied by Dr. Catherine Bacon of Chicago. This patient's conscious self-destructive activities went only so far as scratching herself with the deliberate intent of causing a skin infection, with the expressed hope of death. This is common in malingering. But what determines whether or not these infections shall prove fatal? Can we assume with the bacteriologists that it is entirely a matter of quantitative relationships between virulence and resistance, or, in other words, mere chance? Clinical experience certainly leads us to suspect that such infections become serious in just those cases where there are other evidences of strongly active self-destructive tendencies. It is possible that the available strength of the death instinct determines this biological acceptance of the extraneous opportunities for self-destruction.

There is another straw in the wind that I wish to mention. It has been suggested that the wish for death may be only another disguise for the frequently observed phenomena commonly interpreted as birth fantasies, or, more accurately, a desire to return to the womb. Suicide by drowning is supposed to be particularly clear in its symbolic suggestion of this tendency. It is not impossible, however, that this interpretation is an exact inversion and that birth fantasies and the various phenomena suggesting a desire to return to the peace of the womb may be only pictorial representations of the unconscious wish for death.

We have seen that the aggressive elements in suicide originate in the ego and the submissive elements in the super-ego; it would conform with Freud's postulate to find that the unconscious wish to die implicit in the death instinct originates in the id.

To advance this hypothesis, however, we can offer only negative data as I have suggested above. We can show that many individuals in whom the aggressive and submissive elements of self-destruction are strongly operative fail of a successful suicide because of some unwillingness to die, which, while capable of many explanations, certainly lends some support to the view that in such individuals the life instincts are able to maintain their ascendancy over the death instincts. Alexander in a personal communication states that he does not believe that clear psychological representations of the death instinct can be demonstrated. I agree that they have not been, but I do not see why it is *a priori* impossible that they may not be. I think we must recognize, however, that as yet the theory of the death instinct and therefore the "wish to die" element in suicide is only an hypothesis in contrast to the demonstrated facts of the existence of the other two elements.

RECAPITULATION

So far we have presented the thesis that suicide is a gratification of self-destructive tendencies which upon analysis appear to be composed of at least two elements—an aggressive element—the wish to kill—and a submissive element—the wish to be killed. In addition, it is postulated that a wish to die may be present to a variable degree for which, however, no definite psychological evidence can be offered.

The three components are derived respectively from the ego, the super-ego, and the id. It can be recognized from the clinical phenomena studied that the proportionate strength of these three components varies considerably in various instances, so that in one case the motivation comes most powerfully from the ego, in another from the super-ego, and in still another (perhaps) from the id.

PARTIAL SUICIDE

This leads us directly to a consideration of those incomplete forms of suicide which deductions and analysis alike show to be directly related to the more successful efforts at self-destruction which we ordinarily call suicide. Self-destruction is, as we shall see, sometimes directly and sometimes indirectly accomplished, sometimes completely and sometimes incompletely. We may well speak of *chronic suicides* as well as *acute suicides;* it is probably not too wide an extension of theory to say that many diseases, both those ordinarily called organic as well as those called functional, may be regarded as various forms of self-destruction—*chronic, indirect* suicide.

For, just as neurotic symptoms may be localized, as in conversion hysteria, or generalized as in major hysteria, so self-destruction may be focalized or generalized. Neurotic syndromes and neurotic character manifestations are similarly focal or generalized. It is not impossible that we may some day be able to show that conversion hysteria and some forms of organic disease represent chronic *focal* self-destructive attacks while asceticism and martyrdom represent chronic *generalized* self-destruction. The ordinary forms of suicide must stand as prototypes of *acute generalized total self-destruction.*

19. Some Clinical Examples of Indirect Suicide

In all of us, as has been pointed out by Freud, there are two dominant tendencies, one to live and one to die, or, as they are often described, the instinct of self-preservation and the instinct of self-destruction. These two are constantly in conflict within us, tearing down and building up, preserving and destroying. At the moment we begin to live we begin also to die. As time goes on we gradually sacrifice our hair, our teeth, our muscle elasticity, and when these can no longer be renewed we die.

The act of suicide is a dramatic representation of the instinct of self-destruction. It is as if the person must take the inevitable act of death into his own hands and in this direct way put an end to living. This sudden dramatic triumph of the destructive instinct over the life instinct has been observed by psychiatrists for a long time.

But what I wish to speak of is not the immediate operations of the death instinct so plainly exemplified in suicide, but rather the various indirect operations of the tendency toward self-destruction. We know that even suicide can be accomplished indirectly, that is, without the active, conscious participation of the individual. We know of people who seem to have accidental deaths which, we are convinced from our knowledge of the case, are unconsciously de-

Read in Section on Neurology and Psychiatry, Southern Medical Association, Twenty-eighth Annual Meeting, San Antonio, Texas, Nov. 13–16, 1934. Reprinted from the *Southern Medical Journal,* 28:356–360, April 1935.

termined. I do not refer to actual suicides which the persons, out of pride, consideration for family, or greed, try to make look accidental, but to those cases in which the person would not purposely and consciously bring about his death, and yet gives considerable evidence that he had unconsciously wished for it. I know of a man who had had many disappointments and was quite depressed and in fact had tried several times to commit suicide, but was unsuccessful. A little later, however, he accidently stepped in front of an automobile and was killed. There is no proof that this accident was unconsciously self-determined, but it is plain that the man's own carelessness brought about the accident and to that extent he brought about his own death.

Another illustration, even more dramatic, recently came to my attention. I read in a newspaper of a man who had arranged a burglar trap in such a way that a gun would shoot anyone who tried to steal his chickens. He forgot that he had done so, however, and entered the chicken house himself first and was killed by his own gun. I thought this was a neat illustration of a death sentence, self-inflicted, and I cut it out, thinking it was most unusual. In two months I found another illustration of a man who had put a trap in his garage to protect his automobile. He went away on a trip for a month and upon his return was killed by his own thief trap. I saved this clipping, too, and began to look for more. In a year I got five examples of men who were caught in their own traps, set to kill another man. I do not believe these accidents can be explained as mere coincidence. For a man to be caught in his own death trap it seems there must be an element of (unconscious) guilt, perhaps arising in part out of his desire to kill another man (the thief).

But these illustrations are not very convincing to some because, of course, we cannot obtain clinical proof after the individual is dead. I want, therefore, to leave this somewhat tenuous type of illustration for material which demonstrates indirect self-destruction in forms that are slower and less dramatic, but just as sure.

One of these forms of chronic self-destruction is alcoholism. Even the layman knows that people drink themselves to death. What he does not know is that the original difficulty in such cases is not the alcoholism, but the underlying personality defect which creates great inner tension and leads the individual to seek relief. Alcohol, as a means of escape from inner tension, is more socially acceptable than morphine and other drugs, and hence more popular. Thus, at first, the alcohol is taken as an attempted cure for a psychological illness. Physicians are familiar with patients who use a relief-giving drug, such as barbital, as a means of suicide; so it is with the person who finds temporary relief in alcohol, but eventually destroys himself by its excessive use.

I can illustrate this with the case of a man in whom I was able to study some of the psychological factors which led to his drinking. His father was a celebrated lawyer, a brilliant but domineering man who was determined that his son should follow in his footsteps. The boy was very promising and his father was proud of him, although he treated him with great severity. The boy grew up with a great hatred for his father which he did not dare express. When his father insisted on his going away to the university to study law, the boy, now a young man, did attempt to rebel, but the habit of years was too strong and he again fell under his father's will. His rebellion and his strong hostilities became evident in indirect ways, however, for in the law school he began to drink heavily until finally it was necessary for him to quit school and give up the attempt to become a lawyer. He had thwarted his father's dearest hopes, but at the same time he defeated himself and in the years that followed he continued this course of self-defeat. He went into a number of businesses, each one of which proved a failure. His marriage was a complete failure and he is now separated from his family. The alcoholism, instead of being the cause of all his troubles, was only one of many ways in which he ruined his own career to spite his father and relieve his sense of guilt and inferiority. In every way his life has been a failure, a long-continued rebellion against his father and punishment for that rebellion.

There are other ways in which individuals condemn themselves to a living death. Asceticism, for example, which was so familiar in the early days of the church, is still in existence. I do not mean in religion only, but in everyday life. The Europeans say Americans do not enjoy life, that they are not loving to their women, they are not interested in their children, that they live only to work, eat, and sleep, they cannot allow themselves pleasure. I do not wish to discuss American asceticism, however, except in the form of clinical examples that come to the attention of psychiatrists.

A conspicuous example of this ascetic attitude toward life was furnished me by a patient who, although well-to-do, lived in a mean room furnished meagerly with a bed, a table, and one chair. He did not permit himself the indulgence of going to a good restaurant, although he liked food very much. Instead, he cooked most of his meals in his room surreptitiously. He had scarcely any utensils and his cooking was a dismal failure. When he went out he made a peculiar appearance, for his clothes were of poor quality and usually unpressed. He did not allow himself the luxury of going to a barber, but cut his own hair. Although he was a talented musician, he would not spend money for a ticket to a symphony orchestra. Yet he was not a true miser, for he would spend money freely on things that gave him no pleasure. His conscience demanded that he deny himself all comfort and enjoyment in life.

I have called this self-destruction, for surely such a self-imposed sentence of deprivation is a kind of slow suicide. Furthermore, this ascetic mode of life did almost destroy this man's life, for it denied him all friendships and social contacts; it finally led to his giving up his music, and it impaired his health.

This was even more evident in another patient, a woman who married a man whom she considered an irresponsible ne'er-do-well. Although this girl had been given every advantage in her home, she suffered from a sense of guilt that would not allow her to make a success of anything she undertook. She entered college, but failed in her school work. She went to work, but became slightly ill and immediately gave up her position and became a semi-invalid. She then met the man she married and during the early years of her married life denied herself many pleasures to help him pay off his debts and make a start in business. Eventually he became very successful and distinguished and was able to lavish money upon his wife.

They traveled and met interesting and prominent persons and went out in society. But with this unusual measure of success, the wife became increasingly unhappy. She antagonized her friends and her husband, ceased to take an interest in her appearance, and finally withdrew from everything that gave her pleasure and lived a dull and lonely life in a little village.

The psychological factors in this case were interesting. This woman, as a child, had been the favored daughter. Although she had two sisters, she was considered the beauty and the most promising child. Her parents and her sisters sacrificed necessities to give her beautiful clothes, leisure, dainty food, and opportunities for travel and education. She took all this, apparently, as if it were her due, but analysis showed that she really had strong unconscious guilt feelings which prevented her from enjoying these advantages fully or using them profitably. She felt she must pay for her extraordinary privileges by great suffering. Before she discovered this strong self-destructive trend in herself through analysis, she had managed to lose her home, her friends, her husband, and her career.

There are other forms of indirect self-destruction in which the individual destroys a part of himself rather than the whole. We see many cases of patients who cut off parts of the body. I have collected many examples of striking self-mutilation. One of these was a woman who was under treatment in a sanitarium. She was taken out by her mother, against advice. Soon after she killed her own baby. She became very agitated after this and one day slipped away from her home and ran to the railroad track, where she placed her right arm (the arm that had killed her child) on the track and allowed the train to cut it off. After this she recovered rapidly and has remained well ever since. It has been said that suicide is often the death sentence self-inflicted. This woman's act represented a symbolic suicide, in that she recognized her own guilt for the murder and killed the part of herself that she considered guilty, namely, her right arm.

This same motive has been shown to exist in many patients who mutilate themselves in a lesser degree, as by skin digging, biting off nails, compulsive scratching, and so on. Such neurotic mutilations are often equivalents for masturbation, it is true, but at the same time they are self-punitive and self-destructive.

No less self-destructive, although more difficult to demonstrate as such, is malingering. I refer to that type of malingering in which the individual actually injures himself in order to secure attention, pity, or money. I do not believe that the underlying motive of malingering is to gain money (or attention). I contend, rather, that the malingerer who mutilates himself does so for the same reasons that prompt any neurotic mutilation, and that then his strong aggressions against people lead him to capitalize the injury in a way that is particularly disagreeable and mortifying to the persons who wish to help him, namely, by fooling them. This aspect of the matter blinds us to the fact that the malingerer has actually destroyed a part of himself, and that in addition to this act of physical self-destruction, he has also destroyed (if he is found out, as he usually is) his own prestige and the confidence and respect his friends hold for him.

There is still another form of partial self-destruction in which individuals by one means or another make someone else responsible for their self-punitive attacks. For example, these patients can make the surgeon feel that an operation is necessary or at least that there is sufficient indication for the operation to cause him to give the patient the benefit of the doubt. We know that the neurotic patient can simulate disease unconsciously and we know also that patients are sometimes successful in inducing surgeons to mutilate them unnecessarily. Indeed, it is not uncommon for a neurotic individual to try to avoid a difficult situation, such as the necessity for psychological treatment, or impending marriage, by seeking a surgical operation.

The foregoing examples of self-destruction have to do with the striated musculature and the voluntary nervous system. I believe that the autonomic nervous system and the smooth muscles carry out the unconscious wishes of the individual also, in two ways: first, in conversion hysteria, for example in aphonias and anorexia; second, by structuralization of these hysterical manifestations. I think we all recognize intuitively that self-destructive impulses may be carried out through the autonomic nervous system, as, for example, in the gastrointestinal processes where excessive emotional stimulation of the stomach leads to gastric ulcer. We say such conditions are caused by the emotional state, and that the emotion is relieved by the flowing of hydrochloric acid. But this does not explain why the process goes on to produce organic self-destruction. I think it is because there is working throughout the entire personality a destructive instinct which may be carried out in its entirety in the form of direct suicide, or may be limited to partial or focal forms of self-destruction, in which case it may be carried out by the voluntary nervous system or by the autonomic nervous system.

This is merely an outline of a thesis which I have been investigating for a number of years. I could present a great deal of clinical data which we have amassed, were there time. From the study of many cases we have drawn some conclusions about the destructive impulse and why it is turned inward against the self in some people instead of outward upon the environment as in normal people. We have also determined what causes a certain individual to choose a particular form of self-destruction in some of these cases. These conclusions we have been able to utilize in therapy, but that is a subject for another paper. For the present I have merely tried to suggest a method of approach to further research.

DISCUSSION (*Abstract*)

Dr. A. L. Skoog (Kansas City, Missouri): Dr. Menninger mentioned alcoholism as an illustration of indirect suicide. Possibly quite a few individuals using alcoholic drinks to excess would come under this classification, but I believe that a great many persons indulge moderately or even excessively in such beverages without any suicidal intentions, either consciously or unconsciously. I should like to call the essayist's attention to one individual, a Mr. D., about whom he was consulted at one time, some years past. This individual literally destroyed himself by alcoholic indulgences. He was under my care many times and on a number of occasions expressed himself as not being interested in life any longer and said that he might as well kill himself by drinking. His exitus happened this year and may be ascribed to alcoholism. He could not meet the problems of life as a normal individual should and would have done. Perhaps his was a cyclothymic psychosis.

DR. W. R. HOUSTON (Augusta, Georgia): The topic that Dr. Menninger has developed is one of intense interest and wide scope. I sympathize heartily in his conception that some impulse to self-injury is a plausible and sufficing explanation of many phenomena that we meet with in practice, not merely overt self-mutilation and suicide, but the more numerous and important damages people covertly inflict upon themselves both consciously and unconsciously. This is a conception that explains many obscure behavior patterns, many organ neuroses that would otherwise be inexplicable.

I regret to say, however, that I cannot share the essayist's confidence as to the possibility of analyzing these impulses in any basic sense. I have not been impressed with the analyses that I have heard or have attempted to make. The analyses seem often to be whimsical and shallow, not to reach the fundamental pathogenesis. They are correct, no doubt, as laying bare some of the more immediate and proximate links in the chain of causation, but they fail to reveal the *primum movens.* Not infrequently the analysis overleaps itself or, as La Rochefoucauld puts it, "The fault with penetration is not that it does not penetrate, but that it penetrates too far."

We come nearer arriving at the truth by listening to the interpretations of poets and seers. Dr. Jelliffe, confirmed psychoanalyst, admits that the analyses are for those that creep, that the poet divines in a flash what the analyst laboriously strives for. Nor does the poet always tell all that he apprehends. Shakespeare in the soliloquy in *Hamlet* gives a marvelous rationalization of the arguments for suicide pro and con, but he carefully avoids permitting Hamlet to refer to the real reason why he does not commit suicide. The real reason, of course, is the reason that keeps a wounded cat or chicken from committing suicide, namely, the instinct to preserve life at whatever cost. Is it not true that the cause of suicide direct or indirect is a fundamental failure in this instinct to live? Is it not true that our analysis reaches only to the rationalization? Just as the orderly development of the embryo directed by the intuitive wisdom inherent in the egg sometimes suffers from a fatal change in this order and there develops instead of the symmetrical organism a monster, so the will to live may be altered and perverted by an antagonistic instinct to death which I can but regard as an ultimate datum not susceptible of further analysis.

DR. MENNINGER (*closing*): The psychiatrists are not pessimistic about the possibility of analyzing impulses in human beings. Poets and philosophers are more able to give hints about these tendencies than scientists. These matters are quite beyond the scope of laboratory methods. But I think the psychiatrists are more nearly allied to the poets than to the laboratory investigators. Nor is that as damning as it may sound to some. Our work is very largely verbalization; not pus and blood, but the whole verbalization of life is our material.

But with all due credit to the poets and philosophers, the difficulty in applying their observations to one's patients is that their material is not systematized. Freud realized many years ago that authors had recognized many facts about human nature that physicians and other scientists had missed, but he also saw that this insight had not been made available to the physician in practice. What psychiatry has been interested in for the last several years is bringing some of these intuitive facts into systematized form so that they can be used by physicians.

The work is not complete, but many cases have been analyzed in great detail so that we know, for example, just what causes self-mutilation. These researches do not appear in the *Journal of the American Medical Association,* but you will find them recorded in detail in some of our psychiatric and psychoanalytic journals. I could have presented one of these cases in more detail today, but I purposely spared you because I preferred to give you a hasty general outline of the study I have been conducting for several years.

We not only know what causes some of these things, but we have formed some conclusions which have been utilized in therapy. For example, after we have determined the individual things that cause self-mutilation in a particular case, we can indicate what the next step is, to free the individual from these self-destructive impulses by assisting him to turn his aggressions outward toward the outside world instead of inward upon himself. That is the rationale of what psychiatrists are doing. Occupational and recreational therapy are not devices to keep the patient's hands busy and his mind occupied, but are much more specific treatment. We do not keep patients playing tennis just to keep them busy, but to enable them to return their aggressions outward and thus relieve their need for expressions of internal aggressions. That is why a ping-pong game is sometimes more effective treatment than an appendectomy. These strong aggressions cannot be permanently relieved surgically. The patient is forced to make repeated sacrifices in which one organ is offered for another. But if he can be led to direct these aggressions outward in the form of sublimations he is on the road to health. Physicians can help him to do that only if they understand why the patient is trying to destroy himself in the first place. Therefore, I protest against the belief that we can never find out why these things are, and urge my colleagues to pursue with an open mind the solution of the riddle of indirect self-destruction.

20. Psychology of a Certain Type of Malingering

In an earlier study [1] of the attenuated forms of suicide, I suggested that self-mutilation, appearing under the varying circumstances of psychosis, neurosis, religious ceremony, and social convention, is in all cases the result of a compromise between the self-destructive and erotic tendencies, such that the death instinct is thwarted of its purpose through the sacrifice of a part for the whole.[2] I was able to demonstrate from representative examples of various types of mutilation that in all of them one could find evidence of a simultaneous indulgence in passive gratifications and punitive satisfaction, which at the same time atone for the guilt, repeat the crime (of passivity), and act as a peace offering for the mitigation of the more severe punishment of death, i.e., a sacrifice to permit continued indulgence.

I did not include in that study a form of self-mutilation with which clinical medicine has been familiar for centuries, namely, malingering. Malingering is a word of obscure origin, of which the earliest known definition appears in Grove's *Directory of the Vulgar Tongue,* in which it is defined as "a military term for one who, under pretense of sickness, evades his duty." In the earliest meaning there is some hint as to the dynamic explanation of what would now be called a symptomatic act, which since that time seems to have puzzled and distressed clinicians no end. Although malingering is obviously, in certain forms, a variety of self-mutilation, I was led to

Reprinted from the *Archives of Neurology and Psychiatry,* 33:507–515, March 1935.

a separate consideration of it by reason of two outstanding characteristics which set it apart from the ordinary forms of self-mutilation: first, the large epinosic gain, which is, of course, largely conscious, and, second, the frank appearance of what in every other
form of self-mutilation is entirely masked, namely, the aggressive
elements.

The first of these differences between malingering and the mutilations carried out by neurotic and psychotic patients is in degree rather
than in kind. The malingerer turns his neurotic tendencies to
evident profitable account (or attempts to do so) and takes conscious
cognizance of this. In psychoanalytic language, he consciously cap-
italizes the secondary gain of illness and makes it the predominant
motive.*

In doing so, however, he necessarily thwarts the physician and
other people whose interests run counter to his, and in this way he
carries out aggressions toward a substitute object. Usually in the end
the object is the physician; and because he is the victim of an unjustified aggression, the physician's temptation to retaliate may result in making the patient suffer doubly.

---

* Every neurotic patient makes some use of this secondary gain from illness, as
is well known, and to this extent every neurotic person is a malingerer. To just the
extent that he is conscious of this does the neurotic patient deserve to share in the
opprobrium that attaches to malingering. Freud [3] discussed this in the account
of Dora, his first reported history of a case. Dora made bitter reproaches against
her father, charging among other things that he was malingering, in that he used
tuberculosis to justify expeditions with a woman who was at the same time his
nurse and his mistress. This reproach, as Freud pointed out, while true, actually
rose out of her own bad conscience, and was a self-reproach not only for earlier
states of ill health—aphonia, coughing, etc.—but also for more recent ones. What
she hoped to gain by her immediate illness, Freud pointed out to her, was to de-
tach her father from his mistress, something she had been able to achieve by no
other method. Thus she was also malingering. "I felt quite convinced," said Freud,
"that she would recover at once if only her father were to tell her that he had
sacrificed Frau K. for the sake of her (Dora's) health, but I added that I hoped
he would not let himself be persuaded to do this, for then she would have learned
what a powerful weapon she had in her hand, and she would certainly not fail
on every future occasion to make use once more of her liability to ill-health." (This,
as is known, is precisely what neurotic families encourage certain members of the
family to do.) Freud continued that those "crudest and most commonplace views"
of hysterical disorders, i.e., that they could be cured by some catastrophe, are in a
certain sense correct, but that they overlook psychologic distinctions between what
is conscious and what is unconscious. One can say that the neurosis always contains
a certain amount of malingering, i.e., a certain amount of conscious secondary gain
from the elements, although in some instances this amount may be very small.

This becomes clear if one reads in a detached and impassive way almost any account of malingering in the medical literature. What impresses one most is the apparent irritation, hostility, even righteous indignation of the authors toward the subjects of their investigations.

In their comprehensive monograph on the subject, for example, Jones and Llewellyn [4] returned time after time to the moral obliquity of the malingerer, his knavery, his rascality, his unscrupulousness. Many pages of their book, as well as many of the articles that appear in medical literature, are devoted to the technic of distinguishing between malicious and unintentional deception in disease. The authors assume it to be self-evident that the malingerer's behavior, and therefore his intention, is morally reprehensible and that his success in concealing its factitious origin is even more so. The moral attitudes of condemnation follow naturally from the assumption that the immediate and sole purpose of the simulation is material gain.

It would seem evident that, as to the moral reprehensibility of the malingerer, the scientist has no more justification for forming an opinion than in the case of any other clinical phenomena. The medical scientist is fairly entitled to judge as to whether or not a given condition is injurious to society; he is justified, for example, in quarantining a patient with smallpox. But to decide as to the morality of the illness has never been the physician's function. He does not attempt, for example, to judge the sinfulness of syphilis. The scientist who becomes angry with the subject of his investigations is to that extent no longer scientific.

How then can one interpret the curious attitude which may be detected in those who write on malingering, and in the way in which physicians, lawyers, and employers discuss such cases?

The first explanation lies in the widespread fallacy of assuming that conscious motives can be regarded as explanatory of human behavior. Especially is this lost sight of by medical writers who, accustomed to dealing with physiologic functions over which the conscious intention has a minimum of authority, turn on rare occasion to the analysis of behavior. Behavior cannot be understood in terms of conscious intention alone; unless one considers the unconscious motives which determine an act, one cannot understand the significance of the act to the actor.

A second reason for the irritation exists, however. Intuitively physicians grasp one of the unconscious motives of malingering without clearly recognizing it intellectually; they react to it emotionally. For a man to injure himself so that he escapes responsibility or obtains money is reprehensible from the standpoint of the employer and of society at large. It is an aggression against society, although done in the form of an aggression against the self. But this is not sufficient reason for the many aroused emotions of the physician; he is only too familiar with many examples of aggression against society in the form of sickness. The shoe pinches because malingering is also an aggression against the physician himself. It is an attempt to deceive him, to perplex, perhaps to overtax and ridicule his diagnostic acumen and his therapeutic efforts. If one reads the reports of cases of malingering, one cannot but be struck by the frequency with which the physician describes how a certain wound, for example, is almost healed time after time, only to show exacerbation which puzzled all the consultants. When at last the factitious nature of the injury is discovered, there is almost a shout of triumph in the clinical reports, and some authors even describe how the patient was reproached, sharply spoken to, summarily dismissed, or otherwise punished. It is this which clearly indicates that the physician recognizes intuitively that one of the motives of the patient was not so much the material gain as the unconscious wish to fool the physician and, coincidentally, to make a bid for punishment.*

One often sees the same aspect of this phenomenon clearly demonstrated in the course of psychoanalytic treatment. The patient begins to give evidence of regarding the treatment as a competitive struggle with the analyst. This may be subtle, or the patient may frankly announce it. "You have got to yield; I never will," said one

---

* So dogged is this refusal to confess the deception that patients will go to incredible lengths in their submission to treatment. I know of the case of a man and woman who claimed to have effected a suicide pact and to be dying of self-inflicted poison. They were taken to a hospital and given heroic treatment with a powerful antidote which resulted in their deaths, and it was not until shortly before death occurred that they confessed that they had not taken poison.

of my patients, clearly recognizing, even as he said it, that it was a defensive and, at the same time, aggressive gesture. Such patients are like the skeptic described by Karin Stephen [5] who, when told of the significance of slips of the tongue, declared, "One or two instances like that would never convict [convince] me."

Such a competition with the analyst takes this specific form: "You may be a wise and highly regarded analyst, but now you have met your match. I will show you that you can't cure me." Such dreams as the following are familiar to all analysts: A baseball game is in progress. A man resembling the analyst is the pitcher, and he has achieved a remarkable record. He has struck out nearly every batter that has faced him. The dreamer goes to bat and knocks a home run (he is going to give up the analysis and go home). Or in another and still more specific dream he steps up to the plate and knocks foul after foul so that the pitcher, in spite of his wonderful record, is unable to fan him out and is, on the other hand, worn out with the contest. In such a dream it is almost self-evident the foul balls are the unscrupulous devices for resistance used by the patient to prolong and stalemate the analysis, exhaust the patience of the analyst, and provoke his exasperation.

From this, one can hazard the assumption that the original act of malingering serves chiefly as a provocative aggression, i.e., that it is a minor self-attack designed to excite a major attack from another person. In this it corresponds to the criminality from a sense of guilt described by Freud [6] and elaborated by Alexander.[7]

CLINICAL EXAMPLES

Since malingering is usually imitative or simulated, many forms of illness or sickness can be represented, but in general there are two forms: those in which incapacity is claimed because of subjective evidence (for example, the patient insists that he feels too sick to work), and those in which the incapacity is ascribed to an evident local injury which has been self-induced. Only the latter can serve as illustrations of focal self-destruction. I shall cite only a few examples.

The first is that of a woman, aged 29, whom I saw briefly, in consultation with a surgeon who was certain that she had a basal skull fracture. Her pillow was drenched with blood, and she was tossing about as if in great pain, responding to questions in a confused, semidelirious fashion. She begged constantly for morphine, which was given her. I incurred the surgeon's displeasure by vetoing his intention to perform a craniotomy immediately on the basis that I was not convinced that there was an intracranial lesion.

After a few days' observation the nurses detected her in the act of picking open small vessels inside the external ear, which was presumably the way in which she had brought about the profuse hemorrhages which, by that time, had almost exsanguinated her.

A few days later she disappeared from the hospital. A month later I was urged by a colleague in another city to come at once in consultation on a case, the description of which made it obvious that it was the same patient.

Later, also, I learned from various sources that she had succeeded in persuading a competent surgeon to do a cranial decompression, and that in several cities she had collected money from insurance companies and corporations, to whom she was able to make it appear that they were in some way responsible for her self-induced injuries.

The elements of aggression, exhibitionism, and self-punishment are obvious in this case, in spite of the brief opportunity available for studying it. To say that the patient wanted money, morphine, or attention, or all three, is, to say the least, to disregard the extraordinary means which she used to obtain them. It would be accepting the face-saving rationalizations of the ego at par value, in the teeth of striking neurotic stigmas.

What was most enlightening about the case was the effect it produced on the professional men who saw her. The first effect was to create in the nurses and surgeons great interest and concern. As her shocking condition became more apparent, the emotions changed into pity and a strong wish to give her relief. When, however, the nature of her illness became known, the strongly positive feelings were exactly reversed. The surgeon was angry at the deception and was considerably put out with himself for having expended so much time and sympathy and for having been so completely taken in. Under such circumstances one may properly apply a technical device which experience has proved useful in clinical psychoanalysis. When, in spite of one's scientific training and an effort to maintain an objective attitude toward the patient's behavior symptoms, one finds oneself strongly moved emotionally in a certain direction, toward pity or anger or exasperation, it is a useful measure to ask oneself if it is not precisely this result which the patient is unconsciously attempting to produce. One of my patients, for example, who had an indescribably irritating method of picking flaws in whatever I did or said, suddenly stopped short one day in the middle of a harangue to confess that in spite of a conviction of earnestness and sincerity which he felt strongly, he could not deny that as he spoke there flashed across his mind the image of the leering smile which he gave his father on occasions in his youth when, by similar behavior, he would taunt his father into pursuing and punishing him.

Another typical case was one presented by Dr. Edward Delehanty before the Central Neuropsychiatric Association in September 1929. A youth of about twenty years had, in the course of two years, succeeded in deceiving a dozen physicians with regard to an extensive and crippling burn on his hand and arm. Extensive skin grafting was undertaken time after time; in each instance, after an early show of success, sloughing would reappear. The youth's suffering must have been enormous, and his monetary profit was almost certain to be slight. It was discovered that during all those months he had systematically renewed the wound by surreptitiously anointing the edges with phenol which he purchased for the purpose and kept concealed in his bed. I cannot conceive of an explanation outside of that afforded by this theory for such behavior, which the reports of industrial surgeons, dermatologists, and others would indicate to be rather frequent.

A most enlightening contribution to the understanding of malingering comes from the descriptive accounts given by dermatologists of this type of illness, which would appear to be a rather common clinical entity: dermatitis factitia or dermatitis artefacta.[8]

This is a condition in which lesions are voluntarily inflicted on the

skin of the person himself, with the aid of corrosive chemicals or mechanical agents such as penknives, fire (particularly from matches),
cigarettes, the finger, or some other object, perhaps most commonly
with the fingernails. I exclude from consideration the cases in which
there is an acknowledged compulsion to pick at the skin until the
lesion has formed. This is not malingering, since it is not in any
sense concealed, but rather the result of unconscious impulses which
a patient cannot explain, but does not deny. What characterizes
dermatitis artefacta, as all dermatologists point out, is the persistent
denial of authorship, even in the face of absolute proof.

"Many of these patients," Netherton [9] stated, "are subjected to
repeated and extensive surgical procedures, and may even suffer
irreparable damage and mutilation. In fact many cases are on record
in which an arm, finger, etc., have been unnecessarily removed with
the full consent of the patient.

"In three of my cases the patient submitted to repeated abdominal
operations. Beside the economic loss involved in such cases, the inconvenience sustained by innocent members of the patient's family
is frequently little short of tragic."

In these few words this intuitive dermatologist strikes at the
psychologic factors which I regard as the most important in malingering: the wish to suffer, the wish to conceal, the wish to injure
oneself and, to an even greater extent, the wish to cause other people
pain, distress, and embarrassment. In other words, there are all the
factors one finds in suicide: the wish to hurt oneself, the wish to be
hurt, and the wish to hurt someone else.

In another study [10] I pointed out how surgical operations are apparently sought and demanded as expression of some unconscious
need for self-mutilation at the hands of another person, and I was,
therefore, particularly impressed by the observations of Netherton
and others that this type of malingering was frequently associated
with repeated surgical procedures. In four of the cases Netherton
cited, the self-mutilation began after an uneventful appendectomy.
The first case is particularly striking, since in this instance six or more
major operations were performed subsequent to the original appendectomy, which began the self-induced ulcerations. It was as if the

patient was compelled to have an operation made on her abdomen. Six surgical incisions did not suffice; she must continue the process by making innumerable attempts to open her own abdomen by a frustrated and incomplete, but undoubtedly painful, method. Netherton's account of the case leaves little doubt as to the burden which her continued sickness caused her parents. The vicious circle established depended on the fact that by her suffering she simultaneously made the desired aggression against them, atoned for it, and justified herself in additional aggressions.

Through the courtesy of Dr. Joseph Klauder of Philadelphia, who has made numerous contributions to the literature on the subject,[11] I was able to study briefly several cases in conference with him. The first patient was a feeble-minded woman who presented lesions regarded as dermatitis factitia, that is, self-produced. They were sharply circumscribed areas, as though produced by the application of a caustic. Dr. Klauder had never been able to obtain much cooperation from the family and could not prove that the lesions were self-produced, although he was sure that they were. The only motive he could elicit was that she was very anxious to be admitted to the hospital. Her sister said that the patient was extremely fond of going to hospitals. An interesting feature about the patient was that she had two fingers amputated, apparently for lesions that were self-produced, as far as the evidence showed.

I am indebted to Dr. Klauder for the account of the following case of the same sort. The patient was a woman of thirty-five years who, for six months, had had recurrent attacks of a dermatitis. Her husband was insistent that something be done for her, and the family physician sought a consultation with a dermatologist. The dermatologist, in turn, asked Dr. Klauder to see the patient. She presented curious bandlike areas of erythema encircling her wrists like a wristwatch and below the knee like a garter. These led to the diagnosis of dermatitis factitia. When the patient was taking a bath, her room in the hospital was searched, and a bottle of compound solution of Cresol was found. Dr. Klauder accused her of producing the lesions with it, but she stoutly denied it. Later she admitted using it to wash her hands and to apply to the skin in order to prevent the skin disease, which she had been told was a streptococcic infection. This was a partial confession of the truth. Her emotional tone was normal, and she presented no neurologic abnormalities, except that her conjunctiva and hard palate were anesthetic. This and the dermatitis artefacta justified the diagnosis of hysteria.

Dr. Klauder discovered that her illness had become "town gossip" in the small town in which she lived. Her family physician had been obliged to issue a daily bulletin as to how she was, in answer to the many inquiries he received as to her progress. She was the recipient of many gifts, flowers, and cards, both at her home and after she entered the hospital. She arranged the postcards in a kind of picture-gallery exhibit about her sickroom.

In both of the cases cited it will be observed that the patient endeavored to bring about the confusion and embarrassment of the physicians, as well as to carry out the evident purpose of exciting sympathy and attention. It is particularly desirable to emphasize the absence of any monetary gain, which the industrial surgeon is apt to regard as the only motive for malingering.

It is extremely interesting to compare dermatologic malingering, for which the patient nearly always denies any responsibility, with what dermatologists call neurotic excoriations, several instances of which Dr. Klauder showed me, and in all of which it was frankly confessed by the patient that for reasons unknown to her and beyond her control she was compelled to pick, pinch, or dig at herself until various ulcerations were formed. I mention these cases, which in a sense are out of place in a paper on malingering, only to indicate the theoretical distinction between them, namely, that in these self-mutilations the aggression is almost entirely self-directed and not at all provocative, whereas in dermatitis factitia (malingering) the aggression is chiefly intended for another person and, as has been seen before, seems to serve a provocative function.

COMMENT

The chief elements in malingering of the self-mutilative type are: the infliction of a wound on the self which results in pain and loss of tissue; exhibition of the wound to persons who react emotionally to it and give sympathy, attention, and efforts to cause healing; the deception of the observer as to the origin of the wound and often distinct efforts to defeat therapeutic measures and the obtaining of monetary or other material reward or detection, exposure, with constant humiliation, reproach, and sometimes actual punishment. The cases presented show that one cannot subscribe to so naïve a view as that consciously advanced by the detected malingerer, that he was willing to gamble with his chances in the exchange of a self-inflicted wound for gain. With so much gambling instinct in the race, the infrequency of malingering would, in itself, contradict this interpretation. Again, it is well known that the pain endured is frequently out of all proportion to the anticipated monetary gain. Furthermore, such interpretation ignores the unconscious factors which, however unfamiliar to the malingerer and the public, are now well known to medical science.

The well-known disparity between the great suffering voluntarily endured and the objective gain is to be explained on two bases: first, that the gain is only partly represented by the monetary reward, but includes also the satisfactions in exciting sympathy, attention, perplexity, and dismay, and, second, that the pain is not only incident to the device used for obtaining the gains, but is psychologically demanded by the conscience as a price for indulging in them. Actions speak louder than words, and it is clear that however conscienceless the malingerer appears (or claims) to be, he unconsciously feels guilty and inflicts his own punishment. Unfortunately, there are available as yet no precise instruments with which to measure emotions, but probably there is a precise quantitative relationship, so that the externally achieved punishment is reciprocal with the amount of self-inflicted suffering. The less of one, the more there is of the other. A man who enucleates his own eye meets with less reproach and condemnation than one who burns himself with a match, even though each may do so for the same external purpose. This, to be sure, depends to a large extent on the sense of justice implicit in one, but it is precisely this in everyone and in himself that the patient takes advantage of to achieve an equilibrium of emotional forces.

CONCLUSIONS

Malingering, therefore, of the self-mutilative type may be described as a form of localized self-destruction which serves simultaneously as an externally directed aggression of deceit, robbery, and false appeal. The aggression is of such an inflammatory sort that it, in turn, obtains for the malingerer not only sympathy, attention, and monetary gain (at first), but, ultimately, exposure, reproach, and "punishment." Both aspects of the induced treatment by the outside world are strongly tinctured with the perverted erotic satisfaction incident to masochism and exhibitionism.

From this, one may conclude that the original act of malingering of this type serves chiefly as a provocative aggression, i.e., it is a minor self-attack designed to excite a major attack (both indulgent and punitive) from other persons, the pain involved being the price demanded by the conscience for the unconscious satisfactions achieved.

DIAGNOSTIC AND
TREATMENT METHODS

Unfortunately Karl Menninger has written very little about his concepts of psychiatric treatment. This is a paradox because perhaps his greatest contribution to medical science is his heroic leadership in the reform and reorganization of state mental hospitals. He describes those hospitals where active treatment has replaced shameful neglect as having "an atmosphere of people getting well."

His theoretical convictions about illness and the nature of the recovery process were crystallized long ago into sound treatment methods. In revitalizing the care of the mentally ill in large mental hospitals he has insisted upon the application of these therapeutic principles and methods. Adlai Stevenson was the first of a series of distinguished governors who sought his consultation for the improvement of state hospitals. He has since consulted with a number of them, and his brother, William C. Menninger, has addressed the legislatures of fourteen states telling them about the basic convictions which the Menninger brothers have about the hospital care of the mentally ill and how these have been put to work in Kansas.

A basic lesson learned early by the medical student is the fundamental importance of the diagnostic examination for a sound treatment program. As Karl Menninger attempted to improve his powers of clinical diagnosis and to organize the data gained from his examination of the patient— all of which he conceived as being needed to eventually prescribe treatment for the patient—he began to write about the diagnostic examination and the organization of the findings.

Later, when he had the responsibility of teaching psychiatry to large classes of young physicians, he saw the need for a more comprehensive exposition of the psychiatric examination and published a book, *A Manual for Psychiatric Case Study* (1952). Before the pages of the book were stitched together he had begun a revision of it, and in the last paper in this section he reports his latest revision of one part of the psychiatric case study, the psychological examination. —B. H. H.

21. The Abuse of Rest in Psychiatry

A little over a hundred years ago a man was born in Philadelphia who became pre-eminent in three fields. In 1881 he was described by Sir James Paget as "one of the most distinguished medical men in your country or in any country." In addition to conducting one of the largest private practices in America, he was the author of a book of poetry, one of children's stories, numerous novels, a treatise on neurologic injuries and 250 articles on pharmacology, physiology, toxicology, and psychotherapy. He received honorary degrees from Bologna, Edinburgh, Toronto, Harvard, Princeton, and Jefferson. It is significant that a man of such prodigious labors and accomplishments should have made famous a program of treatment by rest!

Weir Mitchell described his "rest cure" in a number of books, the titles of which indicate his philosophy: *Wear and Tear, Hints for the Overworked, Fat and Blood.* His idea was that nervous illnesses were the result of physical exhaustion, which he combated by complete bed rest, complete isolation, no visitors, no letters, no reading, no writing; the constant attendance of a nurse, some massage and electricity and, withal, high-caloric feeding.

Mitchell's prestige, influence, and persuasiveness were such that his "rest cure" for the treatment of neuroses influenced American medicine for nearly fifty years. The fact that persons with nonorganic

Read in a symposium on "The Abuse of Rest in the Treatment of Disease" before the Section on Experimental Medicine and Therapeutics at the Ninety-fourth Annual Session of the American Medical Association, Chicago, June 15, 1944. Reprinted from the *Journal of the American Medical Association*, 125:1087–1090, Aug. 19, 1944.

illnesses who complained of "nervousness" seem to be wasting energy by unnecessary tensions, anxieties, and fruitless exertions and that they suffer, subjectively at least, from a high degree of fatigability could not but impress physicians who, because they had been reared and trained in a mechanistic physiologic philosophy of human life, saw these cases without benefit of psychologic insight. The fatigue theory of the neuroses which so impressed Weir Mitchell thus continued to impress nonpsychologically-minded physicians, who welcomed a plausible physiologic expansion of these baffling cases. Diagnoses of nervous exhaustion, nervous fatigue, fatigue neuroses, nervous breakdown from overwork, nervous weakness, neurasthenia, and so on continued to fill the records of hospitals, clinics, and private practitioners. Treatment based on these diagnoses and Weir Mitchell's example were developed, exploited, and popularized— modified rest cures, relaxation treatment, vacation treatment, and what I have called "trip treatment"—the sending of patients away on visits to California, Florida, and Europe, or on fishing trips, hunting expeditions, and the like.

Modern psychiatry regards this conception of neurosis and these forms of treatment for neuroses as entirely false in theory and unsound in practice. To relate ourselves again to the title of this symposium I will put it this way: the abuse of rest as a treatment in psychiatric conditions represents a neglect or misunderstanding of the real pathologic condition of the neurotic patient under the guise of a treatment which is not only futile and expensive but very often definitely harmful.

In the brief limits of time available it would be difficult to answer all the questions to which this statement will give rise. In a very condensed form I shall try to outline the modern theory of the neuroses and of the treatments considered appropriate for them in contrast to those which justify the practice of prescribing excessive rest and indicate, in closing, some of the ways in which rest can be used without abuse.

There is no question but that nervous patients show evidences of fatigue and easy fatigability; this fatigue is a symptom of the neurosis. Overstudy, overapplication, overexertion, and all other excess expenditures of energy do not cause psychiatric syndromes; they are often the expression of psychiatric illness. The cure of the psychiatric illness—the neurosis, the nervousness—is the removal of that which impels the individual to make such depletions of his own strength, to waste so much of his energy, or to require so much of it to hold himself in check against explosions or collapse. The modern conception of a psychiatric illness is a dynamic one based on a concept of cooperative and interactive anatomy, physiology, and psychology. The neuroses and psychoses and other evidence of maladjustment on the part of a patient are a result of misdirected energy rather than the lack of sufficient energy. An automobile the engine of which has become overheated as the result of being driven with the brakes set cannot be cured by resting. As soon as the car's proper function, that of traveling along the road, is resumed (with the brake still set), the same overheating will result. The question is, Why are the brakes set and how does one release them?

The problem of treatment of a psychiatric illness thus goes beyond merely arresting any attempt at adjustment by physical exertion. It aims at the redirection of the wasted energy, the removal of interfering inhibitions, and the setting up of requisite inhibitions. Human beings are impelled by instinctual forces to attempt certain modifying relationships with respect to their environment. From earliest infancy they want "to do something." As they grow older and the aimlessness of infantile manipulation of the environment becomes an organized pattern, this something which they do to the environment turns out to be a modification of it in either a constructive or a destructive direction. We perform creative activity and destructive activity—nothing else. Both forms of activity seem to be related to certain instinctual drives, and a certain kind and amount of destructiveness and a certain amount of creativeness appear in the activities of every human being. As long as an adequate amount of both is possible for an individual, he does not develop a neurosis or a psychosis.

For various reasons—a brain tumor, a hemiplegia, an infection with tuberculosis, a reaction of grief to the death of a daughter, a reaction of fear to the treatment of an employer, a reaction of hate to the infidelity of a husband, an ineradicable memory of over-whelming defeat and inadequacy experienced in childhood—for these and many other reasons, the ability to direct energy in a proper pattern of destructiveness and creativeness fails to develop or to be maintained. The resulting incoordinate, awkward attempts to maintain an adjustment is expensive of energy. The patient carries on with his assigned tasks only under the greatest difficulty, with increasing inefficiency, pain, and internal and external dissatisfaction. Perhaps he continues to operate at 40 per cent efficiency plus much complaining, worrying, lamenting, and despairing, plus many "patent medicines," osteopathic treatments, periods of absenteeism, week-end drunks, acerbities with wife and children, quarrels with fellow employees, foremen, and assistants. If his efficiency declines even further, let us say to 20 per cent, he may come to a psychiatrist. The brakes are well set, the heat is enormous, the productivity is minimum, the distress is great.

The absurdity and futility of prescribing rest for such a patient must be apparent. The problem is rather to discover what prodigious internal consumption and blockade of energy has occurred and how it can be directed again to fruitful employment. The technic in doing this is beyond the scope of the paper; it would entail a review of the entire program of psychiatric examination and treatment.

Pari passu with the development of the rest cure there developed in the field of medicine a program of work cure. This concept held that such individuals needed only to be driven to more strenuous efforts, a procedure comparable to driving an overheated, brake-set automobile harder and faster. Obviously, this is an even more absurd philosophy than that of the rest cure. It appealed particularly to hard-boiled industrialists and misguided Army officers whose conception of neurotic illness is that its victims are lazy liars or yellow dogs, feigning disability to avoid duty.

At first glance, the behavior of the neurotic or psychotic patient would seem to lend support to these emotionally colored judgments of the exasperated practical man of affairs. The modern psychiatric hospital provides abundant opportunities for enlisting the interests of patients,[1] and yet despite the efforts of the medical director, the medical staff, the nursing staff and the therapists—despite schedules and regulations and exhortations—many patients manage to evade with an uncanny skill every available opportunity for exercise, constructive craft work, amusement, diversion, recreation, and all the other outlets so carefully planned and devised for them. The temptation is to react to this emotionally, forgetting that this is the primary problem of psychiatry. What malignant energy lock has occurred within them that prevents it? What we find almost regularly in psychiatric patients is that they cannot work, they cannot play, and they cannot rest. They have to be taught to do all three of these things. Fortunately, in most cases it proves possible to grade the assignments so that patients may be taught to play and taught to work and thus taught to divert available energy toward the construction of patterns of creativeness and destructiveness which can be re-employed usefully in the outside world when the patient has made sufficient progress. Meanwhile of course other types of procedure must be instigated which make more energy available for the development of such patterns.

To teach such individuals how to work and how to play is to teach them how really to rest. This is the function of occupational therapy, recreational therapy, educational therapy, and psychotherapy as they are employed in the modern psychiatric hospital.[2] They seek to make it possible for the patient to find an outlet for his instinctual urges in work and play properly guided, properly taught, properly selected for his special needs, interests, and capacities, and properly graded and expanded. All this is in a contrary direction to that of the old plan of enforced rest whereby the patient through moral, physical, or chemical restraint was obliged to surrender to idleness and passivity. Both types of treatment not only were ineffective; they were actually deleterious. The reason for this is not far to seek. Patients deprived of physiologic, mechanical, and psychologic devices for turning their aggressive energy into batting a ball, digging a trench, or making a puppet turn these destructive tendencies in on themselves.[3] The man who commits suicide, who kills himself, is often thought of as the paradigm of psychiatric morbidity. He turns all his aggressive energy on himself and commits a murder with

himself as the object. It is quite obvious, of course, that many self-
destructive persons do not go as far as murdering the object; they
only berate it, abuse it, debauch it, humiliate it, hamstring it, in-
toxicate it. By it, of course I mean the self; this is the way many
people treat themselves. In psychiatry we describe this abuse and
mistreatment of the self as the turning inward of aggressive tendencies. The object of psychiatric treatment for such individuals is to
turn these aggressive impulses outward, away from the self. Failure
to do so results in a virtual suicide, not by placing a gun to the temple
or even by pouring gallons of whisky into the central nervous system,
but by the accumulation of hostile feelings associated with self-
destructive energy that accomplish the same morbid result. We know
that physical exertion, the directed use of the muscles, tends to combat this, and that enforced rest tends to favor it.

Having thus demonstrated as well as I can in the short time allotted
to me that rest can be a very dangerous remedy and do a great deal
of harm, I should like to end my contribution to this symposium by
taking the paradoxical position that rest may also do a very definite
amount of good. If one remembers that the psychiatrically disturbed
patient who cannot work or play efficiently usually cannot rest adequately, one realizes that definite steps have to be taken to improve
this capacity also. It was in that direction that hydrotherapy, prolonged immersion tub baths, wet sheet packs, and the like were
originally developed, and these are still much employed. Chemical
sedatives have improved vastly since the day in which chief reliance
had to be put on bromides and opiates. It is possible now to produce
sleep in patients whose disturbed emotional conflicts and prevailing
fears prevent them from daring to sink into repose without the use
of drugs having deterrent side effects. Some sedatives have the
peculiar ability, when administered rapidly, so to modify consciousness and the psychologic architecture as to permit the emergence of
what might be described as the indigestible toxic material of the
mind. This has been a feature of recent reports from the war theater
made by Grinker and Spiegel,[4] Murray,[5] and others. In some instances exposure to prodigious stress, both physical and mental, has
so depleted the energy reserves of combat troops, airplane pilots, and

shipwrecked merchant seamen that psychiatric syndromes characterized by anxiety, fears, aggressiveness, erratic behavior, and other
symptoms have emerged. In these conditions prompt and complete
rest has proved of enormous benefit, as indicated by the reports of
Commander Daniel Blain [6] of the War Shipping Administration,
Public Health Service Clinics, and his associates. [7] A few nights of
sound, protected sleep under quiet, pleasant surroundings with good
food and manifested friendliness are often sufficient to restore these
individuals to active duty within one to three weeks. Even in these
cases, important as is the element of rest, the importance of the
psychologic factors of safety, sympathy, and admiration are probably equally great. Companionship and planned activities are prescribed as soon as the men are up. It should certainly be borne in
mind that these cases represent a war syndrome and are not comparable to any peacetime pictures. There is a vast difference between
the man who has worked at full capacity for thirty-six hours without
stopping and is then thrown into cold oily waters by a submarine attack and fights for his life in and out of a lifeboat for the next twenty-
four hours—there is a vast difference between his need for rest and
the need for rest of the average maladjusted, neurotic, or psychotic
civilian, whose illness is none the less severe but whose physical energy and physiologic defenses have had no such sudden strain put on
them.

CONCLUSION

The concept of rest as a form of treatment in psychiatry arose in
an era characterized by the total neglect of the consideration of
psychologic factors in the study of human beings. As the mechanistic
conception of personality has given way to the dynamic organismic
conception, the fallacy of curing psychologic symptoms by merely
decreasing muscular activity has become apparent. In the sense of
physical inactivity, rest has ceased to be of any importance in psychiatric phenomena. Indeed, the tendency is in precisely the other
direction; namely, to utilize rather than to blockade further the
available energy of the neurotic or psychotic patient. Such a point
of view extends beyond a treatment of conditions formerly described

as neuroses and psychoses, however; in arterial hypertension, for example, where there is a vascular response to the anxiety associated with emotional conflict, the former prescription of exercise and work seems to have been a step in precisely the wrong direction. I am confident that the death of some hypertensive patients has been hastened by physicians who removed from them the only available or acceptable form of aggression to which they had had access. When I suggested this a few years ago,[8] I received numerous letters from internists confirming this opinion on the basis of their own clinical experience. How widely this may apply to other forms of what we formerly called physical illness and which we now, with equal verbal error, sometimes call psychosomatic conditions has been indicated in part by the presentations in this symposium.

The net philosophical import is that successful medicine must envisage the personality as a physiochemopsychologic unit susceptible of being interpreted and treated from the physical standpoint, the chemical standpoint, and the psychologic standpoint, assuming a working knowledge of the instinctual motivations that impel the adjustment patterns of human life.

22. The Approach to the Psychiatric Patient

The unique position of the physician in contemporary society is apt to be erroneously ascribed by the young doctor to the development and recognition of scientific truth.

The grouping of well-tested observations into an ordered, intelligible scheme and the formulation of conclusions or general principles derived from such a scheme and capable of being used to predict accurately future phenomena are methods of procedure unknown to the ancients. Hypotheses to explain them and the verification of these hypotheses by experiment and subsequent observations logically followed. Adherence to these scientific principles enlists a few millions of intelligent individuals today but the great bulk of the people of the world still knows nothing of them. If it hears of them, it often distrusts them. Religious principles, political principles, economic principles—all of these have far wider allegiance. The world is glad to use the gadgets of science, but its methods, its principles, and its workers are still regarded by the mass of the population with a mixture of amused tolerance and hostile suspicion.

No, the doctor's prestige does not stem from his knowledge of science nor solely from his utilization of its techniques. From time immemorial certain individuals have been set apart in every human society as possessing power to assist in the process of personal reparation, the power to relieve pain, to forestall death and promote recovery from injuries—in short, to minister to an individual upon whom the assaults of a hostile environment have fallen more heavily

Reprinted from the *Bulletin of the Menninger Clinic*, 14:192–201, November 1950.

than upon his fellows. For many centuries these individuals were regarded as not quite human and were always considered to possess supernatural powers. With the development of biological science and its acceptance by physicians, these supernatural attributes were replaced—in the doctors' minds at least—by scientific knowledge, a knowledge dependent upon certain techniques of investigation, of observation, correlation, and confirmation.

It is in these techniques that the greatest changes in medical practice have occurred, and they in turn are reflected in and at the same time determined by the changing concepts of personality through the centuries. From the standpoint of the patient, it has been and still is quite immaterial whether a physician employs amulets, arsenic, or abracadabra; these are the physician's business, not his. His basic expectations from the physician have not changed since the earliest days of human society; they are the same whether the physician be a medicine man, a quack, or the most highly skilled scientist. We may profitably raise the question: What does the patient want from the doctor?

More specifically, in what way does he expect the doctor to render him the aid, the relief, the reconstruction that he needs? Obviously he *expects a change to be effected within him*. He comes making the concession, or the confession if you like, that something is wrong with him, that something in him is not equal to the demands of reality. Something within his personality is at least temporarily defective. What the doctor is going to do, is to be done *to him*—the patient—not to the environment, not the neighbors, not to the husband or wife, but to him, personally. The purification of drinking water, proper sewage disposal, the quarantine of patients with infectious diseases, the counsel of parents, the eradication of lice, mosquitoes, even from his own body—these are not the patient's expectations.

To the patient the affliction for which he goes to the physician is something in himself which he wants changed. He expects that change to be effected in one of three ways:

1. By having something given or added to him (for example, some "iron for his blood").

2. By having something taken away from him (e.g., bleeding, catharsis, appendectomy).

3. By having something "done to him," (e.g., shoulder joint reduction, massage, encouragement).

The idea of altering a patient's condition for the better by giving something to him or taking something from him has been for so many centuries an integral part of medical practice that it requires no discussion. As we all know, the accumulated experience of years has changed the nature of substances "added," i.e., administered to patients; it has changed the nature of the taking-away process, also.

As to what may be done to a patient which is neither additive nor subtractive, one might think of such things as massage, poulticing, and blistering; we do not like to think of a great many less gentle procedures which have been used in the name of medical treatment such as whirling, hanging, stretching, shaking, and piercing. The important principle back of all these procedures, however, is now very important in the types of therapy to be discussed later, which involve neither taking from the patient nor giving to him but helping to make certain modifications within himself, thus, in a sense, "doing something to him."

In exchange for the service of the physician—this *giving to* or *taking from* or *altering* in some form or other, with the object of relieving the patient's pain, disability, threat of death, or whatever— what does the patient give? One's first thought is that he gives money, and so he does (sometimes). He gives something else which is very important to remember if one wants to think through the philosophy of medical practice. Obviously he gives obedience; he does what the physician tells him to do. He also gives respect, trust, and gratitude.

But he gives something more than this. He gives his consent to being examined. He surrenders his right to personal privacy. He submits himself not only for treatments but for examination.

It should be borne in mind that this examination of the patient is not something primarily sought by him. It was not a part of the procedure of the primitive physician or even of the physician of the

Middle Ages. The old chestnut, so familiar a part of the experience of every doctor, in which the patient when asked what is wrong with him, replies "That is what I want you to tell me, *you* are the doctor" is a residual indication of this feeling on the part of the patient that the doctor has magic—a mysterious intuition as to the nature of the patient's disability, sight unseen. Although to some extent many doctors are tempted by this to play a wizard role, scientific medicine repudiates these attributed powers and insists upon procedures of collecting data.

But however much intelligence and common-practice may lead a patient to accept consciously the necessity of such collecting of data, and even to enjoy the procedure, his submission to the routine of examination will always be tinctured by feelings of concession. The extent of this concession is apt to be forgotten by the modern physician, trained as he is in the formula, "Examination is necessary to diagnosis; diagnosis must precede treatment." The résumé just offered of the historical development of the patient-doctor relationship indicates how false this axiom is; the patient comes to be *treated* and everything that is done for him is, so far as he is concerned, treatment, whatever the doctor may call it. In a sense, therefore, treatment always precedes diagnosis. But it should not *preclude* diagnosis; and, for diagnosis, examination is necessary.

The questioning and examining of patients is so ingrained a part of the standardized procedure of modern medicine and indeed the pattern of modern civilized life that it is no wonder the doctors sometimes fail to appreciate the extraordinary uniqueness of this role. The lowliest general practitioner, in however a shabby little office in the remotest country town, has an authority and a prerogative which few kings have ever had, which the Pope of Rome does not have, which the highest judge in the highest court in this land never had. He has an opportunity to obtain an intimate view of another human being which the biographer, the historian, even the intimate friend, is denied. From his special coign of vantage the physician may undertake to scrutinize his fellow man's past history and present status in all of their aspects. The physician may ask questions and expect a truthful answer regarding details of every phase of the patient's life. Nothing is too intimate, nothing is too secret, nothing is too prejudicial.

More than that, the doctor has the right to examine his patient materially. He may ask the patient to disrobe; he may inspect and palpate the patient's body, he may ausculate the sounds made by the patient's internal organs; he may pass tubes or instruments into body orifices or examine the shadows revealed by the X-ray; he may collect from the patient blood, urine, feces, and other body substances for particular examination; he may give the patient adventitious substances and check their specific effects.

The first great boon of this extraordinary privilege accorded the physician is the opportunity it gives him to formulate a precise description of a particular personality; the second is the fact that it enables him to form a comprehensive conception of personality in general. It is, in short, the only conceivable way of approaching the delineation of the total personality concretely or abstractly. The combination and correlation of the two essential techniques just referred to, that of the historical or longitudinal survey, and that of the cross-sectional, as-of-the-moment, survey, give us a truly three-dimensional view of the human being. The one approach contributes data as to development, the other as to status, and by synthesizing the two one is able to describe and define a total personality. One might say that, directly proportional to the extent and the skill with which these two approaches have been used and combined, medicine has grown from the unsystematized, irregular magic of the medicine man to the orderly procedure of modern scientific medicine.

I have directed your thinking in this direction as a background for a mental attitude which I think should characterize the approach of *any* physician to *any* patient. It might be summed up as one of respect for the dignity of the individual human being, even—or perhaps *especially*—the one in trouble. Powys speaks of "plain, simple, humble reverence for the mystery of misfortune." But with this goes a respect for the responsibility and authority of the place occupied by the physician—a self-respect and a respect for one's colleagues and predecessors, for accumulated medical science, and for the nature of human beings that they turn in trust to some of their equally fallible fellow creatures and place their fate in our hands. That this implies a necessary humility and earnest dedication should require no emphasis.

All that has been said here applies as well to medical, surgical, obstetrical, dermatological, *and* psychiatric patients. My chapter title implied special features of the approach to the psychiatric patient. What are they? How does the psychiatric approach differ from the approach to *any* patient?

It differs in that the psychiatric patient differs from all other patients in several important respects. These determine—or should determine—peculiar qualities of the psychiatrist's approach to him.— Let us consider some of them serially.

In the first place, the patient who finally decides to seek the help of a psychiatrist does so in the face of an undeniable social stigmatization. According to our notion, and I refer now to psychiatrists, mental trouble is just as prevalent as dental trouble, and there should be no more disgrace attached to going to a psychiatrist than going to a dentist. Compare the situation of an employee who requests time for the medical treatment of heart symptoms with that of an employee who requests time for a visit to a psychiatrist! A physical illness is often something to boast about; a mental illness never is. Consequently, the pressures internal and external have usually become pretty severe before the patient or his relatives reach the point of taking the step that means, at least to the other people, "There is something wrong with his mind." Both the patient and his family— sometimes more one than the other—endeavor as long as possible to deny that the patient is sick, or at least sick in this particular way. It is not surprising therefore that before the psychiatric patient gets to the psychiatrist he has often wistfully solicited help from the surgeon, the osteopath, the gynecologist, or the faith healer. These individuals, anxious to meet the challenge, not infrequently play into the hands of the patient's evasions and do something for him or to him. It is only the wiser, more skillful ones who may help him overcome his reluctance and his fears and go straight to the psychiatrist.

This fear of social penalization joins hands with another fear which is peculiar to the psychiatric patient. Mental illness is mysterious; in its extreme form it is horrible. The verdict of the psychiatrist may confirm the unspoken dread; "insanity" may be just around the corner. This is a burden of fear great enough for anyone. But added to it always are such secondary fears as the fear of exposure, the fear of being laughed at, the fear of being humiliated by the examination, the fear of "being locked up." All patients come to the physician with a certain amount of fear, but the psychiatric patient with most of all.

One effect of this fear, perhaps the most important effect, is to increase the patient's defensiveness; at the very moment that he is approaching the physician for help he is withdrawing and preparing to conceal that for which he needs help. All human beings, indeed all animals, approach one another at the start with a certain tentativeness in which, as Freud has shown, there is a preliminary phase of hostility. In ordinary human contacts this hostility is quickly overcome by the human equivalents of nosing, smelling, licking, and pawing. We must establish the fact that the stranger comes as a friend or as a foe. This is much harder for the psychiatric patient to do, not only because of the fears just enumerated, but because his illness has disturbed his machinery for establishing interpersonal relationships. It is like a patient with a crippled hand being introduced to the surgeon whose first impulse, before he knows the type of injury, is to shake hands—the very thing that such a patient can't do. And just as a surgeon would have to find other means than the conventional ones for conveying his purposes and attitudes of friendliness to this patient, so the psychiatrist must learn to depend upon many other means than the conventional ones for establishing rapport with his patients.

The psychiatric patient not only is fearful and hostile beyond the average, but is embarrassed. He is like a shy girl, suffering from hemorrhoids, who goes to the surgeon. He is not only embarrassed about the location of his symptoms, but he is embarrassed in a way which the patient with hemorrhoids is not. For the latter has something to show which justifies her appeal, even though the exhibition may be awkward. The psychiatric patient has no protrusions, no tumors, no points of tenderness, no fever, no blood. He has nothing that can be seen. He has only something that can be heard, i.e., something that he can tell about.

But *can* it be told about? *Can* it be described? *Can* it be made clear to the psychiatrist? Will the psychiatrist understand it? Will he believe it? Will he tolerate it? These are the reflections which appall the psychiatric patient.

Harry Stack Sullivan remarked once about the paradox that the beginning student in psychiatry is put to work at the most difficult task, namely that of getting the history of the psychiatric patient. He went on to say that they often do better than we have any right to expect. "What we finally succeed in beating into the heads of our more promising students is that they must take histories with the following in mind: Can they imagine what it would be like to undergo the events they have heard about? To be where the informant claims he was? That is, do they have a sense of its being possible really to follow what he says? If they don't they should say they don't understand! When they cannot follow, they should ask questions. It's that simple. This also calls for competence in language—a remarkable sense of the nuances of communication. . . ."

This competence in communication is a matter of the utmost importance in psychiatry because it is the basis of much of our therapy. For in addition to the fact that the patient has justifiable doubts about the ability of the psychiatrist to understand him, there is the fact that the patient himself doesn't understand himself! It is hard enough to describe something that one is clearly aware of; it is still more difficult to describe something about which one is not clearly aware but is disturbed by, and it is still more difficult to put this in a form which a second party (the psychiatrist) will grasp, and grasp sympathetically.

Finally, the psychiatric patient differs from most medical and surgical patients in that his illness involves not only his interpersonal relationships, and his means of communication, but involves psycho-

logical processes—intellectual and emotional and instinctual manifestations—the counterparts of which exist also in the physician.
Indeed, these may be the very same ones which the physician is using
in his efforts to observe and understand the patient. Hence the patient's symptoms and behavior often awaken impulses and associations and reactions within us which we are having trouble enough
of our own to manage. This tends to upset us, to disturb our objectivity. It may arouse pity rather than sympathy, anger rather than
regret, contempt rather than curiosity, erotic feelings rather than
friendliness, anxiety about oneself rather than concern about the
patient. The patient's illness forces, or let us say permits, him to do
things which we do not permit ourselves to do, and sometimes this
has the tendency to create envy and resentment. The patient may be
provocative; he may be seductive. And the psychiatrist must control
himself.

These are some of the ways in which the psychiatric patient differs
from the medical and surgical patient, requiring a different approach. It probably sounds to the novitiate appallingly difficult and
dangerous. If this inspires respect for the difficulties of the task, that
is good; if it stimulates only fear and inhibition, it is bad. The task
must be done and can be done and is and has been done very skillfully by many people. But it has to be learned; it has to be learned
with much trial-and-error experience. Gradually a certain attitude
will develop which enables one to do it with an automatic correctness.
Even then one will sometimes make mistakes; the most experienced
of us do that.

Perhaps a few practical hints will help the novitiate in his earliest
efforts of this difficult task by serving as rules of thumb. They are all
dependent upon what I have previously said, but they will look
simpler in this form and thus will be easier to follow until an ingrained attitude is acquired:

1. In meeting your patient, you must take the initiative. Of course
he has already taken the initiative, or someone has, by virtue of the
fact that he is in your office or hospital. Now it is up to you to carry
the ball for a little way. Help him over this critical moment, remem-

bering that all patients are afraid, ashamed, embarrassed, a bit hostile, and justifiably distrustful. Put him at ease.

2. Be sure that your patient is as comfortable as he can be. His chair should be more comfortable than yours, not less; he shouldn't have to stare at a window with a light half-blinding him as is considered so proper in medical examinations where visual inspection is so important.

3. Naturally you will see him alone. His story is private and personal and confidential and embarrassing. You may see him occasionally, earlier or later, with relatives and with nurses, but in really getting acquainted with him he must be your sole object of attention.

4. Speak quietly and naturally and in tune with the patient's mood. If he is trying to be cheerful, be the same—but not flippant. If he is depressed, respect that fact. If he is silent, respect his reasons by inquiring about them patiently, not reproachfully.

5. Avoid like the plague such banalities and insults as the following initial statements which one so often hears: "How do you feel today?" "What's the matter?" "How are you feeling?" "What's wrong with you?" "What can I do for you?" "I want to take your history." "When was your father born?" "How much do you masturbate?"

6. Instead, begin in the most natural way possible by telling the patient who and what you are, if he doesn't know, and asking him simple, conventional questions; proceed from the known to the unknown, i.e., from things held in common such as the place, the weather, the circumstances, friends, or current events, to (a) things which the patient alone knows, and only much later to (b) things which you alone know, i.e., explanations, information, and advice.

7. Sincerity, earnestness, and unhurriedness ought to be taken for granted. Unfortunately, they are by no means universal.

8. Tone of voice and manner are hard to prescribe, but the essential thing is to convey to the patient that you are seriously interested in him, desirous of helping him, prepared to listen attentively and uninterruptedly, and capable of understanding and responding. Actions speak louder than words, but one must use both words and actions.

The skillful psychiatrist makes his moves with sufficient smoothness, slowness, and steadiness so that the patient's fears recede in favor of his burning impulse to seize the extended hand of help.

9. Let the patient know that you are on his side. You are, anyway, but while you know it, he doesn't—at first. Even if and where he is wrong in what he says, he is telling you how he sees it, and you must see it that way with him before you can get him to see it differently (which will be much later). Such expressions as "I see what you mean," "Naturally," "I don't blame you," "But why did they do that?" act as catalytic agents in an interview.

10. Avoid patronizing, condescending, minimizing, jocular, reproachful, or preachy remarks. These are so common in us all and so habitual for some people that obvious as this advice is you will probably find yourself violating it.

11. Remember to listen to what the patient says; listen, too, for what he doesn't say. After a rapport is established—not before—you can begin asking pointed questions about what has been omitted, but lead up to these gradually. Thus for example don't come out with a blunt "Are you suicidal?" Rather, "You must have felt pretty bad about it . . . And did you remain pretty low-spirited? . . . Clear down, eh? . . . Did you want to give up entirely? . . . How desperate did you get? . . . Did you think of ending it? . . . Really killing yourself? . . . How were you going to do it?" etc.

12. Be especially reticent in asking questions about sexual matters until the patient is quite familiar with your purpose and methods, and can accept such questions as part of a thorough and systematic examination of his life and habits. Even then, remember that you are a psychological-minded physician and not a statistical-minded contributor to the Kinsey report. You don't have to know all the details.

13. Don't lose your balance, by which I mean this: Don't be so bent upon convincing the patient that you are the best friend he has or ever had that you put him in the embarrassing position of being afraid to tell you the truth later on for fear of disappointing you. You are a physician, not a nurse, and making him comfortable is for you a means to an end. While you must convince him of your trustworthiness and of your genuine interest, you shouldn't seduce

him into thinking you approve of his continuing to do anything he wants to do. Set him an example of objectivity. You want to collect certain facts and look at them to see what they mean; help him to do that with you.

14. At the right time, therefore, you should explain what you are doing and what you propose to do, for example in the way of further history, physical examination, and ward prescription. Don't do too much of this explaining. Listening is your main role for a few hours; perhaps many hours, but don't leave the patient hanging. He wants you to listen, but he also wants you to do something about it. Hence in leaving him, make the next step definite—*when, where,* and *what.* You must also account for the interim. What is he to do in the meantime? You are responsible, you know. He is your patient; you have assumed the responsibility. Let him feel this, and maintain the continuity between the various times of personal contact you make with him.

15. In regard to taking notes, a great deal of nonsense has been written and spoken. Very few patients object to this *after* the first ten or fifteen minutes, by which time you will probably have settled down to serious listening. Most patients are impressed favorably by your wish to make a careful record. Some are disturbed by it, however, and you should notice that quickly and act accordingly—stop! Remember what you can and fill in your forgettings later. It is just as simple as that.

16. A small minority of psychiatric patients will seem to be uncommunicative and psychologically inaccessible. (This number seems *relatively* large when one is working in a large state hospital.) But even such patients are rarely completely uncommunicative or completely inaccessible. Their very silence communicates something. Their gestures and strange language likewise have meaning. Sometimes by quiet, continued observation we can read these "foreign languages." Sometimes, too, we can learn to read the communications of organ speech, as it has been called. The main thing is to make an effort, a patient, persistent, earnest effort. Recently a patient who had not spoken for fifteen years responded to the continued efforts of one of our psychiatric aides who presumably was the first

man who had ever convinced the patient of having a genuine wish to hear what he had to say. Within a few days this patient took a place on the hospital baseball team, and talks freely now with numerous individuals. But there were fifteen years of silence during which no one made a successful psychiatric approach to this patient. This is why we think it is important to learn how to do it.

23. Psychiatric Responsibilities in Nursing-Home Care

Several years ago I woke up to a responsibility of psychiatry which had eluded my vision completely for thirty years. I felt as a patient must feel when his eyes have been suddenly opened to a vista long obscured by a neurotic scotoma. But my particular type of scotoma seems to afflict many of my colleagues.

In every state there are problems of overcrowding in the state hospitals. We have been doing pretty well recently in getting this to the attention of the governors and legislators. We have told them the truth, namely, that because of forced, false economies and because of inadequate and untrained personnel, patients have been starved, beaten, neglected, and unscientifically treated in thousands of instances.

We have told them that nearly three-quarters of a million patients fill our psychiatric hospitals today and that there will be more tomorrow, in spite of the fact that our treatment methods are improving.

What we did *not* tell them is that a very large number of psychiatric patients are being cared for in a semi-institutional way without any psychiatrists at all and without any psychiatric supervision at all, and in many instances with no state regulation or inspection at all. I confess that I was utterly astonished to learn that in my own state the number of residents in nursing homes is approximately one-half the number of patients in all our state institutions.

Reprinted from the *Bulletin of the Menninger Clinic*, 19:16–18, January 1955.

As Dr. R. C. Anderson commented in his recent presidential address before the Kansas Psychiatric Society, "In our zeal to eliminate mere custodial care in our hospitals, and to insure that persons are not hospitalized who are not in actual need of specific psychiatric treatment, perhaps we psychiatrists have contributed to the unprecedented expansion and growth of nursing homes during the past ten years. While it is certainly desirable that all persons who may be said to be unnecessarily hospitalized should be removed from hospitals, there is a question as to whether or not the psychiatric profession is fully aware of its continuing responsibility in these matters.

"There are literally thousands of nursing homes in the nation providing a type of care for the mentally ill with no supervision, inspection, certification, or professional assistance of any kind whatsoever. It is my impression that if this trend continues, and if the psychiatric profession does not recognize and assume the responsibility which is rightfully its own, more shocking conditions will eventually come to light in these institutions than has ever prevailed in the worst of our state hospitals. The psychiatric profession must recognize that it has a medical responsibility to mentally ill persons and that this responsibility is not evaded by changing the location of such persons or by indulging in various kinds of euphemisms, such as nursing homes, intermediate hospitals, rehabilitation centers, and so forth. We cannot cleanse our Augean stables by sweeping them into another which is even more chaotic."

It is inevitable when weak, helpless, dependent, mentally impaired individuals are given over to the care of healthier individuals who earn their living by taking care of these afflicted ones, that abuses of many kinds will develop and continue. It is not surprising that there have been some shocking reports of what goes on in nursing homes. It is only surprising that there have not been more such articles. As one national magazine [1] has recently said, it "has grown into a big and sometimes shady business."

Every psychiatrist who has had experience with the administration of state mental-health problems realizes the very valuable services that a properly run nursing home can contribute. It is a great need. The dedication of some operators to the humble and often trying and laborious tasks is something to marvel at. Of course there are some cruel operators and some vicious ones, but there are also many dedicated and devoted ones. They get little help or attention from psychiatry or psychiatrists. My point is that we psychiatrists who have scotomatized this area of our professional responsibility ought to become aware of it and seek to be as helpful as we can to those who are trying to maintain high standards in the conduct of this phase of care for the helpless.

I am proud of some recent developments in the state of Kansas, where, among other things, a school for nursing-home operators has been developed at the Topeka State Hospital for which there are many more applicants than available positions at the moment. But more important, it seems to me, is the fact that the better operators— in many states, including Kansas—have taken upon themselves the responsibility for organizing and developing standards for their work. The state inspection in the world will never eliminate abuses if some sort of leadership and idealism doesn't develop from within. That it is doing so is attested by such things as the following Official Creed of the Kansas Association of Licensed Nursing Homes, Inc. It speaks for itself, and in my opinion it speaks with eloquence and dignity and a warming of the heart. Fellow blind-men, please take notice!

I BELIEVE in the dignity of the individual human personality and shall respect that dignity.

I BELIEVE in the right of a resident, as an individual, to have a freedom of choice in his way of life and shall respect that right.

I BELIEVE that the requirements of the residents in my care come before my own needs, and shall care for them before myself.

I BELIEVE in the inviolate nature of confidences and personal life of my residents and shall respect those confidences.

I BELIEVE that derogatory comments about other members of my profession are detrimental to the entire profession and shall not make such remarks.

I BELIEVE that my behavior in all respects and at all times should reflect only credit upon my profession and shall conduct myself accordingly.

I BELIEVE in maintaining cooperative relationships with other members of my profession, with all persons and agencies, both public and private, whose function is the betterment of the nursing home and shall extend that cooperation at all times.

I BELIEVE that learning is a continuing process and shall strive daily to improve my professional ability.

24. The Psychological Examination in the Psychiatric Case Study

The one professional function which a psychiatrist performs with every patient is the making of a psychological examination. It is axiomatic that psychiatry depends upon psychological data as well as physical and chemical data for its conclusions and its procedures. These data must be collected, correlated, and recorded.

The procedures of clinical examinations are for the most part of fairly recent origin. Time was when physicians could voice opinions on the basis of clinical history, intuition, or imagination with no examinations whatsoever. The earlier clinical examinations were superficial, local, and unsystematized. Old woodcuts show physicians holding flasks of urine up to the light for the purpose of determining whether or not the patient was in love! Why this should have been a medical problem is not clear, nor how any diagnostic conclusions could be logically drawn. But examination of a kind it definitely was, and other types of topical examinations were widely used.

Systematic physical and chemical examination methods were developed during the late nineteenth century, and were brought to a high peak of technical proficiency with the assistance of the newly discovered X-ray and electrical testing methods of the twentieth century. Post-mortem pathological clinical history and clinical ex-

This is a portion of a chapter in the revised edition of *A Manual for Psychiatric Case Study* (1952), now in preparation, in which the original author, Karl Menninger, M.D., has been assisted by Lewis L. Robbins, M.D., Paul W. Pruyser, Ph.D., and Martin Mayman, Ph.D. Reprinted from the *Bulletin of the Menninger Clinic*, 23:131–143, July 1959.

amination findings began to be systematically correlated. The longitudinal, historical view of the process was correlated with the cross-sectional view (the examinations).

It is only within the past few decades that it has been considered proper to include psychological data in clinical examination. Psychological observations of certain kinds have always been included in history—the reaction to a great bereavement, an experience of horror, an inability to remember. But the systematic examining of a patient's psychological functions as of the present moment was not considered medical. Its chief development came from the psychologists, whose clinical material was sparse and who tended therefore to concentrate on relatively healthy subjects, and from the alienists, whose clinical material was extremely specialized. Even yet there is confusion in many quarters between psychological examining and psychological testing. The making of a psychological examination requires testing, but even more it requires observation of the patient in various life situations. It requires observation of the patient's reaction to the examiner and to the examiner's efforts to observe and understand him. It requires both formal inquiry and measurement.

The acquisition of these data will therefore never be so systematic as in the case of a physical examination or a urinalysis. The data will be obtained on the ward and in the office. They will be obtained by the psychologist, the nurse, the physician. Many conclusions regarding the patient's psychological functioning will be drawn during the taking of the clinical history.

But, however diffuse and varied the procedures of examination may be, the data obtained must be recorded in an orderly, systematic, logical way. This is partly for the assistance of the examiner himself in organizing his thinking and arriving at an understanding of the illness, but it is also for the purpose of informing fellow scientists who wish to review the data upon which the conclusions are based.

From traditional psychology and hospital psychiatry, certain general schemata of psychological descriptions have evolved. These have been considerably modified by new tests on one hand and by new personality theories on the other. Any system of recording will be somewhat artificial and over-simplified. The lack of some skeletal outline, however, results in impressionistic descriptions and precludes accurate comparison of patients and functions. At the Menninger Clinic the psychiatrists have cooperated with the psychologists in working out a general scheme for the organization and recording of psychological data. The revisions of it almost every year since 1946 represent what we believe are improvements from experience and suggestions.

We divide the examination into four parts: The identification of the patient and the circumstances of the examination, the analysis of the part processes (which formerly constituted the entirety of the mental-status examination in psychiatry), an analysis of the integrated functioning of the patient in his environment, and a recapitulation of the most important findings, positive and negative.

I. IDENTIFICATION

Obtaining information, findings, or data from the patient always depends on the context or setting of the examination. The context must be defined because it determines the validity and the interpretation of the findings. The following categories are included under identification of the patient.

A. *File number, age, sex, marital status, special characteristics, and whereabouts of the patient.*
B. *Circumstances of the examination, including dates.*
State whether the psychological examination was part of a total psychiatric case study or was a consultation service, to a surgical colleague, for example. Always state *where* and *when* the examination was made, and name those present. If any data were obtained at another time by another person, such as psychological test results or the observations of a nurse, this should be specified. Give the date on which the data were organized into a formal record.
C. *Special conditions affecting the validity of the findings.*
For example, has the patient taken any drugs which might have a sedative effect or any other psychological effect on him at the time of the examination? Is the patient under sentence or awaiting trial? In case of paroxysmal or cyclic symptoms, state how much time has

elapsed since the last attack. If the patient was unwilling to undergo examination, indicate to what extent he cooperated or was reluctant. D. *General impression conveyed.*

What was the examiner's initial impression of the patient, his gait, posture, clothing, voice, manner of speech, facial expressions, muscular tension, his first reactions to meeting the examiner, his accessibility to inquiry?

II. PART PROCESSES OF PSYCHOLOGICAL FUNCTION

The part processes of psychological functioning contain perception and the reactions to what is perceived. These reactions are emotional actions involving autonomic structures, behavior involving striated musculature, intellectual reactions which presumably slow and refine the immediate responses to stimuli perceived. Each of these reactions has certain normal characteristics. One alertly perceives certain things in the outside world, responds to them with certain appropriate feelings, compares them with previous experiences, traces of which are retained in his memory, examines certain discrepancies and compares these with a line of reasoning about the matter, and finally behaves in a way corresponding to these perceptions, reflections, and emotional reactions. One may promptly exploit the opportunity offered by the original perception or he may inhibit all motion in that direction because of fear of a detected danger.

Obviously, a patient may fail to perceive accurately or he may be distracted by perceiving too much; his memory may be defective or his ability to use it impaired. His emotions may be inappropriate or even lacking. By examining carefully how accurately the patient perceives the outside world, how correctly he tests reality, how appropriately he reacts, how effectively he organizes his experience toward his goals or fails to do so—we have a coherent picture of the intact and impaired areas in the patient's psychological functioning. In reality, the so-called "part processes" occur not in isolation, but in exceedingly intricate patterns of dynamic interaction. Many of them can be further analyzed and reduced to more microscopic part processes, and they all overlap. We are aware of these theoretical imperfections; our groupings are dictated by practical considerations including traditional usage.

Perception is the first step in reality testing—the discovery and identification of environmental stimuli. Some use of memory and intellection is necessary for this identification before perception, but the dysfunctions of memory and thought processes are deferred to the next section of the examination. Sensations usually are almost immediately recognized and become perceptions. Interference with perception may occur at different points, e.g., in peripheral deafness, central deafness, or a still more central type of deafness in which words are incorrectly recognized.

Once data are perceived, they continue to be "studied" by processes of recollection, association, comparison, and the like. In this clinical application, thinking might be compared with the use of a reference library. Before a person can react to what he perceives, he will "consult" his memory of previous experiences. How orderly has this material been stored, how much of it is there, how available is it, how accurate, how coherent? We consider what might be described as the *size* and *content* of the library, as well as its *utilization,* i.e., the quantitative and the qualitative or functional aspects of cognition.

The examiner should try to record what occupies the patient's mind in the ordinary sense of the word. What does he think about? What does he daydream about? What does he talk about? What does he ask questions about? This is not all that is in his mind, of course. He has memories most of which are unavailable to him. He has considerable information in his foreconscious. Even in his conscious mind are thoughts he is aware of but to which he is giving a minimum of attention. Usually, the directed thought content of a patient is about the examination itself and the illness. The examiner must determine to what extent this displaces more important reality factors. Hence, the patient's version of the development of his illness must sometimes be included here in full; for example, there may be irreconcilable discrepancies between what the patient says and what another informant says whose report may not be reliable.

Since much of what and how the patient thinks is communicated in speech, writing, gestures, and in other ways, his thinking as such should be distinguished from its expression or "tools." That the cognitive process has a sequence in which thoughts arise first and their expression or formulation comes second is an erroneous idea. Thought and language determine each other in such complicated ways that it is almost impossible to separate them, except in exposition. For this reason language behavior should come under the larger heading of intellection or cognitive functioning. Yet an assessment of a person's language per se can be of clinical value. Some people are excellent talkers and their language carries them away; others are meticulous about what they say, and their language is precise, sometimes halting, with incessant corrections and modifications. Words may have power and they may also arouse anxiety. Words and gestures may communicate or they may conceal one's thoughts. Certain silences may be highly communicative.

In addition to thinking about things perceived and remembered, there are efferent discharges into the autonomic and neuromuscular systems, giving rise to *emotional* states and muscular actions. Often subjective reactions must be inferred from actions rather than words. The patient may try to restrain the expression of his feelings or to deny their nature or intensity. The affective state of a troubled individual is such a subtle aspect of human functioning that data about it can only be approximately and tentatively estimated.

The end result of reaction to perception is the conglomerate of acts which make up the patient's *behavior*. We attempt to describe the relative appropriateness, quantity, skill, speed, and efficiency of these actions with respect to the patient's purposes and his possibilities. The estimate will be based on observations by the examiner and by reliable affiliates—the nurses, aides, and adjunctive therapists. The examiner will also consider any reliable information in the history.

One purpose of part processes is to establish an optimum relationship between the individual and the environment. This involves the maintenance of combined *internal* and *external* balance or integration. These balances are constantly changing but in making the adjustments necessary for this balance, characteristic individual patterns and techniques develop. Most minor and many major changes (stresses) in the environment will be absorbed without much change in these established patterns. Stress that is too great, too sudden, or too long excites disturbing responses of disappointment, dissatisfaction, or aggression. These in turn impel the ego to use adventitious emergency devices which permit survival but are disagreeable and burdensome, and are symptoms of an illness.

The evidences of an impairment in the mutual adjustment of an individual and his environment may be most conspicuous in the adventitious elements observed in the part processes. A delusion, for example, results from an internal need to alter an interpretation of facts. This necessity may have arisen through some change in the external adjustment, but the delusion itself will, in turn, affect other relationships. Thus failure of the psychological system not only appears in the part processes but can also be observed in the person's external relationships.

Every person relates himself to a number of other people, to material objects, to values, to society at large, to the universe, and to his God. He develops certain attitudes toward himself and "his" illness. These relations make up his characteristic patterns of life adjustment. Integration is thus used in a double sense; the person becomes integrated with his environment to varying degrees and his psychological processes can be considered internally integrated if they have helped achieve a good external integration at not too great a cost.

A. *Perception.*
> *Normal features:* Alertness; accuracy; vividness; range and scope; appropriate selectivity; reality assessment.
> *Deviations:*
> Deficiencies, e.g., anesthesia; * anosmia; amaurosis; distractability; disorientation (time, place, person); confusion; selective inattention; denial (e.g., phantom limb).

---

* The symptoms suggested throughout embrace those seen at one time or another in various patients. No patient presents all of these. This is not a check list of all possibilities, but is arranged in this way because of the relative unfamiliarity of the young psychiatrists with most of these terms.

Excesses, e.g., hyperesthesia; hyperalertness; restless wandering of attention; hyperacusis.

Distortions, e.g., paresthesias; illusions; disorders of body image; depersonalization.

B. *Intellection* (cognitive functions).

Distinguish between the native endowment and what has become of it under the stresses and strains and challenges of life. One person may make efficient use of a meager endowment, while another may waste great intellectual resources. Intellectual deficit may be general, as in diffuse senile deteriorations, or specific, as in the inability of some bright persons to learn mathematics, or agraphia in some persons with a parietal lobe tumor.

  1. Content, level, and range of intellection.

  Normal features: Curiosity; memory; store of knowledge; range and type of ideas; fantasies; dreams; thoughts; intellectual level; special intellectual gifts; talents and skills.

  Deviations:

  Deficiencies, e.g., stupidity; amnesia; hypomnesia; meagerness; vagueness; impoverishment; special deficits or developmental anomalies.

  Excesses, e.g., hypergnosis; hypermnesia; absorbing preoccupation with plans, worries, fantasies; obsessions; fixed ideas.

  Distortions, e.g., memory distortions (in content or chronology); confabulations; gross judgment defect; delusions.

  2. Functional aspects of intellection.

The ways a person uses his memories and his capacity for association in seeking solutions to problems or in achieving goals are considered here.

  Normal features: Tempo (rapidity of association and ideas); rythm (spontaneous, hesitant, halting); style (practical, simple, well-articulated or global, creative, inventive, reproductive); organization and logical coherence; direction; abstraction capacity; flexibility.

  Deviations:

  Deficiencies, e.g., stereotypy, platitudinous vagueness, rigidity, concretism, retardation, blocking, agnosia.

Excesses, e.g., circumstantiality; over-intellectualizing; over-symbolization; syncretism; flight of ideas.

Distortions, e.g., incoherence; irrelevance; condensation; contaminations; neologisms.

3. Language and communication.

Depending on vocabulary size, language may be stereotyped and rigid or highly diversified. Linguists have found distinct patterns and degrees of diversity among normal and pathological groups. The frequency with which certain words occur (e.g., "I" or "me," adjectives, qualifying terms such as "but" or "however") shows certain norms or optima from which individuals may deviate in clinically significant ways.

Extralingual communication processes refer to gestures, facial expression, and muscular movements which have a definite communicative intention. One should distinguish between involuntary autonomic reactions which cause, e.g., blushing or tremor, and acquired muscular patterns (which may become habits and therefore become also quite automatic) which can be brought under conscious control, such as pointing, gesticulating, frowning, raising one's eyebrows. Some people support their speech with massive bodily action, by pounding, swaying their arms, rocking their trunk, or even by physically acting what they say. In others one finds that posturing or more dramatic acting and mimicking totally replaces verbal communication. Significant also is the excessive use or total abstinence of physical contact with others, such as touching, shaking hands, embracing. As communications these gestures may have a loving or an aggressive connotation.

> *Normal features:* Word fluency; vocabulary size; diversity; precision/exactness; stability of meaning; proportionality; cultural determinants; writing; extralingual communication skills.

Deviations:

Deficiencies, e.g., illiteracy; word paucity; stereotypy, clichés, vagueness; asphasic deficits, understatements; inarticulateness; circumlocution; semantic vagueness; agraphia.

Excesses, e.g., garrulousness; over-exactness; pedantic or stilted

word choice; verbosity; perseverations; redundancy; over-
statements; absolutism, excessive use of superlatives, over-
affective, metaphoric, or poetic language.

Distortions, e.g., autistic word usage; excessive or peculiar ges-
turing; neologisms; word salad; paraphasias; incoherence;
jargon; glibness.

C. *Emotion* (affective processes).

Emotions have an "ebb and flow" character; any specific feeling
(as different in tone from other feelings) has a certain rate of acceleration and deceleration in the process of being built up and fading
out. There are significant individual differences in this respect. The
depth of any emotion (we speak of "strong" and "weak" feelings
too) though very difficult to assess objectively, is also subject to individual variation. Some people's feelings linger on for a long
time, while others' feelings change rapidly from one moment to
the next.

The concepts of *stability* of affect and its converse, *liability,* relate
feeling to the varying conditions of the person's external or internal environment. In some, emotions remain rather stable despite
gross changes in surroundings, while others fluctuate rapidly from
one extreme to another, even in relatively stable surroundings or
inner conditions. In still others a definite periodicity or cycle occurs.

Normal features: Prevailing mood; intensity and duration of
emotional reactions; appropriateness; irritability; stability.

Deviations:

Deficiencies, e.g., blandness; blunting; apathy; coldness.

Excesses, e.g., prevalent or recurrent rage, depression, elation;
fearfulness; apprehensiveness; jealousy; envy, suspiciousness;
remorse; panic; sudden shifts.

Distortions, e.g., inappropriate responses to stimuli; inappropriate
guilt feelings; incongruity of feeling and action; dissimulation;
negativism; facetiousness.

D. *Action* (behavior).

Excesses of action refer to states of disinhibition or release. In
normal growth we acquire control over the motor system by delay
of action and a dampening of the intensity of motor impulses.

Normal features: Energy level; vigor; adroitness; directness; persistence; constructiveness; planning and timing; effectiveness;
purposiveness.

Deviations:

Deficiencies, e.g., inertia; stupor; paralysis; inability to initiate
action; inhibition; rigidity; apraxias.

Excesses, e.g., restlessness; hyperkinesis; agitation; assaultiveness;
impulsiveness; destructiveness; gesticulation; expansiveness.

Distortions, e.g., peculiar habits (e.g., in eating, sleeping, smoking, excretory, sexual, others); tics and mannerisms; compulsions; rituals; posturing; stereotypy; catalepsy; aimless, scattered activity.

III. INTEGRATIVE PATTERNS

The third section of the examination deals not with part processes,
but with total or holistic processes. Here, as in the first part, data
are bound to include directly observed facts, reports by other workers, history obtained in various ways, and statements which may
appear to be factual but which are actually inferences. The degree
of probability or correctness of an estimate or conclusion should
be implied by the language in which it is recorded.

We assume that each person is motivated by instinctual drives
which lead him to explore his environment, make selections and
rejections, and in various ways adjust himself to what he finds.
He is attached to others by bonds of interest, fear, desire, dependence, or envy. With Freud, we think these can be reduced to various
combinations and special aspects of *love* and *hate,* representing
integrative and disintegrative instinctual trends. Toward everyone
we have some love and some hate. They may both be present in
equally slight amounts, in some instances the love will far outweigh the hate, while in others the hostile and negative elements
will far outweigh the love. Since these bonds are to other human
beings, there is a constant reciprocal interaction, although the
quantities and patterns will never exactly correspond.

How the patient reacts toward inanimate objects reflects his self-
concept and his maturation. What does he prize most—his wife,

his money, his car, his lands, his books? How does he treat them? How does he feel toward the possessions of others, i.e., how sharp is his distinction between mine and thine? Objects tend to be substituted for persons in the unconscious, and this personalization of them combines with reality factors to form the fabric of the patient's relationships with the accessible pieces of his universe.

The relationship of the self to the self is more difficult to grasp philosophically than psychologically. We believe that the child originally identifies himself with the universe and only gradually subtracts from himself and accords autonomy to the various objects in his environment—first the mother, then the father, then toys or sky. We assume a core of self-investment of instinctual energies from which is drawn the supply necessary for external attachments. Some of this supply is in times of stress, pain, illness, or loneliness, returned to, or redirected upon the self as "secondary narcissism" (visible as self-love, self-pity, self-comfort), leaving less to neutralize the externally directed aggression. This means that if one is sorry for himself, he will likely be more aggressive toward others. Under other circumstances, the aggressive component is redirected upon the self.

Inquire particularly into the patient's attitude toward his illness. One must distinguish between how it feels and looks to the patient, how it feels and looks to others, and the patient's reaction to discrepancies in these views.

Since adaptation is crucial to survival, the mode and degree of adaptation are basic determinants of a person's place on the health-illness continuum. All the holistic and integrative processes, as well as the part processes of psychological functioning, must be evaluated in terms of their efficacy in securing exchange between the person and his material and social environment.

A. *Relations to other people.*
  1. Range, diversification, depth, constancy, and other general qualities of the patient's positive and negative attachments to people.

Is he a man of many friends or few, a "wallflower" or a "joiner," a quarrelsome misfit or a leader? Indicate what his prevailing techniques of social encounter appear to be—kindliness, friendliness, reserve, provocative challenge, quick empathy and identification.

2. Major attachments.

Who are the main figures in the patient's life, his best friends and his worst enemies? Indicate something of the quality of the attachment to them, e.g., anaclitic, parasitic, possessive, intrusive, exploiting, companionate, erotic, or agapic.

3. General pattern of sexual adjustment (if not covered above).

4. Transference paradigm (relationships to examiner reflecting childhood patterns).

The patient's general pattern of interpersonal relationships is frequently reflected in those he seeks to establish with the examiner. For example, he may be more anxious to please the examiner than to conform to truth; he may make innumerable requests and demands and take umbrage easily if these are ignored. Such approaches often typify the social techniques of the patient and one may make inferences about how they were developed in childhood situations. It may be helpful to describe these techniques in terms of roles. See also D-3.

B. *Relations to things and ideas.*

1. Possessions.

2. Time and space.

Persons differ in regard to their time perspective. Some are past-oriented, some future-oriented. Consider also the immediately observable aspects of behavior, such as: always late? always early? claustrophobic? wasting time? expansive? space-demanding or crammed?

3. Authority, power, and responsibility.

The child goes through phases of taking authority for granted, questioning it, opposing it, assuming it without justification, and finally differentiating his reactions so as to distinguish the appropriate time and place for compliance or for the assumption of responsibility. Immaturity of development and regression from maturity are frequently most conspicuously evident in this area.

4. Work.

Consider here interest, intensity, variety, creativity, consistency, skill, efficiency, satisfaction, and, in the matter of play, add sportsmanship. Not only are objects substituted, but the modalities of dealing with the objects may be considered sublimations or useful fusions of destructive and creative impulses, the latter normally predominating.

5. Play (see Work, above).

6. Philosophical, social, and religious concepts.

Assess the form, scope, intensity, and satisfaction toward the intangibles of life—value systems, philosophical attitudes and formulations regarding the problems of evil, misfortune, death, race prejudice, religious beliefs.

C. *Relations to self.*

1. Ego: self-concept; self-esteem; models of ego-identity; sense of freedom.

The self includes several selves or parts. The word ego may be confusing here since we use it elsewhere to describe the executive functions of regulation, steady state maintenance, and impulse control in reconciling conflictual pressures. These functions also assume a *perceptive* function, and it is used here in this sense only because this is all the patient can tell us about. We can learn from him how he sees himself, what his ego observes or "feels," or what it senses in regard to its freedom or restriction. (We cannot expect an individual to tell us, however, what his ego represses or how much, or why.) We can also learn from a person whether he stresses his uniqueness or whether he perceives himself as "just one among many," "a cog in the machine," or "just a member of the species." Obviously, such self-evaluations have far-reaching significance for the total life style.

2. Ego-ideal: level of aspiration; ethical standards; life-goal formulation; sense of responsibility.

This consists of that *complex of conscious attitudes,* evaluations, motivations, ideals, and hopes that can be formulated in answer to the question, What kind of a person does the patient aspire to be? The feasibility of the aspirations, the motivating power or "steam" back of it, and the discrepancies between ego-ideal and everyday behavior are to be noted.

3. Super-ego: evidences of strength; presumptive predominant models (if known); characteristic type of placation required (penance or penitence, mourning, physical suffering, gestures, deprivation, bribery); degree of externalization.

This comprises those *unconscious determinants* of prohibitions and obligations that are rooted in infantile identifications, the *"archaic conscience"* as distinguished from conscience in the ordinary sense. In reporting on super-ego functioning, the examiner must avoid psychodynamic speculations that have no place in a report of examination. Inferences should be confined to the available evidence. Since it is likely to be meager, the recorded data will probably be brief. Self-reproach, perfectionism, asceticism, and oppressive "oughts" and "musts" are common indices of super-ego over-activity.

4. The body: attitudes toward; concept of (body image); treatment of; susceptibility to injury; sensitivity to pain.

The body is certainly part of the self, and yet in other aspects it is sharply differentiated from the self—we speak of *me* and *my* body, sometimes even of "it." The attitude of the ego toward the body may be one of overestimation or underestimation, or nearness or distance. The "body image" each person has of his own appearance, his body conformation, his physical assets and liabilities, is always considerably different from how others see him. This discrepancy is frequently important and complicates the "relations" to the self, but there is a distinction between relations to the body as such and relations to the body as conceived.

D. *Relations to the present situation* (insight).

1. Discomfort experienced (i.e., how much does the patient suffer?).

Subjective distress—psychological pain, tension awareness, anxiety feelings—call into use some of the devices of the ego which tend to diminish this discomfort. Distinguish between what is actually felt by the patient and what would be felt were it not for these semi-relief measures. The examiner should note whether the awareness of the internal distress (anxiety) is constant, episodic, fluctuating, intense, or only nagging, and to what extent it is expressed or accompanied by physiological evidences.

2. Discomfort inflicted. (How much does the patient make others suffer? Who are the ones hurt? How does he hurt them? Does he know it? Does he care?)

3. Patient-society interactions.

a. How do others react to his injuries of them? (Do they regard him as sick, "crazy," criminal, "demented," pathetic?)

b. How does he react to their reactions? (Does he know that he is regarded as mentally ill? Does he concur? If he is unpopular, does he understand it?)

4. The patient's concept of his illness.

How does the patient regard or explain his illness, his unpopularity, or his pain? To whom or to what does he attribute it? Does he see it as more or as less severe than it actually is? Does he recognize his own responsibility in it, or does he regard himself solely as a victim? Do casual observers see his disability as less handicapping than it really is, or as more so?

5. Patient's concept of and attitude toward recovery (i.e., Does the patient have any hopes of recovery? From what source? Does he consciously want help? Does he think this help can come only from the doctor? Does he feel free enough to commit himself to a change?).

6. The patient's attitude toward the examiner before, during, and at the end of the examination.

E. *Relations to reality in general.*

1. General level of "common sense" and reality contact.

2. Degree of reality severance.

We distinguish four levels: (1) More or less disturbing subjectively with no perceptible withdrawal from reality. (2) Partial detachment from reality with the use of compensatory "second order" devices. (3) Quasi-stability with episodic explosions of aggressive energy and dereism. (4) Gross repudiation of reality.

3. Degree of impairment of total effectiveness.

This is often quite unpredictable from quantity and even quality of the psychopathology. Some very disorganized, mentally ill individuals are extremely competent and function, with or without public detection of their handicap, in places of considerable responsibility.

IV. RECAPITULATION

Summarize briefly in telegraphic or tabular style the significant findings of the psychological examinations, including the intact functions which can serve as assets for therapeutic exploitation and the most important pathology found.

PART THREE

The Theorist

Alan Gregg was fond of talking about a certain deep-sea fish and he would often remark, "The most difficult thing for a deep-sea fish to realize is that he is swimming in salt water." Certain men, like Gregg, have an uncanny sensitivity to what is going on in the world around about them, and Karl Menninger is such a man. Part of the perspicacity essential to the theorist stems from this sensitivity.

Perhaps more important than his theoretical contributions are the social changes that he has tried to implement, social changes based upon his theoretical formulations. He is more of a militant reformer—a twentieth-century Pinel—than he is a theorist. But his programs for reform of the care of the mentally ill and for the treatment of the offender are not only visionary ones, but are backed by sound theoretical principles.

When Karl Menninger has an idea he pursues it doggedly. Often he appears more convinced of the idea than he really is, and uses an assumed attitude of conviction to reflect his thinking against the thinking of others. Many find this quality in him irritating and some are angered by it. But thinking about thinking is important in the world of Karl Menninger.

His theoretical considerations, evident throughout this book, are largely an extension of those of Sigmund Freud. Karl Menninger's original contributions to medical theory concern largely the very conception of health and disease. He learned a great deal from Adolf Meyer, who conceived of illness as a reaction of the individual to internal and external stress and who attempted to develop a nosology for these reactions. He studied the organism's continuous and dynamic efforts to maintain a biological *status quo,* and he enlarged this concept to include the psychic functions of the organism.

From Freud he learned the most: the theory of the unconscious—the very cornerstone of psychoanalysis; theories of personality development; theories about the structure of the personality; theories about the instincts and their vicissitudes; theories of symptom formation and their treatment.

But Southard made an imprint upon Karl Menninger that proved indelible—he is restless to bring the lessons learned from the clinical use of the theories of others into an over-all conception of the nature of illness. This includes an attempt at nosology, but one quite different from that imagined by Southard or Meyer. The latest editions of this thinking are included in the last two papers in this section.

Other papers in this section reflect efforts to continue in the tradition of A. A. Brill, William Alanson White, and Smith Ely Jelliffe. These men saw the need to integrate psychoanalytic principles into general psychiatry and were dedicated to accomplishing this. Here, Karl Menninger writes about the results of their efforts which he helped foster—psychoanalytic psychiatry.   —B. H. H.

1. The Genius of the Jew in Psychiatry

If we had no further illustration than the character of Sigmund Freud, we should have a basis for suspecting some connection between the Jew and psychological genius. It would carry us too far to list all the outstanding Jewish psychologists and psychiatrists, nor would it, in my own mind, be fitting to associate lesser names with that of such a master as he. It is one thing to show that proportionately many Jews have an interest in psychiatry and another to show that they have some special abilities in that direction. The fact is well known that Jewish physicians are distinguished for their scientific accomplishments in all fields of medicine, and, in writing such an article as this, one is dangerously close to the dilemma that if one holds that Jews are brilliant in all fields of science, it is the more difficult to show that they have some outstanding genius in psychiatry. Furthermore, as a Gentile, I am apt —like all Gentiles—to overestimate the superiorities and attainments of the Jews (a psychological fact which no doubt contributes in part to anti-Semitic reactions).

Nevertheless, I shall proceed on the basis of my empirical impressions, an unscientific but not necessarily invalid method. Some physicians accuse psychiatry of being more of an art than a science and say that psychiatrists are, therefore, born rather than made (not in the sense of inheriting something, but of coming by their special gifts by very early childhood influences, rather than from later

Reprinted from *Medical Leaves,* Joseph C. Beck, ed. Chicago: Medical Leaves, 1937.

training). This perhaps substantiates me in my belief that some Jews seem to have a special gift which makes them more likely than the average person in those requirements that make for skill, if not genius, in psychiatry, gifts which are peculiarly related to their Jewish origin. Since the recognition of the psychological elements of disease and behavior are so rapidly increasing in scientific circles as well as among laymen, and since the demands for psychiatrists so far exceed the supply, the recognition of such gifts might therefore be of considerable practical value, and it behooves us to inquire into the reasons for it and the possibilities of its being cultivated.

We could not logically begin a consideration of such a problem in a more appropriate way than to consider that extraordinary genius, Sigmund Freud. It is neither necessary nor appropriate that I devote many lines here to show that he is one of the great minds in history. In all those sciences which deal with human beings in the course of his own generation probably no other individual has so largely altered the content and direction of human thought. What appeals to us, who are scientists, is the fact that he was able to reduce to a scientific discipline what had been known for thousands of years by those whose intuition gave them glimpses beneath the surface of things. That it led to extraordinary and unexpected findings which he then had the courage to examine, to correlate, and to present to a reluctant and even antagonistic world of science is to his inestimable credit. In working with difficult patients, with the possibilities of homicide or suicide or psychosis imminent, I have often reflected what immeasurable courage it must have taken for Freud to pursue his earliest researches in the face of the threat of scientific excommunication, legal action, social stigmatization, and above all that feeling of having brought about a disaster through blunder which all doctors dread. Freud faithfully and courageously worked through an uncharted wilderness, blazing a trail for the rest of us to follow and to explore more leisurely and more safely.

I should not have sought to establish a connection between his talent and the fact that he was a Jew, had not Freud himself repeatedly called attention to the relationship between his work and his Jewishness. Some of his own remarks on the subject were:

> . . . Only to my Jewish nature did I owe the two qualities which have become indispensable to me on my hard road. Because I was a Jew I found myself free from many prejudices which limited others in the use of their intellects; and being a Jew I was prepared to enter opposition to renounce the agreement with the compact majority.[1]

It would indeed seem presumptuous to take issue with Freud on any subject involving psychology, except that Freud himself taught us we must distrust our own motives and our own explanations. I shall, therefore, in the interest of the present theme, and encouraged by Freud's own attitude, attempt the formidable task of examining Freud's comments on this subject more carefully.*

If we look very objectively at Freud's quotation above, we see that he did not explain it very fully. For example, he says, *"Only to my Jewish nature* did I owe the two qualities." This, it seems to me, is begging the question. Others than Jews have these qualities and it may well be that Freud might have had them had he not been a Jew. Let us examine what the qualities were.

First, he says he found himself free from many prejudices which limited others in the use of their intellects. Now what prejudices could Freud have meant? Is it true that Jews are freer from prejudices than Gentiles?

That, being a Jew, Freud could have the courage to identify himself with another minority group seems to have obvious validity. It should not be forgotten, however, that the original Jews were, so far as they knew or believed, the majority, and the Gentiles the inconsequential minority. I think it is fair to say that the Jewish

---

* It is well known that some of the hostility which Freud's ideas stimulated was projected onto his Jewishness. This is now being re-enacted in Germany where psychoanalysis is under a taboo because it is regarded as a Jewish science. Such absurdities seem incredible to us, but as psychologists we much recognize this principle of displacement, a principle which Freud himself elaborated. We also know, however, that Freud never overcame a considerable reaction of sensitiveness to a discrimination made against him, thought by his friends to be largely due to the fact that he was a Jew. He was never, for example, made a full professor at the University. [K.M.]

people never became adjusted to the consequences of their dispersion over the globe, and such articles as one often reads extolling the great achievements of the Jews, the great men who have been Jews, are no doubt often motivated by a wish to show that qualitatively at least the Jews are in the majority—a spiritual majority. The wish to feel secure which is back of the wish to align oneself with the majority is certainly not lacking in any human beings, Jewish or non-Jewish; the fact that the Jews have been accustomed to the necessity of being affiliated with one minority may give them a greater endurance of such a state, but, as everyone knows, it also acts in a contrary direction and impels many people to identify themselves with whatever majorities they can, and to do so vigorously and enthusiastically.

I venture to say, then, that Freud's own explanations of the relation between his genius and his Jewishness explain nothing. On the other hand, if he were to have had recourse to his own theories, he would have considered far more important the actual experiences of his childhood. What is there in the experience of the Jewish child which is different from that of the Gentile child which might be related to later psychological perspicacity? This, I think, is our question.

Theoretically, the gift of intuitive perception as well as the interest in those who suffer spiritually rather than merely physically must come from previous experiences which rendered him forever sensitive and forever responsive to similar experiences in others. In other words, I think only certain types of suffering in childhood can make one sufficiently concerned with or understanding of suffering of others to enable one to be of help to them. Perhaps this is a clumsy attempt at scientific expression of the religious ideas connecting suffering with spiritual vision. I have no objection to these scientific ideas being allied to religious ideas, but I think we can be more precise and objective about them than in religious treatises. I think we can see in the sharp and intuitive vision and the scientific concern with the unhappy, which go to make a psychiatrist, a sublimation and social exploitation of the unhappiness which must come to many a child. And since many children suffer and will continue to suffer, no matter what happens, this is one way of exploiting suffering other than becoming masochistic oneself, as is the general tendency of many Jews (and, of course, of many others).

Clearly the psychiatrist or psychologist is one for whom emotional experiences are something very real, no less real than physical substances; and presumably in the suffering of other people there is awakened in him some recollections of his own suffering as a child, a suffering which was perhaps never completely assuaged; in this case, his wish to help the other person, his wish to see into the other person's problems and to set him aright, is in part an acting out of a wish that he himself might be saved or have been saved this pain, and in part a sublimation of the sadistic feelings of resentment that his own experiences aroused in him. The child who suffers more has more of such aggressions to release. Psychiatrists, like surgeons, have to hurt people, though when they do so in the interests of helping the patient, the unconscious aggressiveness is thereby sublimated.

Of course, this theory is not mine but an essential part of the whole psychoanalytic discipline; the point is now to apply it to the Jewish child. Does the Jewish child * suffer more than the Gentile child, and, if so, does he suffer in a way which is likely to increase this propensity for interest in the sufferings of other people?

My impression is that perhaps, if we may generalize, the Jewish child does suffer somewhat more or somewhat more frequently than the Gentile child. However, I do not think that this is due to the immediate effects of Gentile prejudice. My impression is that it is due to the child's reaction to the parents' reaction to the entire social situation in which the Jews live. This includes, of course, their religious and historical traditions.

I believe that some ethnologists hold that from the physical standpoint there is little to support the theory of racial distinctness or character in Jews. Certainly from the psychological standpoint,

---

* I mean here, and throughout the paper, not to confirm the illusion of a Jewish entity except socially and traditionally; by Jewish child I mean the child raised in the Jewish tradition. [K.M.]

about which I am better informed, it is now considered entirely invalid to ascribe specific qualities of human nature, or, for example, of "Jewish nature," to human beings independent of their social situation. Those things which are considered (by anyone) to be typically Jewish must be regarded as the consequences of long-continued custom, ideology, and social attitudes. In other words, from this standpoint (represented by the Gestalt psychologists, the psychoanalysts, and, indeed, most of the psychiatrists, as well as many others) the Jew is not a biological entity, and his distinguishing characteristics are psychological and social rather than biological, hence, changeable and changing.

For the present, our social heritage is such that the average Jew thinks of himself as a biological entity and is so regarded by the average Gentile. The majority of Jewish children are brought up under psychological circumstances distinctly different from those of the average Gentile child, at least insofar as his membership character in the Jewish group is concerned. This results in certain reactions with reference to nonmembers of the group, attitudes of hostility, fear, distrust, and repudiation mixed with wistful and uncertain longings to be liked and to be assimilated by other groups, and reaction formations against these wishes. The corresponding Gentile attitudes of fear, distrust, and dislike, mixed with mystical notions of Jewish magic and divinity, are well known.

The product of this, insofar as the Jewish child is concerned, is an emphasis upon his membership in the Jewish group, the dangers to which he is exposed on account of it, the protection he is afforded by it, and the loyalty he owes it. Granted that there are individual differences in every family, one very frequently observed tendency among Jews is their overemphasis of the family bond and their overprotection and overdemonstrativeness toward the children. How this arises from the parents' own sense of insecurity, bred of social situations, I have just outlined.

The overprotective, separatistic treatment of any child, especially if it is endorsed and supported both by custom and by sentimental rationalizations, produces in the child a high degree of narcissism resulting from the fact that he is encouraged to regard himself as superlative, a misconception about himself which, however much it may be displaced in the course of time to his relatives (e.g., to great Jews who have shown the world what Jews can really do), nevertheless acts as a barrier toward comfortable social relationships with his fellow men. To be sure, it may also inspire a terrific aspiration and a compulsive striving toward superiority which may partially account for the high scholastic ranking which Jews so frequently achieve. But along with this there is a mounting sense of disappointment and disillusionment as the growing child discovers that his parents, being human, were not entirely sincere in their adulation and demonstrativeness. He discovers, too, with a bitterness even greater than that of the less favored child, that nowhere outside of his own home is he treated with the extreme tenderness and solicitude he once enjoyed.

Psychiatrists know that such a wound, received in early childhood—a wound inflicted upon one's self-esteem and implicit faith in humanity—never heals without a scar. The thwarting and rebuffs which an overprotected and petted child receives in his first contact with an unfeeling world produce a reaction of protest in him and often lead to his setting up defenses against people. These defenses (or perhaps the inner insecurity which they breed) lead to the essential individualism of so many Jews.

Separatism and prejudice go hand in hand, and the Jewish child has separatism and the alleged need for it impressed upon him before he has had any actual experience with the prejudice. Thus he sets out to meet prejudice, so to speak. The external dangers in a Gentile society are magnified, perhaps partly because of the parents' own sorrows from this source but also because this is an essential corollary to the preservation of internal unity; the same thing is to be observed, of course, in college fraternities, political parties, and international politics. The effect on the child, however, is to instill fear into him. I have been told by Jewish psychiatrists that they regard this as the greatest sin, or shall we say error, of their parents. The child is thus impelled either to forestall this danger by befriending the Gentile in an obsequious manner, which is often transparent, or to defy the danger by being aggressive and provocative, which is also apt to be transparent (i.e., shows the motive of fear behind it), and when this attitude is responded to in kind it gives him an apparent justification for his fears and his hostility. Perhaps on this account every Jewish child must have some time in his life felt hostile toward his parents for their role in having sustained the separatism and inspired the fear which so affects his sense of security. The confusing thing is that there are actually some dangers from some Gentiles, as we have all been painfully reminded by affairs in Germany, and this would seem an inappropriate time to raise the question as to just how this prejudice arises and why it persists.

The result of this separatism, however one explains its origin, is that many Jewish children grow up with an extraordinary interest in and curiosity about people, reinforced no doubt by the background of religion and philosophy which is their heritage. Their own detachment when successfully achieved enables them to be more objective, more analytical and at the same time more discerning in their judgment of others, partly because they understand, and partly because they have been able to rise above suffering and even feel able to relieve it in others.

There is another point to be made in tracing childhood experiences to the adult vocation of psychiatry. Everyone learns sooner or later that one must expect disappointments in love—that his loved ones hurt him oftentimes as grievously as his enemies—but it has seemed to me that the individual Jew learns this at an earlier and more vulnerable age than do others. He learns it first because of his initial disappointment in his parents; their overtenderness and overestimation of him leads to inevitable disappointment because the least indifference on their part or perhaps the enthusiastic reception of another infant is interpreted by the child as a tragic rejection. Thus the individual Jew learns again what the Jews as a group (from their social experiences) long ago learned, namely, that no one can be implicitly and completely trusted. This saves them the painful disillusionment which the Gentile is continually experiencing because of his more gullible naïveté. The Jew knows from bitter experience that those who appear to love one another most, have a hostile component in their interpersonal bond which may under certain circumstances show itself directly or indirectly, overtly or covertly. They know that in one sense there is no such thing as disinterested friendship.

Theoretically—on the basis of their social experience—this attitude might be thought to apply only to Gentiles and not to fellow Jews. Practically, however, the early disillusionment extends to all relationships. Because of his experience within a closely allied group, the Jewish child has an opportunity to learn what every idealistic person who joins a social group or cause in search of understanding and inspiration discovers—that close association breeds hostilities and jealousies as well as love and sympathy.

This knowledge that even one's brothers, those whom one has been taught to turn to for comfort, are not exempt from envy, jealousy, craftiness, and hate, and, above all, actions of self-interest to the hurt of the others, leaves the Jew peculiarly exposed to *feelings of insecurity*. He has too keen an insight into human nature for his own comfort. He is so aware of the possibility of an attack or a desertion or a "double-cross" from his friends that he often anticipates it, even provokes it. But if he learns to understand and control this sensitiveness, he can turn to account his perception of unseen motives with telling effect, as he often does in psychiatry.

Still another reason that those raised in the Jewish tradition may have some special gift for psychiatry is that of the high value placed by them throughout history on verbal expression of feelings as exemplified by the incomparable poetry of the Psalms and the extraordinary quality of their religious literature, and also upon studious scholarly organization of their thinking. The Irish are gifted verbally but do not have the scientific essential of orderliness; the Swedes are orderly but not so gifted verbally. Now, in psychiatry the reduction of relatively intangible things such as feelings and attitudes to verbal expression is highly important. It is necessary to the scientific evaluation of mental processes and it has been shown by the work of Freud to have a therapeutic value for the patient. It is a very old observation that quarreling Irish may throw bricks at one another, and Italians knives, but Jews throw sharp words.

This is a destructive use of the same gift. To convert this talent for verbalization into scientific purposes is in no branch of science more useful than in psychiatry.

Closely allied with this is the fact that traditionally and historically, spiritual values, that is to say, the importance of certain feelings and abstractions, have always appealed to Jews. It has always been my suspicion that the practical business talents exemplified by some Jews were a reaction against this traditional emphasis on intangibles. Be that as it may, the idea that something nonexistent may nevertheless be a psychological reality as powerful in its effect as some material substance is not hard for the Jew to grasp. It is much more difficult on the other hand for the average Anglo-Saxon, and puts him at a disadvantage in psychiatry.

When so many children must suffer in the ways I have outlined and so very few men become psychiatrists or psychologists, the question as to whether the Jewish tradition favors the development of skill in this vocation is left poorly answered, indeed. I do not believe it can be answered definitely. The psychological fact remains that some possess the saving grace of turning suffering and resentment and fear into constructive and helpful efforts based on a kind of spiritual discernment with a quantum of scientific detachment, and that this seems to occur relatively more often among Jews than among Gentiles. Would that it occurred oftener among both!

2. On Revising Psychoanalysis

Nearly fifty years ago Sigmund Freud published the first of a series of clinical observations and formulations relative to the treatment of neurotic patients. In subsequent publications he broadened and frequently revised his views in the light of further observations. The novelty of the material and the wide departure from the accepted conceptions aroused great resistance on the part of the medical profession, but the intelligence, honesty, and self-criticism of the discoverer of psychoanalysis plus the therapeutic success of the method gradually won for it the respect of large numbers of medical men. Since then the growth and development of psychoanalysis have continued in a decent and orderly fashion, like those of other scientific disciplines, contributed to by hundreds of serious, scientific workers who have added their observations and made their suggestions to their colleagues for the modification of this or that detail in the theory or in the technic.

The author of the book under review was for many years associated with the main body of psychoanalysts. Recently, however, she became convinced that neither Freud nor any of the hundreds of psychoanalysts who have been working during the fifty years since Freud began have been quite right about psychoanalysis. It is almost incredible that anyone should be so ambitious as to an-

A review of Karen Horney's book *New Ways in Psychoanalysis* (New York: Norton, 1939). Reprinted from the *Journal of the American Medical Association,* 113:356–357, July 22, 1939.

nounce, as she does, that the "purpose of this book is . . . through eliminating the debatable elements, to enable psychoanalysis to develop to the height of its potentialities." For nearly half a century these debatable elements have been continually worked over and, in many instances, clarified by the rank and file of psychoanalysts. That this author should essay to straighten the matter out once and for all by her revolutionary discoveries is a confession of a lack of perspective.

The author proceeds to set up a series of propositions inferentially or directly ascribed to Freud (many of them incorrectly stated) and, having made them appear more or less absurd, follows them with ideas which she labels her own (many of which have been standard conceptions for years past) couched in language which is intended to ring the gong of common sense. Time after time there occur such juxtapositions of the distorted theories of Freud followed by the level-headed revisions of Horney. She refers to herself in the footnotes twenty-nine times; Freud is referred to twenty-three times and no other author more than a few times.

All this is the more regrettable because the book contains here and there some excellent points. Her compulsion to revise Freud is so insistent, however, and the commendable pages are interspersed with so much polemic that the book cannot be recommended to medical readers.

The author clearly does not expect it to be read by medical men. She accuses Freud of having a "biologic orientation," contrasting this (unfavorably) with the "social orientation" which she regards herself as having acquired. Setting biologic orientation up against social orientation is an empty, polemic trick without essential meaning, since society is made up of biologic units.

Psychoanalysis is a medical discipline. Its original technics were discovered by a physician. Its development has been largely at the hands of physicians, and its administration in this country is entirely in the hands of physicians. There is, as everyone knows, a widespread tendency at the present time to accuse medicine of being antisocial or at least unsocial in its orientation. This criticism undoubtedly has had some basis in fact. Many physicians are endeavoring to correct their astigmatism and give to the pressures and forces deriving from the social structure their proper consideration. It is unfortunate that this book, which presumably strives toward a greater clarification of the role of these social factors, should have sacrificed its value for the physician by misplaced emphasis and a prevailing tone of disparagement toward some of the principles and personalities of psychoanalytic medical science.

3. Psychoanalytic Psychiatry:
Theory and Practice

Psychoanalysis began as a medical discipline. In its earliest phase it was an observational technique applied by a physician to the treatment of patients suffering from conditions *now* classified as psychiatric, although in those days regarded as falling within the province of neurology.

The application of the psychoanalytic method of observation resulted not only in the therapeutic amelioration of the patient's illness but in the acquisition of a considerable body of knowledge about a previously unexplored and unknown area of the personality, supplying us with information about psychological laws to such an extent that psychoanalysis deserves also to be regarded as a department of *psychology*.

As a method of observation, as a treatment technique, and as a body of knowledge, these functions of psychoanalysis coexist today and the use of the word psychoanalysis, referring sometimes to one and sometimes to another, leads not only to popular confusion but frequently to confusion in scientific discourse. This confusion is particularly evident in the various phases of the increasing recognition of psychology as a basic biological science, deserving to be considered in the pathogenesis of every disease whether the symptoms be predominantly physical or predominantly mental. With their

Read before the New York Psychoanalytic Society, Jan. 30, 1940, and before the Staff of St. Elizabeths Hospital, Washington, D. C., Feb. 1, 1940. Reprinted from the *Bulletin of the Menninger Clinic*, 4:105–123, July 1940.

special interest in the unconscious phases of psychology, psycho-analysts sometimes assume that psychosomatic medicine means psychoanalytic medicine. Good psychiatry has always been "psycho-somatic medicine."

This confusion is best explained as the residual disorientation of physicians, psychologists, and psychoanalysts regarding the division of their particular fields of labor with respect to science as a whole. Psychoanalysis was regarded by its founder and by some of its earlier exponents as a separate department of science; today, in America at least, psychoanalysis is on its theoretical side a part of psychology, and on its practical side a part of medicine. This is a fundamental principle in the constitutions of the component societies of the American Psychoanalytic Association.

I have reviewed this status of psychoanalysis in order to bring out clearly the relation of psychoanalysis to psychiatry. Psychiatry is that branch of medicine, which, long before psychoanalysis, recog-nized the importance of psychology in disease. Before psychoanalysis had contributed to our theoretical knowledge of the deeper psy-chology of the personality, psychiatry was handicapped in its de-velopment in the same way that all applied psychology was hand-icapped. But with the development of psychoanalysis, both as psy-choanalytic psychology and as psychoanalytic medicine, psychiatry was given a new birth. By psychiatry I refer now to the treatment of patients who suffer from diseases the symptoms of which are predominantly nonstructural in character—in other words, patients whose behavior and emotions cause them or those about them to suffer.

In their capacity as therapists for such patients, psychoanalysts are, by definition, psychiatrists—or at least they are to this extent practicing psychiatry. We officially acknowledge this fact and claim to be physicians and psychiatrists. Yet there is a certain ambiguity, not to say ambivalence, about the psychiatrist-psychoanalyst relation somewhat akin to the physician-surgeon relation. Surgery is a tech-nique requiring special training, and when we speak of surgeons we do not forget that they are primarily physicians. No *good* surgeon ever forgets it. Nor should any good psychoanalyst ever forget that

he is primarily a psychiatrist. If, for practical purposes, we sometimes speak of psychoanalysts *and* psychiatrists, we should always
remember that this is a logical inaccuracy, just as is the expression
"physicians *and* surgeons."

At the present time psychoanalysis runs the danger of becoming,
or rather remaining, too isolated from its mother specialty, psychiatry. Psychoanalysis is of such fundamental importance, both
theoretically and practically, that it should significantly modify the
whole nature of psychiatry, and I wish to raise the question tonight
as to whether it has actually done so. Let us ask ourselves this question: *Just what has psychoanalysis contributed to psychiatry?*

If I may answer the question briefly and then elaborate it, I should
say that in theory psychoanalysis has contributed much; in practice,
little. I should say that its small contribution to psychiatric practice
has been due in part to the resistance of those using the established
methods of psychiatry, but also in part to the indifference and separatism of those practicing psychoanalysis. It is so easy to get into the
rut of establishing and continuing the office treatment of ambulatory
psychiatric patients by psychoanalytic technique that a proper concern for the development of effective treatment of the more severe
cases which cannot be thus handled is simply dismissed from mind
or relegated to institutional psychiatrists with a mixture of disdain,
pity, and disparagement. It is small wonder, therefore, that such
psychiatrists have been encouraged in their resistance against the
acceptance of psychoanalytic principles.

THE CONTRIBUTIONS OF PSYCHOANALYSIS TO PSYCHIATRIC THEORY

In the brief time at my disposal I can do little more than list some
of the outstanding contributions of psychoanalytic theory to psychiatric theory. I mean by this to outline what we understand now
about the more severe mental illnesses that we did not understand
prior to the accumulation of knowledge about the unconscious from
the study of the less severe illnesses.

1. The pre-eminent contribution of psychoanalytic theory to
psychology, and, therefore, to psychiatry, is, of course, the concept
of the unconscious. We should not allow ourselves to forget that the

concept of the unconscious antedated Freud's discovery of a method of exploring it. Nevertheless, so long as it was inaccessible to systematic exploration, the unconscious was an exceedingly vague and tenuous concept, and its acceptance by psychiatry may be fairly attributed to psychoanalysis for this reason.

2. Superficially and immediately this concept enabled us to obtain some insight into the meaning of symptoms which had previously been studied merely as empirical phenomena, and to view them as aspects of a continuous process. It made us realize that a meaning existed and should be sought for in such manifestations as depression, exhibitionism, hallucinations, and so forth; these became indices pointing to conflicts behind instead of empirically based prognoses ahead.

3. From these indices and from a reconsideration of the life history of the individual, psychoanalytic theory enabled us to obtain a knowledge of the nature of the unseen conflicts of the patient. His *conscious* conflicts were already a matter of psychiatric concern, but we now learned that these were often disguises for, or minor reproductions of, earlier and deeper invisible conflicts. The phenomena called "shell shock" during the World War were at first explained as automatic solutions to the conscious conflict between the will-to-live and the will-to-be patriotic, or between the fear-of-death-from-the-enemy and the fear-of-disgrace-or-death-from-the-commanding-officer. Psychoanalysis should not and *does* not deny the importance of such conscious conflicts, although in its enthusiasm for the elucidation of underlying material it sometimes seems to do so, thus giving rise to waves of Adlerian emphasis on contemporary forces and conflicts which distract and confuse some observers. Psychoanalysts should not forget that these were a matter of psychiatric consideration and attention years before Adler was born or psychoanalysis discovered, and that psychoanalysis has added to them, but not rejected them.

4. This knowledge of the nature of the unconscious conflicts, plus working hypotheses as to the forces acting to bring about different types of personality disintegration, made possible some important modifications in the concepts of the established psychiatric syn-

dromes, the specific work of Freud and Abraham in cyclothymic psychoses, Jung and Sullivan in schizophrenia. Here, of course, there is a wide discrepancy in the extent to which such modifications have been made according to the psychiatrists one has in mind; in some quarters schizophrenia is still seen in the light of the original Kraepelinian picture as an endocrine disorder; in other quarters it is still regarded as a structural brain disease, and, of course, by Mr. Hitler's official psychiatrists (and I am afraid by a few in this country) it is still considered a product of hereditary degeneration. In other quarters, however, the conception of schizophrenia is one determined by the combined views of Bleuler, Jung, Sullivan, Zilboorg, and other psychoanalysts. To some paresis is still a disease caused simply by the destruction of the brain by syphilis, but by others it is seen as the product of certain personality trends, certain emotional traumata, *and* a spirochetal invasion of the brain.

5. Psychoanalytic theory also called to the attention of psychiatrists what I believe to be the essence of psychiatric symptomatology, namely, the self-destructive goal and techniques of the personality. Symptoms of behavior previously regarded only as empirical evidences of psychosis became recognized as self-destructive techniques impelled by unleashed instinctual impulses. The psychiatrist who had long recognized as his duty the prevention of overt suicide began to see his responsibility for the prevention of those lesser forms of suicide represented by the behavior and symptoms of his patients.

6. The most immediately practical contribution of psychoanalytic psychology to psychiatry was the recognition of the function of therapy as one of releasing and redistributing misplaced aggressive energy and encouraging or permitting the development of more satisfactory erotic objectives. Upon this is based most of the useful applications of psychoanalysis in psychiatry, which we shall discuss next.

THE CONTRIBUTIONS OF PSYCHOANALYSIS TO PSYCHIATRIC PRACTICE

Having outlined the contributions of psychoanalysis to the theoretical structure of psychiatry, let us consider to what extent this appears in actual psychiatric practice.

I begin with the assumption that the standard clinical application of psychoanalysis to ambulatory cases of mental illness, particularly those who themselves elect to come for such treatment, belongs within the sphere of psychiatry, and hence this is one practical application. Psychoanalysis is so pre-eminently successful in the treatment of the neuroses that it has come to be the method of choice of many psychiatrists, including many who are not themselves psychoanalysts. The situation is somewhat similar to that period in medical history when it was discovered that surgery could relieve certain cases of acute abdominal pain. Many of the old-time physicians combated the new treatment, but many others saw how useful and successful it was and were glad to turn their patients over to colleagues who were skilled in the new technique.

Of course, there remained many cases of acute abdominal pain for which surgery was not the best treatment (although some surgeons were loath to concede this). These cases were generally handled better by non-surgically-trained physicians. I think that the analogy still holds and that many psychiatrists handle certain cases requiring minor psychotherapy better than do those of us who devote our chief attention to what might be called major psychotherapy.

But after giving credit to the accomplishments of psychoanalysis in the treatment of severe but ambulatory mental illnesses, we must admit that psychoanalysis has not thus far given to psychiatry any very great assistance in dealing with those patients who desire and even seek treatment but whose conflicts are not sufficiently intense to justify the great expense in time and money of a *complete* analysis. This is a problem which is faced by every psychiatrist with psychoanalytic predilections who works in an outpatient psychiatric clinic, mental-hygiene clinic, child-guidance clinic, or general medical clinic. In theory, psychoanalysis has given us a better conception of personality structure, motives, conflicts, and so on, but in practice, psychoanalysis as a therapeutic technique operates according to the *all-or-none law*. At least this is the general tendency. A few individuals with psychoanalytic orientation have attempted to apply their knowledge of psychoanalysis to the problems of the outpatient psychiatric clinic. Three of my colleagues, Dr. Robert Knight,[1] Dr. Harlan Crank,[2] and Dr. Hanford Auten [3] have reported examples of such an effort. I myself [4] have outlined a method of approach to such patients. These are only a beginning, however, and I think we must look forward to further study of the practical methods of psychotherapy based on psychoanalytic theory but not on psychoanalytic technique.

Traditionally, however, the bulk of psychiatric material is intra-mural and relatively involuntary—and this is still the case. Just as most serious surgical cases must be hospitalized, so most psychiatric cases must be hospitalized—although for quite different reasons. The necessity for isolation from various harmful elements in the environment, the necessity of protecting the environment from the patient as well as the patient from the environment, the necessity of a different kind of nursing supervision and care, the necessity of various degrees of restraint—these have been recognized by psy-chiatrists for several centuries. It is only fair to add that not all these principles were clearly recognized at all times, and that a part of the stimulus toward a more adequate recognition of them came from an American woman who was not a physician. Never-theless, we feel that in America we have brought the external forms of hospitalization to a relatively high degree of efficiency and ef-ficacy, and this was on the way to accomplishment prior to the introduction of psychoanalysis. The question is, What has our psychoanalytic knowledge added to, or modified in, these psy-chiatric provisions?

There are in the United States at the present time 603 hospitals, public and private, devoted exclusively to the care of psychiatric patients. Of these a small but increasing number make available to their patients the application of psychoanalysis as a treatment method, but only a few have as yet organized their regimes of man-agement and treatment on the basis of psychoanalytic knowledge. It is for this reason that I made the statement which I now re-peat, psychoanalysis has had far less influence on psychiatry in prac-tice than in theory.

In these psychoanalytically oriented psychiatric institutions, and probably in a few of those not wholly committed to such a program, there has been a definite trend toward making a practical application of psychoanalytic principles. Since this constitutes an illustrative demonstration of how psychoanalysis *can* modify psychiatric procedure and gives some indication of how it *could* modify psychiatric procedure elsewhere, and since it seems to be relatively unknown even to some of my psychoanalytical colleagues who still think of psychoanalysis only as an outpatient treatment modality, I should like to discuss certain aspects of these experiments in detail. What I have to say hereinafter is based upon personal experience over a period of ten years in one of these psychoanalytically-oriented psychiatric institutions. Detailed accounts of the operative procedures have been contributed to the literature by my brother William [5, 6] and numerous colleagues, especially Knight,[7] Reider,[8] Tidd,[9] Hemphill,[10] Erickson,[11] Anderson,[12] Lyle,[13] Cutrer,[14] McKimens,[15] Medd,[16] McColl,[17] and Olinger.[18] In addition, there have been important reports by Bullard,[19] Fromm-Reichmann,[20] Sullivan,[21] Simmel,[22] and Chapman.[23]

1. In the first place, the architecture and construction of the psychiatric hospital which is to operate according to psychoanalytic principles will certainly not conform either with those of the old-style Kirkbride asylums, or with the new-style factory-and-office-building monstrosities developed by some larger eastern states in an effort to solve psychiatric problems by mass-production methods. Nor, I must add, would an ideally constructed private psychiatric institution follow the pattern set by the old-style sanitarium, with its emphasis upon luxury and physical comfort.

To speak positively rather than negatively, I should say that a psychoanalytically inspired hospital is built not so much according to the ideal of a medical hospital, or (as is sometimes advocated) on the other hand to that of a home, but more nearly like that of a college dormitory. The sanitarium is not a hospital inasmuch as most of its occupants are not bed-ridden; it is not a home inasmuch as its occupants are not relatives and do not expect to live there permanently; it is more closely related to a school than to either of these. But since it is a place of residency and, since its occupants are definitely sick, it must also possess certain homelike and hospital-like features. What it certainly is NOT is a prison; it must not look like one, or be like one in any sense. Nor, on the other hand, should it be a country club. Tendencies in these directions are not in keeping with the facts and purposes of the patients' confinement, and are therefore not honest, and therefore not scientific.

This question of architecture is not an academic one. Architecture, like science, has undergone changes and expansions, and the moving spirit of modern architecture is functionalism. To the scientifically minded and trained architect, it is a crime to construct buildings without regard to the spirit or the purpose to which they are to be put. In the institution with which I am most familiar, an architect spent many months with psychiatric patients and attended psychiatric clinics and psychoanalytic seminars for two years in order to learn exactly what was needed and desired for the structural foundation of an institution devoted to the psychiatric treatment of patients according to psychoanalytic principles.

2. The same spirit that determines the selection of the appropriate architecture, the appropriate ground plan, and the appropriate decoration of such an institution, will permeate the philosophy of everyone connected with it. It is a little difficult to put this into words, but I can give some examples. In such an institution there must be a unanimity of purpose, and this implies a unanimity of basic information. It is useless to expect a dietitian, a housekeeper, a gardener entrusted with the flowers, or stenographers entrusted with the records to cooperate in a treatment program the essential principles of which they do not understand. In the institution to which I refer, the chef attended the psychiatric lectures regularly for a year. The business manager underwent a complete psychoanalysis. The stenographers were required to attend lectures on psychiatry. Doctor Bullard of Chestnut Lodge Sanitarium in Rockville, Maryland, has tried the plan of having many of his nurses analyzed. Such things contribute to a unanimity of spirit and knowledge which I regard as a necessity in the maintenance of a proper feeling-tone among the many units of personnel making up such an organization.

3. Most important of all, of course, are the attitudes of the members of the medical staff. I say attitudes because I think these are more important than specific information. On the one hand, a proper attitude leads automatically to the acquisition of the necessary information, and, on the other hand, information and experience support and improve the attitude.

I should like to be definite about what I refer to as physicians' attitudes. I mean that it is not enough for them to be physicians with an interest in disease, or even an interest in patients suffering diseases. It is not enough for them to have what would be acceptable in many places as a progressive psychiatric attitude. This would imply that they had a wide tolerance for and empirical understanding of erratic, unpredictable, aggressive, and often provocative behavior on the part of those committed to their care. Physicians in a psychoanalytically oriented sanitarium must have more than this. They must have a genuine conviction as to the existence of the unconscious and its predominant influence upon the behavior, the logic, the conversation, the decisions, and the interpersonal relationships of their patients. With such a concept of the unconscious, such physicians can and will take these unconscious motives into consideration in their dealings with patients' relatives and friends. Such a recognition of the existence of the unconscious leads to efforts to understand the expressions of the patients' unconscious and to an attempt to seek for methods of assisting the patients to understand them also and learn to express them in less self-destructive ways. If a young staff member gives evidence of recognizing the unconscious motivation and the deeper meaning of the behavior of a certain patient, I think we need not be distressed with his selection of a nosological label which does not correspond to that of some Kraepelinian chapter title or to the impressions of a more experienced colleague. Such an attitude as I have in mind leads to far more interest in the structure of the personality than in the name of the psychosis, and far more interest in seeking devices for relieving stresses within that structure than in locating diagnostic categories.

We have not found it *essential* that a psychiatrist be analyzed in order to acquire such an attitude, ideally desirable though that is for the purpose of eliminating those blind spots or "complexes" in the physician which interfere with his effectiveness, his understanding of the patient, his maintenance of the ideal attitude. The proper attitude can be taught and, furthermore, it is contagious—it can be *caught*. Young psychiatrists quickly absorb the spirit or philosophy that permeates an institution; if it be a diagnostic, pigeonholing, receiving-station attitude he will acquire it; if it be a custodial, therapeutically hopeless, nihilistic attitude he will acquire that; if it be a pollyanna, back-slapping, kid-em-along-and-nature-will-make-them-well attitude he will acquire that. Similarly, if it be a psychoanalytic attitude he will acquire that.

4. The same is true of nurses. The psychoanalyst sees his patients an hour a day. The average institutional psychiatrist sees his patients a much shorter time. In either case the patient spends twenty-three hours out of the twenty-four in the company of other individuals with whom there is a constant interchange of erotic and aggressive energies. In the case of hospitalized patients the nurses represent, very definitely, extensions of the physician; and yet their technique of handling patients, the attitudes they assume with respect to the demands made by patients, or to the demands made *of* patients, are in many institutions left entirely to chance, or, more accurately, to the personality habits of the various nurses. So far as I know, Harry Stack Sullivan [24] was the first to point out the importance of selecting and training the nursing personnel along these lines; this was echoed by Ross Chapman [25] (both of them psychoanalytically oriented psychiatrists), but I believe my brother William C. Menninger [26] was the first to develop this idea systematically and to indicate how proper attitudes might be taught to nurses and specifically applied in individual cases through the prescription of the physician.

5. Physical environment and personnel attitudes are essential, but the correct management of the patient committed to psychiatric care does not follow automatically. There is a sharp difference in this respect between the operation of a hospital in which psychoanalytic principles are recognized and adhered to by the entire

staff and one in which psychoanalysis is of casual interest only or not considered at all. This applies to those innumerable minutiae of hospital residence which are too often relegated by physicians to uninstructed and uninspired administrative officers. It is an old, established rule, for example, that patients in a psychiatric hospital may not retain in their possession breakable glass objects, but psycho-analytic insight would perceive that in certain instances to take away the prized gift of perfume from a self-depreciating female would be more dangerous than the risk of allowing her to keep it in her pos-session.

A patient in a hospital where psychoanalysis is understood would not be reproached for urinating on the floor; it might be welcomed as an evidence of a positive reaction to the visit of his physician. I need not say what the attitude of the untrained psychiatric hos-pital attendant would be. In one instance a patient began writing on the wall with her own feces but soon substituted for this the writing of idealistic verse with pen and ink. Had her smearing been treated in the standard fashion, the rebuff might have been suf-ficient to have delayed the recovery indefinitely. Innumerable exam-ples of this type could be cited and have been cited by my brother and some of our colleagues, and by Fromm-Reichmann [27] and Bullard.[28] In general, the entire routine of a psychoanalytic hospital is quite different from that in a hospital in which psychoanalytic principles are not considered.

This is especially true with reference to the guidance of the interpersonal relationships of the patients. Isolation, participation in social functions, athletic activity—these cannot be allowed to de-velop spontaneously but are arranged on a basis of careful study of the patient in an effort to discover his unconscious needs. If, for example, an alcoholic patient is dodging his real problem by an excess of affability and vocability, the very thing must be discour-aged which in a lonely schizophrenic would be encouraged.

In the course of recovery the psychiatric patient undertakes more and more extramural activities. He seeks to resume his relationships with individuals and institutions in the outside world. He wants to go visiting or shopping, or to see a movie—or to "have a date." The decision as to whether a particular project of this sort can be permitted will be determined quite differently by a psychoanalytically trained psychiatrist and one who is entirely unacquainted with psychoanalysis. The question of how much money a patient is to spend is also one which can be decided merely according to the wishes of the relatives, but which can also be decided, more wisely we believe, on the basis of the patient's attitude toward money and his purposes in the purchase.

The whole question of diet, which in most hospitals is one of chemistry, calories, and vitamins, is in a psychoanalytic hospital one involving not only these chemical factors but psychological factors as well. I admit that it is not easy to find a dietitian for whom psychological factors assume anything like the importance of the chemical ones, but here again it is largely a question of education, and, I can say from experience, it has been done.

Medication in a psychiatric hospital will also be influenced very considerably by the point of view of the physician. After one has lived with psychoanalytic concepts for a dozen years and guided his prescriptions on the basis of his knowledge of the pathology of oral and anal tendencies, the routine and indiscriminate administration of cathartics, sedatives, and carminatives seems very improper.

SPECIFIC THERAPEUTIC MODALITIES DESIGNED TO EFFECT MODIFICATIONS OF THE PERSONALITY

I have reserved for the last a consideration of those *special* therapies available in a psychiatric hospital in which we are apt to place our greatest confidence. I have just spoken of the question of drugs—chemotherapy—and a little earlier of dietotherapy. For something like fifty years physiotherapy has also been a standard psychiatric technique, one to which psychoanalytic psychology has not been thoughtfully applied. We have recognized that immersion in prolonged neutral baths often means to the patient something equivalent to a temporary intra-uterine existence, but we have not applied this suggestion to the question of whether or not a particular patient should be given this opportunity for symbolic regression. Yet physiotherapy prescriptions in psychoanalytic hospitals must be guided not only by the physiological results ascribed to it by empirical observations, but also by the psychological determinants.

The meaning and function of occupational therapy and recreational therapy have been studied much more intensively from a psychological standpoint. But while there are literally thousands of occupational-therapy departments in the hospitals of the United States, it is safe to say that in only a very few of these is the prescription and the execution of occupational therapy based upon the consideration of deep psychological principles. Wise occupational therapists have insisted for a long time that their work is therapy and not diversion or time-killing trivia. In an unguided way they frequently attempt to use the various modalities of craft work so as to be suitable to the capacities and interests of their patients. But this is something quite different from selecting the occupational therapy to fit not merely the conscious interest of the patient but his unconscious needs. My brother recently showed me a memorandum sent to his desk by the director of occupational therapy who was proposing some instruction in certain new crafts. After stating the material and principles of the craft, the approximate cost, and so on, the director specified under each item the functional value that such a course might have. "This craft," he wrote, "furnishes excellent opportunities for narcissistic gratification (read ego-development, if you prefer) and also for the external deflection of aggressive tendencies in a socially approved form." Of another craft, he said, "This is a hard, laborious task which in the end yields a desirable material product and should be useful for depressed patients." Whether or not his estimate was correct, this will illustrate an entirely different point of view regarding occupational therapy from that which used to prevail in such departments. It is routine in the institution with which I am most familiar for the physician to indicate to the occupational therapist whether the cultivation of esthetic interests, concentration, hobby formation, imagination, or initiative is most important and whether the techniques taught should be simple, intricate, routine, or strenuous and difficult, according to the patient's personality structure. It is routine for the physician to indicate, also, whether the therapist's attitude should be that of stimulating, inviting, urging, or compelling the patient.

According to psychoanalytic theory, sublimation means a deflection of aggressive impulses into work or play. Recreational therapy represents an organized and directed opportunity for play sublimation. All that was said above concerning the selection of the particular occupational therapy for the particular patient applies to recreational therapy. This can be done intuitively or empirically, but it can also be done on the basis of a knowledge of a patient's deep psychology.

A similar point of view should prevail in the development of other special therapies such as educational therapy, project therapy, and bibliotherapy. Concerning these I shall not cite details or illustrations because the practice is similar to that described in connection with the other special therapies already discussed.

To a psychoanalytic audience, it almost goes without saying that psychotherapy is the most important of all the special treatment measures available in a psychiatric hospital. Yet one must remember that this is not the conviction of all psychiatrists, nor is it the practice in most psychiatric hospitals. I refer now to systematic attempts to develop a special interpersonal relationship between a patient and a particular physician by means of regularly recurring sessions of more than a few minutes in which there is some kind of intercommunication. Ideally, of course, this means conversation, but Fromm-Reichmann [29] and Sullivan [30] have shown that silent companionship may be the basis of an increased confidence which later makes verbal interchange possible. Some psychoanalysts seem to make the assumption that if a patient does not spontaneously come to them or talk to them he cannot be helped by psychotherapy. As I said earlier in my paper, psychoanalysis is not the only effective psychotherapy. In a psychiatric hospital where psychoanalytic principles prevail, the potency of psychotherapy is recognized and a personal approach to the patient is made routinely—the technique of which conforms, if not to psychoanalytic practice, at least to psychoanalytic theory.

A much larger percentage of patients in a psychiatric hospital

can be benefited by the standard technique of psychoanalytic practice than is assumed by the psychiatrist not familiar with psychoanalysis or by the psychoanalyst not familiar (as I am afraid some
of them are not) with the nature of the patients resident in a modern psychiatric hospital. It is startling to discover that many psychoanalytic colleagues continue to think of the modern psychiatric hospital in terms of the institutions of thirty years ago, as being full
of screaming or sobbing patients with whom the refined, dignified
patients whom the psychoanalysts are accustomed to see in their
offices could not conceivably associate with pleasure or benefit. Such
an erroneous conception on the part of psychoanalysts would be
more appropriate on the part of laymen. It astonishes many of my
colleagues to learn that some of our patients attend high school and
college during their sanitarium residence, and that frequently dignified and fairly well-adjusted persons prefer small, unluxurious rooms
in the company of other psychiatric patients to the occupancy of
large homes or apartments in metropolitan centers. I don't know
why some psychoanalytic colleagues continue to have the asylum
conception of the modern psychiatric hospital, unless it is because
the nature of their daily practice is such that they unconsciously
develop the notion that patients are all either nice, tractable neurotics
who come to them for analysis, or else wild, maniacal psychotics
who have to be quickly committed, restrained, and gotten out of
sight. The personality characteristics of the alcohol addict frequently
seduce young analysts into believing that these cases can be treated
by analysis extramurally; these same charming, sophisticated, self-
possessed men also sometimes give the modern sanitarium the atmosphere of a club. But those of us who have worked with many
alcoholics realize how shallow and unreliable these surface indications are and how dangerous and futile it is to attempt to analyze
the severe alcoholic outside of a situation where he can be given
psychiatric guidance and restraint during the twenty-three hours
that he is not with the analyst.

Not only alcohol addicts, in our opinion, but severe neuroses and
mild psychoses (if there really is any difference) are frequently
analyzable only under such circumstances, as Zilboorg [31] and others

have proved. This is looking at it from the standpoint of the psychoanalyst. Looking at it from the standpoint of the psychiatrist, I repeat what I said above, that many patients can be cured by psychoanalysis who at the present time are treated unsuccessfully by the routine hospital care and the other special therapies enumerated, or else by attempts at outpatient-department psychoanalysis.

It may be felt by some that such an application of psychoanalytic theory to psychiatric practice as I have outlined has one grave fault. That the psychiatrist, after a comparatively short period of observation, should assume to minister to the specific unconscious needs of his patient would seem to imply that the psychiatrist could easily recognize all the deep unconscious strivings of another person, and had ignored the precariousness of attempting to satisfy these needs with substitutions. There are two answers to this objection. In the first place, it should be remembered that in many psychiatric patients, especially those with frank psychoses, the unconscious trends are much less completely disguised than in the neuroses which form the bulk of outpatient psychoanalytic practice. Hence it is often possible to recognize the unconscious structure more quickly than in the case of the better-integrated neurotic. In the second place, it is true that frequently the initial estimate of the patient's needs and capacities will be superficial, and applications of psychoanalytic inferences must therefore be broad rather than intensive. Treatment based upon the indications afforded only by the preliminary examination would certainly be contrary to the psychoanalytic ideal, were the matter to end there. But when the observation is continued over a period of weeks and months and when the schedule of treatment is modified from day to day and from week to week as further insight is obtained by the patient and by the physician, and especially when any indications given by the patient of his desire to follow the leadership of certain persons or of his wish to take the initiative in some project are welcomed and encouraged—then, I think, one may say that the procedure is truly in the spirit of psychoanalysis. It is, in fact, because of the importance of following the lead of the patient in prescribing therapy that the entire personnel must be permeated with the theory of personality development implicit in psychoanalysis. The concept of the unconscious is important, not only in helping doctors and therapists to understand the needs of the patient, but also in reminding them of the complexity and depth of the symptoms and of the impossibility of solving human problems and "curing" human ills with admonitions and advice or with quick tricks.

If for no other reason than this, I believe young psychiatrists should be trained in a psychoanalytic sanitarium so that they acquire a true humility and awe at the extraordinary complexity of the human personality, and learn to look for the many ways it has of securing its ends through body and through mind, often interchanging one method for another.

Far from leading to superficiality of outlook, I believe that the application of psychoanalytic principles leads to an attitude of dissatisfaction with blanket application of techniques, to an eagerness to discover significant leads with individual patients, to a constant watchfulness and a desire to perfect one's own objectivity. Then, even if mistakes are made, if the patients' unconscious needs are only imperfectly perceived and if the therapeutic methods are insufficient to satisfy them, the patient will nevertheless *feel* the active interest and sympathy of those about him, a sympathy which is the more effective for being intelligently directed. To make this bond between patient and therapist useful as an instrument of cure is the most important principle of psychoanalytic psychiatry, and it is so taught in a psychoanalytic sanitarium.

CONCLUSION

As psychoanalysis develops we observe with deep satisfaction the extension of its influence and of its techniques into the realms of sociology, anthropology, education, and general medicine. In our pleasure at these substantiations of our convictions regarding the scientific truth of psychoanalytic theory and the fruitfulness of psychoanalytic therapy, we should not neglect their application to the medical specialty of which psychoanalysis is an integral part. For every patient now receiving psychoanalysis, there are five hundred patients receiving psychiatric treatment of other sorts. Time was, and this was especially true in Europe, when psychiatry refused to look at psychoanalysis, but this is not true any more; psychiatry has been magnanimously and profitably hospitable to psychoanalysis in this country. Psychoanalysis should not be less hospitable, less open-minded, less aware of its responsibilities to psychiatry. There *is* a psychoanalytic psychiatry, in theory and in practice, but it has only begun. I have tried to indicate the general form of some of these beginnings and the direction of continued research.

4. Presidential Address to the American Psychoanalytic Association

Psychoanalysis was born in 1893 when Freud and Breuer published a paper which laid the foundation for an organized discipline of psychoanalytic theory and practice. Nine years later, in 1902, an informal group of scientists gathered about Freud in Vienna. In 1908 there was an informal conference in Salzburg, and in 1910 the first International Psychoanalytic Congress was held in Nuremburg and the International Association was founded. In February 1911 the New York Psychoanalytic Society was organized; in May of the same year Dr. Brill and Ernest Jones arranged the first meeting of an American Psychoanalytic Association in Washington. In 1932 the American Association became a federation of psychoanalytic societies.

This year, therefore, marks the tenth anniversary of the organization of our Association in its present form, and lacks one year of being the fiftieth anniversary of the inception of psychoanalysis. For these reasons, it seemed appropriate to me to use this occasion to reflect audibly upon the structure and function of our organization in relation to psychoanalysis as a science, and its meaning not only for the world but for us who practice it.

We are gathered today in one of those annual incidents of coming together which characterize all scientific groups and, indeed,

Given at Boston, Massachusetts, May 18, 1942. Reprinted from the *Psychoanalytic Quarterly*, 11:287–300, July 1942.

all human groups. We here have many things in common but the one thing in common which brings us together at this moment and under these auspices is our interest in a certain technique for understanding human beings and for treating some of them who need it and want us to do so, and for organizing and elaborating the conclusions we draw from our observations. We are committed to the principle that as human beings we ourselves are not exempt from the laws we have discovered by this technique; indeed, we believe that until we have made a study of ourselves as individuals we cannot accurately appraise or assist others. It would seem legitimate to extend this principle to the examination of our organization.

I shall, therefore, review for your consideration some of our theories about group structure in general and shall then submit some ideas regarding the structure of our own organization in particular and the effect upon it of three significant events of recent times:

1. The growth of psychoanalysis in America.
2. The death of Sigmund Freud.
3. The explosion of a world war.

I shall begin in a most general way by directing your attention to the ways in which human beings attach themselves to one another in groups in a supposedly nonsexual way. This has been called gregariousness and described by some, more eloquently than accurately, as due to a "herd instinct" [1] similar to that which impels the flocking of certain birds and herding of beasts in large assemblies. But there is no need to postulate any such special instinct. Men gather together at times for practical reasons of greater economy or greater safety or greater power; such gatherings are not motivated by any instinct, either a "herd instinct" or the instinct of love. But there are other gatherings, gatherings that occur daily, hourly, in a million villages and by roadsides and hearthsides, in which the affection of people for each other is the moving spirit. In the custom to which our own country is so particularly given, of organizing clubs, societies, associations, unions, and the like, one can see a spontaneous tendency toward increasing the opportunities for knowing and understanding one another. It is an unusual individual who does not to some extent enjoy meetings and gatherings, and we are all better for them.

Freud [2] ascribed the cohesiveness of the group to a common devotion to a leader, a devotion in which the hostile elements are kept in abeyance through a kind of tacit recognition that ultimately he—the leader—will be replaced by one of the followers, who meanwhile suspend all mutual hostilities. Each follower thus identifies himself with the leader, and hence to some extent with all the other followers. The successful leader must manage to keep the constantly accumulating aggressions of the group discharged by directing them to this or that *external* danger or project. Such a reinforcement and concentration of emotion is like a Leyden jar; it has an enormous potential and can be exploited by psychopathic leaders to accomplish great harm. Examples of this are to be seen in the career of Adolf Hitler, in lynchings and other mob violences, and even in some "good" organizations which suffer for a time under "bad" leaders.

But honest leaders, who will not distort reality to manufacture "enemies" in order to increase internal solidarity, are far more numerous than dishonest and psychopathic leaders; the latter are only more conspicuous. And in organization and group association, formal and informal, there is an investment of love which is mutually reinforcing, and, hence, highly desirable.

In our own work we have had many opportunities to observe this in connection with medical organizations. The average citizen has no idea how thoroughly and intricately medical men are organized. The American Medical Association has been accused of being the most powerful trust in the world and a great many unfavorable things have been said about it. The fact remains that it is largely responsible for having brought American medicine to its present high peak of accomplishment. Selfish and shortsighted it has undoubtedly been at times, but it has held up standards of education, publication, medical research, and medical ethics from which every citizen in this country has profited. It is not my point to attack or defend the American Medical Association, however, but only to comment that this powerful organization is made up of perhaps the most individualistic and unorganizable of all citizens.

But we all belong not only to the American Medical Association and to our county medical societies but to many other medical organizations. Most of us belong to the American Psychiatric Association, which is scientifically the parent organization of the present body. Now that our orientation in regard to psychoanalysis has taken definite form and we recognize that we are physicians first, psychiatrists second, and psychoanalysts third, I feel strongly that our membership in the American Psychiatric Association should become unanimous. The gigantic strides which that organization has taken in establishing psychiatry and, incidentally, psychoanalysis in its proper place in American medicine deserve our unwavering and undivided support. As I said to the New York Psychoanalytic Society two years ago, "Psychiatry has been magnanimously and profitably hospitable to psychoanalysis in this country. Psychoanalysis should not be less hospitable, less open-minded, less aware of its responsibilities to psychiatry."

One often hears complaints from physicians, psychoanalysts not excluded, to the effect that we have too much medical organization, too many meetings to attend. I should like to consider the reasons for the necessity of so much organization. One of these, practical, not psychological, is the need for consultation in the modern practice of medicine because of its growing complexity. The practice of medicine was at one time more art than science and even after it became more science than art its requirements did not exceed the capacities of the average intelligence. At the present time, however, the field of medical science is so broad and so complicated that no human being could possibly master it. The result is that physicians lodge in various corners of the field, so to speak. It would seem entirely logical for groups of them to work together, to cooperate in the study and treatment of the sick patient from the angles of various special fields of knowledge. The Mayo Clinic has proved in a magnificent way the potentialities of such medical cooperation. It is almost unnecessary to mention the fine work it has done for multitudes of patients, but it may be less familiar that this cooperation among physicians has enabled the Mayo Clinic to do two other things. First, it has furthered medical science by research and clinical observations equaling or surpassing those of any publicly endowed medical school in the world. The average physician cannot be expected to turn a considerable portion of his income into financing studies that will promote public health; but that is precisely what this cooperating group of private physicians has been able to do. More than that, there is a spirit of comradeship and affection among the physicians of the Mayo Clinic staff which is for many of them one of the chief rewards of their work together. I know of this from intimate contacts with them, and I see the same thing in my association with the colleagues in our own Clinic. I have practiced alone and I know some of the satisfactions of being so completely independent and self-sufficient; I have also practiced in a group, and I know the satisfactions of cooperating with colleagues instead of competing with them, of admitting one's mistakes and discussing without rancor the mistakes of others, of sharing a common purpose, common enthusiasms, and common disappointments. I know that these latter satisfactions are far greater.

It is surely a relevant question to ask why, under these circumstances, cooperative associations of physicians are not more frequent. There are probably many reasons for this, some of which are not pertinent to our theme. But I have often thought that the unconscious roots of the "rugged individualism" which has so long characterized physicians are to be found in the peculiarly intimate interpersonal relationship between the doctor and his patient. Theoretically, the patient comes to the doctor to be relieved of pain. Theoretically, the doctor undertakes to relieve this pain, expecting nothing from the patient but the payment of a bill; but, actually, we know that the patient is motivated by unconscious expectations and desires in the establishment of this relationship, and so is the physician. The patient thinks he wants the doctor to treat him, but it becomes very apparent in some cases and it is inferentially true in many others that the patient wants more than this—he wants the doctor to give him something, to do something to him, to like him, even to love him. And, for his part, the doctor, while he wants his fee, also wants the patient to like him, to be grateful to him and, in a sense, to love *him*. Doctors do love their patients and their patients love them, and this is not an unhealthy situation, nor a deplorable one; it is a part of the process of healing and being healed. But, on the other hand, it is something which interferes with the association of doctors in a group because the emotional relationship that exists between physician and patient is personal, intimate, confidential, and exclusive. Unless this is clearly understood and full allowance made for it, jealousies spring up. The real reason why most doctors are so violently opposed to state medicine is that they fear, with justice, that this emotional relationship between them and their patients would be seriously impaired by impersonal, mechanistic administration.

I come back to the necessity for organizations, and I shall pass over those practical aspects which will occur to everyone, such as official recognition, cooperation with other organized scientific bodies, the regulations of the principles of practice, the dissemination of new ideas, new experiments, new results. I want to emphasize again the psychological principles which Freud first pointed out and which we have all come to recognize more and more clearly. Organizations, and this does not exclude our own, exist because of the need of human beings for love. We need to neutralize the aggressions that well up within us—often, strangely enough, against those who have the most in common with us. To understand all is to forgive all, and to know one another well enough should not be to hate one another the more but to love one another the more. If we fail in doing so, something is wrong in our organization or something is wrong in us.

I would not have this construed to mean that our psychoanalytic organization is more prone than others to fail in its task of relieving individual loneliness and controlling hostilities. The inherent danger in any group seems to be the tendency to become static, so that the promise of growth in friendship is often unfulfilled.

There is often an insufficiently strong central interest or unity of purpose to keep the group welded together in a common goal; internal dissension, distrust, jealousy, overambitiousness, and envy tend to overwhelm the erotic bond. Afraid of their own hostilities, the members shrink into smaller and smaller units or cliques or compensate for their own hollowness by an overemphasis on the snobbishness and exclusiveness of the group. A typical example is the petty gossiping and mutual hostility of the members of the proverbial small-town sewing circle.

Naturally, the more homogeneous the club, the greater the peril in this quarter. The tendency of all groups to select members who resemble each other in some way, leads to rivalry on the one hand and to staleness on the other. One prophylactic measure against this danger is the periodic infusion of new blood, the addition of new members. This requires a readjustment of the emotional linkages of all members and affords intellectual stimulation as well. If the differences of the new members are as great as their resemblances, the club is strengthened to the extent that it can absorb the new and continue in a more cosmopolitan unity.

These general considerations relate to the particular problems of our own Association, and especially to the very rapid growth which it has been undergoing. Ten years ago we were born, and while we are still very young and very small compared to the great Psychiatric Association and medical associations, nevertheless, we have grown with great rapidity. There are now seven constituent societies and soon more groups will apply for membership. We have in training perhaps two hundred students, so that by two or three years from now our membership will almost certainly be doubled. What was once like a little family gathering has now become as large a meeting as can be comfortably handled in the average hotel convention room. Informality has gradually been replaced by a necessary formality, with certain consequent losses. Time after time we have had to change our constitution to fit our growing needs, and we shall have to do so many more times as we continue to grow. I can remember the New York Society when its average attendance was six or eight physicians who met in private homes. I remember sitting in the hall of an apartment for two hours one evening while the business session was in progress, following which one of the members reported some of his own experiences in analysis with Professor Freud. It is a far cry, too, from the time when teaching was an individual affair between two physicians to our present attempts to standardize and formalize our educational program.

In July last year I wrote each one of you asking for suggestions in regard to the changes that might be made in our Association. I received a great deal of helpful advice. Since that time I have conferred many times with the officers of the Association, with the Executive Council, with our indefatigable Secretary, Doctor Bartemeier. In accordance with the instructions of the Executive Council last year, Mr. Austin Davies, Executive Assistant to the American Psychiatric Association, made a survey of our constitution and made exceedingly helpful recommendations which were considered by the Executive Council. A few weeks ago I called a meeting of some of the older teaching analysts in Chicago and discussed with them the possible changes that might be made to adapt our ideals and teaching purposes to the larger needs of our organization.

On the basis of these various suggestions, proposals are now being discussed in Executive Council and in the Council on Professional Training. I will not go into detail about these except to say that it seems desirable that we should have a stronger central organization, that more authority should be given to the American Association by the constituent societies. We are probably not yet large enough to have a full-time executive secretary, but it is time that we changed from a loose organization of independent groups, to a more centrally directed association. I have long felt, for example, that the appointment of training analysts ought to cease to be a local function and become a national function, or else that it should be relegated to the institutes which, in turn, should be responsible to the national association. The details of these plans will be proposed to you in due time in accordance with the procedure prescribed by our constitution.

We can expect difficulties and disagreements in the many changes that we are obliged to make in adapting ourselves to growth, but

I do not see why we need to expect rancor and bitterness. Psycho-analysis is greater than the association of psychoanalysts, and the association is greater than any one of us or, for that matter, any group of us. If we are loyal to one another, loyal to our teacher and to the principles which he taught us, we shall not be overwhelmed by personal irritations and disagreements.

If these have been somewhat greater in the past year than in previous years, perhaps it can be related in no small measure to the disturbing effects upon all of us of the death of Freud. He him-self anticipated some of these difficulties and I have the impression that he had this very much in mind, either consciously or uncon-sciously, when he wrote his last great contribution to human thought, *Moses and Monotheism*. Freud was our Moses and, like the children of Israel, we feel guilty in connection with his death, no matter how much we consciously regret it, and despite the fact that in reality we can be charged with no responsibility for it. How we react to that guilt depends upon our individual psychic struc-tures. As Freud pointed out in his book, it is unimportant by whom Moses was killed or by whom Jesus was killed. What is important is the fact that the Jewish conscience reacts repeatedly in denial of the accusation, and this is intertwined with the tendency of some Christians to unload their own feelings of guilt onto the Jews in-stead of onto Jesus. Christians and Jews react to guilt feelings and react to them in ways which are superficially different but actually, in the last analysis, the same. Our tendency as analysts is to react to our guilt by attacks upon one another. From our own science we know that the atonement often repeats the crime. Those who feel unable to atone for their sense of guilt may feel impelled to make overt attacks upon some symbol of the leader—his memory, his theory, his principles, or other followers—in self-justification. One recalls the querulous cry of a little man forty years ago: "Must I stand always in Freud's shadow?"

These things we should all face. Our attitude toward Freud should certainly not be a religious one. Superstitious religion is based on the theory that men were made by a God in His own image. To recognize that man creates his God, as the ideal of a benign father and with the highest aspirations of human thought, is to exemplify the spirit of a civilized, intelligent religion not incompatible with rigorous scientific discipline. This spirit should determine our feelings toward Freud. The temptation to abandon the *elohim* concepts of single-heartedness, loyalty, affection, and peaceful cooperation for polytheistic Jahvistic concepts of conflict is to take flight from our unconscious guilt feelings in the vain illusion that by sufficient heterodoxy and a sufficient plurality of loyalties one can avoid the penalties of patricide without incurring the penalties of faithlessness.

Freud was not our God; he was our Moses. But in his death we did not lose our leader. No matter how much more we learn, Freud will always be our leader, as Galileo will always be the leader of astronomers and Newton of physicists. His physical presence was not the important thing; Freud's principles, Freud's integrity, Freud's honesty, and, above all, Freud's discoveries—these are still with us; they will always be with us. It is not only our privilege to add to his discoveries, it is our duty. But it is neither our duty nor our privilege to attempt to accomplish self-advancement in the name of intellectual freedom by proclaiming criticisms of Freud or exploiting great discoveries of our differences with him. Nor is it our privilege to distort and misrepresent what he has said in order to make ourselves seem more sensible, more perspicacious, more "decent," or more pious.

Let us suppose that forty-nine years after Columbus discovered America, an organization of scientifically minded navigators and geographers had been formed who were convinced of the validity of the theory that the earth was round and that another continent existed to the west. All of them had themselves made the trip across the Atlantic and seen for themselves that it was true. Let us further assume that the members of this organization felt that great possibilities existed for the peoples of Europe and for the peoples of the world by making use of the discoveries of Columbus. Let us remember that at that time the vast majority of Europeans were still highly skeptical of such theories, and even scornful of this small group of "believers."

Now let us assume that some of the members of this organization became jealous of Columbus, envious of the credit and acclaim that were being given him as a result of the growth of the knowledge that what he had discovered was true. Perhaps some of these envious individuals began talking like this: "Oh, yes, Columbus was a courageous fellow. He made a great discovery but his theories were all wrong. He thought he had proved that the world was round. He thought he had discovered the East Indies. All these things are absurd. He didn't prove that the earth is round; he only proved that it extends horizontally somewhat farther than we thought. We appeal to your common sense, dear public. We, too, have sailed the seas and, in our experience, it is desirable to sail to the northwest instead of due west. Land is found sooner and, in our experience, it is land of a very different type from what Columbus described—much less tropical. Our colleagues are very arbitrary and dogmatic about this, and Columbus was a very narrow-minded man owing to his peculiar Genoese culture; he was interested only in finding a new route by which to obtain spices and silks. This gave him the peculiar delusion that the earth was round. Pay no attention to it but listen to us."

The other members of the Navigators' Society, feeling that the continuation of exploration was the most important thing and that Columbus had enunciated the essential principles both in theory and practice for this, would be considerably alarmed at these disparagers, fearing that the dissension and counter-suggestions would mislead an already skeptical and ignorant world, and they would object. They would object to the dissemination of these aspersions upon Columbus, these distortions of his motives and theories, these detractions from his greatness: "Either you believe the world is round or you don't believe it," they would say. "Either you follow the technique of sailing in a generally westward direction or you do not. If you do not do these things, it is dishonest to call yourselves Columbians."

One can imagine that some of these dissenters would then say, "You people are no longer scientists; you are sentimentalists. You are attempting to stifle free speech. Columbus is not a God. We do not need to worship him. We are independent. We shall leave you and appeal to the people. We shall prove to them that their common sense is quite right; that the world is not round and that land can be reached by sailing in other directions than merely west. You backward Columbus worshipers can go on thinking the world is round if you like. We are the *advanced* Columbians."

I use this illustration to make the point that nothing is so unscientific as to lose sight of the main principles. These main principles include not only a recognition of the fundamental importance of Freud's discoveries but the recognition that, for the sake of dignity, unity, and prestige, scientific differences of opinion must be confined to the halls of our meeting places rather than used to obtain popular support by appealing to the prejudices and so-called common sense of persons unfamiliar with the details and history of the science.

My final topic is the relation of psychoanalysis to the world war in which our country is an active participant. The president of our Association last year appointed a Committee on Morale which I supplemented by further appointments during my administration. This Committee has been very active and has made its report to the Council. It would certainly seem as if psychoanalytic experience ought to be used in the present war, but it is not so clear just how, where, and by whom it should or can be used. Our Committee on Morale has worked hard without getting as far as they had hoped. I do not think we should be discouraged by this, but I think perhaps we should realign our ideas. We are, after all, a small group, a part of a much larger group of those familiar with human psychology and psychopathology, and it would seem to me to be expedient for us to work through the American Psychiatric Association rather than directly. The Army, the Navy, and the Public Health Services recognize psychiatry; they do not recognize psychoanalysis, and I am not sure that in our present state of knowledge there is any reason why they should. We could not possibly take on an extensive treatment program even if it were requested of us, and our ideas in regard to morale, intelligence, the analysis of propaganda, etc., do not differ substantially from those held by the members of our parent organization. It seems to me that it behooves us as psychoanalysts at the present time to pay prime attention to our patients and not attempt to gain a foothold in political and governmental activities.

On the other hand, it seems to me not only the privilege but the duty of psychoanalysts to contribute to the thinking of those medical men and psychiatrists who are in positions of responsibility in the government and in the armed forces. This we can do by the contribution of pertinent theories and observations relevant to general and specific problems.

The more general principles involved in the war seem to me to be of the utmost importance to us psychoanalysts and it is to these that I think we could contribute the most. As Dr. Samuel Hartwell put it, in his presidential letter to the members of the American Orthopsychiatric Association, "The world's confusion is caused by the fact that human beings, although fully intelligent enough to control the environment in a way to give a good life to all, fail to react to one another constructively, to agree or to understand one another sufficiently well to live together with a reasonable degree of civilized sociability." The fundamental reason for this unsociability seems to me to be one to which psychoanalysis ought to be able to contribute more than any other branch of science, since we have at our hands the techniques for discovering what is unconscious, and surely much of this must be unconscious. Human beings would not, for conscious "rational" reasons, bring so much sorrow upon themselves.

It is from unconscious motives that "we human beings plant in ourselves the perennial blossom of cruelty—the conviction that if we hurt other people we are doing good to ourselves and to life in general. To destroy this cancer of our spirit is our real problem"

(Rebecca West). It is the aggressive instincts, the impulses to self-destruction and the destruction of others, that seize every opportunity to make men miserable.

Basic principles survive all disasters, all threats. Our growing pains, the death of our first teacher, even the world conflagration—these will not alter science, science in general or psychoanalysis in particular. These things will not even retard its development. On the other hand, dissensions, secessions, personal feuds and personal exploitations—while they cannot destroy psychoanalysis—certainly can retard its development and injure its prestige. I am no believer in peace at any price but I am a great believer in the strength of unity and amity. There is enough fighting among the peoples of the earth. Let us, as American scientists, work together in harmony, tolerance, cooperation—and loyalty. In all the history of the world there was never a time in which loyalty was more important. "United we stand, divided we fall" is trite, but it is true—true for our international war, true for our states, true for Americans, true for psychoanalysts. Loyalty is one of the great virtues. Loyalty means not that I *am* you, or that I *agree* with everything you say or that I believe you are always right. Loyalty means that I share a common ideal with you and that regardless of minor differences we fight for it, shoulder to shoulder, confident in one another's good faith, trust, constancy, and affection. This is my ideal for the members of our Association.

5. Present Trends
in Psychoanalytic Theory and Practice

This symposium provides the opportunity for some of us to formulate what seems most significant to use in the present-day trends in psychoanalysis. I am, therefore, offering my reflections upon this topic in lieu of a presidential address.

In the work of every scientist there are to be found two opposed and at the same time interactive principles. In common speech these are described as theory and practice. In traditional philosophy they are known as the principles of induction and deduction. On the one hand, there is the necessity of drawing conclusions from certain observed, collected, and organized facts. On the other hand, there is not only the possibility but the necessity of constructing theories that go beyond these facts and guide us in the seeking for more facts.

Now it would seem perfectly obvious that both inductive and deductive logic must be used in the obtaining of any new truth from the mysterious storehouse of nature. Facts have to be observed, to be sure, but explanations must be hazarded which certainly will not be *entirely* correct but which will lead to further investigations which in turn lead to modifications of the explanations.

Nevertheless, although inductive and deductive thinking can be and must be combined, it is a curious observation that for one

Read as part of a symposium on this subject at the Detroit meeting of the American Psychoanalytic Association, May 1943. Reprinted from the *Bulletin of the Menninger Clinic,* 8:14–17, January 1944.

reason and another, perhaps sometimes temperamental, sometimes opportunistic, sometimes even perhaps neurotic, scientists tend to become predominantly inductive or predominantly deductive in their research techniques and to defend their lopsidedness by a psychoanalytic mechanism known as projection. The inductivists, for example, shake their heads sadly at the "metaphysical nonsense," the "mythologies," the "philosophical vagaries" of the deductivists, and the deductivists shrug their shoulders at the tubular vision and obsessive pettiness of the fanatical empiricists or inductivists.

Freud's early work was predominantly inductive, his later work predominantly deductive. Therefore, he is acclaimed by some for his earlier work, by others for his later work. On the one hand, he is described as the greatest empiricist in the field of psychology; on the other hand, it is declared to be to his abiding credit "that he was the first to help free medicine from the binding fetters of inductive science which since the days of Francis Bacon confined its operations within the limits of naïve materialism. . . . Freud actually occupies a position of defense as it were against empiricism which dominated the official science of his day." [1]

It does not seem to me to be necessary to align oneself either on the side of deductivism or on the side of empiricism. We need facts and we need theories. It may sound very scientific to deplore theoretical conclusions and to urge the collection of more facts but such advices are little more than trite and pretentious clichés; no good scientist can possibly avoid collecting facts any more than he can avoid formulating theories, and to argue that one is more important than another is as academic and meaningless as to argue that the key is more important than the lock or vice versa. For some of us the collection and the correlation of facts will be easier or more interesting than the application of theories to these and as yet undiscovered facts. For others of us whose daily life is a continuous round of collecting facts, the greater pleasure lies in the organization of these facts in certain frames of reference. Call them theoretical speculations, if you like; call them hypotheses; call them anything but give them their due.

To me, the most inspiring contribution of Sigmund Freud was

his revised formulation of the instinct theory. Its pre-eminent importance lies in its wide and far-reaching implications: it points to revision in our whole concept of disease; it indicates new diagnostic criteria; it suggests modifications in our treatment techniques, in our concepts of maladjustment and personality structure, in our approaches to the fields bordering on psychiatry. I think it was the final flowering of his creative genius.

It was a practical axiom of one of my psychoanalytic teachers that if the subtle and veiled aggressive intents of the patient were identified with sufficient clarity, directness, and persistence, the development of the erotic life tended to follow and the neurosis to disappear. This was an intuitive application of the dual instinct theory made before Freud had systematically organized his ideas about it (or at least before they were known to us). Freud had no time, as he himself said, in which to extend his theory to the practical applications of psychiatric diagnosis, of psychosomatic diagnosis and treatment, of medical and psychiatric nosology, and many of the other things which now seem to offer such fruitful fields. For many years at our hospital we have attempted to use the implications of the dual instinct theory in the milieu treatment of psychiatric patients, both adults and children, with results that have been sufficiently gratifying in a considerable number of instances to encourage us to continue it. To find ways in which sublimations may be encouraged and aggressions disseminated through harmless or even constructive channels taxes the ingenuity of the psychiatrist far beyond the use of shock treatment and restraint straps, but it is correspondingly more in keeping with our scientific ideals, and, in the opinion of some of us, more gratifying in its therapeutic efficacy.

My old professor, Ernest Southard, shortly before his death twenty-five years ago, wrote to a good friend and later biographer of his:

> Perhaps it is in definition that I am most interested. Perhaps I be-
> believe that the world can get forward most by a clearer and clearer
> definition of fundamentals. Accordingly, I propose to stick to tasks of
> nomenclature and terminology, unpopular and ridiculous though they

may be. A psychiatric dictionary (to include definitions of every near-lying psychological and philosophical term also) would do more to push mental hygiene on than any other single thing I can think of.

I am still under the inspiration of my old chief, and I am now very much impelled in the direction of working at the revision of our psychiatric and psychoanalytic nosologies. It seems to me it is time that we should have the courage of our convictions and discard old-fashioned, outworn diagnostic categories in favor of concepts which are more dynamic and more in keeping with our psychoanalytic knowledge and our psychoanalytic theories, and more closely related to the *object* of all diagnosis, namely treatment. This would be a contribution to psychiatry which, in my opinion, would be no less fundamental and no less practical than the contributions we can make to assisting in the facilitation of nonpsychoanalytic psychotherapy and other recent trends. Similarly it would be a contribution to psychosomatic medicine which, while less dramatic than the dispelling of symptoms and the curing of individual cases by painstaking techniques of various kinds, would tend to align us more usefully with the medical profession generally, and to correlate our vision and experience with theirs.

In addition to classification, I am greatly interested in the *philosophical* implications of the instinct theory. The need of psychiatric counsel in the planning for a postwar world is one which throws a responsibility on psychiatrists and psychoanalysts whether they choose to accept it or not. I have tried to speak for all of us in my book *Love Against Hate;* perhaps I was presumptuous. But I believe we psychiatrists should come out squarely and courageously for hedonism and lend the support of our convictions and experience to the bewildered, fearful, and hate-inspired peoples of the world. With Rebecca West, "I take it as a prime cause of the present confusion of society that it is too sickly and too doubtful to use pleasure frankly as a test of value." With her, too, I believe that "we need no further argument in favor of taking pleasure as a standard when we consider the only alternative that faces us. If we do not live for pleasure we shall soon find ourselves living for pain. If we do not regard as sacred our own joys and the joys of others, we open the door and let into life the ugliest attribute of the human race, which is cruelty . . . the root of all other vices."

This I think is a message which we, as psychiatrists and as psychoanalysts, can and should give to the world. Important as it is for us to offer the succor of our specialized techniques to the suffering individuals that file through our consultation rooms, it is infinitely more important to offer what we can to those far more numerous sufferers who are either not sick enough or not fortunate enough to be able to consult us. To these we owe it and also to those who cannot consult us because they are too young or perhaps not yet even born. For them the implications of psychoanalytic theory are more important than the techniques of psychoanalytic practice. Ultimately, education is more important than therapy, not only because it can be applied to more people, but because in effect it is prophylactic. The time will come when the study of the child and of the threats to his development will be recognized not as a pretty little hobby for a few earnest missionaries and weary pedants but as a task equal in importance to the directing of a railroad or the compounding of new poisonous gases. If we psychoanalysts, who daily have the evidence before us, do not see this and believe it, how can we expect others to do so?

6. One View of the Kinsey Report

As everyone now knows, a distinguished entomologist, intrigued by the personal problems submitted to him by students in his classes at a Midwestern university, was moved to seek answers to these questions by asking a considerable number of cooperative fellow creatures to tell him frankly what their own personal experiences had been. This inquiry he and three associates gradually extended to some thousands of individuals, selecting his total "sample" more and more carefully in the direction of advice from students of statistical science. Influenced by his professional experience in studying insects, in which the significance of a fact is reinforced by its frequency of repetition, Professor Kinsey then tabulated with indefatigable patience the incidence and timing of atomistic sections of the behavior and sensations reported by his communicants. From this he arrived at various totals, split into subtotals by reference to such extraneous criteria as the economic and educational "level" of the subject interviewed, the existence or nonexistence of a marriage license, the number of years lived, and the relative devoutness of religious conviction—to select only a few.

The first results of this study, conscientiously pursued over a period of ten years, appeared in 1948; the second report appeared last week. They elaborately demonstrate the existence of various phenomena long familiar to psychiatrists, which apparently neither

A review of the book by Alfred Kinsey and others, *Sexual Behavior in the Human Female* (Philadelphia: Saunders, 1953). Reprinted from *GP*, 8:67–72, December 1953.

Kinsey and his colleagues, nor some members of the general public, had previously been quite able to bring themselves to believe. They document with figures precisely what Freud submitted in his famous book *Civilization and Its Discontents,* that civilized man has inhibitions which cost him something in the interest of the total welfare of society. Coming as this does from a scientist skilled in collecting numerical data without contamination by the prejudices of psychiatric experience, the Kinsey material is all the more impressive.

Professor Kinsey's name has become a household word, synonymous with the unveiling of concealed truths, and almost synonymous with the existence of sexuality. The same thing occurred when Freud had the temerity to announce, fifty years ago, that sexual goals were really quite important in human life and that prudery, denial, concealment, guilt, fear, and other factors connected with their attainment in our culture produced evidences of distress in human beings which they might or might not consciously connect with this very normal need. Havelock Ellis was similarly pilloried for having persisted earnestly in the proposition that sexuality was noble and beautiful and not shameful and wicked. But if Professor Kinsey is embarrassed by this repute (and I have no way to know whether he is or not) he will also be embarrassed by the implication that in other ways he resembles Freud and Havelock Ellis. That this is not true, no one knows better than Professor Kinsey. Ellis was a social philosopher, and Freud was a discoverer, clinician, and theoretician. Kinsey is not a theoretician, not a clinician, and not actually a discoverer, but a taxonomist. He had curiosity, the mainspring of scientific research, and he had an ingenious idea; with earnestness, persistence, patience, and courage he listened to, recorded, and tabulated what many people told him of their lives. Thus was produced a set of statistics, which, criticize them as we may, does have a certain scientific validity and does have a prodigious interest for the reading public.

Nothing is more convincing of this latter fact than the extraordinary and unparalleled phenomena relating to the publicizing of the present volume dealing with the results of his interviews with women. The fact that fifty professional writers would make a special trip to Bloomington, attend a three-day series of briefings, read galley proofs, sign commitments regarding releases, and so on is something to arouse the envy, admiration, or contempt—perhaps all three—of many fellow scientists. All this makes it the more difficult for a fellow scientist, particularly one affiliated with a branch of the science for which Professor Kinsey appears to have a somewhat hysterical antipathy, to appraise the new Kinsey volume with complete objectivity. Actually, the real difficulty a psychiatrist has in reviewing the book arises from the sharp difference in our viewpoints regarding the science of man.

I am on record as having declared, after the appearance of the first volume five years ago, that this might prove to be one of the most important scientific studies published in our lifetime. Together with many other psychiatrists and social scientists, I admired the intrepidity, persistence, and earnest purpose of the authors. I heartily concurred in their apparent convictions that individual variation deserves respect and not intolerant condemnation. We all rejoiced in the Kinsey group's success in crashing the iron curtain of social hypocrisy and submitting convincing data in a way that Freud, Havelock Ellis, Krafft-Ebing, W. F. Robey, Margaret Sanger, Victor Robinson, G. V. Hamilton, R. L. Dickinson, K. Davis, and hundreds of psychiatrists whose names I have no room to list, had failed to do.

But along with many of my colleagues I was aware of serious flaws in the first volume. These were carefully pointed out by thoughtful, sympathetic fellow scientists, and I had every hope and expectation that Kinsey and his associates would make use of their suggestions and improve the research before the appearance of a second volume.

In this I was to be greatly disappointed. I have read almost every page of the book and, so far as I can ascertain, scarcely a word of the scholarly analyses and wise counsel of such penetrating critics as Dr. Robert P. Knight, Dr. Lawrence Kubie, Lionel Trilling, and numerous others, does Kinsey appear to have heeded. Kinsey's compulsion to force human sexual behavior into a zoological frame of reference leads him to repudiate or neglect human psychology, and to see normality as that which is natural in the sense that it is what is practiced by animals. Kinsey entered the field of sexuality from entomology and Freud from neurology; but Kinsey has never outgrown his original viewpoint that sexuality is just something that occurs in insects and animals. Freud discovered that in the field of human relations one must recognize the functions of love and hate, as scientific realities interrelated with reproduction; Kinsey did not. The word "love" rarely appears in his book.

Kinsey repudiates the concept of normality as beneath scientific contempt but by implication he substitutes for it the use of two other concepts, that of naturalness and that of prevalence (i.e., high relative incidence). Homosexuality is to be regarded, he says, as a natural form of sexuality, like any other, because it is common in human beings and because animals also practice it. Now this may reflect, as Trilling suggested, "a generous impulse for tolerance, acceptance, liberation, a broad and generous desire for fellow men not to be harshly judged," but it puts the authors in the untenable position of establishing inappropriate norms and setting up the worship of the factuality of the fact, its material physicality, and its numerical strength. (The reporter from *Newsweek* quotes Kinsey as declaring, "I am a fact-finder. I have never evaluated and analyzed my material, and this I refuse to do in the future.") To use these as his criteria "has the effect, ironic in a work that is so clearly directed to democratic values, of removing the human subject from its human implications. [It also] has the effect, equally ironic in a democratic and instrumental document, of preventing the consideration of the consequences of certain forms of human conduct— suggesting a most ineffectual standard of social behavior—that is, social behavior as it exists."

By now most literate Americans have been exposed to the statistical conclusions arrived at as a result of the six thousand or more interviews with women which Professor Kinsey and his associates tabulated, and with the rather different interpretations or implications which the various journalists and readers have put upon Professor Kinsey's conclusions. Thus *Life* magazine's most important conclusion is that women are not very interested in "sex" (a conclusion somewhat belied by the prominence which all the women's magazine's gave to the book!). *McCall's,* on the other hand, is most impressed by the implications that men do not understand women. *Today's Woman* concludes that greater marital happiness for many will result from the startling and revolutionary findings of this courageous scientist. The reporter from *Collier's* was impressed with the differences between the sexual behavior of men and women which, in essence, Professor Kinsey was inclined to minimize. The contributor to *Harper's* felt that despite the "repetitiousness, frequent dullness, occasional confusion, and other faults," the volume was a worthy and honest attempt to throw light on customarily concealed behavior. "The blare of trumpets, seldom long absent from this book, rings loud as Dr. Kinsey proclaims [that], unless it has been conditioned by previous experience, an animal should respond identically to identical stimuli either that emanate from some part of its own body, from another individual of the same sex, or from an individual of the opposite sex." (The utter meaninglessness of this and similar blasts from the trumpet does not seem to have struck the reporter. Need it be pointed out that the verb "should" has no place in a scientific conclusion, or that stimuli can never be identical, or that the fact that stimuli come from different sources itself vitiates their "identicalness," or that every animal is constantly being conditioned by previous experience so that there is no such thing as an animal *not* conditioned by previous experience?)

Of sexual frigidity, Kinsey says, "We dislike the term, for it has come to connote [to whom?] either an unwillingness or an incapacity to function sexually. In most circumstances neither of these implications is correct . . . we do not find evidence in any [unresponsive females] that the individual, rid of her inhibitions, would not be capable of response." What on earth does this mean? If a person has inhibitions from which she must be rid before she has the capacity to do something, is it not obvious that she has a functional incapacity to do that something so long as she is not rid of those inhibitions?

Professor Kinsey's conception of sex as something to be let out (he refers to the "total outlet") is a somewhat scatological concept, and leads logically to two of his most egregious errors. The first is the inference that the orgasm is the total goal and ultimate criterion of sexual satisfaction. No one would seriously hold that, since eating is a good thing and a pleasant thing, the more one can eat, the better. Dr. Kinsey presents not one iota of evidence to support such a hypothesis. The fact that many people would feel inclined to agree with it is likewise no proof. The starving inhabitants of a desert island might easily subscribe to the notion that the more food they could obtain, the better, but any dietitian could refute this. And, furthermore, Kinsey clearly demonstrates that there is no considerable amount of sexual starvation in America.

And as for an orgasm's being the chief criterion of sexuality, everyone knows that one orgasm can differ from another as widely as do kisses. A kiss by Judas is one thing, a kiss by Venus is another, and a kiss by a loving mother is still a third. The orgasm of a terrified soldier in battle, that of a loving husband in the arms of his wife, that of a desperate homosexual trying to prove his masculinity, and that of a violent and sadistic brute raping a child are not the same phenomena. The muscles and nerves and secretions may be the same but the orgasms are not the same, and the sexuality is not the same. They may add up to the same numbers on an adding machine, but they don't add up to significant totals in human life.

Indeed, the psycho-physical separation which the Kinsey associates decry at the beginning of Chapter 16 is precisely what they have fallen a victim to throughout their study. They would seem to be under the impression that it is possible to describe the mechanics of human behavior in purely physical and chemical terms without reference to the mystic vagaries (as they conceive of them) of psychology. This point of view, one must concede, is by no means limited to the Kinsey group. It is the chief *casus belli* between the biological and the psychological scientists, and the reviewer is definitely with the latter.

It would be possible to record the number of times six thousand American citizens went to the toilet and the number of minutes spent there and various other details without in any sense identifying the diet, the health, the cleanliness, the psychological attitudes, or the morals of the people that this sample represented. On the other hand, it might reveal to some still uninformed, misguided, constipated individuals that going to the toilet is, for all its privacy, a common human experience which at the same time allows for considerable individual variation. I say this without any wish to ridicule or demean what Dr. Kinsey has done, because I believe that, insofar as his "facts" are true, they should be known. I do not believe, however, that the truth of these facts or any other such facts can be deduced from the tables and statistics offered. Sexuality is only one expression of a dynamic in the direction of life, an aspect which cannot be isolated from the other aspects, motives, and satisfactions of life, and it distorts the "truth" to do so. It isn't that sex cannot be separated from love; we all know, to our sorrow, that it can. But psychiatrists take the position that this separation itself represents an abnormal state of affairs in the human being, and hence statistics about sex based upon an assumption that the presence or absence of love, to put it simply, is unimportant are vastly disturbing to us.

These very points have been made with startling clarity by a feature writer in a newspaper article distributed by the Spadia Syndicate, the whole of which Dr. Kinsey might take to heart. Among other things, Zolotow wrote: "The Indiana inquisitor seems to regard love as a competitive athletic contest, in which frequency of sex adventure and the number of lovers—one's batting average, so to speak—is more important than quality and intensity of experience. . . . I believe that both Kinsey reports, . . . with their graphs and statistics, may bestow an aura of scientific approval on a delusion that has misled all too many people in the past twenty-five years. I refer to that delusion that sex is an indoor sport and, like contract bridge of scrabble or canasta, it can be mastered by studying technique and practicing as often as possible with as many partners as one can induce to play. . . . Unless the movement toward sexual integration is an expression of love for the other person there can be no normal sexual ecstasy. . . . Love is an intense awareness of the other person, a feeling of respect for him or her as a human being and as an instinctive attitude that the needs of the other person are as important to you as your own needs. . . . Sexual promiscuity or experimentation or athleticizing . . . without feelings of tenderness and affection is . . . destructive."

This, rather than skepticism regarding the sample of the frequency table, would be my chief objection to the book. I, too, like all other doctors, have interviewed a few women in the past thirty years in the course of which they had every reason to be quite frank about their sexual experiences. And, while I had no adding machine in my office, I am quite sure that in my sample the incidence of adultery, for example, was not nearly as high as Kinsey reports it. I have talked with other psychiatrists and their experience confirms mine, but *our* samples are not representative ones, either. I think we psychiatrists would have put the incidence of frigidity much higher than does Kinsey. Let us hope he is correct and rejoice in the evidence he offers that satisfactions in one particular function of marital adjustment seem to be more widespread and general than a few years ago when similar statistics were collected by other workers on a smaller scale. Let us commend Professor Kinsey and his associates for their high-minded dedication to searching for concealed facts about human life as it is, and reducing hypocritical pretenses.

Let us be glad, too, if the book relieves *some* people's minds. When the first volume of the Kinsey study appeared five years ago, Dr. Martin Gumpert commented in *The Nation* that one highly gratifying effect of the book would seem to be that it appeared to lift the feelings of guilt from hundreds of thousands of readers. (How did he know this?) "This mass psychotherapeutic function," wrote Gumpert, "is one secret of its success. People work with touching eagerness through the appalling mass of boring charts and statistics in order to discover with relief that they are not outcasts, not psychopaths, not criminals, when they masturbate or enjoy other 'abnormal' sexual outlets. They learn that they are as 'normal' or as 'vicious' as anybody they meet on the streets of their home town. If this relief from tension and guilt can be bought for $6.50, it is a most happy social accomplishment."

Unfortunately, this guilt lifting is an equivocal blessing; I, for one, think that some guilt feelings are better *not* removed; they belong. Certainly, the ethical rightness or wrongness of an act can scarcely be justifiably determined by the frequency of its occurrence. If human welfare be considered a criterion of rightness, the fact that nearly every person in the United States regularly ran stop lights or exceeded the speed limit would still not make it right to do so. Dr. Kinsey and his associates point to the influence of religious training as inhibiting the violation of laws and customs regarding sexuality, such as marital fidelity. If one believes in the principle that maximum sexual expression is the most desirable goal, then, of course, it is encouraging for one to learn that he is not the only sinner against religion, which holds that certain other principles are more important than sexual "freedom" and that more abundant life is not necessarily implied by more abundant sex. And in this instance, surprising as it may be to some, most psychiatrists and psychoanalysts will be definitely on the side of religion.

To be freed from the torturing delusion that one is a monster, a lone and isolated exception among human beings, is indeed a comfort and a salutary benefit if derivable from such statistical announcements. But that learning that other people have temptations, and sometimes yield to them, will bring about happier marriages, better sexual adjustment, and all the other optimistic results bespoken in the news articles referred to is by no means so certain. Indeed, if one followed Kinsey in his (I believe incorrect) assumption that sexual behavior is entirely a matter of sexual equipment, conditioning experience, and chance, there is no reason to assume or hope that the publishing of his findings will in any way change things.

If human beings *were* only animals, if they were "free" from the restraints and social considerations of civilization, if they could once more be simple savages, perhaps their sexuality could likewise be more free, more independent of emotions, more susceptible to statistical evaluation. It would be—in one sense of the word—more "natural," more "normal." But unfortunately for this hypothetical simplification, human beings are possessed of love as well as hate, and willy-nilly, for better or for worse, civilization has gotten a foothold! That the unrestrained expression of "sexuality" becomes impaired thereby is, as Freud pointed out in his classic, *Civilization and Its Discontents,* inevitable. This, Kinsey and his associates have proved statistically. Is it to weep, or to rejoice?

Freud himself would not say. "It is very far from my intentions," he said, "to express any opinion concerning the value of human civilization. I have endeavored to guard myself against the enthusiastic partiality which believes our civilization to be the most precious thing that we possess or could acquire, and thinks it must inevitably lead us to undreamt-of heights of perfection. I can at any rate listen without taking umbrage to those critics who aver that when one surveys the aims of civilization and the means it employs, one is bound to conclude that the whole thing is not worth the effort and that in the end it can only produce a state of things which no individual will be able to bear. My impartiality is all the easier to me since I know very little about these things and am sure only of one thing, that the judgments of value made by mankind are immediately determined by their desires for happiness; in other words, that those judgments are attempts to prop up their illusions with arguments. I could understand it very well if anyone were to point to the inevitable nature of the process of cultural development and say, for instance, that the tendency to institute restrictions upon sexual life or to carry humanitarian ideals into effect at the cost of natural selection is a developmental trend which it is impossible to avert or divert, and to which it is best for us to submit as though they were natural necessities. I know, too, the objection that can be raised against this: that tendencies such as these, which are believed to have insuperable power behind them, have often in the history of man been thrown aside and replaced by others. My courage fails me, therefore, at the thought of rising up as a prophet before my fellow men, and I bow to their reproach that I have no consolation to offer them; for at bottom this is what they all demand—the frenzied revolutionary as passionately as the most pious believer.

"The fateful question of the human species seems to me to be whether and to what extent the cultural process developed in it will succeed in mastering the derangements of communal life caused by the human instinct of aggression and self-destruction. In this connection, perhaps the phase through which we are at this moment passing deserves special interest. Men have brought their powers of subduing the forces of nature to such a pitch that by using them they could now very easily exterminate one another to the last man. They know this—hence arises a great part of their current unrest, their dejection, their mood of apprehension. And now it may be expected that the other of the two 'heavenly forces,' eternal Eros, will put forth his strength so as to maintain himself alongside of his equally immortal adversary."

And by the "eternal Eros," Freud meant the development of the capacity for loving one another, a relationship which far transcends the achievement of more frequent orgasm.

7. Psychological Factors
in the Choice of Medicine as a Profession

The way in which a man works is a measure of his maturity. It is a criterion of his mental healthiness, and of the degree of the internal and external integration which he maintains. The extent to which it meets his internal needs determines his satisfaction in it. Work in the abstract relates to a constructive use of energy. It represents a deflection to constructive uses of energy arising originally in connection with hostile feelings and a destructive purpose. If we define sublimation as the neutralization of these destructive tendencies through diverting them to objects and goals of personal and social benefit, or by converting them into defensive maneuvers against themselves in the so-called reaction formations, we must regard work along with play as among the highest forms of sublimation.

To psychiatrists, therefore, work appears not as a necessary evil, the price payable for the achievement of certain ends, but rather as a necessary good, a source of satisfaction, of joy, of mental healthiness. It is the easier for us to entertain this view because most physicians make no secret of the pleasure they find in their work, unpleasant and heartbreaking as certain aspects of it are. The average layman, on the other hand, finds this difficult to understand, and perhaps on some dark days we ourselves wonder how and why we ever chose this way of life. We are apt to assume too readily, perhaps,

Portions of this article were read at the Brill Memorial dinner meeting of the New York Society for Clinical Psychiatry on Jan. 27, 1955. Reprinted from the *Quarterly of Phi Beta Pi*, 53:12–23, October 1956.

that, because we love our work, everyone who does not love his work is mentally unhealthy to that degree.* As psychiatry is applied increasingly to the problems of industry, we realize more and more how naïve it is to assume that even in our great country people can work at whatever they wish. Economists and sociologists get out of patience with us for making such assumptions, reminding us that economic realities, educational limitations, social structures, traditions, and horizons all tend to narrow the area of vocational choice to such an extent that for many individuals there is clearly no choice, but a question of "Root, hog, or die." We psychiatrists may counter by saying that, granted sufficient goal-directed dissatisfaction, there will be a continued struggle upward and outward in the direction of discovering optimum engagement; but we neglect the fact that for certain kinds of work—our own, for example—the prerequisites and preparations are so long and expensive that the goal cannot be reached unless one gets an early start.†

CHOICE

But while some have no apparent choice, for some fortunate individuals, whose destinies are not restricted by cultural and economic limitations or by inherent organic handicaps, there appears to be the possibility of *choosing* a preferred life work, certainly one of the most momentous decisions ever made by any individual. Yet, since it must be made before maturity has been achieved, when knowledge of the world is far from complete and when life experiences have been relatively limited, the decision must be made to a large extent on the basis of chance, childhood impressions, and the advice, counsel, or inspiration of others. Such external influences are sometimes conscientiously solicited and utilized, but perhaps most often automatically acquired and unconsciously organized in the process of a definite decision.[3] The responsibility of parents and

---

* Anne Roe [1]: "It seems very probable that concepts of adjustment reflect primarily the type of adjustment that is palatable to the sort of people psychologists are."

† This was tragically illustrated in the life of Morton F. Thompson,[2] author of a very popular novel depicting the life and development of a physician. He himself is said to have always longed to study medicine.

of oldsters for setting the right example, for inspiring, for counseling and advising (if asked), is nonetheless most important.

The so-called aptitude tests are of little help to us. We do not know precisely what an aptitude is, and the helpfulness of the questionnaire method of vocational guidance is rather limited.[4, 5] An approach, through projective tests, to the unconscious determinants of vocational choice has been made by Anne Roe[6] in her studies of eminent scientists manifestly successful in the career of their choice.* Eli Ginzberg, Sol Ginsburg, Sidney Axelrad, and John L. Herma have contributed a most important study in *Occupational Choice: An Approach to a General Theory.*[7] What they demonstrated was that, although nearly everyone has to work, many people have little choice, and those who do, have little to guide them. One point of view is that occupational choice is largely fortuitous or "accidental." Another is the so-called "impulse" theory, for which we psychoanalysts are held responsible, the assumption that internal psychological needs determine or condition the responses of the individual to external possibilities. Finally, there is what might be called the "pedagogic theory," which holds that with proper counseling vocational choice need not be left either to accident or to current impulse.

The authors cited examined the degree to which choice is possible, granted various innate capacities, and recognized that it usually represents a series of decisions, made over a period of years, which are connected with one another but which form an irreversible process and end in a compromise. First there is a period of *fantasy choices,* usually in childhood; then a period of *tentative choices* between ages 11 and 17 with four stages—an interest stage, a capacity stage, a value stage, and a transitional stage. Then comes the period of *realistic choices* with a stage of exploration followed by a stage of crystallization and then one of specification.

I know of no other study that recognizes the need to investigate

---

* Her work, still in its early stages, suggests that the specific vocations chosen by her subjects represented ways of dealing with unconscious conflict, occurring in early life, and that the nature of the conflict, and the time at which it occurs, may be important determinants.

how vocational choices are made, and more than most studies it emphasizes the importance of a better knowledge of vocational choice, for the conservation of human resources. This latter point cannot but appeal to those of us who do what we can to identify those indications favoring or not favoring the large investment of time and money which a proper training now costs.

MOTIVATION

Choice of a vocation obviously ties in closely with motivation. The motives of physicians have become of late the subject of intense popular concern. Attempts to institute so-called socialized medicine or compulsory health insurance in this country stimulated such vigorous and poorly presented rationalizations from official medical spokesmen that the motives of physicians, heretofore taken for granted as benign and selfless, began to be questioned by the public. Doctors seemed to resist efforts to make their services more widely available and less expensive, and laymen became increasingly disillusioned about their idols of benevolent healing. Since almost everyone has either had a serious illness or may one day develop one, it is disturbing to bring into question the integrity and good will of the men in the community who have power over life and death.

As though in response to the growing public interest in the inner life of the physician, several collections of autobiographical material by doctors have been published recently.[8] Of these doctor authors, some evidently felt no compulsion to explain their interest in medicine; either they followed a long family tradition without questioning what they felt as their predetermined course, or else they said, simply, "I have always been interested in medicine." Others stated, as though this accounted fully for their choice, that their parents wanted them to study medicine. Still others were sure they became doctors in defiance of their parents' wishes. Some felt drawn to medical science because of its challenge and mystery—because so much remains unknown about health and disease. Yet others felt an attraction of exactly the opposite sort: the study of medicine offered an escape from uncertainty, a chance to reduce mysteries to solid facts. Doctors for centuries have recognized in themselves the desire for prestige and honor and an adequate income; recently the power of these factors has increased.

The motive generally accepted as primary in all physicians is one which no doctor would disavow: the desire to show mercy, to relieve pain, to correct deformity, to preserve life. But while these familiar conscious motives may account, in part, for the initial desire to study medicine, they by no means account for the fact that doctors continue to practice it in spite of frustrations and disappointments. Similar motives of mercy must be prevalent among many non-medical people. And many doctors, possessed of these same motives, are neither successful nor happy in their work. Memoirs, of course, are not written in terms of the *unconscious* factors that influence *conscious* choice. Even Freud himself (as the recent biography by Ernest Jones and the letters to Fliess show) failed to explain why he elected to study medicine, or what turned him away from his original interest in organic structures and toward psychological functions.

UNCONSCIOUS FACTORS

In the past twenty-five years, several thousand physicians have been psychoanalyzed. About one thousand American psychiatrists are being psychoanalyzed at this very moment, in the course of their formal training. Many other physicians have undergone psychoanalysis for strictly therapeutic reasons. Could the knowledge derived from the study of all these colleagues be pooled, we should be in a position to generalize about the *unconscious* motivations of doctors, especially psychiatrists. There are obvious reasons why this information cannot be pooled in any systematic way, but the situation is not hopeless.

Many of us have ourselves been analyzed, and some of our discoveries we can remember, indeed, we must remember them, every day. Too, many of us have analyzed other doctors and from these experiences certain generalizations take form automatically in our minds. This in turn is reflected in our attitudes toward various problems which we discuss in seminars and committee meetings with other colleagues who have also had these experiences, and who also express their attitudes. The result is a certain tacit recognition of agreed-upon assumptions, based upon a common knowledge of unconscious trends and content with which we are familiar both subjectively and objectively. This is apparent in faculty meetings and selection-committee conferences. Add to this the fact that psychoanalytic theory and the facts upon which it has been based have never been kept a secret.

Now the question arises as to whether we can formulate anything regarding these unconscious motives. If we do so, our efforts should be recognized as but speculations, groping attempts to outline some of the more probable explanations of experience.

Let us begin, for example, with the fact that doctors have doctor fathers. What does this tell us? It may or may not conform with the psychoanalytic specifications for an unconscious identification; often it is a quite *conscious* identification. It may be pedagogically determined.

But let us go further. Sometimes an identification with the father is demonstrated by the wish to surpass him, humiliate him, extinguish him; and at other times it is demonstrated by the wish to follow him, to help him, to emulate him. A benevolent identification may be regarded as a successful solution of the Oedipus complex. But another may solve the Oedipus complex successfully by *not* becoming a doctor that his father was; still another becomes a doctor, not because his father was one, but because his father wanted his son to be one. Still others (this is frequently mentioned in autobiographies) become physicians because they or a sibling or one of the parents was ill, and in a more or less dramatic experience this illness was relieved by the ministrations of the family physician, who came like a great healing god, perchance on only one great, memorable visit. Still other doctors would seem to become physicians, not so much through any relationship to the father as through a strong wish to please the mother (who may or may not have married a doctor) or from a strong identification with the mother, rather than the father, as the healing, restoring, comforting member of the family.

All these adolescent conflicts in regard to pleasing the father, challenging the father, disappointing the mother, pleasing the in-group, challenging the out-group, repeat and reflect emotional con-flicts which occurred first in the infancy and childhood period, when pleasing or displeasing the parent or parents seemed a matter of life and death. The parents, who acted as protectors against these dangers, seemed to the child omnipotent.

Inevitably there occurs a disillusionment about the parents' om-nipotence; the parent sickens, falters, dies, or in some other way betrays his vulnerability, and the confidence of the child is displaced to some more dependable bulwark. This may be a magical charm, a totem, a conceptualized deity, or—as just mentioned—often it is explicitly the family physician. The child later emulates this savior and accepts his gospel and way of life. He puts the same faith in medical science that he once put in the comforting arms of his mother and father.*

Alan Gregg [9] put this beautifully in his paper "Our Anabasis" read before the Association of American Physicians:

> You must have been about 11 years old when it happened. You had a very sore throat and after a night when the lamp never went out and your mother was at your side whenever you called for her, you awakened to see her anxiously scanning your face and heard her ask your father to call Dr. Lawrence. You used to see Dr. Lawrence go up Cascade Avenue in his new horseless carriage followed by his man driving the other older horseless carriage in case the new one broke down or blew out a pneumatic tire. When Dr. Lawrence came into your room he put his lighted cigar very carefully on the marble top of the dressing table. Your mother didn't seem to mind that at all. He smelled awfully strongly of tobacco when he leaned down and put his ear right on your bare chest. Then he asked your mother to get a pitcher of fresh water, turned

---

* How the desire to please the parents may operate unconsciously as a powerful motivating force is suggested by Havelock Ellis's account of his decision to study medicine. His own parents had never urged him toward any particular vocation, and until the age of 20 he was utterly without any idea as to how he wanted to make his living. At this point he read the biography of James Hinton, and when he came to the account of how Hinton's parents decided upon a medical career for him, Ellis suddenly, and without any previous inclination in this direction, made the choice of medicine as a vocation. It was as though, not knowing how to please his own parents, he solved the problem by identifying himself with a man who had had it solved for him. (See Fabricant, op. cit.)

to you and said, "Now watch!" He took a bottle out of his medicine
bag, uncorked it deftly with one hand, and shook some shiny brown
crystals into the water which immediately turned a wonderful purple.
"Let him" (he didn't say "make him") "Let him gargle with this every
two hours," and then, turning to you, "but don't swallow it! Two
pounds of this powder would turn all Prospect Lake purple! By the
way, did you hear the sicklebill curlews night before last? Asleep? Well
I was coming home from the Malones at three o'clock in the morning,"
and, turning to your mother, he added, "Eight-and-a-half-pound boy
. . . and the curlews' eerie crying was beautiful." Then he turned to
your Mother and said, "Mrs. Bacon, you haven't a thing to worry about.
I'll be back day after tomorrow and sooner if you want." Your mother
suddenly looked very relieved and just after Dr. Lawrence had left
you heard her say to your father, "Doctor Lawrence is so *faithful*." It
was her highest praise, as anyone could guess from her way of saying it.

Four days later, sitting in the swing in the bright September sun, an
idea suddenly swept you through and through: "When I grow up I
want to be a doctor." You rather thought that with anything as big
as that you ought to tell God about it immediately—and not just casually
standing up, either. But if you knelt down then and there somebody
might see you and ask why—and you couldn't tell. So you ran upstairs
to the only room in the house that could be locked—the bathroom—
and there you knelt down under three towels, an empty hot water bottle
and your father's back-scratcher, and took the Almighty in on a decision that you never doubted nor regretted from that day to this.

I wish you could read all of this. It is so much better than anything
I could say. He goes on to describe the facing of death, the witnessing
of birth, the taking of responsibility, and so on to the "greatest danger
and the greatest reward in medicine—and so the deepest bond between us all—the First Time a Patient Trusts You—with his life."

Identification with the parents or family physician does not
exclude the expression of aggressive impulses in this identification.
The child's earliest anger against parents is generated by many
frustrations, such as weaning, toilet-training, births, deaths, illness
and absences of parents, rivalries, defects. In our culture, a crucial
point in the development of hostility in the young child is reached
with the dawning of conscious erotic impulses, which the child is

constrained to conceal or deny. The mass of aggressive impulses thus stimulated find a variety of expressions, and many of them are repressed and forgotten, others suppressed and remembered. The impulse toward intended injury may be replaced by the effort to heal, to undo injury, to restore health even by painful methods. In this way the aggression is at the same time enacted, disguised, and atoned for.

The atonement and undoing aspects of this cycle deserve emphasis, for the physician's "mercy" may be seen also as his way of undoing injuries which, as a child, he inflicted in fantasy upon individuals now represented by his patients. Rescuing, restoring, and making whole, are well-known preoccupations of the unconscious mental life of many individuals; some invest much energy in symbolic restitution or atonement.

Another unconscious factor which enters into the election of a medical career, and perhaps more generally of all the biological sciences, is the curiosity about the body of the mother which is so intense in every child. Ernst Simmel first related the childhood "doctor game" to the adult "doctor game." Anatomy remains the core of medical education; and for every child anatomy is, for a considerable period, the core of things to be learned. Yet it is something about which his parents and teachers (in our culture) seem reluctant to instruct him. Nearly everything else is pointed out to him, explained to him, even submitted to him for examination: but not his mother's body. He rarely sees it except variously covered. It remains the great mystery.

The child makes his own explorations, and these efforts at self-education are often followed by punishment. Discovery that he himself came from his mother's body renders the already puzzling mystery infinitely more complicated. He has fantasies of having been cut from her abdomen or passed from her bowels. The fascinating obscurity of the external parts of her body is exceeded only by the inconceivable intricacy of her "insides." Not all children remain in such confusion, and not all children become physicians; but curiosity with respect to these mysteries remains the secret driving force of many lives.

As children grow older, they become interested in pets, which they examine carefully and furtively. They cut open dead animals. They observe with an intense fascination the cleaning of chickens by the cook. They take clocks apart to see what is inside.

When the time comes to choose a career, childish interests are not abandoned in favor of adult interests, but rather rephrased in adult terms. If the grown-up child's inhibitions are not too great, he may attempt to satisfy his old curiosity by some direct investigation; but even this cannot fully answer his questions. There remains a drifting and insatiable curiosity about what is *really* on the inside. The only sure, direct, final method of finding out is to study anatomy. One might speculate that those who actually do study anatomy and later medicine may be more direct and less turned from their original purpose than those who deflect their curiosity to the study of the structure of other mammals or of rocks or of atoms. This is only speculation; I have no evidence for it.

Thus far we have been speaking of medicine generally as a profession of healing. Actually, the techniques of diagnosis and treatment have become so complicated that the specialized sub-divisions which have arisen sometimes seem almost separate disciplines. Perhaps this is particularly true of our own specialty of psychiatry, partly because of our commitment to the broader "holistic" view of man. At any rate, we may advantageously carry our analysis further and speculate about some of the reasons for the selection of these specialties. I would emphasize that we do not know about the full and final facts about these things and any similarity between our speculations and the actual facts must be regarded as possibly coincidental.

Pediatrics is a branch of medicine characterized by the fact that all the doctor's patients are children. A pediatrician may see in his patients little replicas of his siblings or playmates of his formative years. In his professional work he has a continuous opportunity to undo in all sorts of magical ways some of the serious conflicts of childhood. Arnold Gesell, the child psychologist, was the eldest of five children, and was held responsible for his younger siblings when he was a boy; he says, understandably enough, "I have always been interested in children."

Everyone has observed in some doctors a pronounced tendency to mother their patients, treating all of them, regardless of their actual age, as if they were little children. Not only in their manner and attitude but also in their procedures, doctors of this type seem to play the maternal role, lavishing attention upon diet and bowel movements in a way strikingly reminiscent of the mother training her child. I once knew a physician who insisted upon giving his patients enemata himself, not occasionally, but daily. And as he tended them thus, he would admonish and scold them exactly as some mothers do.

How much this permeates the entire medical profession generally, we do not know, but in pediatrics the maternal role is sometimes conspicuous. Many pediatricians would probably not resent being called "proxy mothers." Perhaps in some instances the pediatrician is a man in whose own childhood there was physical illness of importance to which the mother ministered in a way which, many years later, the pediatrician repeats with a higher degree of technical skill and knowledge.

A combination of specialty interests occurs not infrequently. A number of psychiatrists have told me that they had narrowed their choices to pediatrics, internal medicine, and psychiatry, and "nearly" chose pediatrics or internal medicine before they finally settled on psychiatry.

In *obstetrics* the childhood longing to know where babies come from is repeatedly and directly gratified. But perhaps even more significant here than curiosity is the factor of identification with the mother. Historically obstetrics developed from the passive art of midwifery (the Latin word *obstare* means merely "to stand [watchfully] before"!), practiced by women, to a highly technical skill in which the obstetrician plays almost as active a role as the mother herself. Indeed it is difficult in watching a modern delivery (in which the mother is unconscious and paralyzed, and the baby drawn instrumentally through a surgically enlarged opening) not to assume that the obstetrician, rather than the mother, is delivering the child!

In no more thorough way could the obstetrician gratify his unconscious infantile wish to become the mother. In certain primitive
societies this wish is given open ritual recognition, as in New Guinea,
where the puberty rites for boys include the imitation by males of
child-bearing.[10]

The agonies of childbirth are described in exceptionally florid
terms in some of the standard obstetrical textbooks as if obstetricians
felt compelled to emphasize or even exaggerate the sufferings of
motherhood; this might be the expression of an unconscious wish,
a residue of early infantile rage and hostility against the mother. The
urge to relieve maternal pain has been so pre-eminent that, until the
recent development of relatively harmless obstetrical anesthetics,
relief was achieved at the cost of considerable risk for the infant.

In view of the foregoing, it is hardly surprising that obstetricians
have been inclined to take a rather dim view of the modern *laissez
faire* trend in obstetrics, many specialists refusing to deliver their
patients without anesthesia even when the mothers oppose it. One
specialist who had been persuaded by a particularly importunate
young mother to deliver her without medication revealed the degree
of his identification with his patient when at the end of the delivery
he said, "Never again! I can't stand it!"

Certain factors in connection with *gynecology* involve psychoanalytic speculations rather complicated for simple generalization.

Perhaps the *urologists* are the frankest and, in a sense, the most
unrepressed of all the specialists. They have been twitted so much in
regard to some of the implications of their specialty that they seem to
have become immune to ridicule and this leads them to be unusually
open-minded. Many urologists acknowledge that impotence in the
male is primarily a psychological and not a structural condition,
and is best treated by psychological means. To be sure, some of
them continue to believe that instrumentation is a type of psychotherapy, and as a matter of fact they have pragmatic justification
for this, because it frequently "works" as such. My impression is,
however, that many of the urologists know in a general way why
it works. They may not recognize the fact that substitution of
another form of punishment often relieves the individual of the

need for self-inflicted symptoms, but they do recognize that the patient often wants to be hurt, and they do it for him cheerfully, skillfully, and harmlessly—which is more than can be said for a good many mothers, judges, and psychiatrists.

Why urologists should have elected that specialty and what unconscious satisfactions they find in it is not easy to say. Urologists in general have a frank attitude toward sex. From the nature of their practice, one might assume that they believe the penis is the most important organ of the body, which is what every human being believes *at one stage in his development,* the so-called phallic period.

The function of urination is of great interest to every child, and many special feelings and attitudes are connected with it. For most children it is for a certain period of time a substitution for less approved uses of the genitals. Some of the individuals may be expected, in adulthood, to find satisfaction in devoting themselves to the maintenance of the most efficient functioning of the urinary apparatus.

Proctology is so obviously connected with what we refer to as preoccupations of the anal phase of development that certain other features might easily be overlooked. The social taboo on anality in our culture is peculiarly sharp and inconsistent; we Americans are proud of our money, our bathrooms and our plumbing, and many other aspects of our civilization which seem clearly related to anal erotism, while we are highly fastidious regarding smells and cleanliness and erect strong taboos on excretion and the structures related to it.[11] This makes the proctologist perforce a humble man indeed, whose patients—like those of the psychiatrist—are ashamed to admit they need him.

Surgery is associated with the idea of cutting, of giving pain in order to relieve pain. The conscious association of pleasure with the inflicting of pain is considered perverse, but, properly sublimated, this becomes a kind of heroic mercifulness. We all know—or suspect —that some physicians and some surgeons, like some candlestick makers, are cruel—cruel to their patients and sometimes to their wives and other people. It cannot be denied that medicine, and particularly surgery, afford a unique opportunity to conceal conscious or unconscious sadism. In the fantasies of children, and of mentally ill patients, one often encounters the wish to mutilate the living body of some foe. The intensity of the revulsion ordinarily evoked by such ideas indicates how strongly most of us repress them. Yet the extreme popularity of the uncouth Mickey Spillane books suggests how widespread is the craving for some sort of vicarious expression of such destructive thoughts.

It is no reflection upon the surgeons to say that a connection exists between fantasies of mutilation and the skilled, tender handling of body tissues by the trained operator. It does not follow that surgeons are more sadistic than other people, or more driven by blind impulses toward cruelty; in fact, just the opposite may be true. The chances are that surgeons have less unconscious guilt about their sadistic proclivities than most people and hence do not need to repress them, but use them constructively. They can sublimate sadistic impulses in a closely related but enormously more approved form of behavior. That this form appeals to the public is obvious in the dramatic interest which attaches to the surgical operation, in the romantic interest which (so often) attaches to the surgeon. He becomes the great life saver, the performer of miracles, the very incarnation of curative science.

This makes it the more understandable that surgeons sometimes seem inclined to establish their own ethical systems, and take the law into their own hands, as it were—or permit their fellows to do so. I so interpret the casualness with which some surgeons treat the ugly fact of mercenary and unnecessary operations, as even recently again exposed by the College of Surgeons under its courageous and outspoken leader, Dr. Paul Hawley. But here again one should observe that it was the surgeons themselves who first fought this temptation, officially repudiated it, and set up standards and practices to eliminate it.

There is an entirely different aspect of surgery which has nothing to do with pain, cutting, cruelty, and so forth. Some people—and who of us does not have friends like this?—feel more confidence in their hands than in their tongues and voices. Many have asked why Albert Schweitzer, already a theologian, a philosopher, and a musician, should have turned to surgery. It is not a complete answer, but it is his own, expressed very simply in *Out of My Life and Thought:* [12] "I wanted to be a doctor that I might be able to work without having to talk. For years I had been giving myself out in words, and it was with joy that I had followed the calling of the theological teacher and preacher. But this new form of activity I could not represent to myself as talking about the religion of love, but only as an actual putting of it into practice."

Dermatology, like psychiatry, deals to a large extent with perverse expressions of emotional disorders. The psychiatrist listens for hours to verbal descriptions of internal, invisible lesions; the dermatologist makes an almost instantaneous visual grasp of external, visible lesions. The psychiatrist relies chiefly upon his ears, the dermatologist upon his eyes. One wonders if a statistical study would show that psychiatrists lean more toward the appreciation of music and dermatologists toward the appreciation of the graphic arts.

At any rate, they have much in common. The patients of the dermatologist, like those of the psychiatrist, are under a cloud. The public suspects them of being untouchable and loathsome and guilty of exaggerating their suffering. Pyschiatrists, who are so often portrayed as enriching themselves by pampering hypochondriacal old ladies with nothing wrong with them, can sympathize with the dermatologists, who are accused of making meaningless Latin diagnoses and applying placebo ointments to inconsequently ill patients.

For all these similarities, however, there is one striking difference between dermatology and psychiatry. We have considerable data about the psychology of psychiatrists, but we have no source of information about any characteristic psychology of the dermatologists. I have not personally analyzed a physician specializing in dermatology or even having a particular interest in it, and I know of no one who has.

My friend, the late Dr. Paul O'Leary, distinguished head of the Department of Dermatology at the Mayo Clinic, took the trouble to inquire for me of quite a number of his dermatological colleagues regarding their original interest in dermatology. Nearly a third of them had physician fathers, none of whom were dermatologists. The reasons ascribed for the choice of dermatology varied widely: the challenge behind the obvious was mentioned oftenest. Dermatological diseases are puzzling, obscure, often difficult to diagnose and still more difficult to treat. The ostentatious pride with which some doctors announce their ignorance of dermatology (and psychiatry) seems to stimulate some others to attempt to fathom the mystery. Only one colleague mentioned the fact that dermatological patients usually do not die. Quite a number mentioned the influence of an enthusiastic teacher, or the desire to exploit a good visual memory.

But all that this really adds up to is that even the conscious reasons for electing dermatology are as unknown as the etiology of some dermatological lesions.

Finally we come to ourselves. What about us? Why are we *psychiatrists?*

At the Menninger School of Psychiatry, we have had the rich experience of selecting several hundred young doctors from among a much larger group and following them through their training years, month by month, with written reports from their teachers and supervisors on into their early clinical years. How good have our selections been? How accurate were our implied predictions? The findings of Holt and Luborsky, who conducted a seven-year research, have encouraged us on the one hand and kept us humble on the other hand. With the aid of psychological tests and numerous interviews, we can do significantly better than chance but it is impossible to be highly accurate.

For our present purposes the more important part of this research was the light it threw upon the ideals, purposes, and motives of men entering the field of psychiatry. That psychiatrists differ from their medical colleagues in certain conspicuous respects is well known. One of the ways which is frequently mentioned by the public is that there are among psychiatrists more members of minority groups than is the case with physicians and surgeons generally. By this is usually meant foreign physicians and Jewish physicians. We have no statistics and know of none on this point, but it is an impression which might well be true.

This corresponds with the psychiatrist's professional interest in lonely, eccentric, and unloved people. It is one of our axioms that such an interest is apt to be a projection of one's own problems, and the speculations we have applied to members of other specialties must now be applied to ourselves. The implication is that psychiatrists, more than members of other specialties and more than the average man, have at some time suffered overmuch from a sense of loneliness, unlovableness, and rejection. In the sense that the doctor constantly heals himself by his ministration to others, this aspect of the determining factors in an interest in psychiatry is prominent. In deadly fear of misquotation by the casual listener or the hasty reader, I want to emphasize the fact that what I have referred to is usually a strongly *repressed* self-concept, almost totally unconscious. Translating this into the positive, I would say that the young men I meet who seek to enter the field of psychiatry are, by and large, just as charming, socially at ease, self-confident, and "regular" as any other group of young men of the same general group, perhaps more so. Naturally I refer now to "appearances."

Unconscious voyeurism has been ascribed to psychiatrists for the obvious reason that they find in their professional lives much opportunity to learn about the sexual behavior of others. I am sure that the public would seize upon this as most characteristic of us, yet I would like to suggest that it is probably *least* characteristic of us, among physicians. We are just a little less self-conscious about it, that is all. Do not forget that the essence of Freud's discovery was that psychiatrists did *not* investigate these areas as they should. It was possibly *just because* Freud and other psychoanalysts were less critically and frantically magnetized into immobility by this subject that they were able to investigate it more casually and more impartially.

I think, rather, that one should look in the depths of the psychiatrist's mind for some greater interest in function than in form, some greater concern with behavior than with organs, some greater interest in human relationships than in human anatomy. Let us hasten to renounce any special credit for what seems to us a more progressive and sophisticated position here, remembering that according to our best beliefs this is a matter of some special kind of childhood experience.

There is a great temptation for the psychiatrist to indulge in a kind of secret arrogance for, in the sense that things of the mind and of the spirit transcend those of flesh and bone, our professional preoccupations as psychiatrists would seem to be on a higher level than those of some medical colleagues. This disputes our holistic theory, but we cling to it secretly. No one can say that the flower is more important than the stem, or the living room than the basement, but through the centuries many doctors have apparently taken the position that the prolongation of a relatively pain-free existence was the sole goal of their endeavors. But if we believe that life has a meaning and our existence here a purpose, what a man does with his body (including his brain) is more important than the fact that he possesses it, or even that he enjoys it.

If a psychiatrist is less of a voyeur, *frotteur,* than some of his colleagues, is he less realistic? Is it really more difficult for him to face or touch reality, as is sometimes jokingly suggested? Would this indicate that his capacity for fantasy is the greater or the lesser? What are the presumptive differences between the reactions of psychiatrists to the basic problem of castration fears and the loss of parental love as compared to his colleagues?

One gets valuable leads about this from the conscious fantasies of the laymen about mental illness. What do *they* think? They think, for one thing, that mental disease is hereditary. Part of this we have taught them, but part of it means that they consider mental illness either a punishment of God or else a curse of nature. Another thing which laymen believe about mental illness is that our patients are wild and dangerous. Here again is a suggestion of uncontrolled aggression for which punishment is the ordinary expectation. Another thing laymen believe is that mental illness is related to masturbation, if not indeed "caused" by it.

All these fantasies are vigorously and continuously refuted both by our words and by our actions. We all want to correct the laymen's absurd ignorance. It may be that our evangelical zeal in this respect, fortunate as are its consequences, derives from the residuals of our own early fears and fantasies.

But now I have the uncomfortable feeling that you will think I have led you through a chamber of horrors from which, with excellent judgment, we doctors and psychiatrists have run in a terrorized flight, into evangelism. And it would certainly belie the spirit of modern psychiatry to end on this negative note. The practice of medicine is more than merely a lifelong penance for the fantasied sins of infancy, or a thinly disguised perpetuation of them. It is more even than an effort to save ourselves by saving others. To assume that the positive is only a reaction to the negative is one of our professional psychiatric fallacies. There are positive motivations in the human spirit not born of fear and guilt and hate, but of life and love. The life instinct not only battles against the death instinct, it has an autonomy and purpose of its own.

What is that autonomy of the ego or that element of the life instinct which fights, strives, aspires—which is more than the negation of evil? With Whitehead, Wieman, Hartshorne, and others, I think we can usefully call it creativity. Healing is more than repairing, more than not destroying; it is creating. It is an article of faith with us, and one without which we doctors cannot work or live, to believe that things can be improved, that the patient can be helped, and that we ourselves can always be better than we are. We must improve ourselves in order to improve those who seek our help. This aspiration is in itself creative.

David Rapaport cites a story of ancient wisdom in his own able discussion of the same topic.[13] A certain king had heard about the great, wise leader, Moses, and sent painters to paint his portrait. When they brought it back, the king called his phrenologists and astrologers. "Look at this portrait and tell me the kind of a man it is," he commanded. So the phrenologists and astrologers studied it long and earnestly and came forth with this report: "Oh, king, this Moses is a cruel, greedy, self-seeking, dishonest man. We see it in his portrait."

The king was puzzled. "Either my painters cannot paint or there is no such science as astrology and phrenology." To decide this dilemma he went himself to see Moses. At the sight of Moses, the king cried out, "The painters painted well. There is no such science as astrology or phrenology."

Now when Moses heard the king speak thus, he was surprised and asked him to explain it. The king did so. Then Moses only shook his head and said, "No, great king, your phrenologists and astrologers are right. That picture is what I *was*. But I fought against it, and won! That is how I became what I *am*."

8. Regulatory Devices of the Ego under Major Stress

The general point of view taken is that all clinical phenomena may be advantageously viewed as belonging within a continuum between the state of adjustment which we call health and an ultimate state of disintegration or extreme "illness." This would tend to dispense with the controversial and essentially useless traditional designations of nervousness, neurasthenia, neurosis, psychasthenia, psychosis, etc., and would bring into some systematic organization our dynamic concepts of "defense measures," reactions, etc., for use in clinical psychiatry.

One can view the functions of the ego in dealing with external and internal stimuli as those of a homeostatic regulator. The drives of the organism must be so directed and modified, in view of the super-ego system and the reality system, as to permit the maintenance of a level of tension which is tolerable, productive, maximally satisfying, and consistent with growth. Events persistently occur which tend to disturb the adjustments and reconciliations

I acknowledge with gratitude the assistance of my associate, Dr. Martin Mayman. The complete version of this presentation was published under the title "Psychological Aspects of the Organism under Stress," Part I; "The Homeostatic Regulatory Function of the Ego," Part II; "Regulatory Devices of the Ego under Major Stress" in the *Journal of the American Psychoanalytic Association*, 2, 1954, No. 1, 67–106; No. 2, 280–310. I have ventured to submit here, at the request of the editor, a condensation of the clinical application of these theories presented before the 18th Int. Congress in London on 28 July, 1953. [K.M.] Reprinted from the *International Journal of Psychoanalysis*, 35:412–420, 1954.

achieved, and these stresses require the ego to improvise adaptive
expedients for maintaining the integrity of the organism. Minor
stresses are usually handled by relatively minor, "normal," "healthy"
devices. Greater stresses or prolonged stress excite the ego to increasingly energetic and expensive activity in the interests of
homeostatic maintenance.

REGULATORY DEVICES OF THE FIRST ORDER

One of the first evidences of failure of the "normal" devices of
the ego for handling emergencies is the development or persistence
of stress awareness. The subject is conscious of discomfort in connection with efforts at concentration or self-control. Aware of this,
he consciously exerts an extra measure of "will power" in the
mastery or concealment of these phenomena. Perhaps we should
think of this hyper-suppression as the most nearly normal of any
of the secondary defences.

Less uncomfortable because unconscious is the greatly increased
use of repression. Externally this appears as restriction and increased
inhibition.

Another well-known representative of this order of emergency-
coping devices is the increase of alertness, irritability, distractibility,
"tenseness," flushing, sweating, and "nervousness" so typical of the
initial phases of acute mental illness. (To call this "anxiety" is to
confuse the meaning of the term.) It is often most uncomfortable
in its effect upon the sleep habits of the individual. This hyper-
alertness represents a protective vigilance. Almost inseparable from
hyper-alertness are hyper-emotionalism and hyperkinesis. The exaggerated use of crying and/or of laughing is one form; but increased "sensitiveness," touchiness, and irascibility to the point of
rage attacks are also of this order. Other excesses of emotion are also
familiar, particularly fearsomeness and depression. The latter may
represent "mourning" for a real or anticipated loss of love, or it may
be a consequence of some special and excessive introjection.

Depression tends to retard the hyperkinetic phenomena which
otherwise appear characteristically in association with hyper-alertness and hyper-emotionalism. The hyperkinesis may be somewhat

directed, as in the normal "acting to alter." But it is now much more likely to appear as insufficient, impulsive, or compulsive (see below) pointless muscular activity. Beginning with restlessness, jumpiness, and other phenomena often considered quasi-normal, it reaches extremes of various kinds of overactivity and distorted activity. The hostile impulses seem sometimes to be deflected to substitute persons or inanimate objects, sometimes to no particular object (or end) at all.

Instead of acting it out with one's muscles, however, the individual may make persistent attempts to think it out, to worry it through, with distorted emphases in mild "obsessional" thinking or "worrying." Excessive talking is a combination of hyperkinesis and hyper-intellection.

Excessive fantasy formation is a common first-order device, which belongs properly in the broader category of the overuse of compensatory measures. When it replaces necessary reality thinking or effective acting, it is pathological. Hypercompensation is also accomplished, however, in numerous other ways, particularly by elaborate reaction formations (reversing the effect of the aggressive wish) and *ad hoc* identifications (e.g. with the enemy).

Somatic reactions characteristic of "anxiety" probably serve the same purpose as the psychological devices described, namely, that of relieving tension. The patient rarely experiences them as other than uncomfortable, and would be loath to accept the proposition that they relieve him. Indeed, they may constitute his chief complaint. They vary greatly in form, intensity, frequency of recurrence, or degree of constancy in different individuals. Tremor, flushing, palpitation, "weak" feelings, giddiness, anorexia, tachycardia, nausea, enuresis, diarrhea, and other evidences of sympathetic nervous system liability and excitation are the more frequent. To this should be added various quantitative and qualitative disturbances in the sexual function.

To recapitulate, regulatory devices of a first order or degree of pathological nature may be employed by the ego in situations which overtax the ordinary or normal devices. These consist essentially in exaggerations of normal functions, but they now appear uncomfortably and unpleasantly. They are apt to be described as evidences of "nervousness." The more familiar ones are: hyper-suppression; hyper-repression; hyper-alertness; hyper-emotionalism; hyper-kinesis; hyper-intellection, including mild obsessional thinking; hyper-compensation; and minor somatic dysfunctions.

The emergency measures just described, although purposeful, may become more troublesome than the original disturbance or danger by which they were aroused, just as the swelling from a bee sting near the eye may obscure the vision and cause other difficulties more serious than the irritant. They always represent a drain on the energies of the individual, and reduce his efficiency and satisfactions. They are apt, therefore, to become an expensive nuisance, causing fatigue, discomfort, and even pain. The ego institutes them as protective necessities, but the total individual is affected by them unpleasantly, and often tends to regard himself as their victim rather than as their beneficiary.

But whether it be called illness or nervousness, or by some more euphemistic name, the utilization of these devices of a first degree of emergency and pathology is (nearly always) a transient—at least an unstable—phase. The tendency is toward subsidence; presumably the irritation is removed, the occasion for alarm passes, the aroused aggressions are mastered or channelled or dissipated. The need for the emergency devices disappears, and likewise the devices. The patient "recovers," the "illness" terminates.

But not always. The situation may not be altered (or even alterable). The satisfactory rearrangement of energy investments may not be immediately possible. And just as Selye, in his account of physiological adaptation to stress, describes how the resistance reactions of the body to alarm become exhausted in time, so the intensification of psychological defences may be described as having a tendency toward exhaustion. In spite of them, the tension rises.

Something further must be done by the ego. What does it do?

REGULATORY DEVICES OF THE SECOND ORDER

There seems to be a limit to the utilization of first-order devices, beyond which qualitative rather than merely quantitative alterations are necessary. These are in the nature of strategic retreats,* with compensating features. The ego system, burdened beyond the Plimsoll mark, capitulates to the necessity of an altered (lowered) level of homeostatic balance, and effects it by a second order of regulating devices characterized by partial detachment from the world of reality—from loved objects, feared objects, and hated objects. Real objects of cathexis are abandoned in favor of substitutions which may have a flavor or façade of "reality," but which yield a gratification only dereistically. This partial withdrawal from reality is not affected for the sake of getting out of harm's way—for that would be a realistic withdrawal. This is the withdrawal for the sake of the ego—i.e., to diminish the tension resulting from excessive internal pressures.

Simple withdrawal by dissociation is accomplished by or reflected in a variety of internal modifications of consciousness and of the mnemonic such as ("hysterical") fainting, amnestic periods, and amnestic states. Presumably the withdrawal here goes far, for the whole world is temporarily forgotten—but it all returns rather promptly. What unconscious fantasies occupied the internal screen we can rarely discover. These are "acted out" in the more complicated phenomena of "dual personalities," and fugues.

Less dramatic, less extreme, but far more frequent are those *formes frustes* in which there is to be seen only social shyness or avoidance or gaucherie, while subjectively there is a sense of strangeness, of unreality, or even of depersonalization (Oberndorf, Federn, etc.). Since these are subjective phenomena, they may be long concealed.†

However widespread such withdrawal and dissociation may be, it is clinically important (at present) chiefly when it is uncom-

---

* The term "regression" is sometimes applied, rather confusingly, I think.

† One is tempted to speculate, at this point, regarding the extent of this "symptom" in the world's population. We psychiatrists usually think of it from the standpoint of those who suffer from their isolation; both we and they are accustomed to think them more or less "sick." How much less sick are they, perhaps, than the many "healthy-minded" millions who scotomatize the misery of most of mankind, and by means of denial, avoidance, studied ignorance, preoccupation, snobbery, and distractions of all kinds manage to avoid even the awareness of worldwide tragedy, and hence of reality in a larger sense!

fortable. For this discomfort itself indicates that a tolerable equilibrium has not been established; the device (withdrawal) has bettered things, but has added another burden from the diminished object attachment (positive and negative). The ego, like nature, abhors a vacuum! Thus the world of reality is subjectively recreated, modified to fit the needs of the beleaguered ego. New objects in the outside world are substituted for those with which the ego felt unable to cope because of the uncontrollable impulses excited by them. This device of displacement, which Freud so brilliantly rediscovered clinically, is as old as the race, as old as dolls and idols and scapegoats. To what extent it pervades all our thinking can only be conjectured. For, indeed, what are prejudices, extreme aversions, and fanatical attitudes pro or con but the substitution of something symbolic for the truly feared or hated or loved object?

We know more about this device, thanks to Freud, as it appears in obsessional and phobic states than we know about it in crusaders and class-haters. We know that even phobias may be converted into or replaced by a reversal, i.e., a pathological (ungenuine) boldness and intrepidity with particular respect to the thing feared. Anna Freud has elaborated this "counterphobic" phenomenon.

Corresponding to its displacement of fear to a substituted symbolic object, the ego logically ascribes to that object threatening intentions. The selection of this object is partly determined by previous —often forgotten—experience, although propinquity and chance play roles in the choice also. We speak of this device as projection. It must be considered a more desperate measure, particularly when it is accompanied by its often associated phenomena—hallucinations, ideas of reference, and delusions. It is then a signal of gross ego failure.

Closely allied to projection and, indeed, making much use of it, is an unhappily familiar syndrome of rapidly shifting displacements, with alternating reality acceptance and reality denial. The characteristic motivation here seems to be provocativeness; it would seem as if the ego accepted or effected potentially unstable object attachments for the very sake of being able to disappoint them and inciting retaliation as a combined form of love and punishment. Individuals who are forced into a program of this semirational, semirealistic, semicriminal, semipsychotic behavior have been called by many names—most commonly, perhaps, "psychopathic personalities." I have previously described them as characterized by this saltatory phenomenon, this device of transiliency, but probably the basic mechanism involved is the compulsion toward provocativeness. Of course, in its simplest form this device is frequently used by others than the individuals just described who are so completely characterized by it.

The substitution of symbolic objects for the displacement of otherwise uncontrolled impulses differs from the substitution of modified modalities of "dealing" with objects. The high value of symbols in psychic life is such that it is possible to use speech, rituals, and other things in place of the unconsciously formulated intent of destruction. Cursing someone may be a sufficiently satisfying equivalent of ridding one's self of him by magic. There are, as we know, many other ways than cursing in which "murder" may be attenuated. This attenuation may be almost to the vanishing point, so far as practical effect on the subject is concerned, but there is always an effect on the subject. One effect is to release aggressive energy and hence diminish ego tension. But another effect is to arouse the super-ego to require placatory undoing, restitutive, penitential, and similar activities. What we call "compulsions" are acts or strong inclinations toward such acts which symbolically destroy the danger and simultaneously appease the conscience. The balance achieved in this combination will by no means satisfy an objective observer, but because of the impaired reality sense, it partially satisfies the doer. Symbolically doing-and-undoing constitute the essence of a large number of modality substitutions all of which represent a partial detachment from reality and an attempted arrangement for releasing an "irresistible impulse" of a dangerous kind in a disguised "magic" form.

Prominent among these substitution techniques as seen in clinical material are the various perversions of mode or object in the gratification of sexual desire. The sexual urge may be considered primarily a derivative of the life instinct—a partial instinct, some would call it. But it is always "contaminated" or fused with some derivatives of the aggressive instinct. According to the proportions of admixture, a sexual act may be predominantly loving or predominantly hostile (but never wholly either). For some individuals the expression of the sexual impulse in a predominantly loving form, according to biologically "normal" modes and toward the appropriate objects, is blocked in respect to one of these three criteria. This frustration still further increases the proportion of aggressive component (which, in turn, may still further intensify the blocking). A bargain is finally struck, so to speak, by means of displacement, substitution, and—as with all these devices—some reality denial. The conditioning of some egos is such that in spite of the super-ego pressure and in spite of reality pressure (danger, inconvenience, etc.) the perverse act can be tolerated, i.e., permitted, whereas the normal act cannot be. Expression of the "sexual" needs in this distorted, substituted way relieves ego pressure by permitting destructive urges to emerge in disguise.*

Finally, among the second-order devices of stress relief, there are the phenomena in which the ego effects a semirealistic withdrawal through the offering of sacrifices, or, as some (Rado) prefer to phrase it, by a choice of the lesser evil. In the psychological system the sacrifice may be made either to the conscience demands or to reality demands. Most reality sacrifices represent normal choice behavior and are usually conscious ("A half loaf is better than no bread," "A bird in the hand is worth two in the bush," etc.). Sacrifices offered the conscience are more self-destructive and are usually only dimly recognized for what they are. The principle of sacrifice is based on a rather complicated equation, in which a part is made to stand for the whole, and is yielded or offered in order to preserve the integrity of the remainder of the whole. I have illustrated in *Man Against*

---

* Some colleagues will feel that sexual perversion is a *prima facie* evidence of severe ego failures and hence should be assigned to a still higher order of tension-relieving devices. I think this is true only if violence and overt destructiveness characterize the modality. There are self-destructive and externally aggressive elements in all the second-order devices, but they are concealed. If the aggression becomes obvious (and, of course, misdirected) we have sufficient evidence of ego rupture to assign such devices to the next order.

Himself in how many different ways the super-ego can be placated by a sacrifice which involves such magical choice of a lesser evil. The solution by sacrifice is accomplished, in clinical experience, by self-immolation and penalization, as in the case of asceticism and martyrdom; by self-mutilation of one's own body or by exploitation of the opportunity for obtaining surgical operations or sustaining semi-purposive accidents which accomplish mutilation; by self-intoxication or narcotization; by entertainment of the fantasy of a somatic affection, as in hypochondriasis; by exploitation and misinterpretation of sensations of somatic affection as in neurasthenia; by unconscious simulation of somatic affection as in conversion syndromes; by the physiological production of somatic affections as in psychosomatic disorders; by the psychological exploitation of an intercurrent somatic affection.

Recapitulation. Regulatory devices of a second order of pathology may be listed as:

1. Withdrawal by dissociation (intra-psychic).
   Syncope.
   Narcolepsy.
   Amnesia.
   Fugues.
   Dual personality.
   Sense of unreality (estrangement).
   Depersonalization.
2. Withdrawal by displacement of aggression to substituted objects.
   Aversion.
   Prejudice.
   Phobias.
   Counterphobic attitudes.
   Obsessions.
   Projection.
   Provocative transiliency.
3. Substitution of (magic) symbols and modalities for more frankly hostile discharge.
   Compulsions.
   Rituals.

"Kleptomania," "pyromania," etc.

Undoing and restitutive gestures.

Perverse sexual modalities and objects, without violence.

4. Substitution of the self or a part of the self as an object of displaced aggression.

Self-imposed restriction and abasement (asceticism).

Body mutilation (self-inflicted, "accidental," surgical).

Self-intoxication or narcotization.

Somatic involvement (fantasy, sensation, or function).

    a. Unconscious simulation.

    b. Exploitation of somatic affection.

    c. Physiological production of somatic disorder.

REGULATORY DEVICES OF THE THIRD ORDER

All the stress-relieving devices of the first and second orders are temporary and emergency devices. The ego never "expects" to retain them permanently (although it often does!). If a woman sees a shocking automobile accident and faints, she doesn't think of her fainting as a sympton of illness; she doesn't expect to continue fainting. If a man has a fatiguing and discouraging day and takes a few drinks too many, he does not think of this narcotization as a symptom. It is only when the fainting becomes frequent or the alcoholic relief imperative, so that other satisfactions are sacrificed, that the "device" becomes a symptom. We may sometimes refer to these as "habits," but it is not merely the accustoming of one's self to an expedient, but rather the *hypertrophy and solidification of a definitely emergency measure* which makes for pathology.

Nevertheless, the actual intra-psychic state of affairs is never static. The stresses either recede, or they continue and are added to by the necessary compromises. And the trend of pressure is in the direction of ego rupture, which could correspond to the neurophysiologist's "exhaustion state." An already stretched, compromised, injured, wearied, over-taxed ego may simply have to yield. It does the best it can as long as it can, but the pressures may be too great for it; it may give way. This does not mean that the ego is destroyed or annihilated; intact portions or functions persist, of course. But in certain "weak" spots it yields. The result is catastrophe—not for the ego, but for the total organism.

The uncontrollable emergence of dangerous instinctual impulses is always something of a catastrophe. As we shall see shortly, it is not *the* catastrophe, the ultimate and *most* dangerous explosion, but it is always serious, because of consequences to be expected from the environment (retaliation, punishment, etc.) and from the super-ego. In this ego rupture the dangerous impulses are apparently outwardly directed, but the "recoil," the concomitant self-damage, is always detectable also.

Clinically and empirically we know these catastrophes in *two forms*—as continuous phenomena over a considerable period of time, and as relatively brief, episodic, discontinuous phenomena from which there is prompt recovery with a continued tendency for them to recur. It would seem that these episodic explosions serve to relieve enough tension to prevent the development of the continuous forms.

Sudden homicidal violence or less extreme assaults and uncontrollable attacks of rage are the most familiar exhibitions of such primitive impulse explosions. These are occasionally self-directive, either as suicide or self-mutilation. Unhappily the pages of history, particularly those of criminologic and psychiatric history, are full of dramatic illustrations of the catastrophe in the form of "impulsive" homicide. In many such instances there is so much "isolation" that the patient has no explanation at all for his crimes. In other cases there are rationalizations for the deed, and for the selection of the individual attacked, but, as Wertham has shown, these reasons, convincing as they may sound in mystery stories, and even in some criminal trials, usually have little to do with the real motivation of the murder.

Assaultive forms of violence may contain an admixture of sexuality, used chiefly as a cloak. But sexual assaults of all kinds, including rape and the aggressive types of sexual perversion, represent modified forms of ego rupture.

Similar in psychodynamic purpose, but quite different clinically, is the *grand mal* convulsion. A convulsion *—however produced— represents a sudden, uncontrolled, relatively unstructured release of enormous quantities of energy, expressed by muscular contractions and the obliteration of consciousness. It permits an episodic explosive emergence of aggressive impulses. It does not seem to be directed toward anything or anyone (as a rule), but seems to be a primitive expression of violent murder and violent suicide—like an enormous temper tantrum.†

There is another form of episodic ego rupture in which the ego has some modifying effect upon the exploding aggressive drives, enough to create a picture of partial disorganization rather than either directed violence or complete convulsive chaos. Familiar to psychiatrists of military experience (and comparable syndromes are occasionally seen in civilian practice) are the attacks of acute panic in which the soldier suddenly becomes either "frozen" to the spot, heedless of danger and opportunity for retreat, or launches into wild screaming, shouting, shooting, crying, running about, and other evidences of demoralization. In most instances they are of relatively short duration.

In other war cases, however, the initial symptoms were less dramatic, but a syndrome of demoralization persisted for some days or weeks, then disappearing completely (after hospitalization). Such cases were sometimes referred to as "ten-day schizophrenias." In civilian life somewhat similar pictures of dereistic trancelike states or delirious excitement are not infrequently seen, and are called by all sorts of names (some of them improvised). They characteristically recover promptly and fairly completely.

---

* Remember, please, that I am discussing the function of the symptom, not the so-called cause or causes, and not the physiological mechanisms or the anatomical structures involved. Convulsions may, of course, occur under many circumstances and conditions from glioma to uremia and from drunkenness to lupus erythematosus disseminata, but the psychological function performed is conceivably always the same, regardless of the crucial precipitating cortical stimulus.

† The therapeutic effect of the artificial induction of convulsions in shock therapy seems to me to depend in large part on the fact that the patient "dies" without dying, and then is reborn, so to speak. The self-destructive energy (mortido) is discharged, permitting a re-cathexis of the ego.

To summarize, stress-relieving devices of a third order of pathology are represented by episodic, explosive outbursts of aggressive energy, more or less disorganized, including:

1. Assaultive violence—homicidal or suicidal.
2. Convulsions.
3. Panic attacks.
4. Catastrophic demoralization.
5. Schizoid attacks (e.g., ten-day schizophrenia).

REGULATORY DEVICES OF THE FOURTH ORDER
(PERSISTENT DEREISTIC DISCHARGE)

Rupture of the ego permitting an episodic explosion may be sufficient to relieve the tension, and the ego quickly "heals" with or without a "weak spot." Its boundaries are restored (Federn) and a catastrophe has been averted. Freud pointed out how suicide may be a substitute for murder, and Reichard and Tillman have recently proposed and illustrated the idea of murder and suicide as "defences" against psychosis.

Thus, the victory may be a Pyrrhic one. The cost of salvation may be fatal. The damage done may be irreparable. Or, the rupture may be too great for the ego to reconstitute its homeostatic patterns in a quick restoration. The ego may be exhausted or semi-permanently damaged. In that case, a further retreat and detachment from reality must occur. This actually represents the net effect of the aggressive intent: destruction is accomplished symbolically in the form of a repudiation of reality and of reality testing to a penultimate degree. Not only is the process of reality testing abandoned, but the established loyalty to reality is (largely) renounced. With this, of course, goes a disruption of interpersonal linkages and the separation from love objects which presages psychological starvation of the ego (Ernest Jones' aphanisis).

It is this state of affairs to which most psychiatrists refer by the word "psychosis," a word which I earnestly hope we can abandon. (Adolf Meyer, George Stevenson, Karl Bowman, and other psychiatrists have expressed the same wish.) It is illustrated in the delirious states, many schizophrenic pictures, some stupors, and various conditions associated with organic brain damage. I am not concerned now with names of specific "causes," but rather with the psychological picture and the psychological process that is represented.

I believe this stage of the process represents a near catastrophic rearranging of homeostatic balance in which the dangerous impulses, aroused by threat, pain, fear, guilt, and frustrations are controllable only (or chiefly) by absorption into fantasy, including narcissistic preoccupations, denial, and destruction in fantasy of some or all of the real world. Disorganization of a high degree is conspicuous. An internal equilibrium and relative peace are indeed re-established, but at a fearful cost in effectiveness. Edward Kempf described this as the fifth and most extreme stage of personality decompensation—"a further flight from adjustment, really an almost complete failure to compensate, so that the individual is dominated by the uncontrollable elements of the unconscious. Then there appear, as if they were a part of real life, such very unreal things as delusions, hallucinations, etc. These, in short, are symptoms popularly known as 'insanity.'"

This is truly disorganization, and the sacrifice of much of the self to the situation. It is self-destructive. But from the other standpoint, which we have been emphasizing, it is also self-preservative, a device to *avert* a more complete self-destruction. It is not a complete self-destruction. It is not a complete surrender, but a retreat—almost a rout, perhaps. But the organism is saved, even though its productive level has fallen to almost zero. We know that such patients feel, on the one hand, desolate, estranged, and hopeless because of the disruption of their linkages with reality love objects and, at the same time, seek to bolster their egos with omnipotent fantasies of destroying the whole world. The picture is apt to be complicated by numerous fragments of second- and third-order devices which are carried over. Indeed, it is these which give color and form to the various clinical pictures in which this near-total disorganization of psychic function appears. The following are some of the commonly observed varieties:

1. *Erratic, disorganized excitement* with corresponding verbal and motor productions—at times destructive, at times self-injuring, at times only bizarre and ineffectual. These pictures have been called delirious, manic, maniacal, catatonic, epileptic, and other names.

2. *Conditions of extreme hyperthymia*—chiefly melancholy, with or without stupor, agitation, delusion formation, retardation, or restless activity. The characteristic feature is the overwhelming of the wish to live, the mood of resignation and obligation to suicide.

3. *Silly, incoherent, manneristic, autistic speech and behavior,* without excitement or clear meaning or direction. Such pictures are often called hebephrenic.

4. *Extreme and continuous apathetic inertia* and extreme inactivity, sometimes rigidity, often with mutism, hallucinations, and other rarely revealed fantasy indulgences and occasional outbursts. Such conditions are called hebephrenic, catatonic, "deteriorated," "regressed," and other undefinable and unjustifiable names.

5. *Delusion preoccupation* with one or several themes, usually persecutory, and usually supported with defensiveness, suspiciousness, grandiosity, condescension, irascibility, etc., with or without hallucinations. A good façade of "normality" may partially or occasionally obscure the underlying picture. Such states have classically gone under many names containing the adjective "paranoid."

6. *Disoriented, confused, uncertain, amnesic,* bewildered disorientation typical of senile regression and organic brain injury.

7. *Gross intellectual defect,* typical of congenital or acquired hypophrenia.

A great deal has been made, in the psychiatric literature, of the finer distinctions between these different pictures. In the writer's opinion, this is like describing the separate fragments of pottery found in an Indian cave. They all represent parts, parts of wholes that have been broken. To be sure, some are small, some are large, some are sharp, some are dull, some have markings of one kind, some of another. But our psychiatric pieces may change their markings under our very eyes. For indeed they are not different *diseases:* they are different exposures, different glimpses, different constellations of compromise, fusion, and defusion, of compensatory effort and change. The important fact is that an ego rupture has occurred, overwhelming aggressive impulses have emerged, extreme withdrawal has been necessary, effective contact with reality has been severed. What one has left is disorganized rubble, the mangled body of an organism that is still breathing.

At this cost, then, the final catastrophe of dissolution has been averted. A kind of equilibrium has been re-established at a very low level. Here it may remain until death. *But* empirically we know that complete restoration may still occur! Indeed, with any help at all, it usually does! Thus the survival function of this catastrophic retreat is demonstrated, and the ego's regulatory powers seem to be justified even in its so-called failure.

THE ULTIMATE AND IRREVERSIBLE CATASTROPHE:
THE FIFTH ORDER

But despite the successive inauguration of progressively more "radical" measures, the ego may really fail completely. Things may go from good to bad, to worse, to worst. And what is the worst that can happen? From the biological standpoint, one would say death; from the psycho-biological standpoint, and in line with the concept here presented, one would have to say complete disorganization, which is perhaps not quite the same. We might borrow the term "entropy" from physics.

Since the basic function of the ego is integration, i.e., holding the personality together, its complete failure is to be seen in disintegration, which occurs when the destructive drives overwhelm it. Complete failure of ego control releases enormous violent energies of destruction in all directions. Clinically one sees occasionally such dreadful cases of continuous, wild, furious, violent mania ending, nearly always I believe, in complete exhaustion and death.*

---

* Actual self-propelled physical self-destruction in the clinical form of suicide should probably be treated as an indication of *not-quite-total disintegration.* It is certainly terminal and irreversible, and it is certainly a kind of failure of ego control which

INTERPRETIVE ADDENDA AND CONCLUSION

On this dismal note of complete disintegration, we must terminate this analysis of the progressive steps or stages in the temporary arrest of the trend toward disintegration by the various regulatory expedients available to the ego. Please bear in mind that this was, by design, a schematic rather than a clinical presentation. As has been pointed out repeatedly as we went along, the ego always does more than attempt to manage the immediate emergency. In spite of resistances implicit in the semi-stabilized emergency adjustment, the ego perennially endeavors to return to its original normal adjustment level. These restorative efforts of the ego have been little touched upon here for the reason that we have been trying to describe the disease process rather than the recovery process, which in no way diminishes the importance of a further consideration of the latter including those artefactual facilitations afforded by "treatment." That recovery actually may take place, wholly or in part, after arrival at any of the stages described has been repeatedly mentioned, but perhaps needs repeating. That recovery may fail to take place is unfortunately also an empirical fact.

This recovery trend is, indeed, constantly interacting with the trend represented by the five stages of progressive disintegration

---

turns out to be fatal. But it does involve some conscious direction, and hence falls a little short of complete reality renunciation. When Freud outlined his concept of the self-destructive instinct he made it clear that its manifestations are never nakedly visible. This is true even in suicide, as I have tried to point out in *Man Against Himself*. It is possible that those forms of suicide among primitives which are said to be accomplished by sheer determination to die represent an exception to Freud's statement, but suicide in the ordinary form represents a direction of violence toward the self which is always tinctured with elements of the integrative efforts of the ego. In other words, no suicide is ever completely wholehearted. There is certainly a considerable difference between the wish to die, the wish to *kill* (one's self), and the wish *to be killed* (by one's self or by someone else) as I have pointed out elsewhere. And none of these are undisguised representations of the "death instinct," by definition. Suicide as an occasional fantasy, suicide as an obsessional preoccupation, and suicide as a gesture must be distinguished from successful or unsuccessful but *bona fide* suicidal attempts (see Raines). The great excess of suicidal attempts as compared with "successful" suicides (even after one excludes "thwarted" suicides) suggests, as Stengel has recently pointed out, that many so-called "successful suicides" are actually bungled attempted-suicides. The gesture function, the appeal effect, and the ordeal character of the attempt are of great importance. Stengel agrees with us, however, that even the suicidal attempt is "a catastrophic reaction to an intolerable social and emotional situation."

described. As is well known clinically, there can be slow or rapid shifts from one level to the other, both upward and downward.

Nor would I leave the impression that the demarcation of these five hierarchical orders of stress-relieving devices is something sharp, clear, and invariable. As in all scientific description, they appear more so in a verbal description of this kind than in real life. In the course of a progressive maladjustment in which second-order devices, for example, are gradually or even suddenly superseded by third- and fourth-order devices, there is apt to be a trailing or continuing use of some of the devices belonging to earlier orders. It should not be forgotten that we psychiatrists see the patient only after months or years of a fluctuating struggle to attain a tolerable adjustment. By recapitulating the history, we can determine which of the present devices are revivals and which are new, and what former "emergency reactions" had been partially accepted by the patient as inevitable character traits rather than symptoms. These may now have become hypertrophied to the point of rejection as "ego-alien," or they may have been supplanted by a new series. Thus a sequential order may be demonstrable, but often it is not.

I have tried to avoid the use of such terms as defenses, defense measures, and defense mechanisms, because of the narrowness of their implications. They call to mind partial maneuvers which parry circumscribed threats. I have tried to employ terms which accent the more holistic implications of the ego's defense efforts, that is, its use of a wide range of expedients in the interest of preserving the best possible level of integration in the face of disintegrative pressures. At first, those expedients may be chosen which result in an increased state of tension within the system (first-order devices). Ultimately, however, the organism may be forced to adopt devices which will relieve the painful state of tension. The devices it chooses must be the best available for maintaining organismic integrity with a minimum of loss.

Disease may be seen, then, not simply as *lack* of "ego strength," an absence of normality, but as a positive expression of the survival efforts of the organism, inept and costly as they may be. In this paper I have sketched out only in broad strokes and rough outline the implications of such a concept of disease. In the development of this idea, the term homeostasis was used to signify the efforts of the organism to realize its potentialities and maintain its integrity despite descriptive onslaughts from within and without. Treatment may be viewed in these terms as assistance in the effort to re-establish the optimal level of integration which had to be sacrificed for a more tenable level of homeostatic maintenance.

SUMMARY

The essence of my thesis is that the principle of homeostasis or steady state maintenance can be applied to psychological phenomena and psychoanalytic theory. The functions of the ego in receiving external and internal stimuli and in dealing with them for the best interests of the organism can be viewed as those of a homeostatic effector. The constructive and destructive drives of the organism must be so directed and modified as to permit the maintenance of a level of tension which is both tolerable and conducive to safe, productive, and satisfying living and continued growth.

Events constantly occur which tend to disturb the adjustments and reconciliations achieved, and these stresses require the ego to improvise adaptive expedients for maintaining the integrity of the organism. Minor stresses are usually handled by relatively minor, "normal," "healthy" devices. Greater stresses or prolonged stress excite the ego to increasingly energetic and expensive activity in the interests of homeostatic maintenance.

In its effort to control dangerous impulses under such circumstances and thereby prevent or retard the disintegrative process which threatens, the ego initiates emergency regulatory devices which fall into five hierarchically arranged and specifically characterized groups, representing increasingly greater degrees af failure in integration.

I believe that this conceptualization of the ego's regulatory function provides us with a broader frame of reference for understanding mental illness and will enable us to discard some of our vague, many-faceted, traditional terms in exchange for more definite and precise designations of process and stage. It also helps us to align our psychoanalytic concepts with general organismic-biologic theory.

9. Toward a Unitary Concept of Mental Illness

A few years ago I, along with many others, began to pay more attention to the phenomena represented by the word "communication." Perhaps the fact that I have always liked to write, to reduce to simplified written form abstruse facts or phenomena, to teach, and to speak—perhaps all of these indicate that I have always been interested in communication. But then I began to observe myself and observe others in this process. I began to observe how much of our time is spent in trying to get something across to others and in trying to grasp clearly what they are trying to get across to us. I began to think about the double function of communication—that of projecting ourselves into and onto the world, and that of signaling in an effort to get some addition to ourselves from the world.

Korzybski, with his emphasis upon the processes of abstraction in human thinking, Hayakawa, Chase, Ogden, and all the semanticists who made us aware that so much of the time we do not say just what we intend to, nor hear just what it was intended that we hear—I became interested in them and self-conscious about my own ambiguities of speech. I was delighted when the word "gobbledygook" was invented to describe a collection of words whose meaning distressingly eluded me. I was equally astonished to see how guilty I was, and had often been, in creating gobbledygook.

I insisted, to the irritation and understandable impatience of

Presented on Oct. 1, 1958 to the Institute on Chronic Schizophrenia, Osawatomie State Hospital, Osawatomie, Kansas. Previously unpublished.

many of my teaching colleagues, that we require the Fellows in the Menninger School of Psychiatry to submit formal writing to us in papers so that we could call their attention to failures in communication which they, who were learning to understand the imperfect communications of patients, were unwittingly making in their attempts to communicate to us, or to relatives, or to family physicians. We have been gratified, I think, by the developments in this aspect of our training, and even our residents have come to appreciate it.

But during these years I also attempted to apply my thinking about communication to the words we use in describing to one another our interpretations of particular cases. To emphasize my own point of view I proposed allegiance to a unitary concept of mental illness. I doubt very much if this differs fundamentally from the view of illness held by most. Nevertheless, there is a hint in it of intransigence, of iconoclasm, and of challenge. For even though most workers in the psychiatric field are committed to the language of the manual of the American Psychiatric Association, and speak of "schizophrenic *reactions*" and "depressive *reactions*" and the like, I suspect that many forget this and go on talking of *schizophrenia* as if it were a clear-cut entity rather than descriptive of a way of reacting. Indeed, I have tried to eliminate from my own vocabulary quite a number of words which suggest that schizophrenia *is* a disease, a disease which is also a psychosis. Now I not only believe that no such disease as schizophrenia can be clearly defined or identified or proved to exist, but I also hold that there is no such thing as a psychosis or a neurosis. My point is that no one can satisfactorily define these terms in a way which the rest of us can accept so that if we use the terms we involve ourselves in confusion because we are all, or nearly all, talking about different things. It is like a Russian, a South African, a Swiss, an American, and a South Sea Islander talking about freedom.

There ought to be a word for this condition which is just the opposite of the Tower of Babel situation. We are not all using different words for the same thing, but we are using the same words for different things.

This was very evident at the International Congress on Schiz-

ophrenic Reactions at Zurich in 1957. In vain did Bleuler,[1] the
chairman of the entire conference, submit his magnificent monograph on changes in the concepts of schizophrenia. Almost in
vain did he declare, wisely and soberly and with a full knowledge
of the great contributions that he and his father had made to the
subject, that

> The main characteristic of research in schizophrenia in the past decade
> has been . . . the collapse of speculations and prejudices which used
> to be inextricably bound up with the concept of schizophrenia . . . for
> example that it is a disease entity . . . inherited, physically conditioned
> . . . and so on. . . . Most investigators no longer consider schizophrenia
> a disease entity, an inherited disorder, an expression of a somatic disease
> or a disorder susceptible to a specific somatic treatment.

In vain we remember the advice of Alfred North Whitehead:[2]

> Should we not distrust the jaunty assurance with which every age
> prides itself that it at last has hit upon the ultimate concepts in which
> all that happens can be formulated? The aim of science is to seek the
> simplest explanations of complex facts. We are apt to fall into the
> error of thinking that the facts are simple because simplicity is the
> goal of our quest. The guiding motto in the life of every natural phi-
> losopher should be "Seek simplicity and distrust it."

But let us try to take this advice; let us try, indeed, for greater
simplicity, greater clarity, a greater degree of consistency, without
ceasing to distrust our results.

Let us observe that classifying, ordering, listing, and grouping
can be applied to all sorts of things in the universe. Let us reflect,
too, that ordering and listing of symptoms is not diagnostication
nor is it yet diagnosis; it is taxonomy. It is a decision made upon
the assumption that, historically, diagnoses have been arrived at and
that symbolic designations of some kind—disease names in this instance—have been applied. But, as we know, names are only a short
cut to description; they may imply more understanding of that to
which they are attached than actually exists in our minds or even
in the world. In the matter of illnesses we have said that their
classification depends upon the names assigned in the process of

diagnosis. But the diagnosis assumes a concept of the illness, its etiology and its probable course, and concepts change with enlarging knowledge. Names, unfortunately, do not. Classifications owe their existence, as Riese[3] has neatly put it, to an economizing principle of the human intellect.

> Indeed [he said], if we were to renounce classifications and deliberately restrict our decriptions and actions to individual experiences, we would not only at the same time denounce science as an articulated whole, thus as a system of experiences, but we would also condemn ourselves to treat every new experience as the first one, not using previous experiences of the same or of an analogous kind. Our intellect would be overburdened by an ever renewed start *ab ovo,* and increase in knowledge would be at a very slow rate. Since individuals of the same species have very much in common, an analysis of our experiences on exclusively individual grounds would mean endless repetitions and reiterations denounced already by Aristotle.

A prodigious number of psychiatric classifications have been elaborated in the course of the centuries, becoming progressively more complicated.* The height of complexity was reached in the eighteenth century with the school of the "systematists" who attempted to introduce Sydenham's principle into psychiatry, using quite arbitrary criteria. The physician and botanist François de Sauvages classified all diseases into 10 classes with 295 genera and about 2400 species. One of these 10 classes included the bulk of mental disease and it was divided into 4 orders and 23 genera. One genus, melancholia, was subdivided into 14 species!

Toward the end of the eighteenth century a tendency toward simpler classifications appeared. In 1798 Pinel published his large, extremely sophisticated, and complicated classification, similar to those of François de Sauvages and his imitators. But three years later Pinel[5] published a revised classification as simple as the former one had been complex. All mental illnesses had been reduced

---

* From this point on, the material presented is essentially that submitted to the Second International Congress of Psychiatry in Zurich, Switzerland, Sept. 4, 1957, by the author in conjunction with Doctors Henri Ellenberger, Paul Pruyser, and Martin Mayman.[4]

to 4 basic types. His contemporary in Italy, Chiarugi, identified only 3 types, and his successor, Esquirol, extended this merely to 5.

However, the trend toward the multiplication of psychiatric disease entities revived, and the nineteenth century was a flourishing period for new classifications. The nosological labors of such men as Kahlbaum, Morel, and Kraepelin became historic. The delineation of general paralysis as an entity (by Bayle, 1822) whetted the appetite of investigators and resulted in attempts to isolate and designate new disease entities, such as hebephrenia (1864), catatonia (1874), and later dementia praecox (1896) and manic-depressive psychosis (1899).

But the nineteenth century was also marked by an undercurrent of rebellion against nosological distinctions. The trend toward simplification reappeared. In 1820 Georget,[6] one of Esquirol's pupils, declared mental illness to be an "idiopathic affection of the brain" which could be manifest in a variety of ways which were not independent disease entities. This was the first modern enunciation of the unitary concept of mental illness.*

Following Georget, Guislain,[8] in Belgium, contended that the various mental diseases were nothing but the successive transformations of what he called the *phrenopathias*. The basis for them all was *phrenalgia,* i.e., "pain of the mind," occurring with various degrees of intensity. These ideas of Guislain's were repeated and expanded in Germany by Zeller, Griesinger, Neumann, and Arndt.

Zeller considered the various mental illness syndromes as successive *Zustandsbilder* in a single fundamental pathological process. Sometimes the illness was restricted to the first stage, *Schwermut;* sometimes it evolved through the successive stages of *Tollheit* (mania) and *Verrücktheit* (paranoia) to the last stage of *Blödsinn* (dementia).

Wilhelm Griesinger,[9] the first director of the famous hospital Burghölzli, proclaimed that "Mental diseases are brain diseases." He held that psychiatric syndromes should be classified according to their underlying brain lesions, but because of the undeveloped

---

* According to Dr. Bartolomé Llopis [7] of Madrid.

science of pathology one must be content provisionally with a "functional" classification.

But it was Heinrich Neumann,[10] a great pioneer who is too much neglected and forgotten today, who was most definite and thorough-going in his development of the unitary concept. Said Neumann:

> Diagnosis is not simply the designation of a group of symptoms but the key to the comprehension of the case. . . . We consider any classification of mental illness to be artificial, and therefore unsatisfactory, [and] we do not believe that one can make progress in psychiatry until one has resolved to throw overboard all classifications and to declare with us: there is only one kind of mental illness. . . .*

Neumann felt strongly that psychiatric classifications of the kinds he knew were not only artificial and illusory but directly dangerous. "Rather no classification," he said, "than a false one. The lack of any classification at least leaves free space for investigation, whereas a false classification leads directly into errors!" [11]

Neumann's wise words might well be engraved on the staff conference rooms of all psychiatric hospitals! But for all their eloquence and wisdom, the battle for simplicity was again—if only temporarily—lost. During the second half of the nineteenth century the discoveries of bacteriology, pathological anatomy, and genetics seemed to bring irrefutable confirmation of Trousseau's famous

---

* Mental illness, according to Neumann, begins with a first stage, intermediate between health and illness; sleeplessness, illusions, exaggerated sensitivity, and lack of attention are the first manifestations. If the process continues, its evolution is through various successive clinical pictures which are really "not various forms, but various stages." He listed *Wahnsinn* (delusion), *Verwirrtheit* (confusion), and *Blödsinn* (dementia).

Arndt (1835–1900) was the last defender of the unitary concept in Germany. Every mental illness, he said, follows the same course of evolution, a stage beginning with neurasthenia or melancholia, followed by stages of mania, stupor, and finally dementia. This cycle he called *vesania typica*. Arndt tried to explain this typical evolution of mental illness with Pflüger's "basic biological law." ("Feeble stimulations activate vital processes, stimulations of intermediate intensity accelerate them, violent stimulations inhibit and finally paralyze them.") Thus, in mental illness, Arndt said, the initial feeble stimulation determines conditions of neurasthenia or melancholia; when the stimulation increases the condition turns into mania, and its further increase results in inhibition (stupor) and paralysis (dementia). This was in anticipation of modern concepts of stress.

declaration: "The principle of specificity dominates all medicine." [12] The unitary concept in psychiatry was forgotten. The problem became, rather, how many disease entities actually exist and how can one group and classify them in the most logical fashion.

But with the dawn of the twentieth century the unitary principle reappeared. By that time the realization had dawned that *names* do not create illness forms; they only comfort the doctors and impress the relatives. If a patient is poor, said Janet with tongue in cheek, he is committed to a public hospital as "psychotic"; if he can afford the luxury of a private sanitarium, he is put there with a diagnosis of "neurasthenia"; if he is wealthy enough to be isolated in his own home under constant watch of nurses and physicians, he is simply an indisposed "eccentric." Janet [13] devoted an entire chapter to a sharp criticism of the current psychiatric classifications. He himself distinguished only two large groups: the organic and the functional. Sometimes, he said, a car stops because the machinery is broken, sometimes because it is out of gasoline. Essentially Janet was a unitarian.

Freud, of course, while adhering to conventional designations in his scientific reports, abandoned most of the old landmarks to devote himself to the common substructure of psychological disturbances, as Gregory Zilboorg [14] has pointed out. Freud was never much concerned with names.

The most consistent effort in the direction of modern unitary concepts in Europe has been by Henri Ey. [15] "A powerful movement has arisen," he wrote, "against the idea that a mental disease should be purely and simply identified with the somatosis which constitutes its known or hypothetical organic 'substratum.'" "Mental disease," he went on to say, "appears to us less and less as disease entities, more and more as 'syndromes' or 'pathological reactions' resulting from a multiplicity of factors." * Ey considers the various clinical syn-

---

* Other protests began to be sounded against the inadequacy of the official psychiatric nomenclature. Attempts toward a "polydimensional" diagnosis were made, e.g., in France, where Laignel-Lavastine [16] proposed his method of "concentric diagnosis." The examination (and therefore also the diagnosis) of any patient was performed on five levels respectively called: the psychic, nervous, endocrine, and visceral zones and the pathological nucleus. Two other French psychiatrists, Leconte

dromes as the expression of various degrees of "dissolution" in accordance with Hughlings Jackson's principles.

Ey's position is very similar to our own. A similar concept is being developed by Bartolomé Llopis [18] who has recently contributed a history of the unitary concept. Llopis [19] does not distinguish, as does Ey, between acute and chronic conditions but has elaborated a "psychic frame" in which one dimension is the "state of consciousness" and the other the "content of consciousness."

We may not leave Europe in this review of the changing concepts of mental illness without mentioning the outstanding work of Manfred Bleuler and of Jakob Wyrsch, both of Switzerland; Eugen Bleuler had already laid the groundwork for it. Contemporary with him was another Swiss, Adolf Meyer, who fostered in America the Kraepelinean classification, which tended strongly in the direction of specificity. Meyer soon became dissatisfied with it and somewhat dismayed at its "success" in his adopted country. (Like Freud, Meyer never quite comprehended the epidemiology of new ideas in America.) Meyer reverted (or, as we prefer to think, progressed!) to a nonspecific, essentially unitary concept of mental illness. The various classical syndromes he considered to be various reaction types, various patterns of misdirected energy. His "ergasia" concept was based on a holistic personality theory, and was supported by the eloquent psychoanalytic and psychiatric leader William Alanson White.

These two systems developed in American psychiatry side by side—the specific entity concept with which Kraepelin worked and the unitary concept which Meyer developed. The former prevailed. Each worker considered his to be a natural classification, the other's an artificial one.

---

and Damey,[17] suggested that every patient receive a three-fold diagnosis: somatic, biological, and social, which would give reliable directives toward a rational treatment. Ey proposes the following classification:

PATHOLOGY OF CONSCIOUSNESS (Acute psychoses)	PATHOLOGY OF PERSONALITY (Chronic psychoses and neuroses)
Manic-depressive attacks.	Disequilibrium, neuroses.
Delirious and hallucinatory transient attacks. Oneiroid conditions.	Chronic delusional systems and schizophrenia.
Confusional-oneiric psychoses.	Dementias.

During World War I, Ernest Southard of Harvard proposed a simplification of the official nosology of the day into eleven major groups. During World War II my brother, William Menninger, developed another reformulation reducing the basic groups of mental illness to five, and emphasizing Freudian and Meyerian principles of psychodynamics. This classification was adopted by the medical departments of our (United States) military forces and by the Veterans Administration, although it was clearly recognized by all that various inconsistencies had been retained as a matter of practical compromise. A very similar classification, prepared by a committee under Dr. George Raines, was subsequently adopted with modifications by the American Psychiatric Association.

Looking back, then, to the days of Hippocrates and since, we see how psychiatric nosology, after modest beginnings, gradually expanded in size and increased in differentiation; then contracted; then expanded to a great maximum; and in these latter days is again contracting toward simpler, more holistic, and process-oriented concepts. Psychiatry was only lately joined to medicine and science; many of our classical designations were practical, administrative descriptions or fanciful "explanatory" terms rather than scientific concepts. But it is difficult to free ourselves from the misleading implications that have become attached historically to the various labels not necessarily by their originators but by their users. This is true even when the old label is replaced with a new model or the concept revised. "Madness" became "lunacy," "lunacy" became "insanity," "insanity" became "psychosis," and now many psychiatrists (in the United States at least) feel that the word "psychosis" should be abandoned. A hundred names have been applied throughout the ages to conditions which were, by a later generation, called *"délire onirique"* or "hebephrenia" or "catatonia," and by the following generation called "dementia praecox," and by the next generation called "schizophrenia."

The fact remains, however, that in the minds of many young doctors and in the minds of vast numbers of laymen mental illness and particularly schizophrenia is a definite, specific, evil thing which invades the unsuspecting like a fungus or a tapeworm. The word schizophrenia becomes a damning designation. To have it once applied to a young man can be to ruin a career, despite all evidence of subsequent healthiness. A name implies a concept; and if this concept is unsound, the diagnosis can ruin the treatment; the very naming it can damage the patient whom we essay to help. Nathaniel Hawthorne in *The House of the Seven Gables* told us what we psychiatrists should well know: "The sick in mind . . . are rendered more darkly and hopelessly so by the manifold reflection of their disease, mirrored back from all quarters in the deportment of those about them; they are compelled to inhale the poison of their own breath, in infinite repetition."

It was these considerations among others which stirred the beginning of our studies some twenty years ago. Speaking as the senior author, I recall how it once seemed to me of the utmost importance to make a sharp distinction between the various types of what we called dementia praecox, or between them and some otherwise labeled syndrome. Today it seems to me most important that we *not* do that. Have I changed so much? Or is it the times and concepts that have changed? It is not that we decry classification as such; we recognize it as a useful scientific tool. But it is dangerous when it leads to reification of terms.

My interest in this developed from my experiences in teaching psychiatrists, some hundreds of whom are or have been enrolled in the Menninger School of Psychiatry for varying periods of time. The concepts gained in their medical schooling are, naturally, carried over by the young doctors into the field of psychiatry, but often these concepts handicap them. They seek specific therapies instead of ways to help their psychiatric patients to better modes of living, to better social adjustment, to greater utilization of latent powers. We would have them think of the patient, not as one afflicted with a certain *disease* which they must *name* and then battle with and attempt to dispel, but rather as a human being, one somewhat isolated from his fellows, one whose interactive relationships with them have become mutually unsatisfactory and disturbing; to this he has reacted in various ways, all intended to salvage the situation and insure survival, even at the cost of social acceptance.

Suppose that instead of putting so much emphasis on different kinds of illness we tried to think of all mental illness as being essentially the same in quality and differing, rather, quantitatively. This is what we mean when we say that we all have mental illness of different degrees at different times, and that sometimes some of us are much worse or much better. If one sets up a scale of well-being—in other words, a scale in the successfulness of an individual-environment adaptation—at one end of it would be health, happiness, success, achievement, and the like, and at the other end misery, failure, crime, delirium, and so forth. On such a continuum one could mark some practical stages. We can say that some people are relatively healthy, that some are relatively sick, and that the latter are either mildly, moderately, or extremely sick. These would vary, of course, depending upon the culture in which one lives and the duration of the particular episode of maladjustment and many other things.

Modern organismic theory conceives of systems and subsystems relating themselves to one another in the interests of homeostasis, the steady state of the open system, as defined by von Bertalanffy.[20] Pressures from instinctual urges, from somatic needs, from environmental threats, losses and opportunities, from the culture and the conscience all bear upon the ego, whose task it is to effect a reconciliation in order to maintain a steady state of the organism. The effectiveness *and* the cost of the reconciliatory efforts determine the degree of mental healthiness of the individual. Inadequate resolution of the conflicting pressures results in increased tension, a warning of danger to the organism which evokes compensatory shifts. If an imbalance continues despite these warnings, there comes reduced function, perhaps more pain, "sickness," and even death. Successful resolution, on the other hand, insures the continuation of constructive activity and organismic growth. Thus the ego, by reconciling the demands and keeping disruptive, destructive drives in check or neutralized by fusion with creative tendencies, fulfills its function of fostering the welfare and development of the individual.

Mental illness, then, is an impairment in self-regulation whereby comfort, production, and growth are temporarily surrendered for the sake of survival at the best level possible, and at the cost of emergency coping devices. Psychiatrists are apt to look upon mental illness as an indication of ego failure. But now this "failure" acquires a different meaning. Beset by a variety of stresses, the ego tries to insure survival and preserve the best possible level of life adaptation at the least cost and in this it has succeeded. We clinicians are more familiar with the instances in which the cost has been relatively great and the gains small; we are less familiar with the current "price" of "normal living and growing."

We believe it possible to construct an empirical series of the regulatory moves or efforts on the part of the ego, progressively more urgent, more adventitious, more symptomatic on the basis of a combined dynamic-economic scale. First come those mild symptoms called by the layman "nervousness"; a second order of devices would include neurotic phenomena; the third order embraces episodic and explosive discharges, and the fourth order various syndromes of more persistent and severe disorganization. The emphasis is on the *degree of disorganization and its course* or trend of development, and the factors determining this trend. It is common knowledge that some patients become acutely ill rapidly and recover slowly; others become mildly ill and recover rapidly, and so on. This trend and acceleration of the changes or level thus characterize each particular instance of illness.

Such an approach does not preclude the administrative usefulness of recognizing the well-known psychopathologic syndromes to which various conventional designations have been applied. *Of course* one can describe a "manic" or a "depressed" or a "schizophrenic" constellation of symptoms, but what is most important about this in each case? Not, we think, its curious external form, but rather what it indicates in regard to the process of organization, disorganization, and reorganization of the personality in a state of attempted adjustment to environmental reality. Is the imbalance increasing or decreasing? To what is the stress related? What psychological factors are accessible to external modification? What latent capacities for satisfaction in work, play, love, creativity are discoverable for therapeutic exploitation? Is a restoration or reconstruction of adjustment patterns developing? Can this be fostered by discriminating medical intervention?

In summary, we believe that the natural "class" in psychiatry must either be the disturbed individual or all mankind in trouble. There are no natural mental disease entities. An ordering of clinical phenomena on the basis of the economics of adaptation such as we have proposed does justice to the essential unity of sickness and health; at the same time it leaves room for recognizing the latent potentials of every individual. It transcends the distinction between natural and artificial classification, the question raised in our opening paragraphs. The trend toward a unitary concept of mental illness is clearly apparent in psychiatric history, and it seems to us to follow modern trends in other fields of science. It spares us some grievous errors and offenses against our patients. This is what we conceive of as rational therapeutic planning. It is our continuing aim to see the unity in diversity of psychiatric symptomatology as reflecting, from the side of the individual, the nature of an organism-environment interaction. It lets us see the conditions labeled "health" and "sickness" as degrees of relative success or failure on that interactive relationship. It enables us to direct psychiatry toward therapeutic endeavors of amelioration rather than toward mere diagnostic name-calling!

The Teacher

By his very nature, Karl Menninger is a teacher. Not only does he learn by teaching, he must teach what he learns. He is impatient with and critical of those who neglect teaching, which to him is a responsibility that comes naturally with education; he acts in the tradition of the Hippocratic oath—"I will impart a knowledge of the art. . . ." Throughout his professional life, he has done the kind of medical teaching that involves sharing everyday clinical experiences with colleagues. But his career as a teacher consists of far more than teaching physicians, and it had a different origin.

When he returned to Topeka after his residency at Boston Psychopathic Hospital, he had decided to engage in the private practice of psychiatry. But he found himself without a psychiatric practice. He was in the position of having to interpret his specialty and in a sense to help people realize that they were psychiatric patients. Moreover, believing, as did Southard, that psychiatry was something every man should know something about, he looked around for opportunities to tell people about psychiatry. He provided one way when he initiated at Washburn University in Topeka one of the first courses in mental hygiene ever to be taught in a college.

Karl Menninger is a teacher of many kinds. His writings selected for publication here reflect him as an educator of the public about psychiatry, as an educator of physicians about psychiatry, and as an educator of psychiatrists about psychiatry. Although he no longer teaches the course in mental hygiene at Washburn, the course continues to be taught. But he continues to interpret psychiatry to the public, and to try to show the good that can result from the application of psychiatric principles to everyday life. In papers such as "Healthier than Healthy" he essays to translate complex theoretical ideas into simple language, and to keep the public informed of medical thinking.

Although Karl Menninger is known as a psychiatrist, he prizes his identity as a physician. He was threatened by professional suicide at the time he chose psychiatry as a career, and this may account for his attempt to justify himself as a physician. Whatever the personal motives may have been, the results are apparent in his first published writings—a total of nine articles in 1919. Among these early papers is one entitled "General Psychiatry for the General Practitioner," published in the *Journal of the Kansas Medical Society*. He contributed many such articles subsequently to that journal and to other journals designed for physicians other than psychiatrists.

As he pursued his studies as a psychiatrist, he became surer that it was not a departure from medicine and that, indeed, more than any other specialty it would probably enrich all of medicine. Particularly through his psychosomatic studies he attempted to acquaint physicians with the fact that psychiatry is an integral part of medicine.

Karl Menninger is a physician, and he talks a doctor's language. However fanciful his clinical convictions might have appeared to less imaginative medical colleagues, they could not ignore him. He has a particular capacity for talking with physicians who are not psychiatrists, and this is evident even in the small number of papers addressed to physicians other than psychiatrists which are included in this collection.

He has taught his specialty to novice psychiatrists from the time he started practicing it. Recognized now as an outstanding psychiatric educator and the dean of the largest educational program for physicians studying psychiatry, he has written little about it, perhaps because he has been too busy doing it. What he believes about it is almost poetically expressed in the paper "What Are the Goals of Psychiatric Education?" He is also an educator in the other disciplines associated with psychiatry, and his contributions to the development of clinical psychology are difficult to estimate. He has made similar contributions to the education of adjunctive therapists, nurses, social workers, and psychiatric aides.

Nor has he written much about another major interest and activity of his—research. He is a busy researcher, and many of the clinical phenomena which have come to his attention have also been assessed from a research perspective. He has written few papers about research methods, but he has done a great deal of notable clinical research. Included here is one brief contribution about the importance of future research in psychiatry.

—B. H. H.

PUBLIC EDUCATION

1. The Washburn College Course in Mental Hygiene

Who ever gives his mind a bath? Who ever brushes his intellectual teeth? Who ever attends to the climate of his emotions or the purging of his will?

The average person gives some little thought to the subject of keeping healthy. Feature articles and state departments are constantly before us in the interests of physical health. But to the health of the mind few people ever give any thought. It is tacitly assumed that the health of the mind (unlike the health of the body) will look after itself until such moments of desperation as it seems to be hopelessly disintegrating. The fear of losing one's mind is a self-sufficient evidence of having already lost it.

What are the practical points of mental hygiene?

Do you know that there is no such disease as insanity? Do you know that you or any other person no matter how immured may at any time develop a mental disease? Do you know that there are perhaps ten times as many cases of mental disease outside of state hospitals as inside?

The chances are that you did not know any of these rather simple facts. The probabilities are that the average reader is more curious than ashamed at his ignorance about them. Ninety per cent of the readers of this article will be teachers and of that ninety per cent

Reprinted from the *Kansas Teacher*, 15:22–23, August–September 1922.

perhaps one per cent will be correctly informed on affairs which touch the life of every man, woman, and child in the country. Not one teacher in a dozen could write an essay on nervous children, a problem which she is facing every day of her life, which would be anything more than obvious and for the most part misinterpreted observations. The average teacher is herself woefully ignorant on the subject of nervous children and nervous people, herself and her pupils included.

I do not for a moment consider it a fault of the teachers. No matter how desirous of knowing these facts about nervous disease a teacher may have been, it would have been practically impossible for her prior to a few years ago to have secured any adequate or helpful information outside of a regular medical course, and even most medical courses do not pay much attention to nervous diseases. There are no good books on the subject. There have been no courses in the colleges or post-graduate schools on the subject. There have been no efforts to stimulate public interest. The cries of "Inspect the children's tonsils" and "Inspect the children's teeth" have utterly drowned out any weak effort that might have arisen is some quarters toward the direction of a little interest and a little attention to the health of the children's minds.

The war is given credit for many good things which have been gained in the last seven years (and God knows the war needs all the credit that anyone can possibly give it). The war is given the credit for stimulating the present wave of intense interest in the subject of mental disease. The literally millions of soldiers who developed nervous diseases during the war period and supposedly because of the war afforded the quantitative impetus necessary to stimulate the public interest. The fact that in the United States alone we have a quarter of a million patients in state hospitals with mental disease and probably two million or more outside of the state hospitals with mental diseases was for some strange reason never of sufficient interest to attract attention.

Just at the present time we are overrun with books and speakers, mental testers, and pseudo-psychologists. From knowing nothing about the subject the average layman who is at all interested is obliged to be informed of a great deal that is not so.

At the present time most teachers are more or less interested in the subject of intelligence tests and similar schemes for estimating intellectual capacity and recording it with a mathematical score. There are now something like four hundred species of these tests in existence. Hundreds of psychologists over the country have deserted their ordinary academic routine to wallow in a debauch of what many of them call "clinical psychology" or "mental testing."

Now these tests are neither clinical psychology nor are they mental tests. The mind is at the simplest composed of something besides intelligence, namely, emotions, perceptions, volition. These tests do afford us a valuable and for the most part a fairly reliable index of intelligence but concerning the other functions of the mind they tell us nothing. They are accordingly of relatively little value in the study of mental disease. Even in groups of cases in which they are the most helpful, namely the feeble-mindednesses, they are of only accessory value and must be supplemented with a great deal of collateral physical, neurological, laboratory, and psychiatric examination.

None of this should be construed as denying the value or antagonizing the spirit of such splendid efforts in psychometry as developed in Kansas by the State Normal's Bureau of Educational Standards and Measurements under the capable direction of Professor James C. DeVoss. I am simply trying to illustrate the fact that teachers' hunger for information so long unsatisfied is in danger of being satisfied with much that is confusing and some that is untrue. The very fact, however, that this hunger has arisen seems to me to be a most salutary sign and these two facts are, I believe, responsible for the enthusiasm with which a course in mental hygiene has been introduced into the curriculum of Washburn College.

The course in mental hygiene at Washburn College is an extension of the work begun a year or so ago in developing the subject of abnormal psychology. Aware of the woeful ignorance on the subject of nervousness, we thought it wise to introduce for the future teachers, preachers, doctors, businessmen, etc., who receive their academic training at Washburn a course which would give them the general facts about abnormalities of the mind and of the nervous system instead of the silly drivel about dreams and hyno- tism which made up about seventy-five per cent of the average college courses in abnormal psychology.

A number of students come to Washburn from other schools in which they had a course in abnormal psychology, but we give them additional credit if they wish to take the course as we give it at Washburn for the reason that most of the courses they have had are quite apart from a broad conception of the subject. This is not an egotistical thing to say. The fact of the matter is that abnormal psychology is usually taught by a psychologist, who knows little or nothing about mental diseases or nervous diseases and who draws a fine and wholly untenable line between what is abnormal and what is pathological.

Our course in abnormal psychology at Washburn embraces a study of the symptoms and syndromes of nervous diseases. Every student in my class has seen not one but numerous examples of every one of the main forms of mental disease and he has at least a general idea of the early recognition and the particular disposi- tion of each group. How much better this is than that of the aver- age university graduate can be illustrated by the following incident.

I was testifying in a court case in regard to a certain very interest- ing gentleman who had been doing peculiar things, so peculiar in fact that the newspapers had been full of descriptions of his con- duct. The doctors who were to adjudge of his sanity were con- siderably puzzled and listened with great attention to what I said. After they had heard my testimony and my recommendation they committed him to the state hospital, but with some misgivings, and a group of doctors actually talked about the case for an hour and a half before coming to a conclusion. I had noticed that my stu- dents who came to the hearing paid rather little attention to what I said and afterward I asked them why. One of them replied, "Why, because we saw from the very start it was probably a case of general paresis, but we were mostly interested in the difficulties the doctors seemed to be having in making up their minds what to do with him."

It should be remembered that these students were not college graduates and not medically trained. As a matter of fact we make no attempt to teach pupils diagnosis. This would be stepping into the very fallacy from which one should be warned by the present fate of some of the psychologists.

This course in abnormal psychology is largely a technical course designed for students who are seriously interested in the subject and wish to have correct information in sufficient detail to help them with their other work, be it teaching, law, medicine, or what not. It is, however, a three-hour course requiring considerable outside study and reading. We have limited the course to juniors and seniors who have had general psychology. Accordingly we felt a need for a shorter course with no prerequisites and one in which stress would be placed upon the facts about normal minds as well as facts about abnormal minds. This we have done in our course in mental hygiene. Lectures and reading assignments make up the body of the course, but there are also visits to the state hospital and the city clinic for nervous and mental diseases, and illustrative cases are particularly selected and demonstrated. Each student is required to attempt an original research, however trivial, and however much confined to collecting rather than to interpreting data. Last year students singly or in pairs visited four state institutions, especially those for delinquents, and in one case lived in the institution for a week to acquire an intimate and concrete knowledge of the data they presented in their theses.

2. Pseudoanalysis

PERILS OF FREUDIAN VERBALISMS

Ever since Sigmund Freud's first book, psychoanalysis has been a storm center of controversy among both the laity and professional people. Because of its human significance, it has achieved a rapid and enormous popularity. I have seen a bantamweight Italian laborer pause a moment in his toil, lean a pick over a sweaty shoulder, and tell his brawny fellow worker that he had an inferiority complex. I have heard a little girl implore her mother to throw away her inhibitions and take her to the circus.

As Freud himself points out in a recent article, the popularity of psychoanalysis in the United States is no real evidence either of a friendly attitude or a profound understanding on the part of its adherents. If the illustrations above show how generally the tenets of psychoanalysis have crept into the common mind, and its phrases onto the collective tongue, they demonstrate even more how inaccurately, and even absurdly, these phrases and tenets are being applied.

The truth of the matter is that the greatest foes of psychoanalysis have been its misguided friends. It has suffered much from unintentional misinterpretations, from the warm enthusiasms of superficial students, from a spectacular popularization of certain minor aspects. It has suffered more at the hands of those amateurs who think or pretend that they understand it well enough to apply its principles. But it has suffered most of all from the hundreds and hundreds of psychoanalytic chatterers, from those eager folk who

Reprinted from *Outlook and Independent*, 155:353-365, July 9, 1930.

long so passionately to impart their smattering of knowledge. These chatterers have created a specious science which has intrigued a tremendous public with its false and facile formulations. This specious science, in fact, is so far from Freudian theory and so popular that it deserves a christening. Let us name it pseudoanalysis.

The vocabulary of psychoanalysis has supplied numerous useful words to common speech. Human behavior is a matter of common interest, and therefore verbalisms from psychoanalytic literature have been eagerly pressed into public service. These verbalisms have become the property of platform controversialist, parlor conversationalist, and the miscellaneous literary flora and fauna of our times. Certain Freudian phrases have, in fact, grown out of all proportion to vocabulary. They are required to hold more meaning than is possible. Their originator would not recognize them in their present weightily amorphous guises. As Love, Honor, Beauty, God, formed the allegorical imperatives of our grandparents, Freudian designations have become the symbol words of our generation. Their dramatic significance has become inflated far beyond their dictionary proportions, and Freudian words taken in this way are dangerous, apt to become emotional and ethical dynamite.

Perhaps the popularity of these words is due, partly, to their Latinity, their rich and rolling cadences; perhaps it is partly the result of their dignity as "scientific phrases." In any case, they have been a boomerang to their creator; comically enough, their most constant users have never read Freud, or only superficially understood him, and are applying his language and ideas in amazingly inaccurate ways.

I presume there have always been soul-talkers, people who take pleasure in mutual verbal self-revelation, and people who do their spiritual or marital washing in public. Now, such practices in moderation should not be thoughtlessly condemned, as they often serve to release mental pressure. But the psychoanalytic vocabulary has made soul-talking a sport as popular as baseball or crossword puzzles, and as such it is not only neurotic, it is becoming a neurosis of wholesale dimensions.

Of course, everyone can find a personal psychological problem if he thinks about it, and most people love to talk about themselves. Psychiatrists and psychoanalysts are therefore pestered by attempted confessions on social occasions. I am often treated like a fortune-teller, and actually asked to read people's minds. I am credited, instantly, with Jehovan attributes. I am taken for a sort of modern magician and asked to untangle human knots at a moment's notice. When I refuse, my questioners often show me how the thing is done.

Gossip is a general human delight, usually accompanied by a feeling of guilt. To mitigate this feeling the modern gossiper of cultural pretensions puts his comments on a "strictly scientific" basis. He, also, utilizes the vocabulary of psychoanalysis. Rationalization is a human talent, and almost as frequent as breathing. But psychoanalytic misinterpreters give license to the rationalized approval of a science, and have produced a false system of ethics that never was intended, and would never be approved, by the founders and workers of that science.

In the pseudo-Freudian phraseology which has resulted, certain errors have become so popular as to be almost standard. Abuses of certain psychoanalytic ideas have become so frequent as to form a kind of general plagiarism of error. It seems, therefore, not inappropriate to examine a few of the words and ideas most commonly misapplied, and to define their misapplications.

Psychoanalysis began as a method of treating mental or nervous cases. It has become now a philosophy as well. From the material derived from the patients to which this treatment has been applied has grown a body of doctrine. In other words, the psychoanalyst has accumulated a great mass of data from case histories, and from this data he has drawn certain logical conclusions which have, in turn, increased the efficiency of psychoanalysis as a treatment and broadened its philosophic implications.

Now it seems to me perfectly legitimate for an intelligent layman to hold the psychoanalytic viewpoint, just as he may be a pragmatist, a vitalist, or an idealist. The nuclear concepts of Freud are philosophic, and it is natural that thinkers of a metaphysical bent should speculate about them. But as a practical science psychoanalysis is just as dangerous in the hands of laymen as amateur surgery would be. To understand Freud's basic philosophic concepts it is only necessary for the intelligent man to read a few books. To conduct psychoanalytic treatment requires years of study, and, it is thought by many, a medical degree. The usual professional analysis takes from three months to a year or more. What, then, can be the value of the diagnoses of superficial students of psychoanalytic theory after a few moments' conversation in a parlor?

Parlor analysis is not only useless, however; it is definitely invidious. It gives people erroneous ideas, on which they sometimes act; it increases the mental confusion of those already in mental chaos; and it sometimes keeps a person in need of treatment away from the proper physician. It also puts into unmerited disrepute the practice and tenets of a great new branch of the science of curing mental disease.

There are three sorts of physicians of nervous and mental disease that are often confused: the neurologist, the psychiatrist, and the psychoanalyst. Neurology is a branch of internal medicine. The neurologist is concerned with the diseases of the brain and spinal cord. The neurologist is not a physician of the mind as differentiated from the body. Psychiatry is also a branch of medicine, but much broader in scope than neurology. The psychiatrist is a doctor of the mind rather than of the brain. This means that he is concerned with the physical and chemical phases of life, to be sure, but more especially the psychological and social. He studies behavior abnormalities in the large, not merely reflexes and sensation changes. Psychoanalysis is one kind of treatment used by psychiatrists. The psychiatrist who spends most of his time in the application of this treatment may be called a psychoanalyst. To make this clear, let us suppose that a man has lost the use of his right arm. He would probably go to his family physician. His family physician might discover that he had a fractured bone and send him to a bone surgeon, or he might decide that there was a nerve injury and send him to a neurologist. The neurologist, after examining him, might find that he had a neuritis or a spinal-cord tumor, or infantile paralysis or something of that sort. On the other hand he might find no injury and that the cause of the paralysis was psychological. In that instance he might treat the case himself; but more probably he would send the patient to a psychiatrist. (Of course the patient might have gone to a psychiatrist in the first place, but this would have spoiled our illustration.) The psychiatrist would try to find out the facts of this man's psychological, social, and physical life which made it necessary for him to have a paralyzed arm in order to protect his ego. He might find this without much trouble and he might be able to cure the man in a few days or weeks. He might decide to use electrical treatments. He might think it necessary to put him in a sanitarium. Or he might feel that the case was a good one for psychoanalytic treatment, involving six months or a year of psychological delving which would straighten out many other symptoms in the man's life less apparent than the paralyzed arm. In this case, if he were himself versed in psychoanalysis, he could use it in this instance and treat the man so. If he were very busy, he would probably refer him to a psychiatrist, who devotes all his time to the therapeutic application of psychoanalysis. Such a man would be properly denoted a psychoanalyst.

There seems to be a common misapprehension that a psychoanalyst is not a doctor. In America, this is rarely the case. The few analysts here who do not have M.D.s find it difficult to achieve official recognition. They are not admitted to the psychoanalytic associations. There are several lay analysts in Europe, some of the most famous being Otto Rank of Paris, Oskar Pfister of Zurich, and Mary Chadwick of London.

Not Freud but Jung originated the most abused of the psychoanalytic terms—the poor old "complex." To say a man has a complex, particularly one of that pristine pair, the Oedipus and the Inferiority, is to say exactly nothing at all. Everyone has an Oedipus complex—an occasional desire for release from mature existence, and a return to the peace of the womb or the crib. And until evolution grants to the human another metamorphosis we will, all of us, have inferiority feelings—complexes—about something or other. It is just as relevant to say that so-and-so has a complex as to say he has a nose.

When a certain complex becomes fixed, so out of proportion to reality that it distorts the life scheme and cripples the economic and social efficiency of a human being, it requires treatment, and another verbal specification.

The word "complex" is useful in describing those psychological tendencies which, when overgrown, can destroy mental health. When laymen accuse a man of an "Oedipus complex" they frequently mean that he has a persistent mother fixation, that his desires for the return to childhood conditions, and the ever-present safeguarding influence of his mother, are blotting out the pleasures and compensations of his present-day life, and causing him to regress overmuch to early traits and memories.

The same objection might be made to "defense mechanism." This term, properly used, simply indicates the facing of life with an individual combination of protective attitudes that are assumed less to fool the attitudinizer, himself, than to deceive others for the sake of vanity or pride. To indicate that a defense mechanism is abnormal is to admit the abnormality of the race. There is no one who does not use protective poses—however well or mistakenly—to lessen hurt, or avoid admission of disadvantageous positions.

Another word which has crept into colloquial use in a peculiarly inept way is "sublimation." A sublimation is really a symptom on the right side of the fence. Men suppressing sexual desires have been known to go in for dyspeptic attacks, or spiritual and confessional conversations with every female acquaintance. Both of these would be symptoms. But the half-thinker is apt to call the second a sublimation.

A real sublimation takes a man farther than from the boudoir to the drawing room. If, instead of having love affairs, he writes poetry or diverts his vitality into scientific discovery, it would be correct to say he had sublimated his libido in these directions.

Here, as usual, the laity put a sexual interpretation on a Freudian word, and overlook its other manifold possibilities. One rarely hears the word "sublimation" used in a nonsexual sense, while many forms of compensation and overcompensation justify it. A man may sublimate his wish to overeat into the writing of a cookbook or a study of the pyramids. He may sublimate his frustrated desire for children into collecting money for the endowing of orphan asylums. A great surgeon may be sublimating his desire to shed blood.

The words "suppression" and "repression" have also been taken over into this great misinterpretation of Freud. These two words should be correctly used by anyone claiming even the most elementary knowledge of psychoanalysis, either philosophic or scientific, because they are of primary importance in any study of the subsurface mechanisms of the mind. Nevertheless, most of the laity use the words interchangeably. Suppression and repression are the forces opposing instinctive tendencies. But suppression is conscious, while repression is unconscious. An artist, bound by the necessity of supporting a wife to commercial work he hates, may suppress his desire to throw up his job. This same man represses, perhaps, the wish to be rid of his wife so he may be free to paint. This second wish will never "enter his head," but he may some night be surprised to wake in a sweat from a nightmare in which he has enacted, say, the title role of the tragedy of *Othello*.

The users of neurotic vocabularies have also, frequently, a taste for the interpretation of dreams. This is no new favorite. Dream books were hidden under the pillows of romantic servant girls and college students long before the birth of Freud or the popularity of psychoanalysis. But the modern interpreter is, again, a causeless snob who claims the aristocracy of a scientific background.

The telling and interpreting of dreams at teas, informal gatherings, and in drawing rooms have exactly the same scientific status as horoscope reading, fortune-telling by cards, and Ouija-board predictions. Even a trained analyst cannot attempt with any certainty to interpret the dream of a patient until he is thoroughly familiar with the case history.

Let us take, as example, a not unusual dream. A sleeping man pictures himself at a fashionable party among people with whom he immensely desires to be popular. Yet he finds himself disrobing until he is nearly nude. What would the intelligent layman, who has read a few popular books on psychoanalysis, make of this dream? From curiosity, I asked several. Most of them answered that the man needed sexual gratification and therefore wishes to exhibit himself nude in the presence of the female guests whom he considered socially superior and physically desirable.

A more thoughtful interpretation, which one might hazard without knowing anything about the patient, is that he welcomed the idea of disrobing, wished to take off the disguises of everyday life and to get down to the naked truth, and to show this truth to all men, represented by an approved social gathering.

Now suppose the patient who had the dream were psychoanalyzed. During the analysis he would recall certain circumstances, by free associations, which he had formerly forgotten. In the audience, for example, he might remember, were his wife and a Miss X, who reminded him of a childhood friend of his, a little girl named Alice. From this he might also turn up into his conscious mind a childhood experience he had shared with Alice. One day, in a room with a locked door, they had disrobed. It was the first time either of the children had seen a member of the opposite sex nude. The whole incident was heavily accompanied by a sense of guilt and fear.

He would then confess to the analyst—who has also, perhaps, come by this time to represent society to him, as did the social gathering in his dream—that he had been tacitly unfaithful to his wife, and had suffered pangs of conscience really dating back to and linked up with his childhood "sins." His dream thus combined the wish to confess to his wife and to be square with society.

This is a comparatively uncomplicated dream. The amateur who does dream-interpreting rates, at the hands of intelligent persons, complete inattention or ridicule. Such practices are muddleheaded and comic in the extreme. No self-respecting psychoanalyst or psychiatrist would indulge in so undignified, so uncertain, or so untruthful a procedure.

There is almost as much nonsense talked about homosexuality as there is about dream interpretation. To the lay mind, I suppose, it seems a sensational and morbid subject. To the psychiatrist it is just another divergence from the normal, by no means the most alarming, and frequently curable. Certain sections of the metropolitan populace are all agog to show their discrimination in this regard. A woman in a strictly tailored suit, with tailored shirt and striped tie, walks into a restaurant. "Look at that Lesbian," whispers Millicent to Mabel. This, of course, by no means follows.

The study and discussion of abnormal psychology by the laity has caused homosexuality to be grossly exaggerated by portions of the population, and fiercely underestimated by other portions. There are no statistics on this subject, but homosexuality is probably as frequent as epilepsy, although not nearly so serious.

For what Freud and his followers have firmly established is that we all have homosexual components—"we normals"—and that there are many gradations of homosexuality. More homosexuality is unconscious than conscious; more cases are nonphysical than physical. There is the passive type who enters into a love affair with a person of the same sex as a poor substitute for a satisfactory heterosexual affair, which, for some reason, is impossible of achievement. There is the active homosexual who has identified himself, in babyhood and childhood, with a parent of the opposite sex, because the parent of his own sex was so weak or so brutal, or drunken, or in some other way physically ugly, that identification became extremely distasteful.

To treat this special divergence from the normal with horror is to be ignorant, smug, and self-righteous. People who make pariahs of homosexuals have a decided kinship with witch-burners—the difference is in degree rather than kind. Usually those so bitterly contemptuous of homosexuals are struggling with their own unconscious tendencies in the same direction.

Frigidity is a very common symptom in women. One of the results, perhaps one of the causes, of the civilization we have developed is a tendency toward sexual renunciation. To say that a woman is frigid because of an unhappy marriage is usually inaccurate. Marriage, or contact with any individual after maturity, is almost never the primary cause of nervous trouble, though it is frequently the cause of certain symptoms which make the trouble perceptible or acute. Before we leave this subject, we might say that impotence in men is the equivalent to frigidity in women, and is more frequent than is generally conceded to be the case.

The last word on this very incomplete list defines the great conceptual error of the laity about Freudian theory. The drunk who toasted "Another little inhibition won't do us any harm," had much more in common with Freud than he realized.

The most vicious practice of the pseudoanalyst is his glorification of uninhibited self-indulgence. No real psychoanalyst ever advocated anything like that. It is only the abysmally ignorant who accuse psychoanalysts of believing that self-control is the genesis of the neuroses and therefore a kind of modern Mephistopheles. Quite the contrary is true. Freud no more advocated promiscuous indulgences in sex than he did promiscuous indulgences in eating. Actually, the Freudian thesis defines the neurotic patient—the person so mentally ill that he requires treatment—as one who is failing to maintain his inhibitions, and needs help in mastering his escaping desires.

These, then, are the high points of the slapstick comedy—pseudoanalysis. The ironists and satirists who like to see life as a grand show, where tragedy only accentuates comedy—and there is plenty of pie-throwing—are probably having a grand time observing it. But those of us who have a real affection for the human kind must feel that the show is truly sad, its irony a little hateful.

For statistics tell us that one out of every twenty of us is, has been, or will at some time be in a hospital for mental disease. A real consideration of psychoanalysis—and the general modern findings about mental disease—would be salutary and extremely logical to our time and place.

A general realization that the abnormal is usually more interesting than dangerous, that the abnormal gives variety and tang to human existence, that at worst it is a wildly exaggerated growth of some universal human tendency, would bring tolerance, wisdom, and a decidedly increased enjoyment of social contacts. Such new, such literate human understanding would not only result in a decrease of mental illness. It would be, I think, the first step toward an educational system which might make peace more than a word in modern existence.

3. Unprofitable Investments in Love

Strange as it may sound, there are a great many persons whose unhappiness depends upon the fact that they love their parents too much, not wisely but too well. There comes a time in the evolution of the child's life when he must seek outside the family circle for the investment of love which hitherto he has placed entirely within it.

His parents, brothers and sisters, who have monopolized and absorbed his entire love life, must relinquish it and be relinquished.

But just as some persons never get past the stage of loving themselves, so others never give up their dependence upon interfamily love.

This externalization of love is painful, both to the parents and to the child; but it is necessary. Mother love, which is one of the most beautiful of human phenomena, may become a harmful, even ruinous thing unless it is great enough and unselfish enough to renounce itself in favor of better investments. It must even be able to turn up thorns in the nest, as eagles are said to do, so that the eaglets will not find it too comfortable to remain.

Many do remain, however. They remain in spirit, if not in the flesh; sometimes both.

I have often been struck by the frequency with which all or

From 1930 to 1932 Dr. Menninger contributed "a series of discussions about mental hygiene in its relation to family life . . ." to the *Ladies' Home Journal*. The following selection from the issue of May 1931 is one of these discussions which appeared under the heading "Mental Hygiene in the Home."

nearly all of the brothers and sisters of nervous patients have remained at home, unmarried. And inevitably, sooner or later, the pain of this unhappy investment comes to the surface.

I get many letters and I see, as does every psychiatrist, many cases like that of a man of thirty from whose letter I take these excerpts:

My early life was made a nightmare through my father's neglect and the struggles of a saintly mother to keep the large family together. It led me to take my mother as a model, and my life was regulated by the softer influences. Due to her exhortations, I was very careful not to engage in dangerous sports. I did not swear, I did not smoke or drink. I regulated every action to the tender feelings of my mother.

I graduated from college near the head of the class. I have a good position. I ought to be happy. But I am near the breaking point—morbid, depressed, terrified at the future. Everything seems about to go to pieces. The girl to whom I have been engaged is not what I want. Everything seems to fall short of my expectations and desires. Nothing seems worth while.

It is not always so dramatic as this. But these victims of family-love bondage are always being disappointed, and disappointing other people. For this they seem to have the best of reasons. But we should be able to see through them.

Frank Adamson, for example, was a very eligible bachelor. He was always popular; women literally ran after him, and men liked him too. After his graduation from college he lived with his parents. When his father died, he went on living with his mother. "She needs me, you know," he said. "She's lonely since my father died."

A score of love affairs simmered down to one likely girl, who considered herself fortunate and happy. They "went together" and were regarded as engaged. Time passed, and they were still going together. Nothing seemed to come of it. The girl's friends whispered; some of them even questioned her. Her replies were necessarily evasive, for she was just as perplexed as they. There was no doubting Frank's ardor, his sincerity, his faithfulness. But what were his intentions?

After a scandalously long time she took things into her own hands. She insisted upon knowing. It seemed to throw him into a panic. At first he declined to make any reply; he seemed terribly upset and did not come to see her.

Finally he laid it all before her. He had wrestled with it in spirit, he said, for over two years. It was a matter of choosing between his honorable duty to his mother and his selfish and romantic desires for a wife. It broke his heart to give her up, but in all honor and decency there was nothing else to do. He could not expect her to wait until . . .

Frank is still a bachelor. His mother died years ago. He carries the girl's picture with him, and has one set in a little frame on his desk. He has never been interested in any other woman. To a few of his friends he has modestly confided this little tragic romance. Some of them think him a hero, others pity him for a martyr or ridicule him as a fool. To only a few is it really clear why he never married.

Sometimes these poor fellows get married. Then it becomes a case of "poor wives"! A good many such write me letters:

My husband is so dominated by his mother that he is becoming actually dangerous to his own health, my peace of mind, and the children's proper bringing up. In fairness to him I must say that I think she is motivated by a desire to satisfy her ego by weakening him and keeping him dependent upon her.

She discourages him about his business, his marriage, and his health. She constantly tries to make him feel that he is [her] sick, weakly child. She has him scared to death about his health. She sets him against me. She gets him to come and talk with her about my faults and even about our sexual relations.

And he is so distracted by it all that he is almost impossible to live with. He flies into rages and does the most absurd things. And yet outsiders do not suspect any of this. He goes right on with his business.

Daughters as well as sons may be caught in the web of *The Silver Cord* (a play every mother should read). The silver cord is beautiful, but unless loosed at the proper time it cuts deep wounds, and binds hands and feet. Whether it is the parent that binds the child or the child who clings to the parent is like the question of whether the chicken or the egg came first. In theory, perhaps, it is the parent's doing; in practice it is the child whom we strive to release.

The possessiveness of parental love, as John Cowper Powys (in *The Meaning of Culture*) puts it, is a "maternal or paternal cannibalism which desires to hug what belongs to it, even unto death. . . . To this gloating . . . love the victim's faults and weaknesses—yes, its worst vices—are equally accepted as 'dear' and 'darling' with its most desperate idealisms. Who has not watched a mother stroke her child's cheek or kiss her child in a certain way, and felt a nervous shudder at the possessive outrage done to a free solitary human soul? . . . There is something about the parental 'aura,' however kind and unselfish her parents may be, that is deadly to a girl's nature. . . . Here parents indeed may be fussing anxiously about her chastity while they themselves are all the while murdering her noblest culture more wickedly and more effectively than could the most treacherous of lovers."

If you doubt Mr. Powys' strong words, read this letter. It is, I concede, somewhat unusual; these imprisoned daughters usually lack the courage or the heart or the *comme savoir* to lift up their voices so.

My dear Doctor Menninger:

I am a girl twenty-nine years old. My mother died when I was fourteen. These fifteen years I have been my father's housekeeper.

I did not even finish high school. When mother died, father was inconsolable, and would have no one but me about. Knowing so little about the world—my home was most of my world then—I thought it was only right and proper. I think I was flattered; I thought it was an honor. And I am quite sure my father hasn't the slightest idea to this day of how he has ruined my life. That, at least, is how I feel about it now. Not that he has ever mistreated me in the ordinary sense of the word. Just the contrary. I've had everything he could give me, lots more than my mother ever had. He is always thinking of me, devoted to me. That's what ties my hands, or my tongue. [She should have added, "and my heart."]

I have never known people my own age. In the earlier years when I would get an occasional invitation he would look grieved and say for me to go on if I wanted to, he guessed he could get along all right; he had intended for us to go out to dinner, or to a movie, and so forth. Then of course there was only one thing for me to do, and I did it. I used to do it in love, and perhaps underneath there is still a bondage of love. But on the surface I am bitter, now, and resentful.

My father is nearly seventy. He can't last very long. Life with him has been hard, but life without him will be unendurable—so empty, joyless, useless. I look back with regrets and forward with apprehension. But what can I do? It looks hopeless to me, but I'm taking a long shot and writing this. . . .

This is what I wrote her:

I doubt if it is quite hopeless, dark as it looks. In the first place you're really not aged yet, and I see you still think of yourself and call yourself a girl—which is as it should be.

In the second place, you may lack education, as you say, but you certainly don't lack intelligence, which is infinitely more important for most human activities, especially for a metamorphosis such as you must undergo. And in the third place, you are willing to take a long shot and to seize upon the possibility of being shown a way out.

The realization of your hopes depends, however—granted the three fortuitous circumstances just cited—upon your grasping a truth of fundamental psychological importance. You believe that it is your father who has imprisoned you these many years. Imprisoned by his love, you think. Intense, honest, possessive, and very selfish love.

And so you were, in part. Especially during the first few years. But that couldn't have held you all this time. You would have broken away from it but for something else. That something else is the bondage of your own reciprocal love for your father. You feel bitter, you say; you think you see clearly how wrong it was for him to expect you to act as his housekeeper—almost, one might say, as his wife. But you must see that underneath that bitterness of yours is a very great love, a wrongly invested love.

Not that it is wrong to love one's father, but that it is wrong to love one's father so much that one's own life is ruined. You have almost done that. I think part of the bitterness you feel toward your father is really inspired by your anger at yourself. You are bound and held by your own

love investments as much as by his, and it beclouds the issue to blame
it all on the object of these investments.

If you can see this clearly, you are ready to go further. You will be in
a position to dismiss your hostilities and bitterness. You will be able to
contemplate calmly a plan of procedure which you can carry out in spite
of new obstacles which will surely arise.

I don't mean you will be able to do all this unassisted; perhaps so,
perhaps not. Time will tell. If you can't make it alone, however, blame
your own weaknesses and not your father's misdirected strength. Then
you can find assistance.

Many other women are just as securely bound without any of
the external circumstances of the one just described. They don't
know what binds them.

"I have everything to live for," writes one. "My people are generous, and I am an only child. I am engaged to a man who graduated
from Yale last June and we expect to be married this summer. He
has a fine job. Our parents are delighted; we have a really wonderful
future. But I'm miserable . . . never more so in my life. . . . I'm
terribly dissatisfied. I don't know why, but I just don't think I can
go through with it."

Some of them are more experienced, but no more successful in
freeing themselves. Here is one, for instance:

Dear Doctor Menninger:
I have been reading what you say about unprofitable investments of
love, and surely my life has been nothing but that. Just a succession of
love affairs which tear my heart out each time, with nothing to show
for it all.

It began pretty early. I was still in high school when I had my first
serious affair. I say "serious" because it was such a tremendous emotional
experience for me. I thought I was in love and I thought he was the
finest male creature God had ever put on earth. He's a taxicab driver
now, so I presume I was mistaken.

As I recall it there were two or three in high school. They all turned
out the same way. There would be a most romantic beginning, then a
tempestuous wooing and the most ardent love-making on the part of
both of us. I am speaking of emotions. For a while everything was

beautiful: moonlight strolls, firelight musings, letters and flowers and little gifts made very important. Then a period of petty quarreling and increasing distress and dissatisfaction. Finally a blow-up and it's all over.

If this had only happened once, or twice, or even three times, I could believe my own impressions that it is always the man's fault. But it has happened a dozen times; perhaps more. So it surely must be in me.

It seems as if I expect too much. The man never turns out to be what I thought he was, some way. . . . I am always ultimately disappointed. I suppose in some way I precipitate the rows that end the affairs, although it always seems to me that it is his fault, and I suffer terribly for a while.

What kind of a complex do you call that and what can one do to get rid of it?

Here is another letter, illustrating the same thing in a somewhat different tempo:

Dear Doctor Menninger:

When I was nineteen I married a man of thirty whose wife had died, leaving him two children. I have always loved children, and I thought I loved this man. He seemed so wise and kind and strong, and everything that a woman might want in a husband. I was sure we would be happy.

We were, for a year or two. I can't recall just how it began, but gradually I began to be dissatisfied. I found fault with him; he seemed to bore me. He treated me indulgently like a child; if I got angry and cried, he would just get up and leave the room and soon I would be completely tamed again.

We had been married about five years, I think, when I met Harold. He was one of my husband's employees. I liked him because he noticed me and flattered me, I guess. And gradually we developed more and more friendship until I realized we were very much in love. I felt terribly guilty about deceiving my husband, and yet I went right ahead with it, justifying myself by saying he didn't love me anyway. . . .

The letter is too long to cite in full. She goes on to relate how she discovered that Harold was married, but was not thereby deterred from continuing her affair with him until he himself threw her over for still another woman. She was greatly disturbed by this and tried to renew her love for her husband and his for her, without success.

Again, she became involved in a love affair with a professor in the university, a man even older than her husband. Because of the very real danger that discovery of their relationship would cost him his position, he reluctantly withdrew and Mrs. Smith was once more thrown back upon her own resources with a sense of having been injured and rejected.

At first she romanticized this episode, and regarded herself as a martyr of fate, but gradually she assumed a feeling of hostility toward all men, describes herself as "thoroughly disillusioned" and yet not satisfied. She writes to know what she can do to prevent herself from repeating again this cycle of love infatuation and disappointment and becoming permanently soured on life.

My replies to these two women were substantially the same. I tried to indicate to them that their repeated selection of love objects which ultimately turn out to be unsatisfactory is strongly indicative of what we call technically an unresolved Oedipus complex, or "father fixation"—an unpropitious investment of love. They were both driven on by their unconscious necessities for a father to replace the one they had lost, or resigned, in childhood.

This explains the preference of Mrs. Smith, for example, for older men, for married men, for men in exalted positions, for men who treated her as a child. And of course these paternal attributes weren't sufficient to satisfy her.

Such women seek unceasingly for a lover to fulfill an unattainable ideal. They are looking for Sir Galahad, which really represents the idealized image of the perfect lover, but—fortunately—there is no one like the traditional Galahad. But in the child's eye there is an ideal, and that ideal is the parent. This she identifies with a Galahad image and, when deprived of the real parent, she sets out to find for herself this ideal of her dreams.

Some women can effect an endurable compromise between what they unconsciously want in this direction, what they consciously and rationally prefer, and what they can actually get. Not so these two women, and many like them. They need to be freed from an unconscious bondage to a childish love image and the consequent thwarting of their yearnings. The ordinary experiences of life have not been sufficient to effect this for them.

Psychiatric treatment, specifically psychoanalysis, is the best technical means of liberation, in my opinion. Unfortunately it is applicable only to a minority of cases; it requires great patience, it is often painful, and it is competently available only at the hands of a very few physicians.

4. Poor Little Good Child

One of the ideas most difficult for parents and educators to accept is that the "good" child is often more in need of help and attention than the "naughty" child. Because of his aggressiveness the bad boy, so-called, is the object of a great deal of concern and counsel while the good lad receives praise or else is overlooked entirely.

Two brothers, Richard and Martin, show this trend very clearly. Richard, the elder, is large, athletic, inclined to take risks, likes to organize the boys of his neighborhood into a gang, is often tardy to school because of some play activity. He is noisy, boisterous, rough, and tumultuous in play, and somewhat untidy in dress. In consequence of his frequent conflicts with the established order of things and with the peace and comfort of adults, he is constantly being punished and is regarded by his parents and the neighbors as a "trying" boy.

His brother, Martin, on the other hand, is considered a model boy because he causes little trouble to anyone and is very dependable. He has learned to avoid conflicts of all sorts because of a kind of

In October 1929 Nelson Antrim Crawford, editor of the *Household Magazine,* announced the organization of the magazine's Advisory Council on the Mental Health of Children. The Council included Doctors W. A. White, Frankwood E. Williams, Lawson G. Lowrey, Josephine A. Jackson, and Karl Menninger. Readers were encouraged to "submit their questions and problems as to the behavior and misbehavior of their children with the assurance that they will be answered with the best resources of modern science." A column, "Keeping Your Child's Mind Healthy," was written by members of the Advisory Council. The following article from the issue of August 1932 is an example of the articles Dr. Menninger contributed to this column from 1929 to 1938.

timidity which comes from a sensitive nature and a slight physique. He is not so energetic as his brother and therefore finds it easier to conform to grown-ups' ideas of propriety. Furthermore, he has learned from observation that implicit obedience entrenches him more firmly in the good favor of his parents and is the best means of rivaling his older brother who is superior to him in size, strength, and leadership. Unfortunately, however, this conformity and dependence upon his parents' approval and guidance is not fitting him for taking an independent place in the world when it becomes necessary for him to do so.

Richard is learning by doing although he makes many blunders; Martin is merely following the dictates of older persons about him, not because these seem logical to him or because they fit into his own experience in living, but because they are commands and therefore cannot be questioned.

The two boys illustrate the true underlying meaning of "good" and "bad" as the terms are usually employed. "Good" does not mean that which is good for the child, but rather that which is acceptable to the adults about him; similarly "bad" is not always applied to conduct which is bad for the child but to any behavior which conflicts with the parents' conventional standards.

All sorts of crimes are committed against the "good" child because in his dependence upon encouragement and his anxiety to please he lends himself to the uses of older persons, who, sometimes unscrupulously but usually unintentionally, capitalize the child's plasticity and devotion in ways very damaging to the child's emotions. A familiar example is that of the teacher who uses the obedient, docile child to carry tales and report on more enterprising youngsters. Still another misuse of the qualities which are pleasing to adults is that of laying many responsibilities on the dutiful child, such as making a "little mother" out of the oldest girl in a large family, or holding a conscientious boy responsible for chores too heavy or too complex for his youthful shoulders. Sometimes the parent shares his own emotional tangles and worries with a sensitive sympathetic child who seems "old for his years," steady and reliable.

We see the poor little "good child" everywhere; bringing home the perfect report card which means for him the approval and praise of adults; parroting his elders in his manners, speech, and actions, instead of expressing himself naturally on a childish level; quoting grown-up ideas and accepting and preaching adult standards and ideals which he does not understand but which seem to please the people whose praise he desires; obediently closing his eyes to those phases of his environment of which his parents prefer him to be ignorant; carefully placing his pennies and dimes in the saving bank for some purpose, quite obscure to him, which his parents proudly call "thrift." Too often parents read into the child's exemplary behavior, based upon his strong attachment for them, a growth in character and a degree of achievement which are not present.

Frequently the good child is paraded as a showpiece by the parents as if he were a possession or a pet instead of an individual. He is made to do quaint tricks, say pieces, "show off" in public with an utter disregard of his feelings and of the harm which may be done him by overstimulation of his desire for attention. When he becomes older and his exhibitionistic tendencies are no longer considered "cute" by his elders, he is bewildered by the withdrawal of the admiration and attention upon which he has become dependent. Such treatment, whether it results in timidity and loss of self-confidence and makes the child overdemonstrative and unduly anxious to excel in competition, or causes him to be obnoxious or conveniently compliant to his elders, is unfair to the child because it does not aim toward his development and future strength.

A woman once told me that one of her early memories of Memorial Day was of laying a wreath on her father's grave while his military company fired a volley over her. The scene was a pretty one, but from the standpoint of the child's sensibilities it was most pathetic. The poor little girl, with her limited understanding of the entire ceremony, was almost unbearably stimulated by the excitement, and the noise and the sentiment of the occasion still linger with her as a most painful memory.

Parents are the ones who should protect the child against such premature experiences; against orgies of emotionalism; against overstimulation of fear, anger, sympathy; against the child's natural desire for attention and applause; against adult demands which tax the child too sorely. They must prevent the "good" child from subordinating his own wishes too completely to their own. They have the task of protecting him from his own "willingness," directing his capabilities and leading him out. They must recognize that the problem of the quiet, dutiful child is as great or greater than that of the naughty child who comes into conflict with authority more frequently in his healthy attempts at self-expression.

5. The Origins and Masques of Fear

A boy was returning home at dusk. His path ran through a short stretch of woods, in the daytime almost as familiar to him as his own yard but at night strange and a little formidable. The trees loomed unnaturally tall, the bushes were full of moving shadows. He walked along, whistling boldly to assure himself that he had nothing to fear, that he was not a bit afraid. But what was that noise? Only a dog barking some distance away, but it made his heart beat faster; reassured, he walked on. Suddenly he seemed to hear Something creeping stealthily behind him; he listened intently and he imagined it stopping to listen too, only a few feet away. He began to walk rapidly, glancing fearfully back over his shoulder as if expecting to see it stalking him. Soon he broke into a run. Before he realized it he had lost the path and was stumbling over logs and underbrush. He fell down and covered himself with mud but he scrambled up, gasping, and ran on in blind fright, staggering into tree trunks, tearing his clothes on thorns, and finally losing the package he had been sent to fetch. He burst into the house, sobbing and incoherent; but to his mother's startled inquiries he could give no satisfactory explanation of the panic which had seized him and caused his familiar surroundings to assume a new and terrifying aspect.

A famous evangelist was conducting a revival service in a large auditorium. Thousands of people were intent upon his words. By

Reprinted from *Survey Graphic*, 22:217–220, April 1933.

sheer force of eloquence and earnestness he was holding his hearers enrapt. Suddenly a frightened woman shouted, "Fire!" and instantly the vast building was in an uproar. People stampeded like cattle, knocking each other down, even trampling on one another, fighting and struggling in their haste to reach the doors. Far more terrifying than even the din, the menace of fire, and the confusion was the stark fear of the throng which almost instantaneously changed reasoning, intelligent persons into mad creatures.

A country is at peace; its citizens, educated and progressive, talk of brotherly cooperation between nations, of a world state, of disarmament, arbitration of difficulties. Suddenly another nation makes what is considered to be a threatening move. The very citizens who spoke of peace now clamor for war. Immense sums of money are appropriated for armament, the whole country is in feverish anxiety while mobilization is going on. The enemy takes on superhuman powers and is credited with an omniscient secret-service system and with incredible cruelties. Dread sweeps over the country until everywhere there is a kind of madness, not unlike the panic in the auditorium although it is not so easily discernible and not so quickly allayed.

Many months ago another kind of panic spread over the world. Stocks dropped in value and financial credit was disturbed. Many persons predicted a quick recovery. There were waves of revived hope on all sides but stocks continued to fall and prices to drop. Manufacturing was curtailed and unemployment resulted. Each succeeding month has brought more and more faltering predictions of prosperity, and more and more distress, more new situations which disturb confidence at new depths, until finally it has become almost impossible to regard the depression objectively, just as it is difficult for people to regard an international situation dispassionately when their own country is at war, or for an audience stampeding in a threatened building to understand what they are doing, or for the little boy returning home through the woods in the dark to see the trees in their correct perspective.

The common element in each of these illustrations, the factor which prevents those involved from reflecting and acting calmly, is fear. Fear is one of the most powerful and most contagious of the emotions. It occurs in all of us, but in varying proportions according to the particular situation and our particular fitness to meet it. Fear in manageable amounts animates prodigious efforts and Herculean achievements; it is responsible, for example, for such a feat of building as the Great Wall of China. We teach children to fear certain things in a constructive way, to cross streets cautiously, to march in an orderly line from a burning building, to handle firearms carefully. If we tried to keep children in total ignorance of all such common dangers by guarding and overprotecting them, we would cripple their independence.

But fear which becomes panic, excessive fear which handicaps and overwhelms men and takes away their reason, as it did in the case of the stampede in the auditorium, performs no useful function.

ORIGINS OF FEAR

Fear is an emotional reaction which comes when we are about to encounter a danger, real or imagined, before which we feel helpless or inadequate. This feeling of helplessness is always based on previous experience of a comparable sort. From a psychological standpoint all fear is patterned upon the early experiences of the child when in his helpless condition he is overwhelmed by environmental factors which he is incapable of resisting. In every child's life there are many such situations because the child is constantly surrounded by dangers against which he is poorly protected, by reason of both physique and knowledge. The first such experience may be the very act of birth in which the child is suddenly forced from a quiet peaceful home within the mother into a bright, loud, garish world which cannot possibly be so comfortable. Some authorities believe that past experiences of the race are also remembered in some deep organic way, so that the terror of primitive man, before beasts and elements against which he could not protect himself, is also a part of the experience of fear. The important point is to recognize that it is not the threatening thing which frightens us but our own helplessness in the face of it, for fear is our anticipation that a situation in which we have previously felt helpless is about to be renewed.

The two things which the child fears originally are the threat of extinction and the threat of pain. The most poignant type of pain to a child and one which for him is practically equivalent to the sacrifice of life itself is the pain of losing love. To cease to be loved is for the child practically synonymous with ceasing to live. When his mother goes away, when she takes her breast from his mouth, or when she takes herself from the room, the child cries because he thinks he has lost her forever. This same feeling is the chief reason for the child's suffering when he is punished.

Later this fear that because of misbehavior he will cease to be loved is internalized as the fear of conscience. Indeed, we can say that for an adult there are two kinds of fears: fears of real danger from the outside world, and fears arising from the tyranny of the conscience within. In other words there are real fears and neurotic fears.

Everyone knows what real fears are; not everyone recognizes neurotic fears so readily. For example, I have received a number of letters during the last few months from persons who are afraid the world will come to an end. One woman told me that if she awakened during the night and found the window shade drawn so that she could not see the street light outside she was immediately struck with terror for fear the world had come to an end while she was sleeping. We characterize such a dread as a manifestation of neurotic fear because we recognize that it is not warranted by external probabilities and must be stimulated by some impulse within the person.

Research by psychoanalysis has demonstrated that such fears usually represent distorted wishes. For example, think of the woman who complains of men following her on the street or staring at her rudely. She both fears and hopes for this because she has converted her internal fears of her own impulses into external fears of men.

Another example just as familiar to psychiatrists but apt to be met with angry rejection by certain mothers is the way in which great anxiety over children's health covers unconscious death wishes within the mother. Many a mother who did everything she knew to get rid of a child before it was born, or who bitterly resented the expense and labor involved in the child's coming, has forgotten this entirely when ten years later she becomes nearly frantic with anxiety when the child shows symptoms of a slight cold.

A little boy continually ran away from school, not to play truant but to go home and see if his mother was safe. He said he had fantasies of his home burning with his mother in it and he had to go home to assure himself that she was still alive. Since there was no fire and no real cause for dreading it, except some unknown psychic reason within the child, this is a typical example of neurotic fear. It is also an example of the fear disguising a denied wish, for the child was discovered to be angry at his mother for thwarting his wishes; he secretly wished her dead, as most children do occasionally when their parents thwart their wishes in some way, and then, feeling guilty and remorseful because he wished his mother to be burned, he was forced to run home to see if his wishes had come true.

An interesting case came to my attention recently which is more detailed than the foregoing illustrations. A young man of unusual ability and education complained of a great dread of his own voice when talking to other people, a fear that it would tremble and quaver. This it actually did, frequently, but especially when he faced some important decision, or some difficult assignment or test. This dread compelled him to leave college and finally to withdraw from association with people almost completely. When he consulted me he was considering suicide because this obsession had, he thought, cost him his friends and his ability to work.

He told a most dramatic story in connection with his first memories of this quavering hysterical note in his voice. One night, because there were rats in the house, his family borrowed a neighbor's tomcat—a huge formidable animal it seemed to the boy, then a child of two or three. That night he awoke in terror with the sensation of rats swarming over him and choking him. He called to his mother, but his father shouted that he should go to sleep or be spanked. The boy called again and again in great terror. Finally his mother, realizing that something was seriously wrong, came to his bedside and found the great cat coiled up on his chest.

The young man told me that he discovered that what had brought his mother to his side that night in spite of his father's protest was the strange quavering note in his voice which had impressed his mother. He also remembered that in his childhood he was afraid of his father and that the memory of this fear of the cat was connected with his fear and dislike of his father. He was quite aware that his trembling voice was not due to any real threat from the people about him now, but was caused rather by childhood influences. Lacking the opportunity to study the case in detail, it is at least a plausible assumption that this young man, strongly attached to his mother as he still is, may still seek unconsciously to cry out for her help in his present difficulties of resorting to the same tactics which were successful in childhood instead of substituting the masterful aggressive attitude of overcoming obstacles.

Many such symbolic fears come to the attention of psychiatrists. I have known people who were afraid of being stared at, people who were afraid to leave the house, people who were afraid to step on a crack in the sidewalk, people who were afraid of "dark, Spanish-looking men," people who were afraid to eat if anyone was watching them, people who were afraid to climb stairs, people who were afraid to wear shoes—all instances of neurotic fears, externalized and distorted until it is impossible to discover the real source of fear until after days, weeks, or even months of study.

Strange and abnormal as such fears appear to us and far removed as they seem from our own apparently rational apprehensions for the future of our business or our homes, they deserve the space given them here because they represent in exaggerated form the fears which are present in almost all healthy persons but which are more successfully concealed or combated. How many of us have been suddenly beset by the fear that our house was on fire or being ransacked by burglars while we were away, or by the fear that someone had been accidentally injured when he failed to appear on time for an appointment? The psychiatrist recognizes such harmless symptoms as instances of symbolic fear which gratify unconscious motives.

MASQUES OF FEAR

So far we have discussed fear as it is ordinarily experienced by people, in undisguised form. We have shown that the sources may be obscured, but in the instances we have cited the feeling at least has not been disguised. Fear was felt as fear. The human mind has many tricks, however, and fear is often subtly disguised in many ways.

One of the most frequent disguises is this: real fear, i.e., fear justified by external reality, will serve as a cloak for neurotic fear. This is especially true in times of panic. This is because the increase in actual irrefutable external uncertainties gives justification to a freer expression of all kinds of unconscious irrational fears which lie buried beneath the surface of the conscious mind in less anxious times. The real fear present about us calls forth repressed fears which have their beginnings in earliest childhood, perhaps, and are entirely unrelated to present external conditions. The fact that there is excellent reason just now for part of this anxiety makes us overlook the presence of this neurotic fear and to fail to separate it from the real fear present.

This is well illustrated in a letter which I recently received in which a women told me of the dark cloud of apprehension which hung over their home because her husband was afraid he was going to lose his position or that his wages were going to be reduced. For months the whole family had talked of nothing else, until even the children were so affected that they were nervous and unable to sleep at night. The woman went on to explain that in reality there was no great likelihood of her husband's losing his job, although he might receive a reduction in pay; that they were well able to sustain such a blow if it fell because they owned their own home and a large plot of ground on which they raised fruit and vegetables; that if worst came to worst they could make a living from this garden and their cow. She quite sensibly added that the uncertainty and foreboding which had hung over them for the last nine months was worse than almost any actuality which could reasonably befall them. She also added the pertinent fact that her husband had all his life been subject to fears of one kind or another, although the depression had greatly intensified his customary anxiety.

This is a case of external reality working with internal fear of the unknown to produce an extravagant reaction. The unsettled economic condition gives this man opportunity to express lifelong fears. Study of neurotic fear shows us that what takes place in such cases is this: the man fears some impulse within himself, some wish or craving which he does not dare admit even to himself, although it may be something quite harmless in itself; he refuses to admit this fear and so he converts it into anxiety about something external, such as loss of work, and thus continues to worry without any reproach to himself.

A second way in which fear is often disguised is in the inhibition of activity, the expression of love, the carrying out of a constructive program of life, without any consciousness, however, of the fact that it is fear which really inhibits these normal tendencies. True, such inhibited persons will often insist that they suffer from a painful sense of inferiority, and therefore cannot lead fruitful lives. But this sense of inferiority is often only an alibi. Some of these people really suffer from a great sense of guilt, i.e., a very bad conscience, on account of some unconscious reason; because of their sense of guilt they fear punishment and the loss of love and this great fear acts as an inhibitor which they then seek to justify by deprecating themselves.

Another disguise of fear which looks very different but is really the same thing is to be seen in those over-courageous persons who are willing to tackle anything, particularly if it is the sort of thing which will give onlookers the impression that they are unusually brave. This is a reaction of denial to the same sort of disguised fear and inhibitions which we have just described. Unfortunately it rarely works out as successfully as it promises because essentially it is a bluff which sometimes works but frequently fails, and the failure provokes the utmost depression in such individuals.

Another disguise of fear is hate, i.e., unproductive aggressive activity. It is easy to see this in the attitude of one group of people against another group, although the same thing applies in the case of individuals. Because of their great fear of Germany, the nations of the world found all sorts of reasons for hating her; because of their great fear of the Negroes, some people in the South have at times had great hatred for them; because of their fear of the economic worth of the Japanese, some people in California express pronounced hatred for them. This fear is frequently not so much of the external object but of the temptations within the individual which the external object arouses—as we have already seen in our discussion of the origins of fear. One sees this particularly clearly in the aggressive intensity of certain reformers, and Somerset Maugham took advantage of it to write his very clever play, *Rain,* in which the minister finally yields to what he had spent his life denouncing.

A fifth masque for fear is the productive aggressiveness which we can regard as a sublimation of hate in creative activity in both work and play. Fear is sometimes the reason for a conspicuous success in business or in sports.

Finally, fear disguised as hate may be internalized, or turned back upon the self instead of upon the external world. A fear of people, for example, may be expressed as a timid withdrawal from social contacts which injures no one except the person himself. Many other examples of this form of fear which is disguised as hate of the self may be found in the self-destructive tendencies with which we are familiar in the neuroses, neurotic characters, alcoholism, defeatism, and so on. This turning in of fear upon the self may take either of two forms—somatic or behavioristic, i.e., those in which the hostility is directed against the body, as in self-imposed invalidism, and those in which it is directed rather against the career of the individual, as in the case of the "hard-luck artist" who can never succeed at anything.

COMBATING FEAR

What can we do to combat these disguised fears? Against neurotic fear our only weapon is insight. This is the justification for the careful elaboration of these disguises which we have just been discussing. The acquisition of insight will be opposed by forces of repression, difficult to evade or escape. In severe cases of fear-ridden individuals only the long, tedious reliving and realignment afforded by psychoanalysis can be expected to free them. But psychoanalysis is for the chosen few; for most people it is not available. And for the rest of the world we must put our hope in education.

But just what should we teach in order that coming generations may be more free from the trammels of fear? I am not sure, but I believe that if greater emphasis were put on teaching children to think in terms of facts and real consequences instead of in terms of morals and prejudices we could make a little progress in this direction.

But what can we do to combat real fear for which the present situation is surely some justification? I do not wish to dwell on internal distresses exclusively or to give the impression that I think the present financial depression is a figment of the collective imagination. There is much real fear created by the threat of actual losses and when this threat is fulfilled and the losses occur they are followed by depression and grief; this depression weakens confidence and in turn creates more danger of real losses, further losses, and this process continues as the months go by in a kind of vicious circle. Added to this cumulative effect is the effect of suggestion which is felt even by those who would otherwise escape the general panic.

Psychologists do not know just how the contagion of fear spreads so rapidly, so mysteriously. It may be by a process of identification in which one person sees his neighbor frightened, puts himself in his neighbor's place, and shares his fear, just as moving-picture audiences shuddered at the horrors of such pictures as *Frankenstein* or *Dr. Jekyll and Mr. Hyde,* through identification with the actors. At any rate we know that it communicates itself from person to person, from group to group, as certainly and much more rapidly than disease. The more people who are affected by the original fear, the greater the suggestion and the faster the spread of the contagion. In the case of the present crisis the fear has been so elemental and so universal, so closely connected with existence, that it has affected people all over the world and accordingly the total effect is tremendous.

MEANS OF COMBATING REAL FEAR

There is both a negative and a positive way of combating such a contagion of fear; the first way is by recognizing the nature of the contagiousness and avoiding making matters worse by exaggerating and spreading the disease. Nearly everyone becomes a "carrier" in a fear contagion because of the peculiar fascination that is derived from spreading the news of calamity. It is proverbial that bad news travels faster than good news.

The second way of combating fear is by countersuggestion. Although it is true that courage and self-confidence do not spread as rapidly as fear, they are contagious emotions also, as we know from the many examples we find in biography and history in which dynamic leaders have rallied forlorn and disheartened followers and led them to success and victory. The logical way to meet suggestion is by countersuggestion and the most strategic way of making a countersuggestion is through a popular leader. If ever there was a time when people clamor for "giants in the land" it is during a time of depression and despair.

Such a popular leader must have something more than boosting and false cheer to offer his followers, however, or his influence will be short-lived. In hard times people are hypercritical and skeptical of any attempt to whitewash actual conditions or to "kid" the public. He must combine the qualities of leadership with some intellectual control of the situation in order to obtain real confidence. People are never convinced by intellectual argument alone, but neither are they satisfied with ballyhoo. The leader who can catch the imagination of the public, arouse its emotions, and present some intelligent program can establish an effective countersuggestion, with a consequent stabilizing influence.

Once such a countersuggestion is initiated many resources can be used to reinforce it: history, psychology, sociology, economics, law, religion, philosophy, art, music—all in various ways can be utilized to ameliorate current conditions and to contribute to a better adjustment for the future. With each such adjustment fear is decreased because the sense of helplessness is reduced. As people conquer the situation with the weapons of intelligent optimism they become increasingly confident, for in the case of real fear, as with neurotic fear, we can expect salvation to the extent that we can make our intelligence master of our emotions.

6. Psychiatry

The very fact that this volume contains a discussion of psychiatry is an indication of the change which has taken place in its content and meaning since the appearance of the previous similar collection of essays describing aspects of civilization in the United States. A thousand years from now some research student seeking for dates that mark transitions may discover this pair of books[1] along with hundreds that have preceded them and will follow them, and he will make a note that "in 1938 there appeared for the first time, in a study of contemporary civilization, a formal representation of psychiatry."

This will seem interesting to him and worthy of note because perhaps by then or long before then what was until 1938 the small esoteric interest in a tabooed and ostracized group of society on the part of a few may have become the mother science of all systematic investigations of interpersonal human relationships.

If such ambitious, if not presumptuous, dreams about the future of psychiatry seem to the reader improbable of fulfillment, let him not forget that even in 1938 psychiatry has been expanded in its scope by discoveries as revolutionary and far-reaching as the basic discoveries which have recently revolutionized transportation and sound transmission.

When in 1938 Harold E. Stearns edited the book *America Now: An Inquiry into Civilization in the United States by 36 Americans* (New York: Scribner, 1938), he asked Dr. Menninger to write about psychiatry. The following article is Dr. Menninger's contribution to the book.

572

I shall shortly indicate what these discoveries are, but I should point out before discussing them that there is a vast difference in the extent to which they have been assimilated into the life of the man of the street as compared with the mechanical discoveries referred to. In fact, this is probably the most striking characteristic of modern psychiatry. Assume for the moment that my belief is correct that recent progress in uncovering fundamental principles of psychology has been as rapid as the progress in physics and mechanics of the last century, and compare the knowledge of the average citizen with respect to the automobile or the radio with his knowledge concerning psychiatry or psychoanalysis.

It is no objection that the man of the street knows very little of the scientific principles of the radio; the fact is that he knows that radios exist, that they are available to him, and that they are capable of performing certain functions which make life more endurable for him, and these things the man of the street does not know about psychiatry. The words "psychiatry" and "psychiatrist" are not mentioned in those extraordinary studies of the average American community, *Middletown* and *Middletown in Transition*,[2] not because the authors were unfamiliar with their existence but presumably because they found no evidence of any such familiarity among the people of this community, a community well equipped with radios, automobiles, factories, airplanes, hospitals, and other items of American civilization. And if the authors were to demur to this, insisting that they had not mentioned surgery or obstetrics, either, subjects which the citizens of Middletown undoubtedly know about and utilize as needed, I would reply that this would imply that psychiatry is only a medical specialty whereas, as I hope to demonstrate, the discoveries of psychiatry operate in many fields of human endeavor and show their influence there even if anonymously.

I propose to review the development of psychiatry and then to show how and to what extent it has influenced the content of literature, drama, and art, the theory and practice of education, the practice of law and the functioning of industry, the concepts and techniques of sociology and psychology. Finally, I shall indicate its present relation to medicine and its influence upon the science and art of that profession. And I shall return in the end to the paradox that a scientific discipline of such relatively recent development which has already made its mark upon all these phases of civilization remains as yet an enigma or a nonentity or perhaps even a joke to the average citizen.

The art of observing and of seeking to influence the course of mental disorders is not new; it appears as a medical discipline in the writings of Hippocrates (400 B.C.) and competent clinical observations and practical therapeutic techniques had been worked out by the Greeks and were preserved and expanded by the Arabians. In Europe, to be sure, demonology and witchcraft swallowed up the achievements of the early physicians and for many centuries the scientific study of the personality was nonexistent.[3]

Slowly, then, and more the result of sentiment and sympathy than of scientific curiosity, a new interest was awakened in those long tabooed and persecuted members of society who obeyed inner demands and impulses of a nature inexplicable to their associates, and hence regarded by them as irrational or "insane." These victims differed from those other victims of society, the criminals, in that the immediate objectives of their behavior were less transparent. Society, therefore, took a slightly less hostile attitude toward them but they were left without the pale of scientific study.

When the humanitarians, Dorothea Dix in the United States and comparable figures in each of the European countries, finally succeeded in extending a small measure of the protection and decencies of civilization to these sufferers, the scientists once more turned their attention to a systematic description of the peculiar reactions which characterized their patients' behavior * who thus

---

* It is quite natural that the earlier affiliations of psychiatry with medicine should have been with neurology on the assumption that mental pathology was the expression of more or less obscure neuropathology. This was the strictly physical viewpoint characteristic of the medical thought of the day. The chemical viewpoint that mental pathology was essentially humoral in origin was represented later by the endocrinological approach. In this we see a new epitomization of an old cycle. For although the earliest conceptions of the personality (Empedocles) were essentially *psychological*, Galen elaborated the *chemical* theory of personality ascribing it even then (170 A.D.) to various internal secretions and chemistry continued to dominate medical concepts of personality for nearly 1700 years. Philosophers (e.g., Kant, 1798) returned to an emphasis upon the psychological aspect of personality but this was

fared better than the supposedly better understood criminals who remained (and still remain) the scapegoats of society without benefit of science.

These nineteenth-century physicians worked away patiently with their material and systematically, accurately described what was extremely visible in the patients for whom they cared. They established some fairly dependable designations for certain clinical syndromes. They learned something of the technique of describing behavior and the personality as a whole. They detected some correlation between certain physical and chemical symptoms and certain pictures of gross psychological pathology. They learned some very practical methods of sedation and some important principles of custodial care and they learned to know what to expect in the way of improvement or recession in the development of certain syndromes. And they discovered the relationship of one type of acute mental illness to syphilitic infection, and because it was possible to attack syphilis chemically it became possible to cure a few of these forms of "insanity" by chemical means.

As we look back on it there seems to have been a prodigious amount of waste effort in certain directions, but that is bound to be the case on any scientific research frontier. A standardized nomenclature developed and, for all the fallacies that naming things introduces, it had the merit of giving us a tentative vocabulary with which to discuss the large masses of data such as were now accumulating. Much of the psychiatry of the early 1900s consisted in efforts to apply these names correctly and establish some basis for a statistical psychiatry.*

---

not reflected in medicine until much later. Later the *physical* elements seemed more important to the experimentalists and led to such *tours de forces* as the theories of Galton, Lombroso and, more recently, Kretschmer.

* Emil Kraepelin deserves the credit for pioneering in this business of naming and describing psychiatric entities in such a way as to afford some points of international agreement. He made many mistakes and in our present mood we should regard him as extremely limited in his depth of vision, but no one can deny his breadth. He saw in a large number of patients certain similarities of onset, course, and duration which led him to define a precocious dementia in contrast to a senile dementia. It took Bleuler to recognize the essential descriptive characteristic of these cases and give them a better name (schizophrenia) and it took Jung, another psychiatrist who had some psychoanalytic training in his earlier days, to understand the forces determining this split-mindedness.

In the midst of all this effort to name, describe, and recognize different forms of the extreme stages of maladjustment, the psychiatrists in the early years of this century were suddenly called upon in a very practical way by the exigencies of the World War. The army medical corps of all countries were well provided with surgeons, but army psychiatrists were unheard of. Such specialists had been left at home to continue to preside over their medieval castles, the hospitals for the insane. Imagine the astonishment and dismay of the military, therefore, when the psychiatric casualties of many engagements far outnumbered the surgical casualties and it became immediately necessary to obtain some psychiatric facilities and to train a large number of medical men in the elements of psychiatry in order to enable them to handle intelligently these cases developing on the European front. In this way the attention not only of the public but of medical men themselves was directed to the great practical importance of psychiatry. This, in turn, led to a greater interest in psychiatric theory. This interest continued and expanded. Even those medical men who did not themselves engage in psychiatry or limit their professional attention to it began to see in it something other than the mere caring for incompetents and began to think of it as a scientific discipline relative to the study and correction of maladjustment of the individual to his environment.

It is difficult to say just how much of this change in attitude was due to the practical experience of these hastily recruited psychiatrists in dealing with these so-called shell-shocked soldiers. The very designation "shell-shocked" indicates to what extent these cases were at first misunderstood; there were lengthy academic arguments in those days as to whether *all* or only *some* of the acute mental illnesses developed in the war were due to minute hemorrhages caused by the shock of expanding gas.* That the ego could be so repelled by the horror of the war situation as to repudiate all loyalty to reality seems scarcely to have entered medical consciousness. This seems a little strange in view of the fact that novelists have assumed it to be common knowledge for centuries. The issue was clouded

---

* We know, now, that none of them were.

by the fact that in many instances it was not "fair reason" that deserted the afflicted soldier but the use of his legs or arms or voice. These physical expressions of unendurable psychic conflict puzzled the doctors no end and were treated and interpreted in all sorts of ways. The organic explanation to which most of them were committed has already been mentioned; a considerable minority held to an opposite view, that they were all malingerers. This is the conception to which many industrial surgeons had clung doggedly for years, but its plausibility declined with great rapidity as experience with the war cases increased. In spite of the fact that these patients would frequently recover suddenly and spontaneously when removed from the danger zone, long continued contact and observation ultimately convinced all but the most obdurate and obtuse that if this was malingering it was unconscious malingering.

After the war ended, the treatment of these cases continued in psychiatric clinics and hospitals and the conviction gradually gained ground that it was actually possible for such a paradoxical phenomenon to occur as unconscious malingering. In this way medical men discovered for themselves what one of them—Sigmund Freud —had been talking about for nearly thirty years, namely, the existence of an unconscious portion of the personality, a reservoir of powers and determining forces of which the individual was only faintly if at all aware.

Recognition of this fact had already revolutionized the conception and treatment of the neuroses on the part of a negligibly small group of physicians who had caught the spark of Freud's brilliant discoveries. This group had already learned from experience and from the mouth of their teacher that human beings do not accept without great resistance the suggestion that a part of oneself is unknown to him. But the experience of the war did much to pave the way for a rapid extension of the corollary implications of the discoveries of Freud including that of the active participation of emotion in disease.

For in their zeal, the doctors who had so carefully examined in vain the brains and the reflexes and the blood chemistry of innumerable sick patients had forgotten to consider the feelings of these patients, the experiences they had undergone, the strivings in which they were thwarted. They had attempted, in a curious dualistic way, to separate structure and function. One sees this reflected even today in the way in which some colleagues seek to find physical and chemical "causes" for the increased blood pressure of a woman who is struggling against the temptation to kill her husband. Body weight and blood chlorides can be measured in units lodged in the Bureau of Standards at Washington, but temptation cannot. Yet it is as absurd to discard it from consideration as it would be for an engineer to eliminate from consideration the weight of the traffic which a bridge is to bear simply because he cannot measure it but can only estimate it in terms of probability.

The usefulness of the new concepts of psychiatry were increasingly recognized and sought after. For these practical men know that psychiatry is no longer a science of calling strange and incurable diseases by strange and unpronounceable names. The discovery of the unconscious led to the understanding of many previously obscure matters relating to the symptoms of disease and their alleviation. Later as the result of Freud's patient, inspired labors psychoanalysis was born, and this psychoanalysis grew up and married the old, sterile psychiatry and brought forth a new child, who has grown so fast that some of her neighbors—other medical specialties—scarcely recognize her. For the new psychiatry, the psychiatry resulting from the infusion of psychoanalytic knowledge, is no longer a specialty limited to asylums, to hopeless or freakish sufferers from strange or "imaginary" diseases. It has become a specialty in which the motives of human behavior so largely neglected in other branches of medicine have been given the wide recognition as participants in illness, not only mental illness, but all forms of illness.

The war experience had another effect upon American psychiatry.* This was a wave of expanded provision for the proper housing of psychiatric patients. State medicine had its first great

---

* Perhaps this is the best place to remark that European psychiatry, that of England excepted, died with the war. Psychiatry in Germany, France, and Italy today is as dead as a dodo, as sterile and medieval as in 1900. It is too long a story and one beyond our province to outline the reasons for this.

inning in this field and institutions for the care of as many as ten thousand patients were planned, constructed, staffed, and almost immediately filled. Some of the credit for the high plane on which this planning was done should go to the mental-hygiene movement, a popular interest in the better care of the insane stimulated in the first place by the personal efforts of a single individual, Clifford Beers, who had been disturbed not by what he saw happening to others, as had been the case with Dorothea Dix, so much as by what he himself experienced and which he described in his auto-biographical book *A Mind That Found Itself.*[4]

The increase of interest in the phenomena of mental disease, the use of the expression *mental hygiene* in various senses apart from its original connotations, the experiences of the doctors in the war—these things all combined to extend the frontiers of psychiatry. The difference between the psychotic, on the one hand, and the eccentric, the disagreeable, the unhappy, and the wicked began to be looked upon as one of degree rather than of kind.

"Is it possible," pointedly asked the professor of psychiatry[5] of Harvard Medical School, "that our intense devotion to a philan-thropic cause may in some instances be a disorder, rather than an indication of a healthy moral superiority? Is it possible that suspi-cion of employers and accusations of social injustice may be a dis-order, and not the expression of an enlightened and impersonal grasp of economic and social relations? Can raucous patriotism and so-called pacifism be scrutinized in the same way? Is antivivisec-tionism not altogether to be explained by a surplus of the milk of human kindness in those who level virulent and ill-founded ac-cusations at men, working earnestly in the interests even of those who revile them? Is intense intellectual activity, in apparent devo-tion to the pursuit of abstract truth, sometimes the expression of a disorder, rather than the wholesome activity of a well-balanced personality? Can the blameless and model individual, following smugly in the parental footsteps, be the victim of a disorder con-sisting essentially in the repression of the most productive elements in the individual's nature? Can the emancipated and unconventional individual, who is expressing his personality to the amazement of his social circle, be the victim of illusion and be really in the throes of a mild mental disorder? Is it possible that many of our beliefs, attitudes, emotions, habits, standards, are not as valid as we have assumed them to be, but are of the same stuff of which mental disorder is made?"

The implied answers to such questions came more and more to be regarded as self-evident and the whole scope of psychiatry began to change as the field of study broadened. Instead of a few miserable quarantined outcasts, the subject matter of psychiatry began to include persons all about us. Not only the criminal, the delinquent, and the maladjusted child, but the unhappy housewife, the inefficient business manager, the religious and political enthusiasts became the subject of psychiatric study. Psychiatrists developed the courage to think of themselves as scientific students of personality. It is as if a group of workers in an automobile repair shop from long experience in mending the results of various accidents and breakdowns gradually acquired the audacity to think in terms of the evaluation and improvement of the less obviously damaged car. This led inevitably to a more accurate estimation of the environment with which serious conflict was sometimes encountered. Almost without knowing it psychiatrists began to think in terms of the concept so eloquently cast by a nonpsychiatric, nonmedical predecessor:

All of our lives long, every day and every hour, we are engaged in the process of accommodating our changed and unchanged selves to changed and unchanged surroundings; living, in fact, is nothing else than this process of accommodation; when we fail in it a little we are stupid, when we fail flagrantly we are mad, when we suspend it temporarily we sleep, when we give up the attempt altogether we die. In quiet, uneventful lives the changes internal and external are so small that there is little or no strain in the process of fusion and accommodation; in other lives there is great strain, but there is also great fusing and accommodating power; in others great strain with little accommodating power. A life will be successful or not, according as the power of accommodation is equal to or unequal to the strain of fusing and adjusting internal and external changes. [Samuel Butler, *The Way of All Flesh*.]

Such a concept of psychiatry then requires, on the one hand, a scientific methodology for describing the human personality—physically, chemically, and psychologically—and describing it not only in terms of its present state but in terms of its development, its encounters with and readjustments to the more or less unyielding elements of environmental reality. It implies, too, that a careful survey and evaluation of the environment are necessary.

These indeed are the pre-eminent tasks of psychiatry and sociology today. That they are in a state of incompletion, scientists from both groups would be quick to acknowledge. For it is one thing to collect data in large quantities, but it is quite another to put them together in a form that will convey accurately to others something about a personality which careful study has elicited. To say that a man is six feet tall, has sugar in his urine, and is afraid to ascend to high places does not describe his personality, nor would his personality be fully described if similar traits were elaborated in great detail, or if so-called diagnostic designations were appended, such as diabetes or acrophobia. For, without gainsaying the practical benefits deriving from the introduction of such terms as schizophrenia and manic-depressive psychosis (if we confine ourselves to psychiatric nomenclature), it must be admitted that much harm has also been done by these words. I do not refer now to their mistaken application to patients who might have been more successfully treated had they been more correctly classified. I refer rather to the fact that a patient who has been assigned to this or that diagnostic category is so frequently treated as if the category, rather than the patient, determined the treatment.

If our psychiatric designations were something very definite and precise, as in the case of syphilis of the eye, for example, advantages might accrue from this. But as yet we have no basis for such a rigid conception of schizophrenia and other psychiatric syndromes and yet the attitude of physicians and the attitudes which they help to build up in the relatives of their patients are often based upon pessimistic conclusions based on the reputation of the named disease as they conceive of it rather than to the actual patient as they discover him to be.

In the sense that it is a summary of the historical and examinational data pertinent to the description of the personality, a diagnosis should certainly embrace decisions or indicate generic relationships with respect to five items: (1) a personality type or structure for which static crystallized terms are as yet, fortunately, lacking; (2) the physical status, expressed in terms established by long experience and usage in medicine; (3) the characteristic psychological reactions, especially to frustration (the psychiatric syndrome); (4) an estimate of the social situation in which the patient lives and of which he is a part—a social diagnosis; (5) symptomatic diagnoses of various kinds which cannot be implied in any of these generic designations.

Such a complex diagnostic summary is far too unwieldy and implies too great a knowledge of the individual for it to be rapidly adopted into scientific medicine, or even into psychiatry. Nevertheless in some such direction our present efforts are heading, for it is certain that now we have learned how to accumulate data concerning personality structure, psychological reactions, and social interaction, we come into possession of more data than we are able to assimilate or to organize and yet without such organization a genuine comprehension of the personality is impossible and hence the communication of a sufficiently accurate picture to others is rendered difficult.

It would be easy to stop at this point, assuming that we had brought the matter to its point of contemporary emphasis with justice to the more important trends. The reader will assume correctly that additional physical and chemical improvements have been made in the therapeutic devices applicable to the more extreme treatment of mental illness. He will have heard of the metrazol and insulin shock treatments for schizophrenia, of more specific endocrine treatments for some depressions, of improved methods of sedation therapy, hydrotherapy, and physiotherapy, of more skillfully applied occupational and recreational therapies. But all these things pale in significance, both as practical agents and as indicators of underlying theory, in comparison with another discovery of Freud's which is the dynamic essence of modern psychiatry.

I refer to the scientific study of the emotional linkage determining interpersonal relationships.

It will be recalled that Freud, observing the readiness with which hypnotized subjects responded to suggestion, asked himself why such patients would accept the suggestion of the hypnotist to abandon his symptoms when all the influences of everyday life and of the patient's own wish to get well had been unavailing. He worked for a time in complete ignorance of a satisfactory explanation for this, and only gradually and as a result of many observations did he become aware of what seems obvious and elementary to us now, namely, that the patient accepts such suggestions to get well because he wants to please the physician. To this we should add quickly what Freud discovered only slowly and what his predecessors had never discovered at all, that it is not the physician as such whom the patient wishes to please but someone else whom, for the moment, the physician in some mysterious way seems to replace and to represent. For the genius of Freud showed itself in that, unlike almost every other human being that has ever lived and treated patients and seen this same thing happen, he was not egotistic enough (or else he was too scientific) to allow himself to conclude that there was anything in his own personality which so captivated and compelled the unwilling patient. "Not I, the doctor," he thought, "but something the patient reads into me is the effective agency." Having already discovered the existence of the unconscious and of repressed memories, it was possible for him to see that the patient was reliving with him an interpersonal relationship which had been incompletely gratified in its original setting. That which had only flattered or frightened other physicians became to him the most important subject of his investigations. The understanding of this principle and of the subsequent discoveries relative to the proper handling of this transference of affect now forms the basis of all effective scientific psychotherapy.

If one looks back to the psychiatry of 1900, or for that matter of 1920, one is aware of this vast difference, that, whereas then the patient and his symptoms were treated as if unrelated to the physician as a symbol of society, today in the evaluation of the personality and its attempted adjustments with society, psychiatry gives primary attention to the nature of the interpersonal relationship, the extent to which it is determined by irrational unconscious elements, the extent to which it is susceptible to modification by interpretation, the way in which it is formed and modified by the prevailing social structure in which the patient lives or has lived.

THE INFLUENCE OF PSYCHIATRY UPON GENERAL MEDICINE

I have already indicated that psychiatry is in the anomalous step-child position of belonging to medicine and yet until recently not accepted by medicine. It is one thing to say that psychiatric principles are receiving more consideration by the medical profession than formerly, but quite another thing to demonstrate that the general practice of medicine has been in any perceptible way influenced by this process. Chemistry remains far more important in the theory and practice of medicine than does psychology.

It sounds so glib to describe the earlier orientations and the age-long preoccupations of medical science as chemical that I am tempted to give an illustration to make it more vivid. It is particularly striking when one encounters a case such as we psychiatrists frequently do, let us say, an intelligent and attractive woman who presents herself with a history of intermittent vomiting of many years' duration. Such a patient will have been treated by hundreds of drugs, hypodermics, diets, and repeated abdominal operations. As I am dictating, the names and faces of three or four recent examples of this come to my mind; in one instance four operations had been performed, in another three, in another the patient had acquired a morphine habit. In spite of all these procedures, the symptoms had persisted. Subjected to psychological treatment, such symptoms will sometimes disappear permanently in twenty-four hours. Such sudden, astonishing, "miraculous" cures, when offered by charlatans or ignorant persons, have several times in the past formed the bases of new religions because of their dramatic qualities, but the scientific psychological treatment of such cases is scarcely yet an established method. I was very much impressed by my own father's comments, a man who had practiced medicine with what

I am sure was an unusual degree of intelligence and good judgment for many years. He said, "As I look back upon my medical practice before my association with psychiatry, I can think of how many such cases I worried over for months and even years, giving them all sorts of treatments which did them no good and which only made them seem incurable and ungrateful. For many years our only recourse was some kind of drugs; as surgery increased in popularity we turned to that, but with no better results. I cannot quite understand how it was that we did not ever consider the possible psychological factors and the possibility of psychological therapy. But we never did."

That energies can be directed and redirected by physical agencies, we know. That energies can be directed and redirected by chemical agencies, we also know. That energies can be directed by psychological agencies, some of us know and some are still skeptical about. The misdirected energy of a toxic goiter may be corrected by the physical manipulations of the surgeon; it may also be cured by the chemical rearrangements effected by the ministrations of the internist; it may also be corrected (and I mean cured) by the manipulation of psychological forces at the hands of a psychiatrist. These things are so well known to some that it may seem as if I were laboring the point, and yet one must reflect that the organization of the American medical teaching at the present time, fine as it is in so many ways, takes very little cognizance of them. There are probably a thousand demonstrations in progress at this moment in the various medical schools, hospitals, and clinics of this country, serious and earnest efforts on the part of devoted and high-minded medical men to set forth to medical students the physical and chemical facts about—let us say—goiter. Does the reader seriously believe that the methods of observing and manipulating the psychological factors involved in goiter are being systematically presented by as many as a dozen of this thousand?

That psychiatry has come to occupy a much larger part of the teaching time in the medical schools is a matter of statistical record. In at least one of the leading medical schools more actual hours are devoted to instruction in psychiatry than to instruction in surgery. The psychiatric departments of several schools have active cooperation not only with all the other hospital services but with the law school, business school, and numerous other departments of the university. In many institutions psychiatrists are now called to the medical and surgical wards for consultations on cases which in previous days would have been regarded as strictly medical or surgical, the psychological aspects entirely disregarded. It is conceivable that, by such gradual absorption into medicine, psychiatry will ultimately eliminate itself, and that in the future every doctor will be to some extent a psychiatrist. It would be painting too rosy a picture, however, to say that such a state of affairs appears to be coming to pass immediately. The old physical and chemical concepts still prevail in medicine and dominate it to a degree far greater than psychiatrists like to believe. The chances of the average patient with a mild depression reaching a psychiatrist as a result of medical advice may be, let us say, perhaps one in twenty. The chances of a patient with a psychologically determined physical disease, such as gastric hyperacidity or mucous colitis, reaching a psychiatrist are surely not much better than one in five hundred, if indeed they are that great. This is not because the physicians wish in some way to thwart the psychiatrists or that they do not feel that psychiatrists would be able to help the patients. It is in some instances due to ignorance and in some to prejudice and in still others to practical difficulties such as the relative scarcity of psychiatrists; but in the vast majority of instances, it is because the doctors do not think in psychological terms—it simply does not enter the mind of the average physician that the psychological approach might be as effective as an operation or a dose of medicine or a change of environment. The doctor knows from experience that sometimes these latter devices effect a cure and it usually does not occur to him that it is possible either to discover or eliminate that inner psychological weakness within the patient that makes him susceptible to the peculiar environmental problem, chemical disorder, or physical agent immediately responsible for the symptoms which he calls the disease.

Furthermore, even when it does occur to him, the doctor is al-

most helpless in the face of prevalent popular prejudices. It requires
the utmost tact to introduce to a patient the idea that he himself may
be contributing to his present condition, that his illness has some
purpose. He would much prefer to believe that fate, circumstance,
bacteria, or some mysterious influence present at birth or absorbed
from the atmosphere are responsible for his suffering and to believe
steadfastly in the magic principles of exorcism as represented for him
by the paraphernalia and procedures in the doctor's office. This is not
to gainsay the fact that quinine, for example, does kill malarial
organisms, but for every dose of specific medicament like quinine
there are a thousand doses of medicine consumed in the belief that
they will combat these internal afflictions of fate and any attempt
on the part of the doctor to substitute something for this kind of
magic or for the more spectacular achievements of surgical operations is certain to be met with powerful resistance. Patients want
to be dosed and rubbed and cut into. They welcome any evidence
that such methods may relieve them and fight valiantly against the
surrender of secret fears, prejudices, and hates. The development
of the psychological concept in medicine cannot proceed very far
beyond the slowly changing philosophies and protective ignorance
of the general public. Hence for some time to come medicine will
be obliged to partake of psychiatry sparingly, perhaps hopefully, but
with an understandable conservatism.

THE INFLUENCE OF PSYCHIATRY UPON LITERATURE, ART, AND MUSIC

It was Freud himself who pointed out that the poets and philosophers understood the laws of unconscious mental functioning long
before they were known to the scientists. Indeed, the works of
Freud are best described as a reduction to scientific order of the
knowledge about the inner motives of human beings which had
previously been vouchsafed only to those gifted with deep intuition,
and then in an unsystematized, disconnected, and unteachable form.
The masterful psychological studies which comprise the works of
Dostoevski, Balzac, Poe, Thackeray, and many others were written
long before Freud had formulated the principles which they illustrate. It was to some of the early Greek plays that Freud turned

for some of the titles which he used to describe characteristic psychic constellations and interpersonal relationships. The plays of Shakespeare and even the musical dramas of Wagner have, along with many other compositions, lent themselves to illuminating psychoanalytic expositions.

Early in the twentieth century, however, the first reports of Freud's work having become available, alert authors showed a more prompt response to the implications of these findings than did the scientists. It can safely be said that in 1915, and even more so in 1920, the influences of psychoanalysis were much more apparent in literature and drama than in medicine, the realm of their origin. The plays of Eugene O'Neill alone probably introduced psychoanalysis to more people in the United States than all the scientific books put together. To be sure, the theory was not always correctly stated or convincingly represented, but the fundamental ideas of conflict, repression, unconscious motives, etc., were vividly portrayed. The same could be said of numerous novels and poems of this period, to list all of which would be difficult as well as tiresome.

Still another tendency in the literature which bore the stamp of direct influence of psychoanalytic methods and discoveries was the style of writing classically represented by Joyce's *Ulysses*. Heralded as a masterpiece by many, and denounced as meaningless and indecent by many others, this large mass of words, phrases, sentences, ideas is written down as if each thought of the speaker or writer had been recorded without any modification arising from a consideration of the listener or reader. This corresponds closely with the material to which the psychoanalyst listens daily in response to his instructions to the patient that every thought be uttered just as it occurs without modification or suppression from any motives whatsoever. Indeed, I have heard many psychiatrists say of *Ulysses,* and similar compositions, that they cannot enjoy it because it is identical with the material to which they must devote all their working hours. More recently the effects of psychiatry and particularly psychoanalysis upon literature have been less conspicuous and more subtle and appear most definitely in the interpretative biography, fictional or real. Once it was sufficient merely to describe the events in a man's life, the peculiarities of his behavior and environment. Now such descriptive accounts would be considered dull and point-less, and the modern author would attempt to make some connec-tion between the childhood experiences and the adult product. The whole "debunking" tendency which was so popular for a while was a protest against naïve hypocritical representations of people and events without reference to the malignant trends and satisfactions which accompanied them.

Similar stylistic effects have appeared in poetry (for example, that of E. E. Cummings, who attempts to produce a certain effect not only by a certain word and sentence arrangement but by his un-conventional punctuation and capitalization). This same principle of a greater freedom has also found its expression in plastic and pic-torial art and music. Here, however, it is very much more difficult to relate either the product or the technique to the influence of psychiatry. Its analogy to similar freedom in literature is obvious enough, but it may well be that this is an evolution taking place in art and music depending in part upon intrinsic principles of change and acceptance of symbolic representations and in part upon social attitudes, which, in turn, are dependent upon economic and political as well as psychological factors.

THE INFLUENCE OF PSYCHIATRY UPON EDUCATIONAL THEORY
AND PRACTICE

In theory, the influence of psychiatry upon education depends upon this—that we now know what was absolutely unknown before, namely, why any child wants to learn anything. Trite as this may sound, search of all the pedagogical treatises prior to 1910 will give the reader no definite information on this point. It was not until Freud pointed out that the child accepts as true statements about reality given him by someone—i.e., by the teacher, only because he wishes to please that teacher—that we gained some insight into the basic psychological principles upon which every schoolroom operates. This is the more curious in view of the fact that in practice the emo-tional relations of the pupils to the teacher are considered unimportant by-products, sometimes interesting, sometimes annoying, but never worth any consideration. In the light of modern psychological theory, the child turns to the teacher for emotional satisfaction *in loco parentis* and goes about to win such affection in the way prescribed by that teacher. When one reflects that in the primary grades at least the personality of the teacher is of the utmost importance in serving as a model for perfecting the ideal love object of the child, one must be the more disturbed to realize how many unattractive, unlovely, inexperienced and often neurotic men and women are placed in strategic positions. The general custom is to promote teachers to the higher grades and secondary schools and here increase their salaries. It would be more intelligent to reverse the direction of progress from the upper grades to the lower, since the elementary teachers have so much greater responsibility for the formation of the child's personality. Not only should such teachers be the most nearly normal individuals that could be obtained but they should be the best trained, and such training should certainly include instruction in those aspects of dynamic psychology which relate to the interaction of human beings upon one another. Such psychological principles, although basic, have no currency at present except in psychiatry, which is another way of saying that the tendency is to wait until the child becomes impossible before any effort is made to find out how he thinks and feels about his teacher, his parents, his siblings, and others. Such an investigation the average teacher is incapable of making or even of understanding. I owe to the professor of education at one of our universities the suggestion that this training in mental hygiene or psychiatry or the psychological understanding of children or whatever it be called should be one of the fundamental studies of primary teachers instead of one of the subjects of which they are usually completely ignorant.

The use of professional psychiatrists or clinically trained psychologists in the solution of emotional difficulties and behavior disorders suffers from this same fault, the fault of concentrating upon the older children to the neglect of the younger ones. As we shall see presently, many college students have available to them at least some professional psychiatric counsel, but this is true of very few school children.

The behavior problems of the average school child are still treated in most places with a mixture of political expediency, conventional hypocrisy, and so-called "common sense." This prevails generally, but there are many exceptions. In several large cities there are psychiatrists attached to the board of education, or psychiatric clinics available to school children which provide for handling such cases upon a more scientific basis. In some cities psychologists function in a somewhat similar capacity. The net result of this is that the *poor* children in the schools of the *larger cities* whose capacity for adjustment is exceeded by unfortunate environmental requirements to the extent of developing various kinds of emotional or behavior problems are likely to receive intelligent scientific treatment. The well-to-do children, however, attending private schools receive, as a rule, no such help and the same is to be said of children in the average middle-sized towns of the country. It is difficult to render this in any statistically accurate way but let us take two very representative Midwestern states, Kansas and Missouri, situated in the center of the United States, one containing some of the most literate rural population of the country, and the other two of the large, wealthy, and in many ways progressive cities of the country. In some of the towns and cities of this large and populous area the boards of education have employed visiting teachers to investigate the home situations of problem children, psychologists to study the peculiar learning disabilities of certain children, and, in one or two instances, psychiatrically trained social workers for similar purposes. There are very few of these but they do exist and the nature of their work is essentially psychiatric in the generic sense. But in not a single town or city in either Kansas or Missouri is there any actual professional *psychiatric* supervision of this work or any consultation service for the problem children in the schools. This is through no lack of facilities; within the borders of these two states there are three child-guidance clinics, two schools for maladjusted children, several schools for feeble-minded children, forty or fifty psychiatrists in private practice and a larger number in state practice, and a number of psychiatric clinics, to say nothing of three medical schools, five or six universities, and a half a hundred colleges, in most of which abnormal psychology and psychological principles relating to adjustment problems of childhood are studied and taught. And, lest anyone suppose that this is some peculiar backwardness of Kansas and Missouri, I can assure them that, with the exception of New York and Massachusetts, the names of almost any other two states in the Union could be substituted for these two.

I seem to have veered around to a demonstration not so much of the application of psychiatry to education as to a lack of application. The situation in colleges and universities is quite different. In perhaps a hundred schools in the United States there are now well-established counselors in mental hygiene, devoting their energies to special problems of college students. Many other colleges have expressed an interest in obtaining similar services, but here a practical difficulty is encountered in that the supply of men properly trained for this function is yet small. Eleven years ago the dean of one of the oldest and most famous institutions in the country said, "The advance of mental hygiene in colleges and universities has come with such rapidity in the last five or ten years that it is no longer progressive to have an expert in mental hygiene on the staff, and to give as respectable a place in the curriculum to mental as to physical hygiene. It is reactionary *not* to do these things."

An intangible effect of psychiatry upon education which cannot be estimated but is probably more widespread and more influential than more obvious expressions mentioned is the insidious change in teachers' attitudes derived not so much from any formal psychiatric experience or from exposure to any particular psychiatric institutions but rather from the combination of the psychiatric influences of literature, the mental-hygiene movement, the writings of numerous popular psychologists, the implications of speakers on political and economic topics, etc. Some years ago a psychologist (Wickman) compared the attitudes of a group of teachers and a group of psychiatrically trained persons—psychologists and others— toward certain characteristic schoolroom behavior, and the teachers were shown, in general, to attach great significance to behavior which psychiatrists regarded as less serious, and to put less value on behavior which psychiatrists considered most serious. I think if such a test were conducted today in the average school, there would be much less discrepancy. Teachers have come to learn that unuttered hostility, seclusiveness, and extreme quietness, convenient as they may be from the standpoint of schoolroom administration, are not evidences of the greatest mental health. The severe discipline has almost entirely disappeared from the schools. (I submitted this statement to Professor Bert Nash of the department of education of the University of Kansas. "I believe," he commented, "that you are a little optimistic here. There has been some improvement but psychiatry has not affected the teachers in rural areas and smaller towns much. The larger areas usually have better qualified teachers and more supervision by supervisors trained in the mental hygiene aspects of these problems. The superintendents and principals in many small towns are not up with many of the teachers.")

THE INFLUENCE OF PSYCHIATRY UPON LEGAL AND CRIMINAL PROCEDURES

Psychiatry has a natural interest in aberrant behavior, whether the aggressiveness is directed upon society or directed upon the individual himself. The law is particularly interested in the former. The law aims at a proper protection of society from certain individuals; but traditionally it has based its procedure upon so-called "common-sense" principles, many of which run counter to modern scientific findings. Logically, the law should revise its attitude, borrowing from psychiatry such knowledge and techniques as will increase the protection afforded the public. In theory, law, criminology, and penology have made these revisions. The American Bar Association (with the American Psychiatric Association and the American Medical Association) formulated and unanimously adopted resolutions to the effect that every judge hearing a criminal case should have at his disposal a psychiatric opinion concern-

ing the accused and that this person's subsequent disposition should
depend upon such a psychiatric examination; they even went further
and indicated that the detention of such a prisoner in a prison and
his subsequent discharge should be determined by scientific personality studies instead of by statute-book prescriptions, political
expediency, etc. But in practice very few of these principles have
been followed. The contrast between the new-fashioned theories and
the old-fashioned practices in criminal administration is astounding.
The practical application of psychiatry is used in a few places, such
as at Sing Sing prison in New York and in a number of courts and
prisons in the state of Massachusetts, to a greater or lesser extent;
but in ninety-nine per cent of the courts of the United States psychiatry still remains something to be invoked by an occasional
prisoner as a means of obtaining mitigation or suspension of sentence on the grounds that his behavior was based upon sickness and
not upon normal human instinctual expression. A respectable married merchant of 42 eminently successful in his business suddenly
comes before the court charged with having sexually molested several twelve-year-old girls. He is arraigned for trial. The judge becomes involved with such technical questions as whether rape or
only attempted rape is the charge to be entertained, whom to admit to the courtroom, whether certain witnesses are competent,
etc. An occasional judge will wish to protect the subsequent proceedings of the court by obtaining a preliminary "sanity" hearing.
A commission of local medical men is appointed and these gentlemen are called from the surgical operating rooms, from the rounds
of general practice, and from the halls of the nearest state hospital
to pass upon the question of whether or not the accused man is
"sane." The question of why a man of forty-two should wish to derive his sexual satisfaction in this strange way, the question of how
this man's life has gone awry to produce this result, the likelihood
or rather unlikelihood of the court proceedings and the penitentiary
sentence affecting this proclivity favorably or unfavorably, never
seem to enter anyone's mind, least of all the judge's. If a psychiatrist
is called he is not allowed to say how such an affliction might be
successfully treated; he is condemned to attempt to swear that the

man's condition does or does not conform to something which seventy-five years ago was called insanity.

Psychiatry has touched the law to this extent—that, if the offender is young enough, the offense not too flagrant, and if the family has money, the case can probably be settled out of court and the offender placed under psychiatric treatment. Psychiatrists deplore this abominable situation as much as anyone, but it is not something they can change.

THE INFLUENCE OF PSYCHIATRY UPON INDUSTRY

Twenty years ago, when psychiatry was first recognized popularly as a science of evaluating and correcting personality disorders, Ernest Southard proposed that no one should be able to make more practical use of it than those industrialists whose labor turnover was a source of large expense. "Why are men discharged?" he asked. Examination of typical records shows that the same behavior disorders for which we treat people in the clinic serve to bring them into disfavor with their employers. Would it not be logical, he said, to apply our methods to these problem employees just as we apply them to problem children in the schools or problem housewives in the home?

The suggestion was promptly taken up by a number of large organizations and put to some fruitful use. Various books were written reporting the good results of the experiment, but the practice has not spread. On the contrary, there has been a recession. All the factors determining this I could not attempt to list, but among them one would certainly include the changed attitude of labor and capital toward one another, a decrease in the paternalistic attitude of employers. Another reason, I think, lies in the greater adaptability of various quantitative psychological tests to the selection of employees. The selection of ten good employees by appropriate psychological tests can be made at less expense than the psychiatric examination or rehabilitation of one employee about to be discharged. This is one of the reproaches of the capitalistic system which is interested in the product and not the producer. But it should be added that this lack of scientific treatment of the worker is furthered by the attitude of labor itself, which suspects all psychiatry and applied psychology of being devices for further exploiting the worker.

A reason even more fundamental than these is to be inferred I think from an experience I had many years ago. The president of a manufacturing corporation who had received some personal benefit from my services became so enthusiastic over the application of psychiatry that he went with me to New York to study its application to industry with the avowed purpose of introducing it into his plant. Upon our return he had me spend several days surveying his plant in operation and getting acquainted with numerous key employees. Then he called a meeting of the board of directors and outlined what he had in mind. I, properly assisted, was to examine every employee from the president to the janitor, noting such evidence of maladjustment as might require some special management. Most of the directors agreed wholeheartedly. One of them, however, protested violently. The president was somewhat crestfallen to meet with this opposition and action was deferred until he could ascertain the special reasons back of the opposition and win over the dissenter. In this he was totally unsuccessful, for reasons which he did not fully understand until long afterward. The dissenting officer was at that very moment carrying on an intense feud with another man in the corporation whom he was ultimately successful in ousting. Scores of the employees were involved in this, and, while discretion prevents the citation of details, I may give it as my opinion that enormous losses of money and of efficiency in this company were due to the psychopathology of this official who blocked the plan of psychiatric service in an industry rather than have his remissness detected.

THE INFLUENCE OF PSYCHIATRY UPON SOCIOLOGY

Between the fields of sociology and psychiatry, both of them relatively new sciences, there has always been a close practical affiliation with a wide theoretical separation. This is precisely the opposite situation of that which exists between psychiatry and criminology. Psychiatric and criminological theories overlap hugely, but in actual practice, as I have indicated, psychiatry and psychiatrists are but little used in court and prison. Sociology however, until recently, considered the psychological vagaries of the individual to be factors of relative unimportance, negligible errors so to speak. Its chief attention was upon the accurate description of mass phenomena, of large social movements, conditions, attitudes, and preoccupations. There was, to be sure, a counter-movement in the direction of the Carlylean theory of hero leadership, a theory that had more popular than scientific support. Hitler, for example, was the clever psychopath who happened to achieve a position of power where he could then inflict his psychopathic notions and ambitions upon a helpless and pliable German people. Napoleon was another such molder of men and events.

Laswell of Chicago helped to destroy this idea by giving it further scientific scrutiny. He demonstrated [6] by a psychological analysis of numerous major and minor politicians how the careers, the methods, the ideology of political "leaders" had been determined by their own pathological childhood experiences. In so doing he guided sociological thinking toward the recognition that similar and reciprocal psychopathological trends exist in those whom these men "chose" to lead.

The increasing trend of sociology seems, therefore, to lean toward the old subject matter viewed from a new angle. If I, who am not a sociologist and not in intimate contact with the thought of that profession, can estimate it, the trend of sociological thinking is toward a study of the way in which accumulated, reinforced thinking and feeling of the community interact with the thinking and feeling of the individual. Just as the psychiatrist has realized that he cannot study any patient irrespective of the social environment to which that patient has had to adjust himself, so the sociologist has come to realize that he cannot study that mass without some idea of the individual units which comprise it. Individual problems reflect themselves in the social structure, and in turn are affected by the community mores.

One might say that the rise of social psychology is a reflection of these tendencies. It is an indication of the dissatisfaction of psychology with the assumption that human reactions are determined entirely within the individual and a dissatisfaction on the part of sociology with the assumption that the mass acts without any individual psychic determinants. Up until 1908 there was only one modern textbook on social psychology; today texts and treatises appear almost as frequently as do those on sociology and psychology themselves. Two journals devote themselves exclusively to this field.

If this summary seems incomplete, let me assure the reader that the present relations of psychiatry and sociology are as awkward and groping as the first meetings of a brother and sister who have not seen each other for twenty years. Psychiatrists write articles and caution fellow psychiatrists not to psychoanalyze society, but to remember that society is not the same as an individual. Sociologists write articles and caution their fellows not to ignore the importance of the psychology of the unconscious since the efforts of every individual must to some extent influence the whole mass. Writers of serious articles make brave statements like this: "It has been demonstrated that there is a relation between social and personal disorganization." The recent appearance of a number of the *American Journal of Sociology* devoted entirely to articles by psychiatrists and sociologists dealing with the problem of the relationship of the two sciences shows the present tendencies of *rapprochement*.

In general, the present impression seems to be that we should regard psychiatry as the microscopic and sociology the macroscopic study of the gregarious life of the human being. Exactly how much the nature of the relationship between its constituent elements, the interpersonal relations, is determined by internal needs of individuals, and how much by certain external conditions which have been in part determined by previous expressions of individual psychology is at the present time a matter of conjecture.

THE INFLUENCE OF PSYCHIATRY UPON PSYCHOLOGY

Psychology means so many things that one must begin by defining the sense in which it is used in this caption. Psychiatry is, after all, according to my lights, a medical science with a proper inclusion of the psychological factor in our concepts and techniques. It is, in short, the result of the influence of psychology upon medicine. When we speak, therefore, of the influence of this clinical science upon one of its mother disciplines, the basic science of formal psychology, what we really do is measure to what extent the concepts of mind and mental processes have been modified by clinical observations. The union of psychology with the rest of medical science was a fruitful one and brought forth many new ideas, new discoveries, new points of view, which in turn have fructified academic or formal psychology. The older psychology devoted itself largely to the study of how we become aware of the world about us, the faculties of perception and cognition as they were called. These bore a well-established relationship to anatomical facts, to nerve trunks and brain areas, and it was possible to introduce experimental and quantitative methods, not only in regard to the rapidity of the processes of recognition and association but as to capacities of memory and grasp. This gave rise to two important developments in psychology, the experimental projects in the laboratory, and quantitative clinical applications in the form of intelligence tests and performance tests.

Increasingly, however, under the influence of psychiatry and particularly of psychoanalysis, the trend in psychology has been away from these quantitative estimations and perceptions, away from the experimental laboratory and the "brass-instrument psychology" of the early part of the century in the direction of more qualitative studies of the emotional processes. Interest and intelligence tests have given way to a greater interest in tests which show not so much static achievement as dynamic striving; e.g., the Rorschach rather than the Binet has been the instrument of examination. This in turn has influenced the former concepts of perception and cognition; we no longer assume, as was formerly believed, that the intelligence quotient remains fixed and invariable throughout life, independent of the external conditions. In addition, experimental procedures relating to the particular way in which intelligence determines emotions and behavior have been developed at Harvard (Murray), Yale (Homburger), Topeka (Brown), and elsewhere.

In other words, psychologists, partly under the influence of psychiatry, became interested thirty years ago (1905) in measuring certain capacities in the individual which we call intelligence. Under the further influence of their contacts with psychiatry, the clinical interest extended to the investigation of the emotional processes which lay behind this intelligence.

If one looks at a representative psychological textbook of twenty-five years ago, that of William James, for example, and compares it with a modern text on psychology, one will see that the whole problem of the emotional factor and motivation which formerly received scant attention, perhaps a brief discussion at the end of the book, has now become the basic portion of the modern textbook. Encouraged by cooperation with psychiatry and by utilizations in psychiatry of different discoveries, psychology has paid increasing attention to what was formerly called abnormal psychology. The very title shows under what difficulties the subject matter formerly labored; of course there can be no such thing as abnormal psychology any more than there is an abnormal physics or an abnormal chemistry. There are, rather, phenomena which are unusual and which do not seem to conform to the rules which ordinarily determine human reactions, and these have been called abnormal. If psychology is a science, however, it cannot be a thing apart from the laws that determine all psychological processes, but it must be the product of certain less usual or less advantageous combinations of forces.

With an eye to reducing behavior and psychological reactions to general principles capable of more adequate scientific formulation, the school of Gestalt psychology has recently developed. Frustration and disappointment are important factors in human behavior and empirically it is possible to estimate roughly some greater or lesser disappointments, and certain types of deviation in the response to such disappointments. But theoretically it ought to be possible to measure the amount of frustration more exactly and to introduce the various factors which determine the peculiar individual response to frustration that one observes in any particular type of situation. It requires the erection of a defined field of operation and a description both in terms of direction and in terms of quantity of the modifying forces of inhibition, stimulation, deflection, exaggeration, disguise, etc. The great difficulties and complications of this task have so discouraged some as to make them intolerant of the method; others, however, have hopes that this is the beginning of a more accurate statement of the basic principles of psychology. Brown has shown that Gestalt psychology has many aims and methods in common with psychoanalysis and it is certain that they have been of reciprocal value.[7]

In summary, psychology, one of the parents of modern psychiatry, has been reciprocally enriched and reanimated by the developments of its child. It continues to be the basic science related to the investigation of certain aspects of biological phenomena we call mental with an increasing scope of activity, and an increasing interest in the dynamic forces back of behavior.

THE INFLUENCE OF PSYCHIATRY UPON RELIGION

As in so many of the previously discussed fields of activity, the influence of psychiatry upon religion has been both direct and indirect, manifest and subtle. Of its subtle influences and those derived from the increasing popularity of science generally I shall not speak, because to do so would involve an elaborate discussion of the function of religion and the relation of religious theory to religious practice for which I am not qualified.

On the other hand, it is not difficult to observe many direct and undisguised influences of psychiatry upon religious conceptions and activities, and of these I may speak briefly. It was under the religious influences of a church that certain very definite and helpful experiments in psychotherapy were begun very early in the twentieth century. These progressively minded ministers and physicians had the impression that there was a wide border area between medical science and formal religion which could be approached through some cooperation to the benefit of persons suffering from diseases of the soul manifested by illness of the body. These experiments met with prejudice from two standpoints: first, from the standpoint that psychiatry properly conceived should include a consideration of so-called disease of the soul and should do so without

theories about the supernatural; secondly, from the influence of the
charlatanry and intellectual dishonesty of some of the adherents of
Mary Baker Eddy. It is perfectly true that some of the prejudice
which medical men have against Christian Science has arisen from
the fact that this over-reaction against the materialism of medicine
and of civilization in general resulted in the disappearance of many
neurotic symptoms in some of its believers and this success reflected
upon the physicians and their abilities. However, the most fair-
minded physician could not but have misgivings about the empirical
and pragmatic benefits to be derived from fooling people, even if
such deceptions led to an appearance of health. To put it in another
way, conscientious medical men, entirely aside from their professional prejudices, might well have their doubts about the desirability
of substituting an artificial psychosis for a naturally acquired
neurosis, even though the latter may have been the more painful.

Psychiatry struggled valiantly against confusion with Christian
Science for many years, and there are still some reputable medical
men who refer patients to Christian Science practitioners rather
than to psychiatrists, not because they prefer the former, but because they are more numerous and more available and better known
to the public.

Gradually the distinction between psychiatric principles utilized
in religious work, and the distortion of psychological principles
under the guise of a religion became more definitely differentiated
in the public mind. It seems to me that now neither the scientists
nor the religionists (I do not mean the Christian Scientists) are
quite so proud of their authority or quite so certain of their absolutism. There seem to be increasing evidences of *rapprochement*
between them. The most conspicuous evidences have been the appearance of numerous books,[8] some of them by ministers and some
of them by psychiatrists, dealing with the problems of the minister
from the psychiatric standpoint. If one assumes that the avowed
purpose of both religion and psychiatry is to make men more
comfortable, then it is natural that the leaders of those professions
should exchange views. And since the views of the ministers have
been for so many centuries more or less common knowledge and

the views of the psychiatrists relatively unknown it is natural that the didactic information should now come more largely from the psychiatrists.

In addition to what might be called manuals of instruction which purport to give the minister some scientific information about the nature of the personality as psychiatrically conceived, the characteristic forms of adjustment aberrancies, and some conception of the technique of effecting changes in individuals as the result of personal contacts, there has been some scientific research with respect to the precise nature of the function of religion as it can be discovered in the lives of individuals obliged for therapeutic purposes to submit themselves to thorough analysis.[9] Furthermore, there has been an increasing number of books written by ministers giving the results of their own efforts to absorb psychiatric principles and apply them to the tasks of ministerial functions.

It is true that some ministers have regarded the psychiatrists as Antichrists, but this cannot be said to be the attitude of the majority; rather it can fairly be said that the ministers have been more open-minded toward psychiatry than have the lawyers. This open-mindedness has led to certain complications, especially that of lay therapy, which has also been a problem with the psychologists. If anything, the ministers have a rather stronger position here than have the psychologists, since they can logically invoke the authority and assistance of divine forces. In short, the minister can say, "It is my duty and my pleasure to counsel my parishioners, happy or unhappy, sick or well. If my faith and the faith of my parishioner in God means anything at all, it should mean something from which to draw comfort and reassurance. Such comfort and reassurance should not be denied to those who suffer from fears of unreal menaces, nor from those who suffer from pains ascribed to nonexistent organic diseases. And, if, as the psychiatrists say, transference is an instrument of highest therapeutic efficacy, surely a minister in whom a parishioner puts his trust and in whose integrity he believes and with whom he shares a common faith should be one most likely to be psychotherapeutically helpful to him. If, as scientists have declared, relieving oneself of hate and certain other undesirable mental attitudes serves to relieve one of depressions and even of physical illnesses, is it not logical that the minister or priest whose ideal it is to dispel hatred applies this gospel in a therapeutic way?"

Some ministers have bravely accepted this challenge and have set themselves up more or less definitely as ministers to the minds of their parishioners no less than to their souls. Others have preferred to organize within the church mental-hygiene clinics or institutions of similar intention presided over by a psychiatrist under the auspices of the church and with the blessings and often the active participation of the minister.

At first it might seem very narrow indeed for psychiatrists to make objections to such worthy purposes, carried out in the main by such high-minded, intelligent, and conscientious men. It is only fair to say, however, that the objections of psychiatrists have a validity which commends itself to many other ministers. In the first place, it should be remembered that while it is true that transference is a powerful therapeutic instrument, it is also true that the use of it requires long training and expert skill and that its mismanagement is apt to cause much distress to all parties concerned. Many an embarrassing situation has arisen through ignorance of the basic principles involved in the correct management of transference; in plain language, many a minister who has begun by wishing to help a parishioner has ended by being dismissed from his church for complications over which he ultimately found that he had no control whatever. Again, it should be remembered that a minister is without training adequate to enable him to make a differential diagnosis. Relinquishing one's envy of a sister under the inspiration of a minister may indeed cure a neurotic headache, but it will not cure a headache arising from an incipient uremia or brain tumor and may postpone the recommendation of a proper treatment until too late. And, finally, there is the objection that most ministers have too many other things to do. Therapeutic treatment of individuals is a time-consuming task of vast proportions, and a minister who turns psychiatrist in function would best turn psychiatrist in training and in profession.[10]

Nevertheless, what I have cited is sufficient to indicate how increasingly formal religion has become interested in the application of the scientific principles of human personality and to those functions which it performs by virtue of inspiration and faith. To what extent psychiatry will replace religion is problematical; the writer's own opinion is that religion will long continue to supply the healing of the nations to a far greater extent than will psychiatry. One might say that psychiatry will continue to do for the individual what religion has endeavored to do and to some extent succeeded in doing for the masses.

CONCLUSION

We return at last to the question as to why the theories, principles, and discoveries that are massed under the general term *psychiatry,* the healing of the mind, should have so profoundly affected these diverse expressions of human thinking and human activity with so little awareness on the part of the majority of American citizens. The discoveries of Einstein, immensely more difficult of comprehension and of practical application, were such as to make his name familiar to every literate American citizen within a few years. The acclaim with which his discoveries were met is in startling contrast to the blankness, sneers, or suspicion which still greet the name of Sigmund Freud in many quarters, and the general ignorance about him and his work which prevails generally.* Both have been classed with Aristotle, Plato, Leonardo, Columbus, and Newton but such a classification does not linger in the public mind so far as Freud or any other psychiatrist is concerned. Why should there be this enormous contrast? Why should the man in the street struggle to understand the principle of relativity which in no way concerns him and revere the man who discovered or emphasized it, but shut his eyes to material which concerns his own life, the structure of his own personality, his failures and successes, his strengths and weaknesses? Clearly there is a resistance to the ac-

---

* I realize of course that intelligent people the world over know about Freud, know something of the nature and importance of his work and in many instances regard him very highly. The fact remains, however, that he has never even been considered for a Nobel prize, he holds no professorship, he has had nothing like the popular acclaim that has met Einstein and Madame Curie.

ceptance of such unpleasant information, and unpleasant it would seem to be to the average person. Freud himself first showed us why psychiatry would always be unpopular, although he also reminded us that the formulations of Galileo and of Darwin met with a similar resistance, traces of which are still observable.

It would not be accurate to fail to mention the fact that psychiatry has not always had the best of representatives, that it has not been possible to separate it in practice from the cloying restrictions and adulterations of politics, economics, and human inertia. Psychiatry has suffered as have all rapidly developing modern sciences from an archaic and often terrifying vocabulary, partly for the reason that we are tied by tradition to the misconceptions of the earlier workers and partly because the structure of our language is inadequate to cast in verbal form the subtle configurations and interrelationships of our data. Again, the over-enthusiasm of a few whose hopes had been stimulated to new heights by the startling discoveries of psychiatry likewise brought about some disappointments and, perhaps, occasional confusion. The proverbial conflict of opinion within the ranks of psychiatrists and psychoanalysts has weakened the interest and the faith of some who felt that those best acquainted with the human instincts and patterns of behavior should be the most successful in avoiding their untoward expression.

The fact remains, however, that psychiatry in the modern sense has already definitely and in some ways prodigiously affected the life of every American citizen, whether he knows it or not. It is to be expected that it will continue to exert its effect in two directions: first, in its therapeutic application to those who suffer or cause their environment to suffer unduly; and, second, in the molding of our conceptions of the purposes and methods of living and of influencing those with whom we must live.

The psychiatry of 1938 is an organized science, art, and profession linked in a three-way combination with medicine, psychology, and sociology. It is a branch of medicine, a branch in which the psychological factors in human characterology are given more recognition and consideration both in diagnosis and in treatment than is the case in the routine practice of the internist, obstetrician, or surgeon.

Such psychological emphasis, however, cannot ignore the psychology of the rest of the human environment, since no patient lives in a vacuum or on a desert island. In this way psychiatry is, very naturally, and properly, bringing sociologists, psychologists, and physicians closer together, and from this there would appear to be evolving at the present time a new concept of human beings. The essence of this new concept in its broadest sense is that human beings possess a physical and chemical and psychological structure partly self-determined, partly socially determined. This is most apparent in the psychological factor but it, in turn, modifies the physical and chemical reactions of each individual. It is not a question of whether we should think of society as being made up of individuals or of individuals as making up society. It is imperative that we be able to think both ways simultaneously. In doing so we realize that we have much to learn as to the exact nature of the interpersonal relationships linking the parts of the whole, concerning which we have only begun to think scientifically. But that we have begun to think of this is characteristic of psychiatry in 1938.

7. Men, Women, and Hate

I

Two of my friends were engaged in a warm discussion.

"Freud will always be honored as one of the greatest men in medical science," said the first, "because he reduced to a scientific basis what had previously been the semi-organized intuition or wisdom of a few perspicacious individuals. His theory and his techniques are among the greatest forward steps in medicine. My only objection is that he reduced all of the psychological troubles of man to sex. That I cannot accept."

"Show me," said the other, "something that is more painful, more perplexing, more repressed, than matters of sex in the life of human beings, from their childhood up, and I will agree with your objection. If there *were* anything more repressed than sex, *it* would be the cause of trouble in human adjustments. But there isn't! Freud, being intellectually honest, had to report what he found."

At this point they appealed to me, and I had to say, "You are both correct, both mistaken. Freud did discover that sexual repression led to unhappy consequences. But he also discovered later that there is something even more repressed, more tabooed than sex—namely, hate—and that it, rather than sexuality, is really responsible for the psychological ills of mankind. When he felt sure of this he courageously retracted and recast his original concept in favor of the view that the erotic instinct constantly defends us against self-destructive tendencies arising from hate."

Reprinted from the *Atlantic Monthly*, 163:158–168, February 1939.

Many of the disasters of life which are blamed on Fate, heredity, misfortune, or the machinations of foes can be traced to this unconscious destructive force within ourselves. Varieties of such self-destruction are familiar to everyone. Men drink themselves to death, antagonize their friends, throw away their best opportunities for success, stumble into accidents or sickness under such circumstances as would make it appear that they had unconsciously wished to suffer or to fail or to fall ill. In all too many instances they actually kill themselves outright. Whether one kills himself suddenly or slowly and by inches, the suicidal impulses are psychologically the same. They spring in part from an inability to express one's hostilities in an expedient manner upon an appropriate object. Repressed (not merely suppressed) for want of such expression, these destructive energies turn back upon their author. Then from the conscience there comes additional force to swell the power of the now self-directed aggressiveness.

This in oversimplified outline is the theory of self-destructiveness, using that expression in its broadest sense rather than in the narrow meaning of suicide. But fortunately there is a powerful force operating toward the mitigating or counteracting of this self-destructiveness. There is that tremendous power which draws men and women together and which draws men and men together and which draws us all together in varying degrees of intensity and effectiveness. It may seem a little trite to come around finally to the conclusion, as Freud has done, that to combat our self-destructiveness we must love one another. But the greatest truths are often the simplest, and this is a conclusion at which Jesus and Plato and many others arrived. The practical question is, what can be said as to the expedition of this program of loving? It isn't enough to be told that we should love one another. We know that already. But *how* to do so—that is a question which no one answers.

We think of the love of a man for a woman and her love for him as the most intense expression of this life instinct, the force which opposes the self-destructive instinct. To love and to be loved should exclude the possibility of hating, destroying, and permitting oneself to be destroyed. If our theory can be true, where there is a full expression of love between two people there should be no weeping, no sorrow, no recriminations, no resentments; I would go further and say, no accidents and no sickness.

If this seems a little Utopian, let us word it another way: people are permitted to love one another, encouraged in it by society, sanctioned by the law, inspired by the examples of their parents and friends or even by the nesting doves and similar phenomena. Yet, with all this impetus in the direction of mutual affection, men and women are frequently unhappy together. Why? Why is divorce so frequent, and contented marriage so rare? What, in short, is behind the war between the sexes which permeates our society? Instead of aiding toward a better integration, greater constructiveness, it would seem as if the association of the sexes often stimulated a mutual aggressiveness, and that men and women aid and abet one another in self-destructiveness instead of greater creativeness.

I base such conclusions upon clinical experience with unhappy women and ineffective men, and with increasing alcoholism among both, and upon the general unfairness toward women on the part of business and industry, the diminishing interest in children, the increasing preparations for war. Occasionally some woman and less frequently some man becomes articulate about this conflict. James Thurber drew some sadly humorous cartoons about it in *The New Yorker*. Anything which can be made funny must have at its heart some tragic implications.

Long ago Freud made the comment that with a normal love life there could be no neurosis. If neuroticism is on the increase, as is generally agreed, we might infer that an effective utilization of the function of love is diminishing. The so-called abnormalities of sex, those individual peculiarities which characterize every individual and which at first appeared to claim so much attention from psychiatrists, have long since ceased to be regarded by them as other than fragments of an erotic striving broken by surges of uncontrollable hate. Sex and sexuality never made anyone ill and never made anyone feel guilty. It is the hate and destructiveness concealed in them which produce strange aberrations and bitter regret.

Until we have recognized this fact, it seems to me futile to attempt or expect improved social and marital relationships in the world. In the past, efforts to improve matters have been directed chiefly to the strengthening of love—by the blessing of the church, the exhortations of the ministers, the tacit rules of society, the enforced regulations of the law. "You *must* love one another," say these authorities. "You must love and promise to love and keep on loving. You must also love your children, you must love your neighbor, you must even love your neighbor's dog (but not his wife). If you fail in any of these we shall punish you." Meanwhile the ebb and flow of the hatred against which this love must incessantly battle pass unrecognized, unadmitted. Some of the very things intended to enforce the love actually stimulate the hatred.

II

Now that we have some idea of the instinctual nature of man, it is possible to consider the social relationships of human beings in a somewhat more comprehensive and, I believe, fruitful way. We may examine those special forms of hate that develop between men and women, especially in the relationships that should theoretically be dominated entirely by love, and we can attempt to trace their origins. All along the reader must bear in mind that hate and love may coexist, and that whether hate is conscious or unconscious makes little real difference in the net result.

First of all, let me be sure that we agree that women do hate men, and men women. Some would prefer to put it that men *fear* women and vice versa, but we know that fear and hate are almost inseparable. At any rate there is no doubt that men do neglect women, avoid them, restrict them, and discriminate against them in many situations. This has had many eloquent, if bitter, expositions, Virginia Woolf's *Three Guineas* being one of the most recent. Indeed, I should say without reservation that men fear and hate women more than women fear and hate men. I think it is this rather than the male's superior physical strength that makes it possible for our civilization to be called "a man's world." It is not a contest of strength; it is a contest of hate. This hatred of men for women is one of the causes of the retaliatory reactions of women, one of the elements in their hate for men. But it is not the only cause for women hating men. The little girl resents the fact that she is not as strong or as active or as privileged or as influential or as egotistical or as untrammeled by physiological processes as is her brother. Many women appear to have an obsessive drive to take revenge on men for real or fancied injuries, for the feeling that they have been forced into what they regard as an inferior status.

The aggressions of women are not always so obvious as those of men, but unfortunately they are probably just as prevalent. The woman who curbs her husband's initiative, exhausts him with her emotional or material demands, dampens his enthusiasms, wastes his money, humiliates him, nags him, remains sexually unresponsive to him, or, worst of all, pillories him by an attitude of martyrdom— such a woman leaves no doubt by her actions as to her deep resentment of men, however much she may verbally deny it or successfully exclude it from her consciousness.

In the eagerness of winning a wife or the joy of obtaining a husband, both men and women for a time forget these resentments. They cannot believe that any ever existed or ever could exist. Marriage comes, then, representing a *fait accompli*. Both parties have won a victory; both have, at the same time, entered into a contract of obligation to one another which draws upon the emotional reserves—I should say the erotic reserves. These may become heavily depleted, even exhausted, and as time goes on the old aggressive feelings of hostility for the opposite sex which the heightened emotion has held in check are reawakened or renewed within the marital union. For the giving of love to another, necessary as it is for the life of the individual, is nevertheless possible only by withdrawing love from the reservoir of self-directed, self-absorbed love. It is this that we perceive when we say that so-and-so is too selfish to marry, or, if married, too selfish to have children. The process of transforming self-love into object love is extremely difficult for those whose childhood experiences were such as to make them fear the result of attempting to do so.

But it is very difficult for the average person to realize that friction with his spouse is based not so much upon minor contemporary provocations as upon the earlier frustrations and resentments of his childhood. He is more impressed, often, with what seem to be very real and present obstacles to happiness. Some of these may be in the very nature of the social order under which we live, the cultural requirements. And to these we should first give thoughtful consideration. Exactly what are the factors in our civilization which internally or externally lead to unhappy relationships between the sexes? Having come to some conclusion about this inquiry, we can approach the second question: what is the nature of the psychological reactions to these factors in men and women respectively?

I am not a sociologist, but a psychiatrist, and therefore it is difficult for me to think in terms of the social structure except as representing mass crystallizations of the attitudes, wishes, and fears of individuals. On the other hand, the behavior of each individual is to some extent determined by these pre-existent and coexistent mass opinions. Hence there is a constant interaction between the established expression of human instinct and emotion, on the one hand, and the individual's attempts to conform to this expression. From one standpoint it is absurd to speak of the war between the sexes in general terms; the war between men and women is certainly very differently determined and expressed in Persia, for example, than in Alaska. There must be similar differences in regard to the intersexual conflict as manifested in England and in the United States, and even in Maryland and Texas, let us say; or, to narrow it down still more, as between urban and rural couples. The customs and social attitudes in these various localities differ so considerably that the particular external irritant in one place may be entirely lacking in the other.

If one continued this line of reasoning far enough, however, one would say that the exact nature of the hostilities between male and female could be accurately determined only in a particular instance, in a particular locality at a particular moment, and then only by subjecting both parties to thorough psychological and sociological study. This is not exactly a *reductio ad absurdum,* but it ignores the possibility of indicating certain trends which apply more generally, from a consideration of which it might be possible to draw some helpful inferences for those who are not sufficiently involved in such conflict as to make it necessary for them to be psychiatrically studied. Hence I shall have the temerity to indicate some general principles which seem to me to have validity because they are conclusions drawn from a number of such individually studied couples.

III

One's first thought in considering the war between the sexes concerns the familiar questions whether—or, rather, in what way —this is a man's world, as one often hears that it is; whether or not America is matriarchal in its family government; whether or not men or women are more cruel, or more patient, or more effective. What all of these come back to is really the question of who possesses or who exerts the most power. The assumption is that such power is used aggressively against one sex and in the self-interest of the other. Of course there isn't any doubt that the average man has more physical strength than the average woman. However, the combative strength in the sexual war is no longer a matter of muscles. To a considerable extent economics has replaced mechanics in the regulation of all human affairs. Aside from war and some types of common labor, the superior strength of men has long since ceased to be of great practical importance, and in its place has come the power of the purse strings.

This may seem pretty obvious, but, simple as it is, it is generally overlooked in discussions of the subject, because in our primitive thinking the influence of muscular strength remains disproportionately great as a carry-over from our childhood feelings of helplessness. Men still believe it necessary to impress upon women that they, the men, are more powerful, and that this power is not only for the purpose of protecting women, but for the purpose of conquering them and holding them in abeyance. But the women constantly erect some barrier to the direct infliction of this "power"; it is customary to be deferential to women, to give them various minor physical advantages and prerogatives, to refrain from striking them under penalty of the law. But no such advantage is given them in the business world; on the contrary, they are hedged about by many restrictions and handicaps, and they are fair prey to the exploitation of men skillful enough to accomplish it. Women, for their part, have their own special devices and techniques of exerting power against men. Sometimes Samson, sometimes Delilah, wins out. A husband may oppress his wife, but a divorcee may put her husband in prison for alimony delinquency.

In many of the contemporary discussions, this is the sort of material that is elaborated. Virginia Woolf is at some pains to show how gaudy and pretentious men are in their ceremonial costumes— this in a book which, to be sure, contains far more recondite material. Pearl Buck, in a recent article on "America's Medieval Women," is impressed with the false promises men make women, particularly in the educational system. Others point out how the church abets women in maintaining an unnatural control over the sexual propensities of men. But it is to none of these familiar topics that I would call attention, because I believe all of them are secondary in importance to the question of reproduction. In the light of modern psychoanalytic theory, living and loving are almost synonymous; one may say that eating one's food and kissing one's bride are merely differently directed expressions of the same drive.

Hence the significant sociological factors contributing to intersexual warfare must be those which restrict the opportunity to live and to love—that is, to subsist and to reproduce. Now I am not sufficiently versed in economics to know definitely (if, indeed, anyone knows) whether it is actually or relatively growing more difficult to subsist. My impression, and I suppose the impression of most people, is that such is the case. We don't work as hard, and perhaps the average man has more money than in the days of an earlier existence—let us say, one hundred years ago; but, on the other hand, unemployment, depression, and actual starvation seem to be more extensive now than ever. Certainly the discrepancy between what a man *may* have and what he almost *must* have in order to keep up with his neighbors is now greater than ever, and keeping up with the neighbors means maintaining a rapidly expanding conception of the proper standard of living. The point of all this is that economics has undoubtedly been one factor in the reduction of the birth rate.

As we shall see, this well-known and prosaic fact has immense psychological significance. For it has become too expensive to have children, or rather to have as many as are wanted. Children are no longer the assets they once were when they worked for their parents and had distinct property value. The state of the world seems increasingly uncertain. Frontiers and virgin resources have disappeared. The threat of world war grows daily greater. Economic theory is only a little less confused than the actual state of economic affairs. And after all, since the prime objective of the erotic drive is the preservation of the species, and since this includes the production of children, these increasing interferences with its expression act as smothering blankets upon the fires of life.

For a long time it has been recognized, as Freud beautifully points out in his *Civilization and Its Discontents* and other papers, that the progress of civilization has been made at the cost of the erotic life of mankind. This might be taken to apply primarily to the increasing frigidity among women and impotence among men. (That these conditions *are* increasing cannot be doubted by anyone familiar with the intimate personal life of any considerable number of individuals. The startling increase in alchoholism goes hand in hand with this phenomenon, since, as all competent observers have remarked, the alcohol addict is nearly always sexually inadequate, even though he may appear to be sexually overactive.) But the point I am making now is that not only is the *immediate* sexual life of human beings impaired by our efforts to be civilized, but the ultimate *purposes* of the erotic instinct, the bearing and rearing of children, are also interfered with, and life itself thus threatened.

The most important consequence of this in relation to our main theme is the effect it has had upon the women. For, whereas child-bearing was once the mark of a woman's success and the most important thing she could do, now it is likely to be an indication of her resignation, her carelessness, or her lack of ambition. It is no secret that many women, perhaps most women, now dread to have children. By far the majority of illegal abortions are performed upon married women, women who have a legal right to bear children but who do not want to do so or feel they cannot.

Thus far I have put the blame for this chiefly upon the economic system, but I remain true to my central thesis, that in the last analysis this must be checked up in part to something in the psychology of the individual. One would expect instincts to rise above economics. When they do, as in the case of the poor families on relief who go on having more children whom they cannot support, we charge it up to slovenliness—criminal improvidence. The very fact that these people do not have enough food or shelter or anything else which gives them a sense of security increases the need for the psychological support which reproduction gives them. It is much easier, of course, to describe this in terms of moralistic condemnation, as is often done, but it is not very philosophical and it allows us to sidestep the psychological necessity of reproduction. Thus we fall again into the fallacy of minimizing the importance of the erotic life, including childbearing.

The point is that the more intelligent people *think* they can substitute other gratifications; that they are mistaken in this appears in the neurotic consequences. Hence such thinking is in effect a cloak for self-destructiveness. There are many women who could well afford to have children but who, following the tradition of the times, think themselves more comfortable without these responsibilities. Still other women consciously desire children—so they think —but find themselves sterile. Both types, to my notion, represent unconscious self-destructive inhibitions. Certainly nothing in our civilization is more disgraceful and tragic than the millions of women who are childless in part because they are unmarried, and unmarried in part because of their inability to adapt themselves to the precarious role of a married woman.

Since the bearing and rearing of children is woman's greatest achievement and the climax of her erotic development, one would expect it to be not only her greatest joy but the source of her greatest power. By means of it she comes into a genuine sense of security and is thus in a position to counteract not only her own aggressive impulses but the occasional eruptions of aggression and self-destructiveness on the part of her husband. Hence to be thwarted in this objective, whether by the restrictions of economic reality or by lack of socially approved opportunity or by conflicting wishes engendered within her by her early childhood experiences, makes for a deep inner resentment. To put it another way, it deprives her of her primary safeguard against her own aggressive impulses.

I have dilated upon this great frustration of women because it seems to me to be the most fundamental one. I am not unaware of the charge that civilized men, and particularly American men, are distressingly inattentive to women. They are so engrossed in their business affairs and the struggle of making a living that they have little time or energy to devote to the constructive purposes of love. Foreign psychiatrists and psychoanalysts have repeatedly commented upon the apparent sexlessness of Americans, the extent to which men get along without women or else treat them either as mothers or as prostitutes. They speak of the neurotic, sexually inhibited American businessman who is a success in practical affairs and a failure as a lover, husband, and father. But the same observers also comment upon the aggressive, grasping, managing American women. "Super-normal," I have heard them called. Such women are reacting, they say, to the neglect that they receive from men by a retaliatory assumption of masculine techniques. It is as if they set out to control and punish the men for being too busy to make love to them. All this they ascribe in large measure to the puritanical tradition of sexual suppression in this country.

Although I am not convinced of the greater happiness of European wives and husbands, I do not differ with this interpretation in the main, but I think the point I discussed above is more basic. For if women were not frustrated in regard to their most important objective, and their position as women were not depreciated by the popular attitude toward childbearing, their resentful aggressivness which my European colleagues observe and blame upon sexual frustration would certainly diminish; and if this aggressivness were less and the soft feminine qualities more in evidence, the erotic reaction of men to them would be greater, and these secondary frustrations would thus disappear.

IV

My belief is, then, that most American women are deeply and critically frustrated in their childbearing function, and that this results in compensatory reactions of masculine strivings on the one hand and aggressive retaliation on the other. The success of many women in taking the place of men and leading men's lives in all important respects—in politics, in sports, in business, and even in foreign affairs—may be said to represent the most favorable and least harmful reaction. These things do not really hurt men, however much bellowing they may stimulate. What really hurts the male is the impact of feminine resentment against him, especially while he is still a little boy. Far more serious than the aggressions of the wife against her husband are the effects of the unconscious attitudes of resentment on the part of the mother toward the child. It may seem paradoxical to say that a woman frustrated in regard to having children expresses her resentment over this frustration toward the few children she does have; nevertheless this is evidently the case, for, with the prevalent social attitudes, those few that she does have (if she has any) are apt to fail her as a gratification and to serve rather as a source of hated responsibility and even as a kind of degradation.

Mothers betray in a hundred ways their genuine resentment of the child and of the obligations he imposes upon them. They turn him over to hirelings during the most important period of his development. They send him to camps and boarding schools; they farm him out with relatives; they separate their interests entirely from his. I am constantly amazed at the way even well-to-do parents, parents who think nothing of spending thousands of dollars upon their own pleasures, will demur to relatively trivial expenses connected with their children—for example, the attempts of physicians and teachers to relieve the children of neurotic complications which the attitude of the parents has helped to produce.

The secret cruelties that parents visit upon their children are past belief. It is said that the American Indians looked with horror upon the white settler's practice of whipping his children. To scalp an enemy, a contender in war—this they could understand, but to strike a helpless child seemed to them incredible. I share this prejudice with the Indians, and in my capacity as a psychiatrist I shudder at the tales of brutality I am obliged to hear. Many people imagine that, in the intimacy of the psychiatric consultation room, shocking secrets are revealed pertaining to abnormal sex practices, perverse yearnings, and the like. But it is not these that shock the psychiatrists. It is the daily recitations of almost unbelievable cruelties systematically practiced by parents upon children. I despair of conveying to the average reader either the extent or the extremity of these, because the natural protective devices of the mind are such that the reader is bound to regard them all as exceptions. There are a few letters and case histories in my private files that even after a good many years of clinical experience I cannot bear to reread, and I hasten to add that these people are not, like many of the characters of such novels as those of William Faulkner, poor and ignorant, but often wealthy and socially prominent.

But far more significant in the war between the sexes than these dramatic episodes are the subtle cruelties inflicted by unconsciously resentful mothers upon their defenseless children. Smothering a child by anxious concern over every detail of his life, robbing him of all opportunities to express himself naturally and to discover the world for himself, rebuking his early efforts to explore and direct his dawning sexuality, may be more crippling than beatings and curses. One mother made her son practice pushing his ears to the side of his head and squeezing his nostrils together so that he would not look so "burly and masculine and Negroid." Another mother put a diaper upon her seven-year-old son and exposed him to her friends in ridicule to cure him of bed-wetting (the latter being, of course, one of his protests against her rule). I could fill many pages with similar illustrations.

Such tactics and such an attitude serve to rob the child of that sense of masculinity which he must have in order to love confidently and live constructively. And for this robbing and suppressing of his masculinity (as for all other manifestations of hatred by the mother) the growing boy bears a deep resentment. The state of being curbed and controlled and wounded by a woman is one which breeds in him an eternal distrust of that woman and of all other women.

To be sure, this protest against interference with his natural pleasures is probably felt by every child, male or female, and the interference comes chiefly from the mother. It is she who enforces the weaning, who forbids the satisfaction of indiscriminate evacuation in favor of the methods approved by adult society, who must say "No" many times, and many times "You must." All this the child resents, and focuses his resentment upon the agent of his thwarting, the mother. But my point is that the necessities of reality, *plus* the restrictive puritanical mores of the times, are enforced upon the child with an aggressive technique that bespeaks unconscious, if not conscious, hostility, which is still further augmented in the case of sons by the special envious resentment toward males that is present in so many mothers. It is this envy which leads a mother so often to want to rob her child of the masculinity which she begrudges him. Because she is usually not aware of this, and, even if she were, would fear to show it in any overt way, she is more apt to use such petty but nonetheless effective methods as over-protecting him, keeping him in curls, snatching him from the company of other boys whom she regards as rough or dangerous, insisting upon manners, and the like.

That these devices actually do have the effect of crippling the masculinity of the boy every psychiatrist knows from clinical experience. It is the sort of thing that has happened in childhood to men who consult us many years later because of impairments of masculinity which may show themselves in an unsatisfactory sexual life, or more commonly in various attempts to compensate for an unsatisfactory sexual life, such as alcoholism, hypochondriasis, neurotic illnesses, all kinds of marital conflict, and even actual psychoses. Call them the extreme cases if you like, but they are extremes that indicate what I believe to be an increasing trend of a most malignant sort. I think one can see in the hysterical suppression of women by the Hitler regime a violent reaction to this fear on the part of men that their masculinity has been or is about to be taken from them. That the women should be blamed for this instead of the Allies, or civilization, or corrupt politicians, is explicable in the light of the fact that, in times of panic, childhood fears and prejudices dominate individuals.

The ultimate result in the son of the specially aggressive mother is that he grows up to fear women and hate them to such an extent that even his erotic instincts, which normally overcome these negative emotional feelings, cannot triumph. This reduces his capacity to love, which in turn thwarts the woman whom he tries to love, and this thwarting increases her resentments. As a result he turns for his love to such sublimated forms as can be obtained in male organizations of various kinds—business activities, clubs, athletic associations, scientific societies, pool halls, bars, poker parties, and so forth. The brotherly camaraderie of men is therefore not so much an indication that love now prevails to a greater extent than in the bellicose days of old as evidence that its expression is being forced out of its most natural channels. Much as such men may fear and hate one another, they feel safer with one another than with women. Whether one explains this as due to the fact that less is expected of them in such company, or that they are anxious to be free from the dominance and surveillance of their wives, or that they are positively attracted to one another, it all comes to the same thing.

The danger of such a solution is that men's destructive impulses are not sufficiently neutralized by this dependence upon one another. Sooner or later they must foment a war with someone, and wars are always self-destructive. That is what is happening now in the Fascistic countries, where masculine association is so greatly favored.

V

We are left at a rather hopeless impasse. The social and economic structure deprives women of children and antagonizes them toward children. The children reflect this in their subsequent associations with other adults and with the next generation. Men turn from women to the company of other men and thus thwart women further, and they in turn inflict more aggressions upon men and upon children.

We cannot change civilization or the social structure, so at first blush the outlook would seem very pessimistic. This was Freud's conclusion in an essay [1] published in 1912:

> So perhaps we must make up our minds to the idea that altogether it is not possible for the claims of the sexual instinct to be reconciled with the demands of culture; that, in consequence of his cultural development, renunciation and suffering, as well as the danger of his extinction at some far future time, are not to be eluded by the race of man. This gloomy prognosis rests, it is true, on the single conjecture that the lack of satisfaction accompanying culture is the necessary consequence of certain peculiarities developed by the sexual instinct under the pressure of culture. This very incapacity in the sexual instinct to yield full satisfaction as soon as it submits to the first demands of culture becomes the source, however, of the grandest cultural achievements, which are brought to birth by ever greater sublimation of the components of the sexual instinct. For what motive would induce man to put his sexual energy to other uses if by any direct disposal of it he could obtain fully satisfying pleasure? He would never let go of this pleasure and would make no further progress.

I do not entirely agree with Freud here, and I believe that in the quarter of a century that has passed since he wrote those words he too has come to be willing to revise them somewhat. It is the aggressive impulses, not the erotic ones, that need to be sublimated; indeed, it is the erotic impulses that enable us to sublimate our aggressions. Van Gogh did not hurl paint at the canvas because he was sexually starved; such love as he was capable of infused itself into his violent resentments to the extent that their plastic expression was acceptable to us as art instead of repulsive to us as criminality or beastliness.

Nevertheless, for the general outlook it is difficult not to share Freud's pessimism. It would seem as if only a complete social and economic revision would enable us to break up the vicious circle which certain features of our civilization encourage, but in individual instances I think the application of intelligence may be considerably effective.

For one thing, in spite of the difficulties and hazards, in spite of the hostile social attitudes, I think that the bearing of children and the recognition and relinquishing of our hostilities toward them could be encouraged as a definite step in self-preservation—not for the purpose of race preservation or of army replacement or of religious compliance or of the justification of improvident irresponsibility, but for *self-preservation*. I have already dilated on this point.

Then also it seems to me that the development of sports and athletics and the participation of women in them offer an exceedingly healthy form of diversion of the aggressive impulses. I have seen many couples who were able to live in comparative harmony because one or both of them succeeded in unloading hostilities in the form of athletic contests. I happen to think of one husband and wife who did not quarrel verbally but who fought violent tennis battles with each other. They didn't always enjoy the games, but they enjoyed relative happiness between games, so to speak. I have elsewhere suggested some other devices along the same lines for diminishing the aggressions.

The participation of wives in the support of the family and their activity in the business world may serve the same purpose. For women to divide their interests between homemaking and business life may not seem an ideal arrangement from the point of view of either traditional standards or psychological theories, but it may be an advantageous compromise in the case of the woman who would otherwise build up too much unrelieved resentment at what she regards as a humiliating or at least uninspiring assignment.

Finally, for those whose resentments have already reached uncontrollable heights, there is now the merciful relief of psychoanalytic exploration. We should regard it as barbaric to allow a friend to suffer indefinitely from a condition easily relieved by modern surgery, and yet many people endure agonies of depression and bitterness and guilt who could be relieved by psychological surgery if they but knew it.

The theory of psychoanalytic therapy rests upon the assumption —an assumption borne out by clinical experience—that intelligence has some influence in directing the investment of instinct. This it cannot do, however, so long as it remains blind to its own defections. As I have said elsewhere, if it is our nature to be self-destructive, our best defense lies in becoming aware of such tendencies. The principle of recognizing the ways in which one destroys his own happiness, and applying one's intelligence to forestalling or repairing the damage instead of devising more ingenious forms of retaliatory destructiveness, offers hope to everyone who utilizes it, apart from its special application in therapy. While it is true that we cannot change society suddenly, some of us are bound to put faith in the ultimate effects of education. It is conceivable that in spite of economic pressure, in spite of prejudice and superstition, we may gradually achieve a somewhat less artificial, more psychologically and biologically sound sexual morality. If we do, it must come, I believe, not through legislation, but through an awareness of internal aggressions and mutual hatred—self-perpetuating hatred that is reflected in the evils of society, rising anew like the phœnix from the ashes of every social revolution.

The furtherance of peace in the multiple miniature conflicts in the lives of the individuals that make up communities, states, and nations is, it seems to me, our first concern; for behind the problems of class wars and international war is the problem of interpersonal wars, the wars between man and man and between men and women. Hence in the future, as at present, wars will continue to seem honorable and inevitable, to be fought "in the service of humanity" in spite of their cost in human life and happiness, until we declare a lasting truce in that most ancient and deadly feud, wherein new wounds are opened every day—the war between men and women.

8. What Is Economy in Mental Illness?

My brother, Will, has outlined how a large group of integrated institutions has developed in Topeka, Kansas, from the modest beginning of a small medical partnership. When we began, we were told by fellow physicians that it was impossible to make a living in the private practice of psychiatry except in big cities like Chicago and New York.

But we soon had plenty of patients, in fact too many. We kept adding doctors to our group and we all kept busy. Patients have kept coming from near and far and by the prevalent scale of values we were fairly successful.

But we were not satisfied. Even at minimum charges proper psychiatric treatment is very expensive because it is necessarily so personalized. We found ourselves increasingly occupied chiefly with a few well-to-do patients—few I mean in comparison with the thousands of people who needed treatment and couldn't afford it. These thousands were not necessarily poor people, although many of them were. We treated a good many of them free, but there was a limit to what we could afford to do in that direction, and we began to realize that the needs vastly exceeded our capacities. We discovered, for example, that in the entire state of Kansas there was no place for the treatment of disturbed, bewildered, neurotic children. A cursory

The following talk was given at the meeting of the Board of Governors of The Menninger Foundation in Chicago on June 13, 1950. Reprinted from the *Menninger Quarterly*, 4:12–19, July 1950.

investigation indicated that there were at least five thousand such children in Kansas, and so we set up a little children's hospital which we called a school, and we took about twenty of these children—twenty out of the five thousand. But what we have learned from that little hospital-school is influencing programs of child care all over the United States.

We were discovering something else, namely, that if we continued to concentrate on doing our best for these patients, many of them indigent and some of them wealthy, we were so busy that we could not spend the time we wanted to in the research investigations regarding unsolved problems of treatment, which both my brother and I had been taught to regard as most important. Furthermore, we had little time to give to the young doctors and others who applied to us for the psychiatric training which they could not get in the graduate departments of the medical schools. When my brother became the assistant to the surgeon general in World War II, he left a heavy burden on those of us who remained behind, but on the other hand he assumed responsibility for the largest number of psychiatric patients ever put under one doctor in the history of the world. With hundreds of thousands of patients to provide for, my brother realized in an unforgettable way, as the Veterans Administration has come to realize since then, that *there are not one-fourth enough trained psychiatrists* in this country to take care of the patients who are now sick and in need of care, and not one-tenth enough psychiatrists in the entire world for this problem.

In the United States alone every day of the year one thousand new patients enter psychiatric hospitals. One thousand new patients a day! This has been going on for a good many months, a good many years! Picture in your mind's eye a hospital big enough for a thousand new patients. It is true that some are also discharged each day, and some die, but the accretions to the total number are overcrowding all our hospitals. The tragedy of it is that most of these patients are curable if treated in time.

While these new patients come in at the rate of seven thousand a week, we are adding new psychiatrists at the rate of one or two a week!

It was things like this that forced upon us the realization that the private practice of psychiatry, no matter how successful by ordinary standards, would never satisfy us. We realized that we had to make a choice between economic success and idealistic success. We deliberately chose the way that we thought would give us the most satisfaction. We contributed our entire assets, savings, good will, private practice, books, everything else to the Foundation, and dedicated our own lives to the continuance of an ideal for which our trustees assumed the responsibility. In spite of extravagant rumors to the contrary, neither my brother nor myself have any material possessions except our homes. On the other hand, we have a priceless possession, we feel, in our opportunity to work in an organization which has certain ideals of scientific treatment, research, and education. About the latter I should like to tell you a little.

When we set up the Foundation as a nonprofit corporation we provided that every professional individual on the staff should divide his time so that a part of it was devoted to treatment of patients, either pay patients or free patients, a part of it to teaching others in our field, and a part of it to scientific investigation. The inclinations and talents of each staff member were to be the chief determinants of time distribution.

The department of work for which I am personally responsible is that of education. It is my responsibility to organize and direct and participate in the training of psychiatrists, social workers, psychologists, nurses, aides and other personnel. Over a hundred other faculty members assist me on a part-time basis. For my own part, much as I enjoy actual treatment of patients, I now limit that activity to about an hour a day. The rest of my time is spent in education. Now the treatment of patients can easily be a self-supporting proposition; education cannot be. Consequently, this shift in my activities represented an enormous financial income reduction for the Foundation. It was one of the chief reasons that the trustees were forced to the decision of appealing to the public for contributed funds. I feel obliged, therefore, to justify what may seem to some to be our extravagant program.

Let me catch up an echo from my brother's remarks. I wonder if you realize that in the medical world at the present time there is one great anomaly. The cancer campaign has endeavored to bring to people's minds the fact that promptness in obtaining treatment is the hope of salvation, and there is no delay in surgery. If anyone in this room develops pneumonia today, God forbid, he can be receiving the best medical treatment before nightfall. A sick child—providing it has a physical illness—can get treatment anywhere almost immediately.

But not so the mentally ill. They form long queues everywhere, waiting to be accepted for treatment. While medical and surgical patients are being successfully and promptly treated all over the country, psychiatric patients stand waiting at the door. To be more exact, they wait in sleepless agitation in their homes; they drink themselves into insensibility in bars; or they walk the floor of cells in county jails. If anyone in this room should develop a mental illness today—unlike the case of pneumonia—the chances are he could *not* get treatment, even in this great city, for a considerable time.

There are five hundred patients on the waiting list of one of our hospitals in Topeka, and the same thing is true to a varying extent of every state hospital and every Veterans Administration hospital in the country. Even patients who come to private clinics with money in their hands, so to speak, and no favors asked except one— that they get treatment—must wait weeks and months before they can even be seen, and *many of these patients are just like cancer patients; if they have to wait too long, as many of them do, the condition is beyond repair*. Why is all this? For just the reason I have already mentioned—there are vastly too few trained psychiatrists in the world and even in our country.

This is the urgency, the compelling demand, for psychiatric training. One might think that it would have an immediate answer. But it never has had, and it doesn't have now. Ever since 1930 we have put *some* emphasis on education at the Menninger Clinic—now The Menninger Foundation—at our own expense, and education is always expensive. We trained a score or more of excellent young men. In 1945 the war having ended, we personally solicited from Topeka friends a few thousand dollars with which to implement the ambitious program of training twelve men *selected from among the six hundred* doctors who had applied to us. At the time our program in Topeka was established in 1946, there were *in all the medical schools of this country combined,* places for only ninety-two physicians to be trained in psychiatry. Bear in mind that at the same moment there were needs in the federal and state hospitals of this country for five thousand psychiatrists. Bear in mind, also, that it takes from three to five years after the completion of an internship for a doctor to become a psychiatrist. Bear in mind, too, that most young physicians upon leaving the medical school have no interest in going into psychiatry.

We had a larger number of applicants for training than any other center. This was one reason that the Veterans Administration sent representatives to Topeka to see if we would undertake the training of a larger percentage of these applicants than we could ever have hoped to do alone. The Veterans Administration offered to build a hospital here, to staff it, and to support in large part the training of a hundred psychiatrists at a time—not twelve but a hundred. With them we would also undertake the training of psychologists, psychiatric social workers, psychiatric nurses, aides, and other personnel to the number of about eight hundred.

Besides our long list of applicants we had other things the Veterans Administration wanted. We had a fine array of teaching talent of which we were and are proud. We had developed a plan of team work in psychiatric treatment. We had an active, mobile organization. Finally, we had an ideal of psychiatric education which coincided with that of such men of vision as General Omar Bradley, Dr. Paul Hawley, and Dr. Daniel Blain, who could foresee the insistent needs of the Veterans Administration for the next twenty years.

For these reasons the Veterans Administration decided to invest what will amount to more than $150,000,000 in this project, knowing that if, in addition to the patients actually treated in this hospital, we could train a thousand psychiatrists over a period of years, their investment would have been a very good one. This is good mathematics. For while the costs of training a psychiatrist are great, let us say $50,000 apiece, it should be remembered that any psychiatrist who is any good at all will save the Veterans Administration a million dollars a year. Or, if he works for an industrial organization, or for a state hospital, or for a community, he should save them at least a million dollars a year.

Do you wonder how I get this figure? It has to do with prompt and efficient handling of psychiatric patients. It is difficult for the average layman to realize how costly mental illness is. It is the costliest illness in the world, as my brother said in his presidential address before the American Psychiatric Association last year. One patient who is made to wait too long before treatment is begun, one patient who is inadequately or unsatisfactorily treated and becomes what we dismally call a chronic custodial case, costs *you and me* and the rest of us, from $50,000 to $150,000 (depending upon the type of custodial care given him). Every such patient whose illness is arrested and who is returned to society thus represents a saving to someone of approximately $100,000. Of the five hundred patients waiting to be admitted to Winter Hospital alone, as you sit here this very moment, perhaps a hundred will be able to get along some way even without treatment, and another hundred will become chronic custodial cases regardless of our efforts. But the fate of the other three hundred is equivocal. It depends on what happens. Adequately treated and restored, they may cost the government an average of $3000 apiece—that is about a million dollars; too long deferred, left untreated, or unsuccessfully treated, many of them will become chronic, permanently disabled custodial cases—assuming an average life span of seventy years, they will cost the government $25,000,000.

I have tried to show from this that the Veterans Administration made a very good investment in its contribution to the educational program of The Menninger Foundation. The legislature of the state of Kansas came to the same conclusion and in their last session they voted a million dollars for the first two years of an educational program at the Topeka State Hospital, with the understanding that a similar program of cooperation should be entered into with The

Menninger Foundation. It is the only way, they thought, that we can at the same time raise the standards of our state hospitals to the proper level and insure a continuity of professional personnel for them.

How it has worked at the Topeka State Hospital is now observable there even to the most casual visitor. A dreary, silent, hopeless atmosphere has been replaced by devoted volunteer workers, activity programs for patients everywhere, and an energetic staff. A patient confined for seventeen years responded to intensive treatment, and was cured and dismissed in ninety days. Forty medical and surgical consultants make regular visits. Psychiatric residents and medical externes are on duty. Neurosurgical operations are restoring individual cases and the curative influence of love has infused the staff. Hopefulness has replaced despair.

Yes, it was a very good investment for the Veterans Administration and for the state of Kansas. But was it a good investment for The Menninger Foundation? What did it mean to The Menninger Foundation? It meant the realization of our ideals to do psychiatric teaching and extend our work out of Topeka to every state in the nation and to the far corners of the globe. In that sense it was a good investment. But *financially* it was not a good investment and is not a good investment, because it means the diversion of professional talent to teaching services. This is a very costly indulgence. Why? Because neither the federal government nor the state of Kansas can or should pay for education what patients pay for treatment. The Veterans Administration and the state of Kansas do pay some tuition for each of the young doctors trained by our staff, but these tuition fees, like those of every medical school of the country, are far below what it costs to actually supply this training. Does anyone here imagine that the federal government would pay me as much for teaching young doctors as Mr. John Smith of the Smithtown Steel Company would pay me for treating his wife? Multiply this discrepancy by one hundred faculty members and you will see what I mean. Actually the federal government pays me for working all day, or most all day, at Winter Hospital about as much as Mr. Smith would pay me for seeing his wife for thirty minutes. And if you come to Topeka most any time of the day you will find me at Winter Hospital. In addition to that, unlike the medical schools of universities, The Menninger Foundation has no endowment, no funds to pay overhead. But on the other hand, as I have already outlined, whatever investments The Menninger Foundation makes in this work pay enormous dividends to the nation.

Very much the same thing could be said for research. One of our research experiments last year resulted in the cure of a patient whose illness had already cost $20,000 and would have gone on to cost someone another $130,000. This experiment cost about $5000. Of this amount, only a few hundred dollars went to the compensation of the physicians. Our three psychiatric hospitals in Topeka cost about $10,000,000 a year to operate; for funded research we spend a total of less than $110,000. Think how many millions we could save the taxpayers of America if we had at our disposal the money it costs to feed our chronic patients for just one day!

I can tell you something of the things I would do. I would support the investigations our surgeons have begun into new ways of operating upon the brain to relieve unbearable pain and intractable misbehavior, returning patients to their homes who would otherwise remain in public hospitals the rest of their lives. I would expand the methods by which we have feebly begun to treat patients in groups by mutual discussion, conference, project development and the like. I would multiply by one hundred our present encouraging efforts to salvage cases of schizophrenia by intensive, individual attention and psychotherapy. I would expand the use of creative and productive work of various kinds, including artistic projects and plain hard work for the rehabilitation of patients who are now idle. I would explore the value of some of the many new powerful drugs and chemical elements that have been discovered with respect to their ameliorative influence on mental illness. I would encourage and expand the small program we have developed for the rehabilitation of patients who are being ruined by irresistible alcoholic addiction.

These are not basic research projects; these do not endeavor to get to the basic weaknesses of personality structure. Such research is also important, but I am speaking only of practical trends that have al-

ready been developed and which languish because a promise to produce a three-thousand-per-cent yield on an investment is not taken
seriously by public administrators. In this respect politicians are different from businessmen.

I am practical enough to realize why this is so in part. It is not
because we scientists are not trusted. It is because there is really such
a vast ignorance about these matters in the places where decisions
have to be made concerning them. I would venture the guess that
not one Congressman in ten who votes on the appropriations for the
medical projects of the government knows either in dollars or cents
or in scientific formulations what he is undertaking.

We in The Menninger Foundation cannot offer this excuse for
ourselves; we know that every thousand dollars invested in psychiatric education will pay back dividends in the hundreds of
thousands and that every thousand invested in research has the
chance at least of paying back dividends in the millions. Knowing
that, knowing the need and knowing the talents which we have at
our disposal, and the eagerness of these people to do whatever can be
done with the funds available, it is our obligation—we have felt—
to give our message to the sympathetic ears of those intelligent laymen who have the means and the vision and the purpose and the
heart to respond to them, and help make this a continuing reality.

We are in desperate need of money. We pay our way currently—
but we have no capital and no reserves to meet the increasing demands. What my brother and I and a few friends donated five years
ago is all too small for the present program. We could make money
—at the cost of giving up a national service. This we don't want to
do. We must, therefore, appeal for help. We can't expect—we don't
want—the government to give all this help. We want generous, socially minded friends to do it. And we believe they will. For this is
not just *our* problem. It is *yours*.

9. Healthier than Healthy

I want to report four observations to you. I would call these "facts," except that I have an aversion for the expression, "Let's get the facts." One of the most untruthful things possible, you know, is a collection of facts, because they can be made to appear so many different ways. I was somewhat interested in sleight of hand when I was younger, and what always intrigued me was that the obvious facts could be so untruthful. It was a fact that here something was and a minute later it was there. It was a fact but it wasn't the truth, because what was over there wasn't what was here. There was something phoney about it.

Here are four observations I want you to consider. The first observation is that mental illness is something that may occur in the lives of any of us. It always develops rather unexpectedly. Nobody plans to get mentally ill, you know, and nobody expects to get mentally ill. We all expect we may get pneumonia or we may get a bad cold next winter. We expect physical illnesses of certain kinds, but no one expects a mental illness.

Nevertheless, mental illness does come; it strikes down friends and acquaintances, the prominent and the lowly, rich victims and poor ones. It is no respecter of persons. It may come to any one of us.

I do not want you to be alarmed by this statement. But I do want to break through the barrier of misapprehensions that divides the

---

A lecture delivered at Chautauqua, New York, on Aug. 5, 1958, and taken down, without editing, by a stenographer. Previously unpublished.

world into "those people"—meaning this time those impossible, out-
landish, afflicted "crazy" people—and "us"—us sane, sensible people.
That is the perfectly understandable, aristocratic view, but it is a mistaken one.

Mental illness used to be thought of only in the extreme forms or
stages which render its victims incapacitated by reason of such
symptoms as overwhelming depressions, paralyzing fear, delusional
misapprehensions, or uncontrolled impulses toward unprofitable or
undesirable behavior. Such individuals have to be taken in hand and
cared for, even over their protests. True.

But surely many of us have experienced *some* degree of depression,
some inhibition from irrational fear, some loss of self-control in social
behavior. And, while it is true that one swallow does not make a
summer, these *are* the symptoms of mental illness, and mental illness
can be mild in degree, or severe, and it can be "in between."

This, of course, is not quite like the notion of some physical
diseases. One can have many degrees of arthritis. But one either
has malaria or does not have it. The same is true with many other
diseases. But in the case of mental illness, it seems that any of us can
—indeed, all of us *do*—have some degree of it, at some times.

That is my first observation. Now for a second observation.

The general notion has long prevailed that, once mental illness
has appeared, the victim is doomed. The illness progresses, the disability increases, the specter of dementia looms inevitably ahead.
"Once insane, always insane," they said. Mental illness is incurable.
Kindly and well-meaning doctors in state hospitals sometimes used
to counsel relatives to go home and try to forget their poor father
or sister or whoever it was; "He can never recover and you should
remake your life as if he were dead."

This all seems incredible to us today, because we have quite the
opposite view. Most attacks of mental illness subside; most of the
patients recover. The trend of mental illness is *usually* back toward
health, not toward permanent disability and incurability, and we
believe that we know some ways to encourage that return to health,
one of which is the sustained and sustaining love of friends and

relatives. This is something *they* can do, while the doctors (and nurses and therapists) do what *they* can; all contribute to the patient's recovery from mental illness.

The third observation I am going to make is that some mental illnesses seem to recover for a while and then stop and other mental illnesses recover slowly and others may recover more rapidly but may recur. They come back again. People often ask me, "You say that eighty-five to ninety per cent of all the patients in the state hospitals that you know about are out within a year. How many of them come back?" They always say this with a knowing look in their eye. "Ah, we've got you there." They haven't got me at all. I admit that something like a fifth of them come back, perhaps even as many as a fourth. "Well," they say, "in other words, they weren't cured." "Well, I do not agree with that. I have had pneumonia three or four times and I don't consider that I wasn't cured of it." Well, I guess I am likely to have another attack. I expect to get over it if I do. Similarly, I think people with a mental illness can have another attack. It is something they will recover from, in all probability. But now you see this is a different attitude. This attitude of, "He is probably a little crazy underneath and just waiting for it to appear," is the old medieval, suspicious, devil-possession attitude toward mental illness which we psychiatrists and those interested in mental health wish so much that the public could learn to renounce. They will learn to renounce it when they have had more experience. That is why we wish everybody could have more exposure, more contact, and more communication with the mentally ill. It is a pity that every one of you can't visit some of our patients and make life a little more enjoyable for them. Go and read to them if you like; go and talk with them; go and chat with them about things, they would enjoy it. They would like to have you. You do have to be screened by the hospital authorities, but they will be glad to do it. Most state hospitals now have hundreds of volunteers.

The fourth observation I wanted to make is that some patients may have a mental illness and then get well, and then may even get "weller"! I mean they get better than they ever were. They get even better than they were before. This is an extraordinary and little-realized truth—and it constitutes the main point of my talk today. Take an instance familiar to all of you. Abraham Lincoln was undoubtedly a far more productive, a far bigger man, and a far broader and wiser man after his attack of mental illness than he was before. Prior to it he had seemed to fail at everything—in his profession, in politics, in love. After his terrible year of depression, he rose to the great heights of vision and accomplishment for which we all know him. And Lincoln is not the only one; there are many others, but he is a conspicuous one. Now I ask you, does this occur in physical illness?

It was noticed in England by a very observing doctor, Dr. Jenner, that some of the milkmaids caught a disease called "cowpox." They subsequently seemed to be a little healthier in some respects than did the other people. Particularly when smallpox came, which was one of the great plagues of the world, as you know, it was noticed that these milkmaids didn't get it. From that it was gradually discovered through a process of some numerous steps that if you get cowpox, you are in some way or other protected against getting smallpox. Now this idea of inoculation, giving you one disease to prevent your getting another, is a kind of a way of making you "weller" than you were before, in that you are protected against something that you previously haven't been protected against. Cowpox being less serious than smallpox, most of us are glad to have it. Of course most of us have had it now. Cowpox got to be one of the great popular diseases of the world and everybody tried to get it, just as we try to have our little girls and boys get the German measles to protect them against serious trouble later.

Now for another illustration. People who have arthritis noticed long ago that if they have a fever of some kind from another cause, their arthritis gets much better. So the treatment was tried of giving them a fever artifically in various ways. We tried giving them an abscess. Now an abscess is pretty painful, but not necessarily as painful as the arthritis, and so a severe abscess will sometimes seem to improve the arthritis. We have better ways of producing fever now with fever machines which don't cause infections. I am just giving you the principle.

Another discovery with which you are probably familiar was made accidentally when a drug being used experimentally seemed to cause convulsions. It was not meant to cause them, but after the convulsions had occurred it was noticed that some of the sick people were improved in ways that had no relation to the disease for which they were being treated. This is the way that electroshock and insulin shock were discovered, by accident during an attempt to cure some other condition—diabetes, for example. The point that I am trying to develop is the old principle that sometimes one illness can, in some way or other, drive out another illness.

I remember an old story which I am sure you have heard. My dentist told it to me when I was just a little boy. If a tooth was to be extracted he would guarantee that the pain would go away if I would do exactly what he told me. Of course I said, "Well what is it?" He said, "I will give you a hatpin, and when I tell you, stick the hatpin the full length right in your leg and you won't notice that your tooth hurts!" That principle sort of stuck with me and I wrestled with it quite a while! Then I ran across the fact that Hippocrates, who was a kind of father of scientific medicine, believed in what he called the healing powers of nature. However, he thought that nature was outside the body. He didn't think of the body as being nature so much at first. Later he did. He thought sunshine and fresh air were great healers, but he also noticed that a great many diseases were cured if *hemorrhoids* developed! Now why on earth he made that observation—and I doubt the accuracy of it—I don't know. The question is, supposing that that were true; how would we be able to repeat that experiment of nature in a therapeutic way? I don't know.

This idea that illnesses can be replaced or changed is one that I am asking you to concentrate on because I want to go back now to mental illnesses. We have thought for a long time that various drugs could cure illnesses in various ways by neutralizing the infection, or by stimulating certain responses in the body to combat them. Now I want to invite your thinking for a few minutes on what the word "recovery" means. In what way does the hatpin illness cause one to recover from a dental illness, so to speak?

Suppose you think of somebody who is ill—not yourself, somebody else; there one can be more objective. He is ill, but somebody says he has recovered. Now who says he has recovered? Let's say that *he* says he is recovered. What does he mean? I suppose he means that he doesn't have any pain any more; or perhaps he means that he doesn't have the disability he had had . . . he doesn't limp so much, or he can move his arm more freely; or perhaps he merely means that he doesn't feel so hopeless and the world looks bright again; or maybe he means that he is not so aware of a rapid degeneration and disintegration of his corporal frame and in that sense feels that death is somewhat postponed. Obviously, none of us recovers from death. In one way of looking at it, we are all marching slowly, slowly, slowly toward disintegration. From that we never recover. We know that we don't recover from that progressive march, and what we recover from subjectively is discomfort rather than disease in that sense, or from a particularly rapid disintegration, or from disability.

Now look at it from the standpoint of the observer. The observer cannot see the pain, and he cannot feel the pain. He can only be told about it. If the patient says "I have pain," you have to believe it; or if he says, "I don't have pain," you accept that. But the observer, who might be a physician, has other ways of examining. *You* may say you feel perfectly well and think you have recovered, but *I* don't think so. The doctor may say, "I think you have recovered," and the patient says, "I don't think I have, as I still feel awful." Or it may be the other way. The physician may say, "I have evidence from tests and from X-ray that you haven't recovered. You'll have to stay in bed a few more days." But the patient says, "But doctor, I feel fine. I want to get up." Now you have two judges. You could have another judge, couldn't you? What do the neighbors say? They may say, "Well, *he* may think he has recovered and the doctor may think so, but *I* don't think so. And I'll tell you why." And they tell you. Well, the neighbors have a point of view about this and it is one that we shouldn't neglect. Maybe the neighbors are the best judge of all; they may say, "He has never done a constructive thing for this community. He doesn't act like there was anybody but him on this earth. I don't call that recovery."

Suppose the neighbors say, "Oh, he looks fine; he has recovered." Let's suppose that the doctor says, "I have X-rayed you, I've made some blood tests, I have made some urine tests, I have observed you, I have taken your temperature, etc., and I think you have recovered." Suppose the patient himself says, "I am glad I have. The doctor says I have recovered, the neighbors say I have recovered, my wife says I have recovered; I guess I have recovered." Now suppose we give psychological tests to such an individual. A psychologist might conceivably say, "He is able to fool people pretty well, even himself, but he just thinks he has recovered. He hasn't recovered." In what way hasn't he recovered? He still continues to think loosely. He continues to misjudge people slightly. He still tends to project the blame to others. The question of whether and to what degree a person has recovered is all relative and is capable of being judged differently by different people.

This abstract case I am giving you, you may find a little dull. Let me give you a more dramatic one and you will see immediately what it means. Suppose I ask you if a certain person in your community, who has done a violent crime, has recovered. First you will say, "Recovered from what?" I'll ask you. "Did you think he was sick?" "Well," you say right away, "I don't think a healthy-minded person would do what he did." Well, then you assume that he must have been sick. "Do you think he has recovered?" "No, I don't. I think he is dangerous." Very well, let's all agree with you for the moment. Let's say, here is a person whose illness took a form worse than cancer, worse than pneumonia, worse than hemorrhoids, worse than diabetes, worse than any of these things. It took the form that made him hurt one of his fellow men. He has become dangerous. Certainly, then, somebody has to deny him liberty for a while. Let's leave vengeance and punishment and smug righteousness out of it. Let's just treat him objectively and say, "This is a dangerous person and he mustn't be in the position to hurt other people as he has a tendency to do. So let's watch him. We will watch him all year, and we will watch him next year, and the next, and the next." So we do, and this man develops a good many talents and becomes useful and decorous. Has he recovered? Let's ask the doctor to examine him. The doctor examines him and says, "I find no sickness. I find no evidence of sickness." Let's ask the people who have been in his vicinity—his neighbors. They say, "Well, he doesn't offend us. He is not a difficult person for us to adjust ourselves to. We find nothing that can be called a sickness. If he had one, so far as we are concerned, he is recovered." Then let's ask the person himself. He will say, "I think I am perfectly safe to be trusted. I don't think I would hurt anybody. I think I am recovered." Then let's ask the psychologist.

Now suppose they all agree. There will still be other people in the general public who will say, "We don't think he has recovered. We don't think he has ceased to be dangerous. We don't want him near us." You ask them on what basis they say that and they reply, "We just don't think he has. We don't want to believe that this could be possible." Now this isn't just a theoretical matter; it is one of the most puzzling problems for the federal government and the state government at the present time.

We don't want to be responsible for releasing people who are going to be dangerous, but we are just as alarmed today about retaining people in custody at your expense—and a very considerable expense—who are not only not dangerous but who are capable of doing splendid things, doing useful things and being community assets. The man committed his crime, but in my opinion that does not justify the state in committing a crime. That is why I am irrevocably, to the last ditch, opposed to capital punishment. I think the state has no right to commit a crime any more than an individual does, and taking peoples' lives is a crime and immoral in my opinion. Besides being immoral, it is unscientific, and it frequently defeats justice. It constantly leads people to be so afraid to take any responsibility of saying that a man is dangerous that they find him not guilty.

Nevertheless it is hard to say, when an individual has been detained in public custody for a while, that he is well enough to go. Everybody in the country has been angered, at times, by reading that such-and-such a terrible crime had been committed by a man who was recently discharged from such-and-such a prison. You know why. Many times the prison officials would like very much to keep the man; they know he is dangerous, but the judge didn't sentence him to stay until he was cured, or until he was recovered. The judge sentenced him to five years according to the statutes of the state law, or whatever it is. Therefore he served five years and then he is out. Penological people are very much distressed by this because the men that ought to be released they can't release and men they ought not to release they have to release, and this is because of the present rigid structure of the penal system.

I want to talk about the fact that people improve and we don't know how to handle people who have improved. If you have pneumonia, or if you have bronchitis or a bad cold, you don't feel as well as before you had it. You wait until it has run its course and then you say, "I am well again. I am just as well as ever. I am my old self." Of course you are not your old self. You are a different self because time has moved on. You have learned something. Maybe the cold did you some good. You theoretically could be better. Now in the case of mental illness it is very definitely and obviously true that frequently you are better.

Mental illness is frequently an experience from which the individual learns and profits and develops and grows. The fact that this can happen seems to me to illustrate a principle which some clergymen might seize upon to make the basis of quite a little inspirational thinking. Even Nietzsche, who was far from being a clergyman, said something like this: "This secret spake life herself unto me. 'Behold, I am that which must ever surpass itself.'" Now this tendency to constantly surpass one's previous state of existence is, of course, from the biological standpoint, comparable to growth. So we say of a person, "Is this man living up to his maximum potentialities?"

Have you read *Christie's Big Toe?* It is an incredible story. In a little tenement crowded with eleven or twelve children, one child who was born a spastic was regarded as being mentally deficient. He was noticed, however, scratching with his toe, which was the one part of his anatomy over which he had any continuous control. Gradually he began to draw with his toe and then to write, and under the guidance of his very busy mother ultimately to go beyond that and get some excellent training at one of the fine places in New York. Ultimately he wrote his autobiography, which is a unique document of the boy who could communicate only with his right big toe at first.

The ill individual narrows his vision till he ceases to see the multiplicity of opportunities. Is the recovered individual now a constructive social factor? Is he giving to the world as well as receiving from it? Giving money is a very good criterion, in a way, of a person's mental health. Generous people are rarely mentally ill people. On the other hand, let's not get critical of some of our stingy friends. Remember that stinginess is an illness. Stinginess is a symptom of some kind of a fear, so that they don't dare give of themselves even if they have money. They might run out. My dear friends, of course you are going to run out. You can't take it with you! I don't know how many hundreds of my patients are now asleep in the graveyard, leaving behind them far more money than they could handle. Far more money than their children can amicably divide, causing endless trouble and worry and oftentimes injury.

I remember I said to a man, "What on earth are you going to do with all that money?" He said, "Just worry about it, I suppose!" I said, "Well, do you get that much pleasure out of worrying about it?" "No, but I get such terror when I think of giving some of it to somebody." I said, "Well, you have quite a symptom there. But you are not alone in it. That is a fairly common symptom at your age. You are older, now, aren't you?" "Yes, I'm fifty-seven now, but I still feel just like I did when I didn't have anything."

Sometimes some people have a mental illness and grow beyond that. They begin suddenly to see they want to have fun in the broad sense of the word. They want to grow. They want to enjoy the gratitude of people. "I want to enjoy trees, I want to enjoy music,

I want to enjoy the world." This represents a kind of growth that we frequently see in our patients who have been mentally ill and some who don't know that they have been mentally ill, and even some who haven't been ill at all. I think, in short, that this is my notion of the gradual and progressive growth that we all make in the direction of mental health. This is what I think mental hygiene is. Now, as I have been speaking perhaps you have been thinking, "Well that is what is done at Chautauqua." That is the whole spirit of Chautauqua and that is what I meant you to think. That is what I think mental health is.

10. The Cinderella of Medicine

The title I have selected may have led you to expect a fairy tale. I shall begin what I am to say, however, with a special version of one of Aesop's fables.

Six blind men sat by the gate of a great city as an elephant was led slowly past. Inspired by scientific curiosity of the highest degree, the six blind men rushed forward to palpate the great beast and to determine the nature of his being.

The first man's hands fell upon the elephant's tusks. "Ah," said he, "this creature is a thing of bones; they even protrude through his skin." Later on, years having past, this man became an orthopedist.

At the same time the second blind man seized the elephant's trunk and identified its function. "What a nose!" he exclaimed. "Surely this is the most important part of the animal." Accordingly he became a rhinologist.

The third man chanced upon the elephant's great flapping ear and came to a similar conclusion; for him the ear was everything, so he, in time, became an otologist.

The fourth blind man rested his hands on the huge chest and abdomen of the elephant. "The contents of this barrel must be enormous," he thought, "and the pathological derangements infinite

Read at the annual meeting of the Medical Society of the State of New York, New York City, May 10, 1938. Reprinted from the *New York State Journal of Medicine,* 38:922–925, June 15, 1938.

in number and variety." Nothing would do but that he should become an internist.

One of the blind men caught hold of the elephant's tail. "This," he said, "would appear to be a useless appendage. It might even be a source of trouble. Better take it off." The blind man became a surgeon.

But the last of the six men did not depend upon the sense of touch. Instead he only listened. He had heard the elephant approaching, the rattle of chains and the shouts of the keepers. It may be that he heard the elephant heaving a great sigh as he trudged along. "Where is the creature going?" he asked. No one answered. "Where did he come from?" he asked. No one knew.

Then this man fell into a deep reverie. What was in the elephant's mind, he wondered, in having left wherever he was and having come to this great city. Why does he submit to the indignities of our curiosity and the slavery of chains? And while he was wondering how to find out the answers to these questions the elephant was gone.

This man became a psychiatrist.

The other blind men were disgusted at this impracticality. They turned their backs upon their visionary companion. What difference does it make, said they, what the elephant's purposes may be? And his chains—they constitute a legal not a medical problem. The important thing is to recognize the animal's structure!

Then they fell to quarreling among themselves as to whether the elephant's structure was primarily that of a nose or that of an ear or that of a tail. And although they all differed flatly from one another on these points they all agreed that the psychiatrist was a fool.

It would be pleasant for me to assume that this allegory no longer represents accurately the attitude of the specialties of medicine toward one another and toward psychiatry. In some respects I think that the proper continuation of the allegory would represent the six blind men taking counsel with one another and making some concessions that the elephant had ears as well as a nose and that he had purposes and feelings as well as tusks and a tail. The tendency

in all scientific research is to lose one's perspective in the intensity of
one's special interest. Psychiatrists may do this no less than surgeons
or otologists.

But in the main it is true that physicians have forgotten or ignored
or repudiated the psychological factors in their patients. Modern
medicine is based upon three basic sciences—physics, chemistry, and
psychology. Of these chemistry is the oldest. For many centuries it
completely dominated medicine. The physics of the body were considered unimportant and physical methods of treatment were considered unethical, undignified, unscientific. It was only in very recent times, relatively speaking, that some members of the barbers'
guild became surgeons, that bonesetters became orthopedists and that
stone crushers became urologists. It was only in recent times that the
mysticism and magic that permeated the recipes of the pharma-
copoeia were purged by the cold light of pharmacological science.
But it has been still more recent that psychological data have assumed some recognized validity of their own and ceased to be a
vague compilation of theories, variously derived from philosophy,
religion, and superstition. A systematic physics of the body was arrived at before a systematic chemistry, but both became the common property of physicians long before a systematic psychology was
known to anyone.

It cannot be said that psychology has been incorporated into medicine as yet, either in theory or in practice. In practice, medical science
has long since become so great in its scope and complex and in its
detail as to favor the development of three kinds of physicians, those
depending chiefly upon physical concepts especially in their treatment methods—and here I have in mind the surgeons—those depending chiefly on chemical measures—and here I have in mind
the internists—and those depending on psychological methods—
and here I have in mind the psychiatrists. What a physician should
be called who utilizes all three of these basic sciences in his work I
do not know, unless it would be that we come back to a new and
prouder use of the simple word "physician." In that case what I am
extolling are not psychiatrists but that kind of a physician for whom
physical, chemical, and psychological data have equal validity.

As a general thing, however, I am afraid this does not prevail. Patients are much more apt to get good physical and laboratory examinations than to get good psychological examinations, or good psychological treatment. I have previously made the statement that if a psychiatrist were to make a diagnosis of appendicitis on the basis of a psychological examination alone he would be justly criticized; yet many doctors are quite willing to make a diagnosis of psychoneurosis on the basis of a physical examination alone.

Suppose I should ask you—and you are representative, progressive physicians—did you in examining that patient yesterday make any psychological examination? Did you, for example, ask him anything about his dreams? No? Why not? Are they not a part of him, a product of his anatomy and physiology and psychology? Meaningless? Negligible? Compare the reactions of a practitioner of medicine fifty years ago when a youngster, recently from medical school, proposed that he examine his patient's urine. "What? Urine? I *did* examine it—it was dark and stank. What more is to be examined? Urine is of no importance—it's only an excretion, to be thrown out quickly." And can you imagine the old fellow's scorn when his son diffidently asserted that it was considered by some doctors to be really possible to examine urine with a flame, with chemicals, and with a microscope—for the purpose of understanding better the organs and the human being from which it came?

And is it really so very different from the proposal that dreams, too, can be analyzed—if one studies the techniques?

I am reminded of course that there are practical reasons why surgeons, dermatologists, and others feel justified in omitting some of the technic of a complete personality inventory. "Psychiatrists," they say, "are overwhelmed with too many data. They can't use all they have. We don't have time to get so much information about the patient. A patient might die while we are getting it. Furthermore it is unnecessary for the determination of the best practical treatment in many cases."

I won't deny the fact that short-cut methods of examination are desirable. What I deny is that one has any right to make this short-cut method at the total expense of the psychological factor. If a man breaks his leg, it is perfectly true that he doesn't want his surgeon to spend three or four hours getting a family or social history or making an intelligence test or analyzing dreams before he puts the leg in a splint. On the other hand, a complete omission of the psychological factor might lead, and I think often does lead, to serious errors in the treatment. Such an investigation in this case, for example, might prove that the man had broken his leg while in a fit of rage, trying to kick his dog or his child, or that his insurance policies paid him $500 a month disability, or that this was the fourth time that he had fallen in this particular spot and the second time he had sustained a fracture in such a fall, suggesting that there was something more than mere chance involved. In other words, a broken leg is a piece of local destruction and may be a covert form of self-destruction. One can confine himself merely to repairing the destruction as a carpenter repairs a broken joist and wait for the next piece of self-destruction or the next accident or the next infection—or one can look at it in the broad sense and compare this with other self-destructive events in the life of the individual and relate them to some more fundamental patterns.

All this sounds so logical—at least *I* think it sounds logical—that the question ought to be, Why is not psychiatry the queen of the medical specialties—in a sense the mother of them all, the integrating and synthetic phase of medicine itself? Or at least why is it not better integrated with the rest of medicine? To some extent, as my brother Will has said, the psychiatrist himself is responsible for this. For many years he contented himself with his assigned but very limited task of looking after an esoteric group of individuals in a secluded cloister on the periphery of a village. He spoke infrequently and then chiefly about such imponderables as dementia praecox and depersonalization, sometimes about dairy barns. He seemed closer to his patients than to the profession and the rest of life.

Thus for years psychiatry remained, as I have indicated in the title, the Cinderella of medicine. She sat alone by the fire in the kitchen, while her proud sisters Ophthalmology and Pediatrics strutted in the parlor. Sister Surgery was there, too, forgetful of her humble origin in the barber-shop, and Mother Obstetrics was never reminded of her poor relations, the Midwives. When, by the Fairy Godmother's aid, the transformed Cinderella appeared at the Great Ball (the war), she outshone all her sisters. It was there she won the Prince's favor (popular esteem), and thereafter she came out of the kitchen and consorted with her fashionable and now deferential sisters, and at last married the Prince.

Thomas Salmon, of New York, first used this figure, a man whose broad vision, whose keen mind, and whose winning personality did much to favor the ascendancy of this Cinderella. And while it is true that the laity has assimilated the principles of psychiatry more rapidly than have some parts of the medical profession, I do not think it was the public alone whose good graces put psychiatry where it is today. I think the intelligent, honest realization of an important portion of the medical profession itself that the psychological factor in medicine could no longer be ignored, forms our most dependable support. Some have felt, not without justice, that psychiatry has been oversold; this is true if one means that a greater need for it exists than our present supply of psychiatrists can fill.

For it was inevitable that science should have gradually displaced the ancient superstitions and taboos attaching to the medical man whereby it was inconceivable for him to be imperfect. So long as the medical man could not bear to examine his own psychology he could not logically concede it to have any importance among the clinical data of his patients. Among the discoveries of Freud, perhaps the greatest are those pertaining to the scientific study of the emotional bonds which develop between the patient and the physician. So long as it was taboo for the doctor to ask himself, "Why am I a physician? Why am I interested in disease? Why does the specialty of pediatrics appeal so to me?" and similar questions, it was necessary also to avoid, "Why did the patient expose himself to syphilis? When did the gastric-ulcer patient begin to hate his wife? What is the purpose of this woman's illness?"

For are not the wishes, the dreams and desires, the fears, and hates and envies of a patient as much a product of his being as his urine, his blood, his spinal fluid?

Are they not as deserving of analysis and as amenable to treatment measures?

What I have been saying may have carried some of you beyond your convictions or my persuasions, so I shall pursue that line of thinking no further, because it is not necessary to explain why psychiatry, the Cinderella, left the kitchen and married the Prince. The fact is that she has done so. If you doubt this, reflect upon the fact that in several medical schools more time is devoted today to the teaching of psychiatry than to the teaching of surgery, that more hospital beds are filled with psychiatric patients today than are filled with all the medical and surgical and tuberculous and orthopedic and all other cases combined. That the state of New York spends many thousand times as much upon the care of psychiatric cases as upon the care or prevention of medical and surgical diseases of all other types. And if you reply that this is because of the social importance of psychiatry I should reply that all disease has social importance and that the failure as physicians to recognize this has laid us open to criticism and to error. I do not mean by this to indicate my approval of the state care of the ill. It does not have my approval. I only mean to remind you that the state has for a long time been in the business of caring for some of the ill and that this some is a much larger number than many of you realize. As a psychiatrist in private practice, I can get no satisfaction out of the fact that the state is my largest competitor and that, although we are friends, we are not cooperators. And I strongly feel that had we physicians recognized from the first that *psychological and social factors are a part of medical science,* we could have made a better arrangement for the care of the mentally ill than now exists and better arrangements for other illnesses that now threaten. Those of you who fear that state medicine will compete with private initiative in other forms of illness might take this as a warning. I must tell you in frankness that some physicians whom I have heard loudly declaiming against state medicine, sometimes do everything possible to prevent a patient from receiving the psychiatric care he needs and resort in the end to sending him to a state hospital without any inkling of the inconsistency of this program. It is this very inconsistency—this blindness to the psychological and social aspects of the human being, a blindness of which a few of our colleagues seem even to be proud—which is one reason for the rise of state medicine.

I am sorry to have injected this serious note into the hour of relaxation afforded by this banquet after the heavy program of the day. You see, I have had some theories about the instinct toward self-destruction, the way in which man fights against himself. I have extended it from clinical phenomena such as martyrdom and suicide to social phenomena such as crime and even to nations warring against nations and against themselves. Our profession, too, sometimes betrays this human trait of fighting against itself. As a psychiatrist my daily occupation is the recognition of such tendencies and the outlining of programs for their circumvention or redirection. You must forgive me if I cannot resist the application of my professional technics to the problems of my own—our own—profession.

I do not know what the future of psychiatry will be. I would certainly not leave you with the impression that we psychiatrists have so great a lack of modesty as to assume to guide the development of all medicine. We have no monopoly on the comprehensive study of the human being, unless by neglect you force it upon us. From the indications of your courtesy in having invited me here to speak for my fellow psychiatrists and having listened so graciously to my strictures and suggestions, I have the impression that you have no wish to do so. On behalf of Cinderella, ladies and gentlemen, my appreciation and my compliments!

11. The Psychological Factor in Disease

No feature of the modern medical scene presents more alluring prospects, both in theory and in practice, than the increasing recognition of the emotional factor in organic disease. The growing interest in this aspect of medicine is reflected in the research now in progress in numerous centers, and in the ever-expanding bulk of pertinent medical literature. But even if none of these researches had ever been published, the daily experience of every thoughtful, intuitive physician must have led him to similar conclusions were it possible for him to allow himself to think what he has been taught never to believe.

For there is a strange paradoxical situation in this matter, in that what we all know in private life we do not discuss in our public scientific sessions. Every doctor in this audience knows that it is impossible to separate human psychology from human physiology and human chemistry. Yet look at the program of this meeting; look at our exhibits; look at the curricula of our medical schools—and tell me why the psychological factor in disease is avoided as if it were taboo.

As a psychiatrist, I have for a long time been interested not only in the psychology of my patients, but in the psychology of myself, and of my colleagues. Logically, therefore, I have reflected on this curious

Read before the Section on General Medicine of The American Medical Association, San Francisco, June 16, 1938. Reprinted from the *Bulletin of the Menninger Clinic,* 3:14-19, January 1939.

fear of or aversion to the discussion of psychological concepts, and I believe numerous factors contribute to it, to summarize which would be impossible in the time allotted me today. I will concede, however, that one factor is a charge to be laid at the door of us psychiatrists, who have not always remembered that we are doctors first and psychiatrists afterward, and that we must speak to our fellow physicians in the common language and not in a psychiatric jargon.

Perhaps, too, if psychological factors in disease had not been made the basis of a so-called religion, one of the tenets of which is that all doctors are wicked, physicians might not have been so slow to acknowledge the truth back of the distortion. They forget that this creed arose in part as a reaction against the static materialism of a medical practice which ignored psychological data completely.

But there are other reasons for this reluctance of doctors to consider scientifically the psychological factor in medicine. There is a group of thoughtful medical men whose stumbling block is their inability to reconcile their knowledge of the physiochemical operations of the body with what they regard as the unproved claims of those who use psychological techniques. A representative of this group recently voiced these objections to me in these rather typical words: "I hear what you say about gastric ulcer and arthritis and prostatitis and hyperthyroidism and asthma being cured by psychotherapy. I know what has been written about ulcers and hemorrhages being produced by suggestion. As a gentleman and a fellow scientist, I may not doubt your word, but to me it just does not make sense. I am familiar with your theory about self-destruction and I can see how a man might voluntarily cut off his nose to spite his face, but how could he inflict such damage upon his prostate or his stomach or his thyroid? There are no voluntary nerves to these organs. The autonomic nervous system does not carry such purposive impulses. There isn't any known way that one's thinking, conscious or unconscious, can affect one's organs except in a very general way, such as bodily tension or fatigue. I can't repudiate my belief in anatomy and physiology, and therefore I can't accept these research reports about emotional factors in physical disease even though they are attested to by credible scientists and colleagues. I am compelled to believe that they are coincidences or misinterpretations of fact."

To such colleagues, and I believe there are quite a few of them, I would make the following reply: In the first place, it *is* possible to account for many of the organic responses to emotion on the known facts of autonomic innervation and function, especially in the light of the newer knowledge of the hypothalamus.[1] Hence, even on their own grounds, such objections are unsupported. But in addition to this there is a new line of supporting evidence coming from the experimental physiologists which I think should be widely disseminated. The work of some of the Russians,[2] Rasenkov and others, have shown that cortical stimulation evokes hormonal substances capable of producing the same effects as does the direct stimulation of the brain itself; the injection of blood and spinal fluid obtained after the stimulation of the brain will affect the pancreas, for example, in the same way as did the original cortical stimulation. The same principle underlies the work of the American, Bender,[3] who demonstrated that the facial and ocular reactions characteristic of fright could be produced in monkeys after destruction of the nerve supplying these muscles. Bender showed further that the same muscular contractions could be invariably reproduced by administration of acetylcholine. This would suggest that the emotion of fright stimulates the production of acetylcholine or a substance like it which in turn can produce reactions which we have for hundreds of years supposed to be dependent exclusively upon direct nervous stimulation. Hall[4] of Toronto has gone further and shown that injections of acetylcholine are followed by the production of pathological organic lesions of a wide variety and Gardner, Smith, Strong, and Allen[5] have shown that lesions of various types and in various organs may be produced in animals through the use of large doses of estrogen. This is a continuation of work begun twenty years ago by Lathrop and Leo Loeb[6] and represented more recently by the experiments of Lewis and Geschickter[7] correlating the estrogenic hormone with various tumor growths.

What does this all sum up to? Simply this: that it is no longer possible to say that there is no experimental evidence for the existence of physiological mechanisms by which psychological activity may result in organic damage. This principle may even be extended to include neoplasms. It is astonishing that laboratory physiologists should thus have come closer to the consideration of the psychological factors in cancer than have the clinicians.

To all this I shall add some of the positive evidences from other fields than those of anatomy and physiology as to the validity of the concept of the psychological factor in disease. Time prevents my more than listing some of these with a few comments on each.

1. We know that physical symptoms and signs may be induced by stimuli which are essentially psychological in nature. Both hypnosis and hysteria afford clear and acknowledged evidences that just as a blister or a paralysis may be brought about through a mechanical blow, they may also be brought about by a psychological blow. If they *may* be brought about then they *are* brought about. If they are brought about under a set of known conditions there is no logical reason to dispute the fact that they might be brought about under other conditions less well controlled or understood. In other words, the fact that we understand the psychological process involved in a hysterical paralysis does not mean that there are no psychological processes in an organic paralysis.

2. It is a matter of empirical observation that in some diseases the psychopathology is just as conspicuous as the physical pathology and it is illogical and unscientific to assume that they have no connection. If a man who has been found to have hypertension is also found to be living in mortal terror of being declared bankrupt, it is perfectly legitimate to attempt to explain these two symptoms separately but it is also legitimate to attempt to understand them conjointly. Those of us who believe in the unity of the organism cannot be persuaded that there is any sense or science in limiting personality study to piecemeal consideration.

3. No one denies the therapeutic effect in some organic diseases of a purely psychological or sociological approach. It would be very tiresome to this audience to recite even the classical illustrations of this. It is more important that I point out that the psychological amelioration of an organic disease does not prove its psychological origin. In fact, I have repeatedly posited that it is philosophically

impossible to conceive of any disease being purely psychological in origin. But such phenomena do show that pathological energy disbursements can be altered in a favorable way by recourse to psychological techniques just as we already know this to be possible by recourse to physical or chemical techniques. That goiter can be cured sometimes by surgery, no one will deny. That it can be cured sometimes by iodine, no one will deny. That it can be cured sometimes by psychoanalysis, no one who is informed will deny. This does not mean three different kinds of goiter or that one method is as good as another. It seems a little trite to say that there are more ways than one to kill a cat, but we doctors seem to have to be reminded of it, because we have groped along for so many centuries on the assumption that psychology was taboo and not to be touched by scientific zealots.

4. A corollary source of evidence is the empirical observation of the alternation or substitution of predominantly psychological and predominantly physical disease syndromes as if they stood in some reciprocal relationship to one another. I refer not only to the structuralization of symptoms which are at first "hysterical" in nature, later becoming organic, but more especially to the less familiar but more convincing phenomenon of patients ill with a physical disease who, cured of that illness against their wishes, as it would seem, replace it with a mental disease, and vice versa. We have all seen this many times.[8]

5. Finally, we cannot take it to be pure coincidence that the same motives, the same psychological structure, can be demonstrated to exist in illnesses which are predominantly psychological and illnesses predominantly physical. Both have the same destructive consequences, and it is difficult to conceive that they do not have in the deepest layer of the personality the same self-destructive purpose. Whether this be called instinct, energic trend, regnant process, or something else does not matter.

In conclusion, I should like to say again what I have said many times before—namely, that the word psychogenic as applied to a disease confuses the issue and misses the point. If we assume that the terms psychological, physical, and chemical describe three different aspects of the same phenomenon and relate primarily to different techniques of investigation, approach, or management, it logically follows that in every disease process there are psychological factors, physical factors, and chemical factors. For this reason there can be no such thing as a psychogenic illness. But there can also be no such thing as a physiogenic or chemogenic or bacteriogenic illness. There are physical and chemical factors in every case of hysteria and there are psychological factors in every instance of ulcer, hemorrhage, infection, and cancer. The progress of medicine demands that we seek for these, and ignore no longer that which is attested to by our experience, our experiments, and our philosophy.

To recapitulate, I have submitted some evidences from physiological research that psychological processes represented by the wish to fall ill may be correlated with the structural or functional disease of an organ. I have submitted psychological and empirical evidence in the same direction. I do not expect these intellectualizations to overcome the emotional resistances of some of my colleagues, but for those who see the human being and his environment as a totality of interacting functions—and not as a collection of independent parts—the material cited may afford reassurance as to the equal validity of psychological, physical, and chemical data in the study of the sick patient.

12. Psychiatry and Medicine

To obtain a proper orientation as to the relationship of psychiatry to the general practice of medicine, one must consider its historical development. For our purposes it is unnecessary to go back farther than the Middle Ages, since psychiatry in its present-day form had its incipiency in that era. Medicine, on the other hand, was already an ancient discipline and its development in the Middle Ages was coordinate with religion and with the crafts. I select these three phases of human activity because from them developed what is now psychiatry.

Medicine, at that time, was largely a *chemical* discipline, dependent upon alimentary therapy in both theory and practice. This it had inherited from antiquity. But from the practical guild and craft men there developed various *physical* and mechanical devices applicable to medical practice and these were gradually assimilated by Mother Medicine. From midwifery (a craft) came obstetrics; from tooth-pulling came dentistry; from barbering came surgery. What we now call neurology was always an integral part of medicine, an elaborate, interesting, but unproductive part. The marriage of practical surgery with respectable neurology resulted in a very lusty child—neurosurgery—which revived neurology and made it useful as well as respectable.

An address delivered before the St. Louis County Medical Society, May 5, 1936, in conjunction with addresses by Dr. Adolf Meyer and Dr. Abraham Myerson. Reprinted from the *Bulletin of the Menninger Clinic*, 1:1–9, September 1936.

Meanwhile, from the vague assemblage of ideas represented by religion, philosophy, alchemy, and astrology, there developed a descriptive interest in certain unclassifiable, unpredictable, irregular psychological phenomena characterized chiefly by social incompatibility. The persons exhibiting this behavior were called criminals, witches, the bewitched, or the insane, and these names gradually became established as *legal* designations. From among them, finally, the most unpredictable, incomprehensible, and paradoxically behaving individuals were singled out for political detention and gradually fell into the hands of scientists, who studied the behavior and found it to be less incomprehensible than had been assumed, indeed entirely understandable once all the facts became known. These scientists were, although working with persons acknowledged to be sick, haltingly accepted by Mother Medicine, at first, but with the unexpected demands of the World War, psychiatry became the Cinderella specialty and advanced to great favor. The most important result of this was that the psychological component in the human personality was recognized along with the chemical, mechanical, and physical derivatives.

The sudden great popularity of psychiatry almost ruined it because the great promise held out by the recognition of this previously ignored element in disease was not fulfilled. Too much was claimed by, and too much was expected of the new science. As had been so often said of neurology, psychiatry could offer diagnosis but not cure. This was vividly true in the cases diagnosed as psychopathic personality, psychoneurosis, and schizophrenia.

Fortunately, in the nick of time, psychiatry, like neurology, took unto itself a fertile bride and its marriage to psychoanalysis had the same rejuvenating and fructifying effect as did the union of neurology and surgery. This does not mean, of course, that all psychiatric therapy is psychoanalytic, any more than all neurologic therapy is surgery. But the advent of psychoanalysis ended the era of therapeutic nihilism in psychiatry.

From exclusive application to those patients with obvious and extreme psychopathology, psychiatry was gradually extended to other fields—criminology, sociology, pedagogy, and recently, with increasing intensity, to the parent field, general medicine. To it psychiatry brought techniques of approach to the patient, of personality evaluation, and of therapeutic management with which general medicine for all its perfection of laboratory procedure and clinical measurement had been only vaguely familiar. Here and there an intuitive old general practitioner had discovered for himself in the "art" of medicine the importance of dealing with the *feelings* of the patient and of influencing his recovery by a proper consideration of these intangibles. But psychiatry, with the aid of psychoanalysis, has made progress in the reduction of this intuitive technique to systematic, scientific principles, the application of which need no longer be limited to a gifted few.

As a result, the emphasis on *psychological* factors in disease (and in health) is slowly permeating the entire practice of medicine. No longer the exclusively *chemical* concepts of the Middle Ages and earlier, nor the chemico-*physical* concepts of the nineteenth century, but a concept of interacting physical *and* chemical *and* psychological factors begins, now, to characterize the theory and practice of medicine. Once it was considered ridiculous to record a temperature; later it was considered ridiculous to examine a specimen of urine; and when these procedures became generally accepted it was still considered ridiculous to inquire into the details of a patient's dream. Now we know that dreams and urine and fever all may and *must* be examined if we are to truly and fully understand a patient. No intelligent or informed physician thinks any of these procedures absurd today—even though in practice he may sometimes omit one or several of them. For every thoughtful physician knows that psychological factors are as real and as effective as physical or chemical factors. His training, however, makes him feel more proficient and sure of himself in the old traditional modalities of physics and chemistry, and he is often afraid to venture into the psychological investigations that he fully realizes his patients merit and need.

The result is that certain rather sharp differences persist in the points of view and techniques of most medical men, on the one hand, and psychiatrists on the other. The psychiatrists sometimes feel that they alone actually look at the human being as a whole, instead of as a creature with certain extraneous pathological attachments or invasions. The general medical man, on the other hand, suspects the psychiatrist of ignoring or underestimating physical and chemical data and of exaggerating psychic factors beyond their proper degree of importance. He thinks, too, that psychiatrists are apt to see the whole world a little askew, as if all people were "more or less crazy," and this strikes him as ill-founded and distorted.

Then, too, the time concepts in psychiatry and in most other medical specialties (phthisiology and orthopedics excepted) differ considerably. Psychiatry, along with the two specialties mentioned, thinks in long-time terms; treatment extends over a long period, prognosis considers a long interval; the patient's whole life is under consideration rather than an acute episode or relatively brief illness.

Again, the patients with whom psychiatrists deal are often under some degree of social taboo which does not apply to the patients of most other specialties, that of the urologists perhaps excepted.

Finally, the psychiatric modalities depend more upon aural than upon oral ministrations. Words, i.e., ideas are "poured into" the patient rather than drugs, with, however, no less palpable—often identical—effects. This is a difference which the general medical man accepts with grave misgivings, because he feels suspicious of anything which resembles, even remotely, the unsavory procedures of quackery and faith healing. Unfamiliar with the deeper mechanisms of psychological reactions, he cannot understand the therapeutic results which shrewd cult leaders often achieve, but has a strong feeling of condemnation for them because of their unscientific and often obviously dishonest methods. Because psychiatrists work with the same raw material and must use scientifically some of the tools which have fallen into the hands of unscrupulous and unreliable persons in some instances, the reproach attached to the faith-healers has often been turned against them unjustly.

But the essential differences that yet separate psychiatry from general medicine go deeper than this. They may best be illustrated by indicating the points of routine psychiatric inquiry and comparing these with general medical practice.

To the psychiatrist, how the patient *acts and reacts* (behaves and feels) are important data. To the average physician, they are not. To the patient, they may or may not be.

For example, a cardiac patient may describe in detail his subjective reactions during a moving-picture show or during an attack of decompensation; in either case the average physician listens only from courtesy, if at all. The psychiatrist, on the other hand, puts great stock in such data. The patient may or may not see any sense in so doing.

Similarly, the psychiatrist is just as interested in how a patient reacts to the making of a physical examination as he is in the other data obtained from such a physical examination. He is just as interested in observing what the patient's emotional reactions are toward his office nurse or the hospital manager or himself as he is in discovering what the patient's blood pressure or leucocyte count or vital capacity may be.

The psychiatrist considers it the first task of a physician to observe these ordinarily neglected data, to recognize them, to appreciate that they have meaning, to seek this meaning, to try to evaluate them. He feels that only having done this can he decide what should be done next with any degree of scientific precision. This "next" may be a chemical manipulation, a mechanical adjustment, or psychological therapy.

It is, of course, impossible definitely to separate diagnosis, prognosis, and treatment; and the psychiatrist feels not only that attention to these data of action and reaction are necessary for a diagnosis and for the prescription of treatment but that often the first indicated treatment is to let the patient know that he, the doctor, is actually interested in these data; he also feels that the prognosis can be accurately determined only by considering them.

For that reason the psychiatrist routinely investigates elaborately the historical data connected with the development of the personality as well as of the present illness. At the same time he does *not* neglect (as he is sometimes thought to) an exhaustive physical inventory, including the routine physical, laboratory, and X-ray investigations, specialized neurology examinations as well, and, finally, a very careful, systematic psychological study.

Throughout these examinations he is particularly interested to observe what the patient has been faced with and how he has responded or attempted to adjust himself to it, and how he has failed. The general medical man also takes these things into some consideration, but, as a rule, without a systematic or persistent attempt to correlate the successive failures or successes of such a patient.

Accordingly, a complete study of the patient, from the psychiatrist's point of view, would also include the analysis of the emotional patterns displayed by the patient in each of the basic situations of life—the home, the school, the vocation, the marriage, and society in general, i.e., his techniques of failing or succeeding with the personnel composing these groups. Finally, a systematic, scientific study of the development of the patient's sexual life cannot be neglected except from hypocrisy or slovenliness.

With all this data (physical-chemical-psychological-social) in hand the psychiatrist asks himself:

1. What is the insuperable difficulty in the situation which this patient is trying to meet, i.e., what are the extraneous factors impeding normal adjustment: What opportunity does this patient have—now or hereafter—for normal living—physical, mental, sexual, social?

2. What, on the other hand, is the fundamental weakness or defect in his personality (a) from the standpoint of physical structure; (b) from the standpoint of physiological or chemical functions; (c) from the standpoint of psychological intention and inhibition?

3. What is the primary purpose of the present illness, and what is the secondary gain accomplished by it?

4. In an effort to expedite better adjustment of patient and universe, (a) to what extent can his environment be changed; (b) to what extent can his personality be changed; (c) in what way and to what degree may the positive functions of the illness be combated or replaced by more expedient devices?

Once these questions are answered, the psychiatrist feels it is possible to make a diagnosis and outline a treatment in the direction of alleviation, counteraction, correction, and digression. This treatment may utilize not only physical, chemical, and mechanical agencies but psychological and social agencies as well. It will be seen from this how different the technique and the point of view of psychiatry are from that of general medicine. It is chiefly a matter of a broader view of the patient and his illness.

The question naturally arises as to whether there is any justification for attempting to bring closer together the viewpoints of the physicians and the psychiatrist. Is it or is it not helpful to consider these instinctual, purposive, emotional factors in general medicine? To the physician they seem unnecessarily elaborate and cumbersome. To the psychiatrist it seems impossible to ignore them with scientific justifiability. Both physicians and psychiatrists are apt to fall back upon the explanation that, after all, they are dealing with different sorts of patients entirely. But is this really true?

I should not go so far as to say that there is not some pragmatic truth in the distinction that is made between patients who consult psychiatrists and patients who consult general practitioners, but I am certain that these groups are not separated so widely as is ordinarily assumed. The fact of the matter is that the psychiatric approach has never been applied in any systematic or extensive way to the problems confronting the general practitioner. Recently some researches in this direction have been undertaken at the Institute for Psychoanalysis in Chicago and at the Presbyterian Hospital in New York with extraordinary results both investigatory and therapeutic. To speak of the emotional factors precipitating the arthritis, the psychology of colitis, or the psychotherapeutic cure of gastric ulcer would have been regarded as prima-facie evidence of lunacy or chicanery a few decades ago. Yet all these have been matters of serious scientific consideration by eminent physicians (*not* just psychiatrists) within the past few years.

I should like to suggest a theoretical point of view which might go far toward reconciling these differences of opinion between psychiatrists and general practitioners. This requires a rather radical revision in the ordinarily accepted notions of what disease is and what we, as physicians, are trying to do. Nevertheless, it is a hypothesis which has gradually developed of late on the basis, originally, of empirical observations.

It is generally assumed, I believe, that the sick man comes to a doctor because he has been overtaken by fate, ill-fortune, bacteria, or some other invader—and the disease is looked upon as something the patient hates, fights, and wants to be rid of. He applies to the doctor, who accepts the responsibility and focuses his energies upon combating this foe. But there are many bits of evidence that such a view makes incorrect assumptions and ignores an important principle. It does not require great intuition to detect the fact that the foe with whom many patients fight is not something outside of them but something inside—a part of themselves. They are often ready enough to let the doctors do the fighting for them; some even do their best to oppose his efforts, and, even though bacteria, bad food, and sharp corners do exist and do inflict wounds, it is often observable that such wounds are invited.

If, in addition to this, we think of the persistence with which some patients cling to their illnesses, the compulsive way in which patients frequently force surgeons to operate and re-operate upon them, the extraordinary repetitiousness of afflictions to which some patients fall victim—these, together with such clinical syndromes as alcohol and morphine addiction, neurotic invalidism, voluntary asceticism from other than religious reasons, malingering, and finally that most dramatic of all human acts, suicide—if we consider these things we must begin to suspect as Freud did that self-preservation is not the only instinct which dominates mankind. On the contrary it would seem as if a self-destructive impulse waged constant battle with the will to live and took advantage of every opportunity to wreak its purpose upon its possessor.

Ordinarily the self-destructive impulses are presumedly held in abeyance. Sick people, on the other hand, may be conceived as of persons in whom the battle has erupted so that they are trying to destroy themselves and at the same time fighting against it, imploring aid in this from the doctor. Such a hypothesis might be applied to such immediate and sudden self-destruction as is represented by suicide, or to more gradual and diffuse self-destruction such as neurotic invalidism. Perhaps such a thing as tuberculosis in which the individual seems to yield, sometimes all too willingly, to the in-

vasion of an available assailant, and even the more localized or
focalized diseases of the body may be thought of as further illustrations. Such an extension of the theory to organic disease was not
made definitely by Freud and we are not yet in any position to support it with convincing evidence; it is, however, a logical conclusion
from the theory that, if there is a self-destructive impulse with the
strength which Freud has postulated and which much clinical evidence supports, then we should not be surprised to find that it had
an active part in the production of physical as well as psychological
disease. Concerning its activity in the latter (i.e., "mental" disease),
we psychiatrists now have no longer any doubt. Concerning its function in the former, we must wait expectantly the result of research.

In terms of this hypothesis, the therapeutic indication is regularly
the same, whether in psychiatry, orthopedics, criminology, or cardi-
ology. The physician must throw the weight of his knowledge, his
skill, his experience, his chemical, mechanical, and psychological
adjuvants on the side of the embattled life instinct and in opposition
to the destructive tendencies. This is actually what is done at the
present time in both medical and psychiatric fields, and we know
that it sometimes saves the day for the patient. This success, in turn,
saves the life of the physician, in a very literal sense. It diverts his
own destructive tendencies to the attack on the destructive tendencies of others, and by losing our lives we save them. This probably
accounts for the prevalent optimism characterizing physicians in
spite of their often dreary experiences and for their conviction that
they have this responsibility and this power. Whatever the reasons
may be, we physicians well know that our deep feelings and our
professional ideals do not permit us to stand by inactively in the face
of a life-and-death struggle. Our daily lives consist in a participation
in innumerable miniature wars between life and death, and our
constant striving is to increase our perspicacity, our skill, and our
discernment, and, for all this, our efficacy in the opposing of self-
destruction.

And although the phenomenon of war, which now looms again
upon the horizon, would seem to be the most dramatic exemplifica-
tion conceivable of this human wish to destroy one's self (along

with one's neighbor) we are simultaneously aware of the weak but growing opposition set up against it by the cooperation of intelligent minorities who struggle with humanity's ills as we physicians wrestle with those of the individual patient.

This is my conception of psychiatry and of general medicine as well, and I feel sure than no one of my colleagues, medical or psychiatric, will deny that from this standpoint, at least, we have more in common than in controversy. What techniques we shall evolve to discover and rout or counteract this self-destruction will differ widely, varying with our talents and training. But with this concept of disease and medical science we are less likely to be misled by the naïve assumptions, false optimism, and easy discouragement which the older views of man versus environment inevitably induced.

13. Changing Concepts of Disease

In deciding what I as a psychiatrist might present to this representative body of internists, I considered several possibilities. I could talk about something which I understood fairly well but with which you are less familiar, such as the psychodynamics of schizophrenia. This might impress you with my expertness, but it would also probably puzzle you. Or I could talk about something which you know all about and I very little about, and this would amuse you. I could talk about something which we all know about, and this would bore you. So I concluded to talk about something which neither of us knows much about, hoping that this might at least intrigue you.

So I begin by assuring you that I am well aware that I know almost nothing about the subject I am presenting except that it is important for us all to think about it.

Perhaps I can enlist your interest in the topic if I recite briefly how I came to begin thinking about it. I have said that I was a psychiatrist. So I was for over twenty-five years. Recently, however, I have had to become a physician! In my position as director of a graduate school of medical education which includes young surgeons and young internists as well as young psychiatrists; and also in my capacity as director of a sizeable general hospital, I have had to think of medicine as a whole. I have had to try to relate in principle and in practice the functioning of many different kinds of

Presented before the twenty-ninth annual meeting of the American College of Physicians, San Francisco, April 19, 1948. Reprinted from the *Annals of Internal Medicine,* 29:318–325, August 1948.

doctors. I have had to revise my comfortable notions about a lot of things which we doctors get into the habit of taking for granted.

For example, I used to think that the accepted formula for any properly trained medical man was very simple—collect data about a patient, organize them, establish a diagnosis, and treat the patient according to the diagnosis. Examination, diagnosis, treatment; patient gets well and lives happily ever after (unless, of course, an error has been made in the diagnosis!).

I am somewhat ashamed to say that it has taken me a quarter of a century to realize that this formula rarely works out this way in actual practice and that it may well be that it is the wrong formula.

What I got out of medical school was the conviction that the world was full of healthy human beings, and that now and then a victim was struck down by a cruel blow from an unheeding Nature—an infestation, a lurking bacterium, a malignant cell. Now and then an inexplicable perversity seized the liver or the pancreas or the bone marrow. As a result, a "disease" developed and a patient appeared on the doorstep of the physician. With the proper questioning and the proper application of a few indispensable gadgets, the diagnosis was correctly established and the proper treatment instituted.

It never occurred to me in those days to realize that *most* people in the world are sick, and not the exceptional individual who came to the out-patient department of the Massachusetts General Hospital. It never occurred to me in those days that the pain produced by a sickness might be experienced by everyone else in the patient's environment more than by him. It never occurred to me to consider how much society determined the illness of a particular individual or how much the individual himself determined, desired, and even inflicted upon himself the suffering for which I as a physician was asked to offer relief. Disease, as I viewed it, and I think I fairly accurately caught the spirit of my preceptors, was an entirely unwanted, useless, purposeless misfortune, acquired inadvertently through an unfortunate concatenation of forces emanating from the best of all possible worlds or from the defective architecture of a hereditary constitution.

It is not often that we discuss the basic philosophical assumptions of medicine, and perhaps most of my audience has been so engrossed, as I have, in doing the daily job with the presenting patient that we haven't stopped to reflect, as I had to in writing this paper, how much our daily experience has taken us away from such concepts. Don't we all agree, really, that whether we call them psychiatric problems or psychosomatic problems or allergic problems or cardiovascular problems or something else, most of the patients—far and away the majority of patients—that you and I treat day after day cannot be given an accurate, specific, meaningful diagnostic label and do not represent any disease entity?

What shall we call the "disease" represented by a man who has always been frail but has worked very hard to support his widowed mother, did not feel he could afford to get married, buries himself in the details of a complicated job, develops paralyzing headaches, loses time at the office for which pay is deducted from his wages, worries about this so much that he loses sleep and begins vomiting after each meal? Just to make it complicated, he has a leucocytosis and an enlarged spleen. Does not such a case defy diagnosis?

Even in the simplest cases it seems to me misleading to make a diagnosis in the old-fashioned way. A middle-aged puritan spinster appears in my office with a chancre on her lip. Isn't this a simple diagnosis? I don't think so. Nor would you if I told you the circumstances of how she acquired that chancre, whom she acquired it from, how she happened to select that type of man, or why she permitted him to kiss her. Her sickness cannot be accurately diagnosed just as syphilis. She did not come to me because of it. What she came to me for was a more serious thing. She was so depressed about the implications of the infection that she now wanted to kill herself. What is the name of that disease? Is it a part of the syphilis? The doctor who is giving her penicillin was wise enough to know that penicillin alone would not cure her.

Diagnosis in the sense in which we doctors have used it for many years is not only relatively useless in most cases; it is an inaccurate, misleading, philosophically false predication. Many doctors know this intuitively. When patients ask, "What is this that has gotten me down?" such doctors reply, "Oh, its a respiratory thing," or "Apparently you caught a bug that is going around," or "You have a cardiovascular involvement; it's tied up with this worry you have at present. Your blood pressure isn't dangerously high and your heart's making an adjustment to it. I think things will improve when that contract is signed." These are not diagnoses in the old sense; they are evasions of diagnosis. Such doctors might be embarrassed if we pressed them, and I think we have no right to do so because these doctors feel the untruthfulness, the unscientific nature of a diagnosis according to our former schedules. We used to think that a doctor who indulged in such vagueness was an unscientific doctor, that all that was the matter with American medicine was the failure of "the old fellows," as we patronizingly called them, to see the necessity of establishing a diagnosis as a basis for treatment. Of course, there was a certain truth in this, and there was also a certain great falseness in it, and it is the falseness that I want to examine today.

I realize that throwing doubt upon the desirability of making a diagnosis as I have done is bound to be disturbing to many physicians. "Granted," they will say, "that one finds many cases in which he cannot make a diagnosis and many in which he has to make a multiple diagnosis; the fact remains that we ought to try to decide what is wrong before we plunge wildly into some kind of therapy. You are attacking a basic foundation stone in scientific medicine. You are encouraging eclecticism and opportunism and shotgun therapy. You are going against everything that we have spent hundreds of years trying to establish."

No, I am not; really I am not. I suffer from the same uneasiness that you do about the consequences of a misinterpretation of what I am saying. But I ask you to listen carefully: *I have not said that we should not attempt to make a diagnosis.* I have merely said that this simple formula of *diagnosis determines treatment* can no longer be carried out as we originally conceived of it, because diagnosis is too complex and attempts to make it simple and definite lead us into error. I have given you some cases to illustrate this, and I shall give you some more.

A traveling salesman of 25 had kept at his job for several years in spite of an increasingly extensive exudative and distressing dermatitis. He had had all sorts of treatment for it, to no consistent avail. Because of it he felt unable to make proper social contacts and, feeling increasingly excluded from the company of "nice girls," he felt obliged to force his attention upon prostitutes. When even prostitutes were dismayed at his appearance he convinced himself that his sexual life would have to be a choice between masturbation and rape.

About this time he was inducted into the Navy and after about a year of unsatisfactory service he was discharged. In his own words, "I guess I just scratched myself out of the Navy." He then proceeded to scratch himself into another hospital, where I saw him.

Everything else having failed, the man was quite willing to see a psychiatrist and proceeded to take advantage of the doctor's invitation to tell him all about his problems. He talked on and on; and the psychiatrist listened on and on. He became intensely emotional in his recollection of the various complications of his life; for the first time the entire pattern began to unroll. The psychiatrist continued to be attentive, permissive, and noncommittal.

And now what do you think happened? Having thus relieved himself of guilt feelings, shame, fear and other stored-up emotion, the patient recovered? His dermatitis disappeared? Not so; it promptly became very much worse! Somewhat disturbing to the notion that psychosomatic afflictions can be deftly cured by emotional catharsis, isn't it?

We doctors are all only too painfully aware that our most logical and best-intended treatments often make patients worse instead of better. It is a blunder we all make; it derives in part from the fact that we cling to an outmoded practice of making disease-picture diagnoses. This leads to a treatment regime based not on the patient's condition, not on his real disease, but on the preconceptions of the particular person who sees the patient. In the case of the clerk which I related first, the sociologist would make a diagnosis of bad labor conditions, the internist might make a diagnosis of anorexia nervosa, the neurologist might see it as an aggravated migraine. In the case of the spinster, the syphilologist made a diagnosis of syphilis, and the psychiatrist a diagnosis of melancholia. In the skin case just related, five different diagnoses had been made—sexual psychopathy, vocational ineptitude, several kinds of dermatitis, and conversion hysteria.

"Very well," you will say, "perhaps he had all of these; multiple diagnosis is all right. But we must have diagnosis." Yes, but the question is, who is the "we"? Do you mean we internists? We neurologists? We pathologists? We sociologists? We psychologists? We psychiatrists? All of us are interested in the same individual; we all believe in the same scientific laws; we are all studying the same interrelated phenomena. Yet each of us has our own little list of syndromes, and we look for symptoms to fit a preconception without reference to any other "we," and call that a diagnosis. And just as surely as we do that, we violate the basic principle of the modern holistic or totalistic concept of the human organism. In theory there cannot be any such thing as a simple, uncomplicated diagnosis of anything, not even measles. The child with measles has at the same time some educational interruptions, and some social complications, and some disturbed relationships with parents and siblings. The only scientific right that we doctors have so to label the total situation in which a school child goes home sick with "measles" is the practical usefulness of a term, the full implications of which are fairly familiar to the general public. Any case of measles is far more than measles, any case of syphilis is far more than syphilis, any case of dermatitis is far more than a skin rash.

If, then, there is some practical advantage in adhering to conventional labels, and if in the back of our minds we remember that the total human organism is a physical-chemical-social-psychological interacting unit, what is the harm in continuing to use these convenient medical handles?

In many instances, none—provided we realize that any such diagnosis is a misnomer. But the tendency is to forget this and to assume that sick patients can be treated like automobiles—properly labeled and then passed down an assembly line of specialists for a punch here and a wrench there—without the guiding principle of an over-all perspective.

I recall a young banker in a small Wisconsin town who had built up his bank from a hard start by dint of assiduous application and good judgment. He began to suffer increasingly from indigestion, and his family physician, who was a member of the board of directors of the bank, studied him in the appropriate medical way and made a diagnosis of peptic ulcer. For a matter of eight years dietary and medical treatment kept the pain under control, but as guardian of the health of one of the community's most important citizens his family physician was disturbed by the possibility of hemorrhage, perforation, or chronic invalidism. He had repeatedly urged upon the banker the advisability of surgical treatment. The patient had strenuously resisted. Finally the conscientious doctor insisted upon the operation, and a successful gastrectomy was skillfully performed. He made an uneventful recovery and returned home.

But he did not return to work. He had become depressed. He appeared physically well, but he felt melancholy, pessimistic, unable to take interest in his work, his customers, or his friends. Month after month passed and his depression deepened rather than lifted. His very much worried family physician now urged that he go to a sanitarium. To this the patient demurred. Finally, under the pressure of friends, family, fellow citizens, and doctor, he agreed to go.

While his wife and his physician were making preparations to carry out this plan, the patient committed suicide.

To this day that family physician doesn't understand that tragedy. He keeps wondering what he did wrong. According to our false principles of departmentalized diagnosis and *ad hoc* treatment, he did nothing wrong. The patient had an ulcer and he received appropriate treatment for that; then the patient perversely developed depression and the doctor arranged the appropriate treatment for depression. It never occurred to him that the patient's ulcer was not his disease, depression was not his disease. His disease was something defective in his total life adjustment. While the bank was struggling he had no physical symptoms, but he had worry; when the bank got on its feet he had no worry, but he developed gastric pain. So long as he had gastric pain, his life adjustment remained in balance. But when this source of suffering was taken away from him he developed another type of suffering, and when this final type of suffering was threatened with removal he killed himself.

What was "the disease" of that banker?

What is the diagnosis in a patient who has coronary symptoms whenever he takes his wife to a party? Or in a woman who has migraine on the week ends that her son is home from college?

What kind of arthritis is it which becomes activated with each quarterly meeting of the board of directors?

If a young wife's dysmenorrhea disappears when her husband is drunk, or if a child vomits each morning just before school time, or if an educated young Negro trying to establish himself in a decent business in an average American city develops vascular hypertension at 35, or if the mother of five children who has been working an eighteen-hour day starts coughing up a little blood, or if a man reared in a home where the drunken father regularly abused his family develops syncope when he goes to his employer's office, or if a rugged individualist who believes in free enterprise exhibits his belief by bullying his employees five days a week and concealing his own feelings of insecurity by week ends of alcoholic anesthesia—if these patients come to see us, as they do every day of the world, what shall we say the disease is, in each case? What are the diagnoses? And what conceivable relationship do any medical diagnostic terms we might apply to them have to the necessary treatment programs?

We cannot make diagnoses to fit such disease pictures as these because our medical diagnostic categories depend upon traditional formulations some of which date back to prehistoric times. Séguin of Peru has, in a recent brilliant article,[1] called the bacteriological era of medical history the "Golden Age for the demoniac concept of disease, when germs became the scientifically named demons." In giving temporary support to the fallacious causality principle, the discovery of bacteria vastly retarded progress in our scientific medical thinking. Every thoughtful person knows that no thing or event in the world can have *a cause,* and that while the impulse to seek causes is, as Tolstoi says (in *War and Peace*), innate in the soul of man, "the combination of causes of phenomena is beyond the grasp of the human intellect." The early Greek physicians knew this and concentrated not on causes but on the phenomena of disease—the symptoms. Rivaling this "phenomenological concept" were theological concepts which equated disease with sin or with punishment, and then the humoral concepts which later found some representation in endocrinology. Virchow fought against the *sedes morborum* concept of disease which had been crystallized by Morgagni, distinguished by great conflict between the humoralists just mentioned and the "solidists" who sought to locate the "seat of disease" in organs. But in the end Virchow himself fell victim to the very theory he was combating by locating the seat of disease in the cell.

In common parlance we talk irrationally and childishly about the patient "fighting the disease," "facing it," "resisting it," and the like, forgetting that disease is not something external or alien but it is *of* the patient, and largely his own doing. The real problem is, what forces him to do it so? How have his defenses handled some new situation? And to what extent have those malignant self-destructive tendencies, which are in us all, combined with external forces to result in pain and faltering and sometimes death? It is somewhat shocking to read, even in some modern textbooks of pathology, statements which imply that disease is a *thing,* a horrid, hateful external thing, which invades the human organism like a snake in a dove's nest. Clinical medicine, with the fructifying stimulation of psychiatry and the psychoanalytic study of the unconscious processes, has a far more dynamic and progressive view than a pathology still couched in descriptive phenomenologic and demoniac terms.

For I believe that clinicians have come to think of disease more and more in terms of a disturbance in the total economics of the personality, a temporary overwhelming of the efforts of the organism to maintain a continuous internal and external adaptation to continuously changing relationships, threats, pressures, instinctual needs, and reality demands. The concept of biochemical homeostasis of the organism, which Cannon so beautifully described, has been extended to include a recognition of a concomitant and interrelated psychological homeostasis and sociological homeostasis, contributing to the total personality. The thoughts, feelings, behavior, and social relationships of patients, no less than their tissues and their body fluids, follow the same principle, the principle of continuous adaptative shifts and reciprocal balances.

When any one of these elements is disturbed from within or from without, the recovery of balance is attempted through a readjustment of all the others. The *agent provocateur* may be bacterium or a bayonet, a cancer cell or a seduction, a starvation of calcium or a starvation of love. Whatever the upsetting influence, many elements cooperate to restore the balance. Sometimes they overdo it, and the last state is worse than the first. For some aspects of this imbalance we have medical terms, for some aspects we have only sociological or common-speech terms. But a meaningful diagnosis cannot be confined to the terms of any one discipline. To do so is to mislabel the condition, to misconceive its essential nature. What we conventionally call "disease" is sometimes the *agent provocateur,* sometimes the wound; it is sometimes the overaction of systemic defense measures and sometimes the consequences of mismanagement by relatives, friends, and even doctors. It is sometimes the picture of a triumphant malignancy, and sometimes that of a quiet renunciation, the sacrifice of a part for the whole, as with Polycrates' ring. All these we have called "the disease."

It is the imbalance, the organismic disequilibration, which is the real pathology, and when that imbalance reaches a degree or duration that threatens the comfort or survival of the individual (or his environment), it may be correctly denoted disease. The protean manifestations of that imbalance must be looked for by the doctor in all the spheres of human life, identified in their relationships, understood in their totality, recognized as symptoms of the imbalance, and labeled in any pragmatically useful way. But they must *never* be mistaken for *"the disease."*

14. The Doctor as a Leader

It is an ancient convention that upon the occasion of a group's completion of a prescribed course of study, such as that of the medical school, some seasoned warrior is appointed to array himself in vestments symbolic of his long battle with the mysteries of the universe, and to indulge himself in platitudes and rhetoric as the one last torture to which the novitiates are subjected. It is a significant occasion—a time for welcoming, cautioning, exhorting, and inspiring. It is an appropriate moment for administering again in spirit, if not in words, the oath of Hippocrates. It is an occasion for someone slightly removed from the interpersonal processes of teaching and learning in which you and your faculty have been engaged to offer you and them the congratulations of the rest of the profession and of the people of the world to whom you will minister—to *you* and to those dedicated men in your faculty who have given their best to give you a good start in the lifelong process of learning.

It is a temptation to indulge in the privilege and the honor accorded me by continuing in a philosophical vein some reflections upon teaching and learning. Unhappily doctors are too often led to believe that philosophical reflection is a vice to be shunned, and I have known some of them to exemplify a stern renunciation of the temptation by delivering as a commencement address some exceed-

Commencement address to the graduating class of the University of Rochester Medical School, March 27, 1948, in Rochester, New York. Reprinted from the *Bulletin of the Menninger Clinic,* 13:9–15, January 1949.

ingly dull observations regarding the cultural media best suited to the cultivation of a newly discovered bacterium in the left ears of some Abyssinian primitives.

I shall try to avoid both errors. I could easily discourse on the subject of psychiatry, because for thirty years I have practiced psychiatry and for most of that time I have taught psychiatry. More recently I have tried to combine the direction of a large Veterans Administration hospital, in which we have tried to develop some new principles of medical integration and hospital treatment, with the equally fascinating task of organizing and directing the graduate training of over a hundred internists, surgeons, and psychiatrists. My knowledge of psychiatry has stood me in good stead in this, especially in helping me to realize the importance of leadership. I have often asked myself: Why have we so few good leaders? Is it possible to train leaders? Is it something which we can deliberately inspire and cultivate? Or is leadership something that is inborn in a few? At any rate it is something we can talk about because it is a function and a responsibility which falls to every doctor—usually to his very considerable surprise.

In a remote and isolated section of South America there was discovered in 1915 a small tribe of Indians known as the Nambikuara. A few years ago they were made the object of a careful study by a French anthropologist, Claude Levi-Strauss.[1] In the consideration of the basic psychology of leadership I know of nothing more stimulating than his report of these studies.

Each year at the end of the rainy season, the semipermanent dwellings in the forest near which the primitive gardens of the Nambikuara are tilled, are abandoned and the population splits into numerous bands formed on a free-choice basis consisting of two to ten families, each of which has a chief. Theoretically these chiefs hold office for life and name their own successors, but the nominee is not always willing to serve; chieftainship does not seem to be coveted.

Nearly four hundred years ago Montaigne asked a representative of another tribe of Brazilian Indians what the privileges of the chief were and received the answer, "To walk ahead on the warpath." In one of his essays (*Des Cannibales*) Montaigne dilates upon his proud

definition. Four centuries later Levi-Strauss received the same answer! Actually the Nambikuara word for chief seems to mean "the
one who unites." Of this Levi-Strauss says, "This etymology suggests that the native mind is fully conscious of this extremely important phenomenon . . . the leader appears as the cause of the
group's willingness to aggregate rather than as the result of the
need for a central authority felt by a group already constituted."
Each chief is entirely responsible for the management of his group—
orders the start of their wandering period, selects the route, chooses
the stopping points and duration of stop, organizes the hunting
parties, and, in short, takes the full responsibility of everything the
group does.

His authority depends entirely, however, upon continued approval or consent. Therefore, the structure of the group might seem
to be very weak. How does the chief maintain it? one might ask.
By generosity. The chief must continuously give of food, tools, weapons, ornaments, etc., to the members of his group. He must be chief
entertainer, singer, dancer, ball player, and general stimulator. He is
by far the hardest working man in the tribe. Levi-Strauss describes
one particular occasion when the group which he was observing ran
out of supplies. The hungry natives simply lay down in the shade
and waited. The leader did not wait or discuss, but took the problem
as a matter of course and left the camp, accompanied by one of his
wives. Late that evening they returned heavily laden with baskets
filled to the brim with edible grasshoppers which they had spent
the day catching and which they now donated to the group.

The chief is the only member of the group who is permitted to
polygamize. The function of the polygamy is a curious one; it
creates a permanent imbalance within the group as between the
number of marriageable boys and girls. It constitutes the functional
device placed at the chief's disposal by the group which enables him
to carry out the exacting duties. The author believes that *consent*
is at the same time the origin and the limit of this leadership. The
relationship between the chief and the group is a perpetual process
of arbitration where the chief's talents and authority, on the one
hand, and the group's size, cohesion, and willingness on the other,

constantly interact. This (mutual) consent is the psychological basis of leadership.

Levi-Strauss inquires why anyone is willing to take this arduous job of chieftainship. He thinks the polygamous privilege, highly valued though it is physically, sentimentally, and socially, would not be sufficient to determine the leader's acceptance. He thinks there is something more which he felt rather than actually proved to himself: namely that "there are chiefs because there are, in any human group, men who, unlike most of their companions, enjoy prestige for its own sake; feel a strong appeal to responsibility; and to whom the burden of public affairs brings its own reward." These individual differences are certainly emphasized by different cultures and to unequal degrees. But their clear-cut existence in a society as little competitive as the Nambikuara strongly suggests to my mind that their origin itself is not cultural. "Men are not all alike; and in primitive societies . . . those individual differences are as keenly perceived and worked out as in our so-called individualistic civilization."

I have cited these observations about a tribe of Indians to lead your thinking in the direction of the function of a leader and the meaning of leadership in our own society. Doctors have traditionally assumed the responsibility of leadership almost without knowing it. The profession inherits this responsibility from centuries of social custom. Doctors have been given special privileges of education and they are afforded special privileges of social prestige and legal permission. Every doctor, therefore, has the obligation to assume that degree of leadership of which he is individually capable.

Dr. Romano of your faculty, Dr. Bartemeier of Detroit, Dr. Whitehorn of Baltimore, Dr. Kubie of New York, and I were sent to the European Theater of Operations shortly before the end of the war to make a study of the disintegration which occurred to so many men under the stress of battle conditions. Most of our conclusions could be summed up in one simple sentence: There were too few good leaders!

On the other hand, however, there were many fine leaders who understood intuitively or by training what leadership meant and what it required. Among these fine leaders, I am very proud to say, there were a very large number of men who probably did not consider themselves leaders at all. They were the young doctors who served as battalion surgeons in the very forefront of combat. By their example of courage and devotion and scientific absorption without loss of the essential human qualities that a doctor must preserve, they were real leaders.

Colonel Marshall,[2] a military observer, has written forcefully about leadership in the war, describing how officers were continually discovering powers of strength in individuals whose earlier service had been "lusterless." Men suddenly became leaders under certain situations of stress; sometimes they actually took the leadership away from their superior officers to the annoyance of the latter (who, for example, sometimes refused to decorate really great heroes). "Those were not small men, moved by jealousy. They were puzzled men who were groping their way through one of the most complex of all human relationships. Someone had failed to counsel them properly" (with respect to leadership, of course). Marshall contrasts, in this regard, command as a prerogative with leadership as a responsibility and technique.

Then he develops the point that although gunfire wins battles and everyone assumes that soldiers in combat shoot their guns, repeated and thorough investigations discover the astonishing fact that only about one-fifth of them ever do so! Occasionally, "in the most aggressive infantry companies, under the most intense local pressure" the figure rose above twenty-five per cent; the average seems to have been about fifteen per cent.

Marshall keeps coming back to faulty leadership as the main thing in military failure. He brings out the great importance of proper communications and especially lateral communications, feeling that a lack of these was one of the most demoralizing influences. He points out that there is a lot of pressure from above to get reports back up, but not enough effort to get reports back down and across. He cites some dramatic examples to show how communication routines sometimes blocked rather than furthered leadership. For example, "In the Burton Island fight during the invasion of the Marshall Islands, one of those prodding demands for more progress raced from division right through lower headquarters to a platoon which had been stopped cold by Jap fire coming from spider holes arranged in great depth along the beach. Lieutenant B—— got the message and, crawling forward to his most advanced rifleman, told him to get up and go on. The boy screamed, 'So the whole God-damned Army wants to kill me, does it? O.K., Lieutenant, here I go, but watch what happens.' He was shot dead almost before he had gotten out of his tracks. That incident seared deep into the brain of every man who witnessed it. It was a final judgment on the futility of that kind of leading.

"As I went about my work, I came to see, more fully and more surely than I have expressed it in the tactical portions of this book," wrote Marshall in conclusion, "that the great victories of the United States have pivoted on the acts of courage and intelligence of a very few individuals. The time always comes in battle when the decisions of statesmen and of generals can no longer affect the issue and when it is not within the power of our national wealth to change the balance decisively. Victory is never achieved prior to that point; it can be won only after the battle has been delivered into the hands of men who move in imminent danger of death."

"In every society there is a leading class born for leadership and without which nothing can be accomplished." (Lyautey, quoted by Marshall.)

Less dramatic leadership than that of war and less primitive leadership than that of a tribe of Indians but leading to the same conclusion, is the leadership a good teacher gives to his students, the leadership that a good dean gives to his faculty. You graduates of the University of Rochester Medical School have good reason for considering the significance of leadership and the influence of a great leader. For the equivalent of four years you have worked under the eye and the hand and the heart of one.

Dr. George Whipple, who has been your pilot—the pilot of your class, your school, your faculty—has all the attributes of a great leader. Every one of you is personally known to him; every one of you has been personally followed and guided and helped by him; every member of your faculty looks to him. It was he who built up this school; it was he who projected its unique ideals and its fine standards; it is he who has given the best years of his life toward making it a justly famous center of scientific education. One thousand excellent physicians have gone forth from this school in its quarter of a century of existence and they have gone forth with the ideals of their leader held firmly in their minds and hearts. The greatest tribute you can pay your leader is to try to be like him, and I know that Dr. Whipple is the kind of a leader who will be proud and happy to see some of you become even greater leaders than he. For the world is really very short of leaders—it is sick today of leaderlessness. Medical scientists more than anyone else should realize this and should do their part to remedy it. The practice of medicine is not to be viewed as an opportunity to live well, to do great operations, to earn big money. It is an opportunity and obligation to work very hard, to make much self-denial, to give much, to assume much responsibility; in short, to be a leader.

In emerging from the status of student to the status of self-supporting citizen, you will find it necessary to assume leadership in directions that you have never thought about before—in community planning, in school-board administration, in park programs, in social-welfare problems. You will discover that you have much more to do than to treat your patients and care for your family; much of your time will have to be spent in counseling the relatives of your patients and the friends of your family. Your counsel cannot be armchair advice; it will have to be to a considerable extent counsel based upon example.

Finally, I would like to say a few words about your responsibility to help us teachers do a better job of what we are trying to do for the next generation of students. For it will be your duty to think how we might have done a better job in teaching you. I have tried to fancy what you might say to us after you have come to feel in practice the dilemma of the modern physician. I think you might feel then like giving some good advice to the medical educator in *his dilemma*.

For our dilemma—the dilemma of the medical educator—is simply put in ancient words: Life is short and the art long, the occasion instant, experiment perilous, decision difficult. What shall we teach the medical student today that will be truly useful to the physician of tomorrow?

I think perhaps you might say to us something like this:

"Remember, please, that these men who are in your charge for four years must not only acquire technical knowledge; they must acquire self-knowledge; they must acquire a realization of the role they are to play in the complicated social structure of a complicated world.

"Hence, they must know more about that world than it is given to the average citizen to know. They must understand their role in it as leaders, as guides, as counsellors, as givers—as well as their role in the alleviation of pain and the forestalling of death.

"We know you teachers have all too little time in which to give these young men this knowledge and this inspiration. Hence, don't let them spend too much time smoking kymograph drums and preparing culture media. Don't let them try to memorize two thousand anatomical terms. Don't teach them some of the ponderous nonsense which, in all good faith, you laboriously taught us.

"Teach them to feel some responsibility and some authority in fields outside the laboratory and the surgical amphitheater. Teach them all you can about human beings—human beings in a changing world—human beings that have feelings as well as sensations, and ideals as well as organs. Teach them something about the paralysis of frustration as well as the paralysis of poliomyelitis, and something about the malignancy of hate and prejudice as well as the malignancy of streptococcus viridans.

"Teach them the sophistry of deterministic causality and show them how there can be no such process as something *causing* something else, and no real sense or wisdom in a search for a cause. Teach them rather to look for meaning, meaning in what the patient does, what he feels, what he says, what he suffers from.

"Teach them a new concept of disease, one that really fits the facts instead of reiterating the old shibboleths. Most of the things that we call disease are efforts of a part of the organism to restore the internal balance that has been disturbed by external traumata, and we know that the external traumata are as often psychological as physical or chemical.

"Teach them, as Plato told the Athenian army physicians after the Phrygian campaign, '. . . so neither ought you to attempt to cure the body without the soul; and this is the reason why the cure of many diseases is unknown to the physicians of Hellas, because they are ignorant of the whole, which ought to be studied also; for the part can never be well unless the whole is well—for this is the great error of our day in the treatment of the human body, that physicians separate the soul from the body.'

"Teach them the words of Oliver Wendell Holmes something about the psychology of bedside manners:

> And last, not least, in each perplexing case,
> Learn the sweet magic of a cheerful face;
> Not always smiling, but at least serene,
> When grief and anguish cloud the anxious scene.
> Each look, each movement, every word and tone,
> Should tell your patient, you are all his own;
> Not the mere worker, purchased to attend,
> But the warm, ready, self-forgetting friend,
> Whose genial presence in itself combines
> The best of cordials, tonics, anodynes.

"Teach them, finally, something of culture; that, in the words of John Cowper Powys, 'There is nothing more expressive of a barbarous and stupid *lack* of culture than the half-unconscious attitude so many of us slip into, of taking for granted, when we see weak, neurotic, helpless, drifting, unhappy people, that it is by reason of some special merit in us or by reason of some especial favor towards us that the gods have given us an advantage over such persons. The more deeply sophisticated our culture is, the more fully are we aware that these lamentable differences in good and bad fortune spring entirely from luck. . . . At any moment fortune's erratic wheel may turn completely around and we ourselves may be hit by some totally unforeseen catastrophe. At any moment we are liable, the toughest

and strongest among us, to be sent howling to a suicidal collapse
. . . hence, the more culture we have, the more deeply do we resolve
that in our relations with all the human failures and abject and
ne'er-do-wells of our world, we shall feel nothing but plain, simple,
humble reverence before the mystery of misfortune.'"

PSYCHIATRIC EDUCATION

15. Psychiatry and Psychology

It is difficult to make ourselves realize *emotionally and intellectually* the *valence* in significance of such landmarks in time and such cornerstones in the development of a human institution as is represented by this occasion. On the one hand we experience the pleasant glow of meeting old and new friends under new auspices, the comfort of mutual converse and association in the contemplation of a common objective, the mild excitement of employing new names, new phrases, new resolves in what is now a legal and official way. It is like those strange and mixed emotions of joy and hope, and sober, saddening contemplation that one experiences in attending— unprofessionally—the birth of a baby. It is quite certain that, for all their hopes and fears, the friends and family members who stood by the cradles of General Eisenhower, of Albert Einstein, of Mussolini, and of Adolf Hitler—little imagined what these seven- or eight-pound parcels of protoplasm would ultimately do for and to the world.

And so I think we cannot look with safety or reliability very far into the future of the infant whose birth we are celebrating tonight— especially those of us who in some degree participated in the parturition. All we can do is formulate and declare the hopes and ideals of

An address delivered at the inauguration of The Menninger Foundation–Kansas University School of Clinical Psychology, Oct. 21, 1946. Reprinted from the *Bulletin of the Menninger Clinic*, 11:45-49, March 1947.

the parents, trusting that some of them will become structuralized in the life and work of the child.

The Menninger Foundation–Kansas University School of Clinical Psychology springs into corporate being as the result of many forces —forces not born or generated over night. Many years of devotion to the patient instruction of students have given Dr. Wheeler and Dr. Morrison, of the University of Kansas, a vested right to feel proud of a new development in an old science which they have taught and fostered through years of less promise and less allurement than the present holds. The stimulating projects and formulations of Dr. Rapaport and Dr. Brenman, of the Foundation, were preceded, I can assure you, by the slow and painful drudgery of years of work. The same is true of the clinical experience of Drs. Challman and Holt and Dunn and Escalona and all the rest.

It is the experience of all these men and women put together that has gone into the naissance of our school.

Not only experience, but a spirit of cooperation, a moving urge for mutual cooperation and for collaboration with others of similar interest—this too has gone into the parentage of this school. This cooperative spirit is reflected in its organizational structure. Never before in history have the federal government, a state government, and a private institution combined to set up a teaching machine.

But this spirit of cooperation is even more important in connection with the basic idea of this school of clinical psychology. It is related to a development in the philosophy and techniques of medicine. Concerning this I should like to remind you of a few things you all know, but which we should remember in particular upon this occasion.

There is a saying current among us that psychiatry has arrived— or at least that it has emerged. If we are more conservative, we say it is emerging. I think we picture a lowly, obscure medical discipline, practiced by a small number of, for the most part, undistinguished but devoted physicians rising to heights of considerable importance through sheer force of clinical necessity. We are not even quite sure ourselves why psychiatric patients should have suddenly seemed to become so numerous. So long as the selection of a medical category was left to the public, so long as patients could select an obstetrician, a surgeon, an eye doctor, or a heart specialist according to their own conception of the nature of their illness, guided to be sure in part by medical prejudices—the only psychiatric patients were those whose friends and relatives forced this classification upon them with the aid of the sheriff and the judge.

But when the differentiation became dependent upon cooperative groups of physicians representing these specialties, when the triage began to be made by medical scientists, the assignment to the psychiatrist suddenly loomed very much larger. Under a relationship with the public such as that of the Veterans Administration, where every patient who needs help must be proffered it, one after another, just as they come, the great majority of cases do not turn out to be medical or orthopedic or dermatological or surgical. They turn out to be psychiatric.

And so because large numbers of patients are now being handed over to psychiatrists, of which there are a very small number, psychiatry has become a magical word. It would almost seem as if all medical science might have to be reorganized and reconceived so that, instead of being one of many smaller specialties clustering about medicine as a nucleus, psychiatry might become the center, with surgery, gynecology, ophthalmology, urology, internal medicine itself ranged about it as adjuvants.

My impression is that precisely something like this is actually coming about. I have long thought it would, and said so often—and long ago. Do not ascribe this to any prophetic vision on my part. I think it is the logical conclusion from a deductive hypothesis which the course of human events and the evolution of medical thinking seem to have justified.

That hypothesis is not one for which I or any of us here would claim any credit, but it is one which older leaders in psychiatry and in psychology—a few of them—proclaimed early in this century, and which Plato and other wise men perceived and defined centuries ago. In an allied sense it has been the burden of the teaching not only of the philosophers but of every great religious teacher and leader.

I refer to the hypothesis which has many technical names—the "holistic theory of personality," the "psycho-biological principle," the "total personality concept," and many others. In religious terms it reads this way: "Man, whose body you perceive, whose voice you hear, and whose warmth you feel, is more than flesh and bones; he has a soul." The philosopher would say, "Of human beings there are material aspects and there are nonmaterial aspects; man has a spirit." And now doctors, borrowing the cue from the psychologists, say the same thing in new words: "Psychology is a basic science necessary to the understanding of human beings and their vicissitudes no less than the basic sciences of physics and chemistry upon which we have hitherto leaned exclusively."

It is fascinating to contemplate the possibility of identifying those factors in social evolution which suddenly bring medical scientists— some of them—back to a truth known better two thousand years ago than it is today. It is almost equally fascinating to review the history of culture and the history of medicine and to trace the divorce of what we call psychology from the science and practice of medicine and its transilient affiliation with mysticism, with philosophy, and with religion. Perhaps it is medicine that has wandered rather than psychology—but that, too, is another train of thought. . . .

The fact is that today here we are—a group of us—all with the same vision. Skeptics might say that we all have the same faith. At least we all speak the same language. We all have the same password; we are all concerned with the psyche.

Some of us say it in Greek, and some in Latin. We say it in German, in Hungarian, in Spanish, in French, and in English. We say it—some of us—with clinical procedures in mind, some of us with research projects, some of us with educational programs. But we all say it, we all use it, we all center our thinking and our living about it. In such a union, whether one is a psychologist or a psychiatrist or a psychoanalyst or a psychometrician is of minor importance.

To this union of kindred minds the traditional practice of medicine brings a rich heritage. In my introductory remarks to the students of this first class, who have come here for training in clinical psychology, I have stressed the fact that the word *clinical* is one for which they should have profound reverence. It carries with it the highest ideals and best traditions of the medical profession. It implies the consideration given by one who is well to one who is sick—who lies abed. "I will not take advantage of, or misuse the advantage I have over one who, because I am in a sacred profession, has appealed to me for help. My immediate and my ultimate objective is the relief of suffering, his and that of others like him." That view becomes the professional responsibility of the psychologists coming into clinical work, into the clinical applications of what was once a purely academic science.

The discipline of psychology, on the other hand, not only brings to medicine that essential *vitamine,* that too long lacking element, which it needs, that we have stressed above; but it brings to medicine also a tradition of objective measurement, of clearly defined logic, of proper methodological procedure which clinical practice and clinical thinking tend to make us forget and neglect. Traditional psychiatric nosology has finally been forced into open bankruptcy, largely by the penetrating symptomatological analyses made by the psychologists. And a very healthy state of affairs it is, I say. We can now begin to define with a precision long absent from our work the clinical factors—psychological and otherwise—which characterize similar syndromes. The diagnostic function of the clinical psychologists is now so well established in psychiatry that the competent psychiatrist, in my opinion, would no more exclude the special techniques of the psychologist in his diagnostic studies than would a capable internist routinely exclude the findings of the roentgenologist. This has led to our irrevocable affiliation.

Whether, in the course of events, the therapeutic function of the psychologist will develop and find its proper place in the same way that the therapeutic function of the X-rays has found its place, we can only guess. I should expect it to do so.

Psychiatrists should not be surprised that psychologists are not yet fully accustomed to their new clinical role. Psychologists similarly should not be surprised if the medical profession, jealous of its historical and traditional responsibilities, is somewhat slow in welcoming the psychologists. In my own mind there is no doubt that the time will come when the assistance of the psychologists in the diagnosis, let us say, of cancer or arthritis will be taken as a matter of everyday routine by the internist, and when the treatment of certain types of illnesses by the psychologist associated with the psychiatrist will be taken as standard procedure. Such a time is not here yet.

And so in all our work at this clinic and in this school, I think we should remember that we have a triple function: that of learning to do better what we are trying to do, that of teaching others what we do and setting up procedures worthy of more general trial, and finally that of seeking out more of the answers to the mysteries of the unknown.

It is to this triple purpose that our school of psychology, like our school of psychiatry, is dedicated. Similarly our other schools to be, schools for social workers, schools for nurses, schools for internists and surgeons, will be likewise so dedicated. It is this conception of education and it is this conception of research and it is this conception of psychiatry which The Menninger Foundation was established to perpetuate. The word psychiatry as we use it means all that I have implied in these paragraphs—it includes the work of all who have taken the oath of fealty to scientific and Hippocratic ideals, who have surrendered individualistic narcissism to a spirit of mutual cooperation, and who have accepted the password. To the students of the school, the members of this first class, to the faculty which has already worked so hard but has far heavier tasks ahead, I offer my congratulations and my promise to work with you in the achievement of the common purpose.

16. Research in Psychiatry

There lies before me a list of the research projects, investigations, and explorations now in progress in the psychiatric community in which I work. This list was not prepared for the purpose of the present contribution; it is a routine report of the work of the research board created to maintain a general supervision of such matters. There are eighty-seven items on this list.

It might not be too wild a guess to say that perhaps a thousand such research projects in psychiatry are under way at the present time in various psychiatric clinics and psychiatric hospitals over the United States. At each meeting of the American Psychiatric Association over a hundred scientific papers are presented and there are

This paper represents thinking which cannot properly be credited to the author alone. It is the substance of scores, one might well say hundreds, of conferences and discussions at the Menninger Clinic over the past ten years. These have taken place not only under the direct auspices of the research department but across the luncheon table and across the conference table of the clinicians, psychiatrists, psychologists, social workers, nurses, and administrators. Portions of the paper have appeared in various reports and informal proposals made by individuals and departments. Several years ago Dr. David Rapaport, then Director of the Research Department of the Menninger Clinic and now of the Riggs Foundation, Stockbridge, Massachusetts, and Dr. Carl Tillman, then a staff psychiatrist of the Menninger Clinic but now director of the Piedmont Clinic, Oakland, California, set down some of the material approximately as it appears in this paper. Again on Oct. 2, 1946, the author opened the forums of the school year at the Menninger Foundation School of Psychiatry at the Winter Veterans Administration Hospital with the presentation of some of this material under the title of "Unsolved Problems in Psychiatry." I am indebted to the persons mentioned and to a great many more who cannot be listed for their contribution to a frame of thinking of which this is an informal statement. [K.M.]

Reprinted from the *Bulletin of the Menninger Clinic*, 13:73–82, May 1949.

more than a half-dozen psychiatric journals replete each month with the reports of investigations and observations.

Empirically, what do such researches pertain to? I have scanned the list on my desk and find that five of the projects deal with an examination of the nature, symptoms, and concepts of the condition we call schizophrenia; ten of them concern psychological concepts and psychological testing; three of them relate to the evaluation and study of personnel, including psychiatrists themselves; and a few of them concern the study of sociological and cultural relationships.

But far and away the majority of these projects are very practical. They deal with what we call psychiatric treatment. Some are concerned with hypnotic treatment, some with electro-shock treatment, some with treatment by drugs, by nitrous oxide, by brain surgery. There are projects in the study of treatment with the use of art, treatment with the use of music, treatment with the use of properly directed reading, treatment with the use of dramatic role taking.

Fully conceding that this is not a fair sample and that it represents only the trends in this particular center, I think it would not be incorrect to assume that most psychiatric research at the present time is of this practical nature. It is directed toward the question: What can we do in a more effective way to improve the personal adjustment of a patient, to re-establish a better inner and inter personality balance?

It might be—it no doubt is—disturbing to a philosopher of science to discover how little consideration we psychiatrists give to the basic principles of psychiatry. Psychiatry like every other science has its postulates, its assumptions. They are the foundation stones upon which the entire structure is built, and yet which themselves stand in constant danger of demolition through the discovery of new facts. Perhaps the most pressing need for research in psychiatry at the present time is in answer to the question: Exactly what do we assume in the delimitation and development of the field of psychological medicine?

I have some convictions about this. I have tried to list for my own use some postulates which I personally believe to be basic ones. I am not sure that the items in the list are correctly defined; I am quite sure that there is some overlapping; I am quite sure that the list is incomplete. But I feel that I have made some progress in my own thinking, and that I am of some help to my students if I have done no more than remind them (and myself) that psychiatry is built upon postulates or assumptions which must be continuously re-examined. I plan to elaborate these elsewhere, and I list them here only to indicate a line of thought. Here they are:

1. In the consideration of human material, psychology is a basic science comparable to physics and chemistry; therefore psychology —plus its societal manifestations, i.e., sociology—must be included in the scientific concept of personality. This could be labeled *the principle of the inclusion of the psychological disciplines.*

2. Since the whole is more than the sum of all its parts, the parts or aspects of the human personality—physical, chemical, psychological, and social—must be envisaged as an integrated, balanced totality. This is the well-known *holistic* or *total personality principle.*

3. Every person is in some respects like all other persons, in some respects like many others, and in some respects like no one else. This is *the principle of uniqueness.* It does not invalidate the study of personality by means of abstract concepts and scientific as well as artistic methods.

4. The individual is constantly in the process of adjustment internally with respect to forces and components of his own personality and externally with persons, forces, and objects with whom he has various kinds of contacts and relationships. This is called *the adjustment principle.* It is perhaps the most familiar in clinical psychiatry.

5. The total personality tends to maintain itself within optimal conditions with a minimum expenditure of energy; to put it another way, there is a constant internal and external movement aimed at maintaining a homeostatic equilibrium in all spheres—physical, chemical, psychological, and social. This can be called *the homeostatic principle;* it has also been called the stability principle, inertia principle, Freud-Fechner principle, Bernard-Cannon principle, and equilibration principle (Child).

6. By long-standing convention and tradition, a physician or his

representative has the authority, and empirically the ability, to alter the adjustment or balance (or lack of these) in a patient under his care, by various devices—physical, chemical, psychological, and social—with the object of permitting the re-establishment of a more stable total equilibrium. This is *the treatment principle*.

7. Just as in physics knowledge is derived from the continuum of the physical world and physical events, so in psychology conclusions can be derived from the continuum of the psyche and psychic events. Hence it is possible to study these internal and external adjustment processes, and the internal and external manifestations of maladjustment, and relate them to one another. This is *the continuity principle*.

8. Certain patterns of behavior and physical functioning characteristics of the individual are formed in infancy and early childhood and have a tendency to remain constant. This is often called *the principle of infantile genesis* or *the genetic principle*.

9. It is possible to explain the continued movement of the personality in the direction of growth, object contact, adjustment, etc., only by the assumption of motivating forces or drives; this makes the personality an energy system and conceives of behavior of all kinds in terms of directed energy. This is *the instinct theory* or *motivation principle*.

10. Certain tendencies or patterns occur in repetitive patterns or cycles (cf. catamenia, heartbeats, manic-depressive attacks, etc.). Such cycles tend to act as a counter-force operating against or in the opposite direction from the evolutionary trend or growth of the personality. This is known as *the repetition compulsion* or *cyclic principle*.

11. The fluidity and constant state of internal and external adjustment of the total personality is modified by the tendency or capacity of the human personality to learn and to remember, and to make modifications in its formulae of adjustment based on previous experience. This can be called *the principle of learning and memory*.

12. Communication between human beings is of many orders, all of which have to be understood by the student of personality who attempts to record in language various phenomena far more com-

plicated than the melody of a symphony or the fragrance of a rose, which acknowledgedly defy such verbal description. While this task cannot be done accurately, proper forms plus a sufficient emphasis upon precision and selection of word and expression, enable us to translate into conventional speech and writing phenomena characteristic and explanatory of personality reactions, for the purposes of communicating with colleagues, affecting the patient in certain ways, and guiding movable portions of the patient's environment, including relatives. This could be called *the semantic principle*.

Upon these postulates we have developed a complicated "science" of psychiatry, the proof of which rests upon five methodological pillars—which as yet stand relatively isolated and uncorrelated. The five pillars are the nosological pillar, the phenomenological pillar, the ontogenetic pillar, the dynamic or psychoanalytic pillar, and the experimental pillar.

The *nosological* pillar, although the oldest, is still the least substantial. It is that method of science which attempts to establish order through arrangements and groupings, the establishment of hierarchies. Inevitably it leads to the iniquitous necessity of name-calling, from which derives the false sense of security that because we have given something a name we know what it is.

I have listed the *phenomenologic* or "examinational" method next because it is perhaps the next oldest. Having given names to certain things, the ancients attempted to describe the manifestations and appearances of what they had named.

The *ontogenetic* method, the study of the case history, arose much later in a vain attempt to establish etiological roots of maladjustment. The "trick" was to coordinate historical events with observed findings (examination).

The *psychoanalytic* method, supported by deterministic and structural hypotheses, is a comparative infant of less than three-score years of age. It has been applied thus far chiefly to maladjusted persons: hence its conclusions regarding "normals" have little substantiated data.

Finally, there is the *experimental* pillar, the youngest and least tried of all.

I should like to make a few additional comments about each of these methods, dealing somewhat at length only with the experimental method.

As for the nosology in psychiatry, the most optimistic thing to be said is that today everyone is dissatisfied with it. We have run the gamut from a nosology of three items in the days of Hippocrates to a nosological list of many thousands of items, and from the attempt of Linnaeus to order these according to his hierarchial principle to a prevalent but somewhat inarticulate tendency to minimize the number of entities and classify quite generically the various reactions. Great practical advances have been made in the recent general adoption in this country of the so-called Army nomenclature formulated by my brother, Dr. William Menninger, with the assistance of many of us. This classification was the product of compromise between adherence to a basic theoretical principle on the one hand, and the empirical observations of many authorities on the other, with various established practices and precedents as a further complication. A more nearly "truthful" nosology is likely to emerge only when we have better clarification of our basic concepts regarding the nature of mental illness in general.

The ontogenetic or case-history method which has become basic practice in clinical medicine and hence also in clinical psychiatry contains sources of error which cannot but be alarming to the methodologically cautious research scientist. Such histories as we now routinely take and depend upon, believing them objective and comprehensive, are certainly neither. At best we are able to record only what someone, either the subject himself or someone who has known him, says about him. We who record such data are ourselves human and biased. Perhaps the most significant discovery of the psychoanalytic method has been to show that we cannot depend upon the accuracy or completeness of what one remembers about himself, and this implicitly denies the validity of the anamnestic record. This at best we know how to get only a macroscopic, not a microscopic, life history, and one distorted by the patient as well as by the recorder. Nor have we yet learned any shorthand device that will render the recorded details of a life history into a form capable of decently rapid comprehension or total visualization by a third party—either listener or reader.

The psychoanalytic method has been praised and criticized so much that it would be impossible to summarize its strength and weaknesses in a definitive way in less than many pages of manuscript. Its enormous popularity bespeaks an internal conviction regarding its validity for which it is true we have no experimental proof. The logicalness and coherence of the concepts derived from it encourage the pragmatic acceptance of the assumptions. But we are still unclear regarding the methods or the material of proof. Psychoanalysis itself is a complicated and expensive method and is applicable for the most part only to such subjects as have subjective motivation for wishing to participate in the process. This eliminates necessary "normal" control material.

The multiple effects upon the field of psychiatry of Freud's discovery of an approach to the unconscious could scarcely be described within the necessarily brief confines of such an article as this. It should be noted, however, that the general content of the field was vastly modified by the side-door entrance to the problem made through the study of what we formerly called the neuroses. It should be borne in mind that fifty years ago when Freud began his work the neuroses were not a part of the field of psychiatry. They were regarded as falling into the province of the neurologist because it was considered that they were curious and perverted physiological manifestations of some mysterious brain affliction. Freud was not unique in suspecting otherwise; in fact he drew his inspiration from the brilliant and iconoclastic departures of his French colleagues. However, having demonstrated certain underlying hidden mechanisms in the production of these numerous afflictions, he not only tied them up more closely with the psycho-pathological phenomenology of the psychoses, but provided a tool of investigation and framework of conceptualization which led psychiatry directly to an interest in somatic manifestations arising from the same roots, to such chronic maladjustment patterns as that of alcohol addiction and habitual antisocial behavior of the type long called "psychopathic." Yet our expanded field of psychiatric interest remains full of unknowns, both theoretical and practical. Thus, in spite of many records of psychoanalytic study of alcoholic addicts, we still do not understand chronic alcoholism or know what to do to control it in individuals or in society.

We come finally to the experimental method proper. Experiment means that a question is put to nature, formulated in such a way that the outcome of the experiment could be considered as a response revealing laws of nature. Modern methodology calls this method the hypothetical-deductive, implying that in order to ask a sensible question from nature one must already know certain facts into which he is now inquiring further, and has already formulated a hypothesis concerning the interrelation of these facts which the experiment might prove or disprove. Such a theory of experimentation has much practical achievement to its credit but it entails the following difficulties: (1) One must have factual data to begin with, and it is questionable what is to be considered a "fact" in psychiatry. (2) The experiment usually consists in producing phenomena under controlled conditions which occur spontaneously in nature, and while a stone falling under controlled conditions can be identified with a stone falling accidently, it is debatable whether a human emotion elicited under controlled conditions is identifiable with "genuine" emotions. (3) A great many phenomena of importance in psychiatry have never been experimentally elicited and it is a question whether social and moral considerations would ever allow this or whether we will ever have the means to do it.

Such considerations have brought home the realization that some of the classic postulates of experimentation, namely, the repeatability of experiments and consequently the statistical method of proof, are not the essence of experimentation. Thus a new concept of experiment has developed in modern psychology as in modern physics. In the latter the astronomical proofs of the theory of relativity consist of the observation of stellar phenomena predicted on the basis of this theory rather than on laboratory experiments with artificial setups. This new conception of experimentation seeks not reproducibility but predictability, not statistical frequency but lawfulness of the individual event.

It appears probable therefore that experimental psychiatry must bring the human being into as many varied conditions as possible in order to understand the laws according to which adaptation to these varied conditions comes about and from these laws erect hypotheses that attempt prediction. Variegated attempts to this effect have been undertaken. For example:

1. The Lewinian topological and vector psychology attempted to reproduce experimentally tensions similar to those which are present in the human being when he remembers certain things, acts according to his ambitions, finds himself in a state of uproar or confusion, etc. By varying the conditions under which these tensions were present, the Lewinian school learned how human beings *might* behave under certain conditions and the laws regulating such possible behavior. While this permitted certain predictions which tended to "come true," no proof has been offered as yet concerning the relation of these tensions to those normally present in life situations. No satisfactory answer has been made to the obvious objection that these tensions are but derivatives of real tensions, and, although there are probably life situations in which such derivative tensions really exist, there is no proof that the dynamics and economics of such derivative tension systems are the same as the dynamics and economics of the tension systems revealed by other methods of study, e.g. psychoanalysis.

2. Experiments with hypnosis on the psychopathology of everyday life (Erickson and others) have confirmed the Freudian assertion concerning parapraxias, symbolic activities, etc. The difficulty with hypnotic experimentation is the lack of sufficient knowledge concerning the nature of the hypnotic state. Schilder, Wells, Erickson, Leuba, Gill, and Brenman hold different theories concerning it. The old saying that in hypnotic demonstration one never knows who is the cheater and who is the cheated, remains true. A special difficulty in the way of hypnotic experimentation is that the subjects have to be trained or conditioned for the more elaborate hypnotic

experiments and this significantly affects the fundamental reliability of the procedure. A person knowing enough about Freudian theory and theatrical enough to put up a show could easily act out all the experiments in which Erickson demonstrated the psychopathology of everyday life. A good clinical observer could certainly decide whether or not the experiment was a "show" and would most likely find that the consistency of the behavior of the hypnotic subject is an observed phenomenon pleading for the reliability of the experiment. Methodologically, however, the above criticism still has to be maintained.

3. Drug experimentation is likewise a developing but insufficiently investigated field. Fairly early in the development of psychiatry it was realized that certain drugs bring about effects which are similar to certain neurotic and psychotic manifestations. The effects of hashish, opium, alcohol, cocaine, morphine, marijuana, mescal, and recently sodium amytal and other barbital derivatives, as well as insulin and metrazol, have been repeatedly observed and described. These observations have been for the most part casual, not very systematic and not directed to any theoretical aim. Wertham in 1926, and more recently Berrington and Kenyon, Lozoff, and Rapaport have been attempting to study drug effects with a definite theoretical aim. Wertham used mescal, the latter authors sodium amytal, metrazol, insulin, histamine, and alcohol, and implied some theoretic aims in his investigations. It is regrettable that while physiological and neurological studies for a long time dominated psychiatric research with a phenomenological aim, drug investigations so much related to these physiological investigations have been undoubtedly neglected, largely because no satisfactory means for clinical and neurological investigation of these effects have been developed as yet.

4. Physiological observations and measurements in the course of clinical psychoanalytic treatment have been undertaken, for example, those of Wolff and Mittelmann, of Rubenstein and Benedek, the asthma study with the thematic apperception test and the gastrointestinal studies using predictions made on the basis of dreams. In most of these, however, it was not always clear whether predictions

were actually made or whether the physiological facts and the dreams and analytical material were merely compared and interpreted. Here again we do not maintain that the experiments were unreliable.

5. The experimental field also includes psychological testing. While tests in physics or in biochemistry derive from experiments and measure facts, the significance of which is established by the previous experiments, psychological tests appear to be of another nature. If they are good, they describe something about the human being. We usually do not know how they do so. Thus psychological tests, instead of measuring understood facts, indicate facts about human behavior, the significance of which is subject to vague theories and the conceptual definition of which is usually not clear. Thus they lead into the field of psychological and psychiatric phenomenology, the structure of which is unknown. Psychological testing is based not on theory but on empiricism. It is true that no psychological test can be used successfully unless he who gives it knows something about human beings, about human nature, and about different theories of psychodynamics. Everyone who maintains, however, that these psychological tests are based methodologically on psychoanalytic concepts or any other theory of psychodynamics pretends and maintains something which is misleading.

The five scientific methods upon which the science of psychiatry rests are, as I have suggested above, somewhat shockingly disconnected in our current research operations. To some extent each psychiatrist, each research worker, uses them all but leans principally upon one or two of them. It is very difficult indeed for anyone to get a grasp of the total personality as a moving, constantly changing, interacting unit, determining and determined to some extent by a complex and similarly moving environment, and approachable from disciplines as apparently discrete as physics, chemistry, and psychology. It is difficult for any scholar to think of cellular function, the process of repression, and the so-called hysterical contracture simultaneously.

The necessity of attempting to do so, however, has led to the great emphasis now coming into vogue upon integration—integration of concepts, integration of disciplines, integration of data. We all believe in the importance, the indispensability of this integration, but none of us know how to do it. We believe in the existence of a continuum of phenomena, but our gropings are like those of the builders of the tower of Babel; there is no universal language.

One might say that the main trend in psychiatric research at the present time on the theoretical side centers about an attempt to harmonize and coordinate and integrate the data obtainable in the study of the personality from many different aspects. And on the practical side this has been less difficult. Psychiatrists, psychologists, psychiatric social workers, psychiatric nurses and therapists have learned through trial and error that they *can* cooperate with one another productively in the study and treatment of human beings in trouble. The technique of the group approach is far from having been perfected, but its general principles are understood and practiced. We have the beginning there for a practical integration of disciplines and approaches and the research of each discipline is in practice related to that of the other disciplines. To a certain extent the development of psychology and psychiatric social work, like the development of nursing, implies that psychiatry in practice cannot be the work of the doctor alone. How to extend his sphere of influence most widely and most effectively through the aid of these adjutant disciplines is the practical problem faced by every progressive psychiatric clinic.

This and other practical problems are being not only faced, but to an increasing degree solved. The theoretical problems of psychiatry, on the other hand, remain a challenge to the science, a challenge to be met by concerted teamwork research by psychiatrists, psychologists, and cooperating scientists in other fields. In these hectic and bewildering days when the demands for the services of psychiatrists and their associates are so insistent and so widespread, when the patient load is so far in excess of the available clinicians, it is difficult to know just where the emphasis should come in teaching. It is true that a physician may handle his patients very well without ever having learned or convinced himself of a single one of the postulates above suggested; he may help a great many patients and do much good in the world. Empirically we know certain things that can be done, and hence that can be taught, which will make for such practical efficacy. But we also know that our therapeutic results are not as good as they should be, our knowledge neither as broad nor as deep as it should be, and fundamental concepts are poorly defined and inadequately substantiated.

In the long run, empirical practicality will defeat itself, unless an appropriate program of research accompanies it. Professor Donald G. Marquis [1] in discussing research planning in psychology has outlined the necessary steps for a research-program design. Dr. David Rapaport [2] has listed the crucial problems which await solution from research investigations in psychology and psychiatry. Such a research program must embrace not only developmental and applied research, but also basic and fundamental research. My brother has written of the difficulties facing the accomplishment of these aims,[3] but he and many others have stressed its importance. If and when we are all convinced of this importance, the difficulties will decrease, the workers will multiply, and the science of psychiatry will develop.

17. A Psychiatric Fable

There was once a psychiatric resident here named John Smith. He was a rather ordinary-looking fellow, a bit self-conscious and perhaps somewhat lacking in social graces, but he was a pleasant, quiet chap. One might not notice him on the first glance around. Even after several months he wasn't very well known. He wasn't very outstanding. Psychological tests didn't rate him "very superior." He wasn't made chairman of anything or secretary of anything, or even sergeant-at-arms.

But gradually this John Smith began to be heard about. His *patients* liked him! They seemed to feel he was their personal doctor. If he was absent for a day they asked, "Where is Doctor Smith?" "Can't I see Doctor Smith today?" New patients were tipped off; they wished he was their doctor, too. He seemed to remember his patients even when he was off duty.

He didn't write easily but he put down his observations simply, clearly, and with conscientious thoroughness. He made no glib references to "adjusting" or "relating" or "identifying" or "acting out." He didn't use "libido," "Oedipus," "psychotic," "syncretistic," and other impressive Greek words. But he spent time listening to his patients and then tried to record what he saw happening to them and in them, written in a way that fellow workers could understand, including the aides and nurses. And he got his reports in on time.

He didn't rush to make application for a training analysis; he

Reprinted from the *Bulletin of the Menninger Clinic*, 14:129-130, July 1950.

said he felt there was plenty of time to learn more about his own unconscious after he had studied the multiform behavior of his patients, and learned from experience his special points of difficulty.

In reading groups and other seminars, he read the assignments—and sometimes more. He spoke up often in the discussions, but only to ask questions, and his colleagues concluded that he really didn't know much about the subject. He took notes in the lectures, so it was concluded by some that he had a poor memory.

Dr. Smith knew all the nurses and all the aides and all the patients on his wards; and they all knew him. "We felt quiet and comfortable and secure when he sat down with us," one of them said. He went with the patients on their picnics; he helped the nurses plan a Christmas party; he sat and talked with the aides at length about their problems.

Then, too, there were a lot of little things. The radiator in the men's toilet stuck one cold morning, and Dr. Smith fixed it before the maintenance men could arrive. When one of the adjunctive therapists lost his wife, Dr. Smith went to the funeral. He spent an hour (at home) fixing a patient's cigarette lighter and took a patient's mother to the contact office because he was afraid she might lose her way. He listened sympathetically to a social worker tell a very long, weary story about her nephew's alcoholism without giving her the impression that he was very busy or bored. He was frequently seen on his wards on Sunday afternoons and holidays.

Toward the end of his third year of residency John Smith was wondering where he should go when he finished his training. He assumed that no prize position would be open to him. Sometimes he doubted, in view of what he realized he didn't know, whether he was competent to go anywhere and take the responsibility of being regarded as a psychiatrist. When he was offered an appointment as assistant section chief, he felt greatly honored, and he was pleased that he had the opportunity to go on learning and helping others to learn.

Toward the end of the three years, the residents were asked by the faculty to help them decide whether the training they had received seemed to be in the direction of helping them to become the kind of psychiatrists they wanted to be. There was a good deal of discussion among them as to just what constituted a *good* psychiatrist, and how success in professional achievement could be evaluated. As an experiment, they decided to vote on which of them seemed to most nearly typify their conception of a good psychiatrist.

The result of the poll was astonishing. It was almost unanimous. One vote only was *not* for John Smith!

18. The Psychiatric Aide

The appearance of this report of an experiment in the education of psychiatric aides is for me like the birth of a grandchild. It fills me with the same mixture of nostalgic recollections and hopes for an effulgent future. I am proud of what the report communicates regarding the work, dedication, love, and vision on the part of its young parents (not to omit the avuncular benefactions of Dr. Alan Gregg).

Seldom does a day go by that we psychiatrists are not reminded of the path our healing science has traveled from the black magic of the witch doctor and the gray limbo of the asylum to the present methods. In less than a half-century the transition from a custodial indifference to intensive therapy has taken place, but the tangled underbrush of outmoded ideas and practices still threatens to restrict by sheer dead weight the growth of new ideas and new ways of doing things.

Of the many prejudices obstructing the development of psychiatry, few have done more to deprive sick people of the benefits of intensive treatment than have those which surround the role of the psychiatric aide—or "attendant." I say this with a certain sense of shame, since I did not fully come to this realization until shortly after the last war, when I had the challenging opportunity of ex-

This statement was published as the Foreword to a report of an experiment in the education of psychiatric aides conducted at The Menninger Foundation from 1949 to 1952. (Hall, Bernard, et al. *Psychiatric Aide Education*. Menninger Clinic Monograph No. 9. New York: Grune and Stratton, 1952.)

changing my quiet private consultation office for the public forum and busy council chamber which characterize the office of a hospital superintendent. In the combined roles of organizer, manager, educational director, employer, and general spokesman for the new Veterans Administration Hospital in Topeka, I found it at first an almost bewilderingly complex assignment.

With only the outer shell of a hospital to start with—a sprawling physical plant built hastily by the Army as a temporary wartime measure—I had the task of recruiting a task force of seventeen hundred employees, and then organizing, teaching, and inspiring them so that the ungainly buildings might become in fact a hospital.

To a considerable extent, my greenness was an advantage, for if I lacked experience I lacked also some prejudices and blind spots which I might have acquired had I developed as a psychiatrist in a system which had long taken for granted the handicaps and obstacles and outmoded practices that had accumulated over the years.

It came as a startling surprise to me that, in sheer numbers of personnel, psychiatric aides *are* the hospital. Fifty per cent, or nearly a thousand, of our new employees fell into one job category— psychiatric aides. I had thought of the psychiatric hospital as a place where doctors work, assisted by others; I began to think that it would be more appropriate to say that psychiatric hospitals are places where aides work, assisted by nurses and doctors.

If these aides were to play such an important part, numerically at least, in the conduct of our hospital, it behooved me to examine the criteria by which they were to be selected. One of the most important considerations in selecting a psychiatric aide, I was told, was his physical size, the strength of his muscles, his ability to command the obedience and "respect" of patients by physical power.

This conception of the prime qualifications of a good psychiatric aide conflicted sharply with my own. I believed that the aide— more than any other hospital employee—was in a position to exert a potent and continuous therapeutic influence on the patients in his charge. It is the aide who is with the patient from minute to minute and hour to hour, day after day and week after week, for month after month and even year after year. It is the aide who sits by the patient in lonely vigil, who works with him, plays with him, waits upon him, takes him to the toilet, gives him food, lights his cigarette, diverts his belligerency, shakes his hand when he enters the ward and when he leaves. It is not only by his number, but by virtue of the role he plays in the patient's recovery or otherwise, that the psychiatric aide is the essence of the large mental hospital.

A second prejudice, closely related to the first, was the lack of prestige and respect associated with the position of psychiatric aide. By the physicians and by the nurses the aide was all too often regarded as the one who did the dirty work; if his charges became well or improved, the credit went to the physicians, and perhaps a little of it to the nurses and other trained specialists. I must confess that at first I shared this prejudice.

Yet the last person to appreciate the importance of the aide's position, I discovered, was the aide himself! He readily applied to himself and his work the attitude of others that his role in the psychiatric community was a menial one, without the dignity, respect, and responsibility of professional status. The quality of his work reflected this attitude. Many aides with a high sense of dedication and responsibility quickly became dissatisfied and quit their jobs, while others who were content with their menial role and with mediocre standards of performance helped to perpetuate the misconception that the aide was a combination guard, janitor, and baby-sitter.

These problems continued to occupy my mind as I employed first dozens, then scores, then hundreds of discharged veterans to help us in the care of other veterans.

Three convictions grew upon me. The first was that these men should not be hired for their muscles, as in days gone by when concepts of psychiatry, now obsolete, made us look for guards and bouncers. Nor should they, strictly speaking, be selected for their superior intellect, for many people of superior intellect lack the patience and the humility to dedicate themselves consistently and contentedly to a task which they feel to be somewhat homely. No, it is for neither muscles nor brains alone that we must look but for certain qualities of character, in persons motivated by the wish to give compassionate service to the friendless and bereft. Are they well-adjusted human beings? Are they prepared by education, experience, or training for the responsibilities and complexities of their job? Are they psychologically prepared for the taxing requirements of their job? Are they gifted with the supernormal patience, self-control, sympathy, willingness to give personal service that must characterize anyone who shepherds the confused, impulsive, erratic, querulous, desperate, irrational patients committed to them? Have they the intelligence to know where secret dangers lurk and the alertness to deal with the recurrent emergencies which characterize the daily routine of a psychiatric hospital?

My second conviction was—and is—that we must increase the self-respect and the prestige of the psychiatric aide. Specialized therapists, technicians, secretaries, psychologists, social workers, and, above all, physicians themselves, must be brought to realize how important it is, for the work they are jointly undertaking, that we get the right kind of aide and that we respect the important function that he can and should perform. I feel that this is possible only if we at least recognize that the aide is carrying out therapeutic nursing activities. In this sense, his work is professional and should be so regarded. Only by giving the aide due respect as a member of the psychiatric team can we increase his self-respect.

To justify this conception of the professional status of the aide and his work, it is necessary to establish an appropriate level of training for these men and women, most of whom come into their jobs without specialized preparation. It was my third conviction, therefore, that effective psychiatric treatment can be achieved only if every aide is carefully, wisely, and thoroughly instructed in all aspects of the work he is assigned to do.

To that end we instituted at Winter Hospital a program of in-service training which we have continually improved and expanded. But we soon recognized that in-service training of the ordinary apprentice type was not enough, and that, until a more formalized and more comprehensive training program was set up, the psychiatric aide could not take his place as a member of a professional group. From this recognition, and with the help and blessings of The Rockefeller Foundation, our experimental Psychiatric Aide School was born.

In the past few years the psychiatric nurses have recognized their responsibility for participating in a program which many formerly viewed with misgivings and suspiciousness. The relationship of aides to nurses is one of the most important problems in working out methods and procedures. In my opinion the work of the psychiatric aide *is* psychiatric nursing at a level administratively subordinate to that of the psychiatric nurse. In the future, the aide will belong to the nursing team, a representative of which will function on the total psychiatric "executive committee" consisting of adjunctive therapists, social workers, psychologists, and other specialized workers under the leadership of the psychiatrist.

In this direction a beginning must be made. Indeed, it has been made; the in-service training efforts of a dozen large hospitals attest to this. The experiment in an autonomous training program with a prescribed curriculum described in this report is the second step. This project was, I believe, impressive in showing what can be done in the space of three years. May it encourage others to go farther!

19. The Goals of Psychiatric Education

This catalogue describes a program of training in psychiatry which has developed at The Menninger Foundation gradually over more than twenty-five years. Many changes in the methods and content and purpose of the teaching have been made during this period. Psychiatry itself has grown in its Cinderella-like change from an ignored specialty, which required no training and erected no set standards of competence, to a branch of medicine with prestige and responsibility equal to that of any other medical specialty.

The residency training of today goes far beyond the apprentice-ship system of the 1920s which, for all its advantages in the way of personal contact and counsel, would be totally inadequate for the needs of present-day physicians. The field has expanded greatly; the subspecialties are numerous; the theory, as well as the practice, has become rapidly more complex. To insure adequate preparation of the physician seeking to become a psychiatrist, the educational methods and scope of training must reflect this expansion and maturation.

The *practical* goal of training may be stated simply: it is to convert a physician who has had general medical training into a qualified specialist in that field of medicine which relates to the diagnosis, treatment, and prevention of mental illness. By official standards, this means three years of supervised practice and clinical instruction as a hospital "resident" plus at least two years of "experience," and then the successful demonstration of the candidate's proficiency before

Introduction to the 1959 Catalogue of the Menninger School of Psychiatry.

examiners of the American Board of Psychiatry and Neurology.

These, however, are but the mechanical steps in a process. What are the *theoretical* goals of the process of psychiatric education? What characterizes a well-trained psychiatrist? How is this training best provided?

Any comprehensive answer to these questions would have to begin with formulations regarding character, integrity, intelligence, sensitivity to human suffering, and numerous other such attributes necessary to psychiatrists—attributes which transcend and antedate all medical training. The psychiatrist must be, in the platonic sense, a *good* man. By definition, he is also a scientist committed to open-minded, but critical, search for empirical truth. Further, he is, *a priori,* a physician, dedicated to the care and treatment of sick people. For reasons to be offered later, he should be a man of broad cultural interests and background, conversant with the principal social, scientific, literary, and artistic developments of his own time and of the past.

If a man (or woman) does not have these assets by the time he has finished medical school, it is probably too late for him to acquire them. Psychiatric training will lean heavily upon these traits and should foster their development. Over and beyond this, psychiatric training will aim at two specific objectives: first, the inculcation and development of a certain philosophy, a certain point of view, a certain scale of values; second, the transmission of technical experience and knowledge to the point where the novitiate can cope, competently and responsibly, with psychiatric problems.

Consider, first, the inculcation of a certain point of view. Psychiatry contemplates the human being as an entity, subject to scientific study and therapeutic ministration only if psychological, social, and cultural factors are given status equivalent to physical and economical factors, and only if all these factors are considered in their interacting and interrelated aspects. Expressed simply, the psychiatrist must avoid that "certain blindness in human beings" of which William James wrote in regard to people's inner feelings. A good psychiatrist is no less interested in the peculiar antics of a two-year-old child than in the dramatic assaults upon the community of a psychopathic criminal, no less interested in the woman covered with the scabs and serum of weeping neurodermatitis than in a soldier screaming that he cannot shoot the enemy. The feelings of people—a nun at prayer, a child at play, an old man intently watching a television screen, a patient weeping in his pillow—these become his pervading interests.

The psychiatrist must have such self-possession that even the most bitter personal attacks on him by a patient are felt as neither insult nor injury, but rather as evidence of a kind of perverted trust. He must not have contempt for a clinical phenomenon, for the most unprepossessing patient, but must remember always that the stone rejected by the builders may become the headstone of the corner.

Furthermore, he must believe in the inherent capacity of even the sickest individual for reconstruction. Without such confidence he will not be able to sustain the discouragements of the short-term view which his day-to-day experience provides. He must believe that people *can* be understood, and that they are thereby helped. He must believe that only in re-examining his efforts constantly in the light of results obtained can he discover and affirm a workable principle. He must become convinced that long-term results are more important than immediate results. He must believe that the mentally ill *can* be helped, and that they *should* be.

The practical aspects of implementing such a point of view by a formal didactic and clinical program of instruction involve many problems. These are the mechanical necessities of providing "case material" in sufficient amount and variety, of arranging adequate supervision of clinical practices by competent supervisors who *like* to teach, of planning a curriculum that is coordinated with clinical activities. But, in addition to these administrative problems, there are less tangible difficulties.

The novice, the young physician fresh from his internship or from a few years of medical practice, is likely to enter his period of psychiatric training in a state of bewilderment. He is in a strange new world. Attitudes, procedures, terms, symptoms, treatment methods, all seem very different from those which he associates with the practice of medicine. To allow a young doctor in this frame of mind to flounder about, observing this patient and that one, following one staff physician or the other, picking up a few things from fellow residents and a few from cryptic discussions or sharp arguments at staff meetings—this kind of experience certainly cannot be considered good training. To be sure, the intelligent physician will absorb something from the exposure, but he will do so at the cost of much time and motion and sometimes with considerable emotional disturbance.

More specifically, his training should be effected by systematic shifting and rotation of assignments and instructors so that the resident comes to understand the implications of hospital admission; the techniques of diagnostic study, of case analysis and of case presentation, the indications for prescription and application of therapy; the techniques of various special kinds of therapy; working with and guiding relatives, handling discharge procedure and patient follow-up; the direction of a psychiatric team; the functions of the clinical psychologists, psychiatric social workers, psychiatric nurses, phychiatric aides, occupational therapists, physical therapists, and recreational therapists; and the responsibilities and relations of the psychiatrist and the psychiatric institution to the community. Only after he has gained familiarity with these fields of psychiatric functioning can he go on to the problems of psychotherapy, child psychiatry, and the function of the psychiatrist in general medicine, surgery, and dentistry, now often called "psychosomatic medicine." A psychiatrist today must know far more than what to do with a patient; he must know how to work with those to whom he assigns the care of the patient and upon whom he depends for effective care and treatment of the patient. This, therefore, must also be a part of the training.

Among thoughtful educators in psychiatry there is a growing conviction that adequate training in specialties within psychiatry cannot be encompassed by the traditional three-year period of residency training. The first three years are largely devoted to instruction and experience in basic techniques of psychiatric practice. Then more specialized training is available—for example, child psychiatry, psychoanalysis, psychosomatic medicine, psychiatric criminology, administrative psychiatry, or psychiatric research. This is substantially the program in operation at present in the Menninger School of Psychiatry; graduates of the basic three-year course are appointed to special fellowships or junior staff positions in one of the associated hospitals or clinics while they pursue special training.

In addition to being doctors, psychiatrists are scientists, and every scientist should consider himself responsible for adding to the fund of knowledge. In the course of psychiatric training, the young psychiatrist should experience a quickening of the spirit of critical inquiry into accepted dogma and established methods of treatment, and a heightening of interest in the progress of his own field and of other branches of medicine and science. Above all, his capacity to look upon each new patient with fresh eyes should be nourished and sustained. The spirit of scientific inquiry probably cannot be taught, but it can be stimulated by precept and example on the part of staff and faculty members and by specific provision in the curriculum for instruction in the elementary principles of the methodology of research and of scientific writing.

The psychiatrist as a person is more important than the psychiatrist as a technician or scientist. What he *is* has more effect upon his patients than anything he *does*. Because of the intimate relationship of patient and psychiatrist, the value systems, standards, and ideals of the doctor are very important. To be sure, these are for the most part features of character which become part of the man before he goes to medical school. Selection of those persons most likely to become good psychiatrists is a responsibility of the School of Psychiatry, but those selected should be reminded frequently of this elementary fact: their effectiveness as clinicians and therapists relates in large measure to the structure and breadth of their own personalities.

Hence, throughout the training period in psychiatry, emphasis on general culture should be implemented by courses, seminars, lectures, and recommendations concerning reading which focus upon the relation of psychiatry to philosophy, sociology, anthropology, and religion. It might be too broad a statement to say that no doctor can become a good psychiatrist if he has not listened at fairly frequent intervals to some of the world's best music or read some of the world's best poetry. But it certainly could be claimed that lack of general acquaintance with the best formalized expression of human emotions seriously compromises a psychiatrist's therapeutic effectiveness. Many psychiatrists in the early days of their training need to be directed to a better acquaintance with the Bible, Aesop's Fables, Grimm's Fairy Tales and Dostoevski's novels rather than to technical treatises on Gestalt psychology and psychoanalysis.

The concept of personal development just referred to should not be taken as one representing only the pleasurable and satisfying development of the doctor's own personality. Only if the acquisition of technical skills proceeds in a context of general cultural enrichment will the young psychiatrist be likely to develop a sense of social responsibility which is both his inheritance and his obligation by reason of professional selection and training. *For unto whomsoever much is given, of him shall be much required; and to whom men have committed much, of him they will ask the more* (Luke 12:48).

To this end, the psychiatric student must obtain and retain a vision of the broad areas of human activity beyond the doors of office or hospital, where his special insight and knowledge and skills can be effectively applied to the understanding of human motivation and adjustment. How to coordinate his professional interests and activities with those of teachers, ministers, and leaders in all areas of public service is a problem which he should be made to feel is his responsibility, one tacitly assumed by him when he made the decision to study psychiatry. To help him in this direction, a psychiatric training program should include opportunities for observing and discussing with those concerned the relations of psychiatry to the work of ministers, industrialists, lawyers, judges, and others.

In all his training experience the resident needs guidance. He needs prescribed reading; he needs didactic instruction; he needs tutorial counsel; he needs clinical supervision; he needs to be a participant in seminars. Residencies, which are essentially only medical assistantships, save the hospital money, but they do not sufficiently train the residents. To train a psychiatric resident adequately will cost money, considerably over and above what his services are worth, for at least the first two years. Any attempt to exploit residents as hospital manpower works injustice on both patients and residents.

The problem of guidance emphasizes the tremendous importance of the teacher's role in a psychiatric training program. The phenomenon of identification, which occurs between parent and child, pupil and teacher, is repeated in the relation of the psychiatric resident to his instructors. One teacher is likely to become the student's ideal, and toward this ideal he will consciously and unconsciously strive throughout his life. Hence, the character of the teachers, and the opportunities afforded to residents for becoming personally acquainted with them, assume great significance in the consideration of educational goals. The continuous dedication of the teacher must be insured by the setting up of guarantees that he may be free to teach and act according to his ideals. Regarding himself as the perennial student, he will be inspired, rather than deterred, by the eternal dilemma of the teacher—whether to present the clear, simple, but inaccurate fact or the complex, confusing, presumptive truth.

It is important that the psychiatric novitiate be exposed by plan and design to the right doctors, the right atmosphere, the right books, the right topics of instruction, the right staff instructors, the right patients, and that he be exposed to all of these at the right time. There always will be differences of opinion among thoughtful teachers as to the meaning of the word "right" as here used. But it is a step forward to recognize that whatever is considered "right" must be that to which the psychiatric resident is systematically exposed.

Something has been said of the general philosophy of teaching and learning which is followed in the Menninger School of Psychiatry. Nothing has been said about our scientific views or, more specifically, about the general position taken by the faculty members in regard to psychology, personology, psychoanalysis, psychotherapy, and other subjects.

Psychiatry has changed greatly since the senior members of the faculty began their training forty or more years ago. At that time there were some thousand members of the American Psychiatric Association; today there are more than ten thousand. In that day there were no psychoanalytic institutes; today there are fourteen in the United States. Psychiatry is variously described as having come of age, as having multiplied its facets, and so forth. American psychiatry of the present day is a composite of the Kraepelinian typography, introduced in the early part of the century; Meyerian psychobiology, emphasizing total personality concepts and the integration of psychology and biology; Ernest Southard's emphasis on the social aspects of psychiatry and its integration with industry, engineering, social work, and the law; and Sigmund Freud's psychoanalytic theory and practice. American psychiatry is a psycho-socio-bio-medico-psychoanalytic composite.

The Menninger Clinic, from which The Menninger Foundation and the Menninger School of Psychiatry developed, early introduced psychoanalysis into its concepts and therapeutic practice. The C. F. Menninger Memorial Hospital is one of the first hospitals to introduce psychoanalytic ideas into the care and treatment of psychiatric inpatients. The treatment modalities include psychotherapy, but also the various forms of adjunctive therapy, as well as the concept of milieu therapy and the application of physical therapies and even pharmacological therapy, all conceived of in terms of their relation to unconscious needs and conflicts. When the Menninger School of Psychiatry was established, psychoanalytic principles so permeated American psychiatry that emphasis upon this in the school was no longer unique. The psychoanalytic theories of personality and the theory of psychoanalytic treatment are either implicit or explicit in all the teachings here, clinical and didactic.

In recent years, the Menninger community has become known for its emphasis in two or three other directions; these ought to be mentioned. For one thing, the faculty always has stressed the multi-disciplinary approach to psychiatric case study. The internist, the surgeon, the neurologist, the psychologist, the sociologist, the social worker, the nurse, the adjunctive therapist, and the aide all belong to the diagnostic team, to the therapeutic team, or to both.

Furthermore, members of the faculty have increasingly accepted implications of what is called general system theory, in which are emphasized the principles of adaptation directed by the ego of one personality with regard to its internal adjustments and its external relationships with the persons and things of the outside world. As physicians, psychiatrists will aim at the relief of suffering—either of the patient or of the environment or both—the deferring of death, the improvement of performance and comfort in the direction that they become healthy.

But the psychiatric conception of health goes beyond the disappearance of symptoms. A patient who ceases to be a patient because he has ceased to suffer may still be a marginal and unproductive member of society, despite potentialities for growth and for creativeness in work. It is a part of the task of psychiatrists to further personality development past the point of mere disappearance of symptoms and to carry this development to the point of enhancement of personality.

Shortly before he completes the program, each of the senior Fellows spends an hour or two with one of the faculty members and later with the dean discussing his retrospective impressions of the three-year training course. Many valuable suggestions for improvement of the program have been derived from these terminal interviews and many words of appreciation and encouragement have been recorded. One recurring declaration, perhaps more than any other comment, has gratified and reassured those responsible for the direction of the teaching. "I came here," the graduating Fellow often will say, "to learn psychiatry. But it turned out to be something more than that. This is not just a school, not just a residency for clinical training. It is a way of life. That's the most important thing I learned."

PART FIVE

The Psychiatrist Afield

Southard's dream of the future of psychiatry included the extension of psychiatric principles into many fields of knowledge. It was only natural then that Karl Menninger should become interested in crime and the law, the public schools, and religion. The papers in this section have been selected to illustrate his views of problems in these fields from the standpoint of the psychiatrist.

One of his earliest interests was crime and the law. As early as 1925 he wrote a paper, "Psychiatry and the Prisoner," presented at the National Conference of Social Work, in which he showed clearly why the psychiatrist must condemn the penology of the time. A year later he was writing for a semi-popular magazine, *Survey Graphic,* in an attempt to arouse the public for a reform of penology. Although there have been isolated exemplary changes in our penal system, it remains by and large unscientific and illogical. Karl Menninger has continued to write about it and in his most recent paper on this subject, "Verdict Guilty—Now What?" he attempts to arouse the members of the American Bar Association to a concerted action that will lead to change in our treatment of the offender.

A psychiatrist soon learns how decisively important the schoolteacher is in the development of the human personality. Karl Menninger has long championed the cause of the teacher. In the one paper included here about our public schools he discusses primarily the people who work there—the teachers. If we want better schools, he points out, then we had better examine our attitudes toward our teachers.

Karl Menninger is far too interested in the unknown and concerned with the mysteries of life not to be interested in religion. More than that, he is intrigued with the origin and history of things. So great has been his interest in the Judaeo-Christian heritage that he has become a biblical scholar; every Sunday morning he teaches a course in the Bible to interested patients at the Menninger Clinic. He is equally interested in Oriental religions—ancient and modern.

He has a religious faith which, like that of many scientists, was not come by without a great deal of intellectual and emotional searching. It is hard to compress the questing spirit of Karl Menninger into the mold of any organized religion—at times he seems strongly identified with the Roman Catholic heritage; at other times, irritated by certain aspects of that heritage, he is a militant Protestant. At other times he is militant for the Jewish people—he remains sensitive to their centuries of persecution and to the contemporary discrimination against them, and he often identifies himself with them against these outrages.

Karl Menninger, like most men, finds a need for a religious faith. Its origin may be, however, more influenced by his clinical experience than by any religious tradition. Certainly religion is both implicit and explicit in his life. Nothing will lead one to a greater preoccupation with the purpose of life than thousands of hours spent with weary, troubled, and despairing patients. Somewhere within him springs a boundless faith; part of it originates from his scientific convictions, part from a belief in God, part from a belief in man. Whatever its origin, it is not naïve or superficial. His favorite quotation—"The stone which the builders rejected, the same was made the head of the corner"—represents his clinical commitment to the rejected in whom he finds both beauty and promise. He has often proposed this statement as a credo for psychiatrists.   —B. H. H.

CRIME AND THE LAW

1. The Psychiatrist in Relation to Crime

I am very happy to be granted an opportunity to speak for a few moments on behalf of the report* which is to be submitted to you for your consideration and explain briefly what it is.

The psychiatrist in relation to crime is no longer a mystery, however much his function may be a moot and debated problem. Every speaker this afternoon talked about the psychiatrist, and every one of them from a somewhat different angle, every one of them with a little different amount of information and a little different attitude. The psychiatrists have been perfectly aware of their ambiguous status. They naturally have been a good deal more distressed and concerned about it than you are, the more so because of the sensational newspaper reports putting them in a false position in the matter of criminal trials.

I want very briefly to tell you what the psychiatrist's position is, because in telling you that I shall tell you what the report is about.

An address delivered at the meeting of the criminal law section of the American Bar Association in Denver, Colorado, July 13, 1926. The address was published in the proceedings of this meeting.

* The report of the Committee on the Legal Aspects of Psychiatry made to the American Psychiatric Association in New York, June 10, 1926, and now under consideration by that body. The members of the committee are Dr. Herman Adler, Chicago; Dr. L. Vernon Briggs, Boston; Dr. Bernard Glueck, New York; Dr. William Healy, Boston; Dr. Smith Ely Jelliffe, New York; Dr. Raymond F. C. Kieb, Beacon; Dr. Lawson G. Lowrey, Cleveland; Dr. Thomas W. Salmon, New York; Dr. Frankwood E. Williams, New York; Dr. William A. White, Washington (vice-chairman); Dr. Karl Menninger, Topeka (chairman). [K.M.]

This report was made by a special committee appointed by the American Psychiatric Association, an organization about eighty years old formed of the psychiatrists or physicians specializing in mental diseases (formerly "alienists," a term which we have abandoned some twenty years ago but which the newspapers still use). This organization comprises practically all of the medical men who are limiting their work to the special problems of diseases of the mind. They are the ones from whom you or your confreres select your expert witnesses in the field of psychiatric expert testimony. Consequently they are very intimately concerned with the problems of expert testimony and alleged miscarriages of justice due to psychiatric misinterpretation.

It seems to me the general crime situation can be likened to an enormous plague which the doctors and nurses (representing the legal profession actually) are struggling very fervently to combat. It is a plague like cholera or typhoid fever, and it is spreading throughout the land in spite of fierce efforts. One group of doctors is working on it from one angle and another group of doctors is saying, "That is not the way to deal with this plague. Here is a drug that will cure it." Still another group says, "Those doctors over there are just killing patients, just letting the cholera increase. It ought to be handled this way." But they all work feverishly and earnestly, and ineffectually.

Out on the side somewhere there is a group of rather diffident plumbers, or sanitary engineers, and they are saying, "It is very singular that these doctors never consider one thing which is very familiar to us. We are familiar with the sewage-disposal menace which these doctors, directing their attacks against the cholera plague, do not take into consideration at all. We wonder why they don't think of the most important thing in connection with it. But still, we are not doctors. We cannot butt in and tell them how to run their business. We cannot tell them how to stop this cholera plague, because it is not our business. Yet we think they would surely want us to tell them if they knew we could help them a little bit."

I think the psychiatrists are in exactly that relation to the lawyers.

The psychiatrists have something with which they could help the lawyers, "lawyers" in a broad sense, meaning lawyers, lawmakers, judges, enforcement officers, and everyone else concerned with this whole problem. The psychiatrists could help, just as the sanitary engineers help the doctors and nurses with such a plague as cholera, and without that sort of assistance cholera and typhoid fever cannot be stamped out.

Similarly it seems strange to me that in all this talk about law enforcement, to which we all listened with a great deal of interest, with such very masterly papers as the one by the president of the Denver Bar Association, and other interesting ones—in all these papers about enforcement of the criminal law, nowhere did the speakers take into consideration in the slightest degree upon whom it was that the law was to be enforced.

The thing that appeals to the psychiatrist, the plumber, or whatever you want to call him for the moment—the thing that appeals to us the least of all is the assumption of the speakers that this law should be enforced upon a lot of people, all of whom are *alike*.

Now psychiatrists as mental-disease specialists, if you want me to emphasize the phrase, are familiar with queer people. They are very familiar with the queernesses of people in the nth degree. Of the people whom the experts call queer, there are some half-wits, some three-quarters witted, some seven-eighths witted; and we see people who are very, very queer, and some people who only once in a while are very queer, and some who only once in a while are a little queer. But no two are just alike. Their queernesses differ both quantitatively and qualitatively. They have been found to be capable of measurement and of analysis, and to be subject to discoverable scientific laws.

From the study of these people, psychiatrists do have some idea as to the motivation of their conduct. We do not know why particular people do particular things, why certain queer people do queer things, until we study them. We are now especially interested in certain queer people who do certain queer things who are called criminals. It was pointed out this afternoon very vividly that one-third or one-fourth of the criminals who have reached penal institutions have already been recognized and listed by statisticians as "mentally" abnormal criminals, to say nothing of the unrecognized cases, yet all have been handled alike.

The psychiatrists, of course, feel that you cannot enforce the same rules on everyone alike. The problem child often comes under the care of a psychiatrist, a child whose eccentricities, temper tantrums, or whose mental retardation, sluggishness, dullness or what not, make him difficult to teach. These children have to be taught individually, and the rules that apply to one child do not apply to the other. We feel very much as if the same thing might be true in regard to criminals.

The psychiatrist comes to the front to give some help from the standpoint that he knows something about the queernesses of the queer people. We don't care whether you call them the abnormal group, the queer group, or the criminal group. But at any rate, the *different* group, the *misbehaved* group, is made up of persons acting according to the psychological, biological, chemical, and physical laws which science has to a certain degree ferreted out or correlated and summed up in such a way that we can now make some definite prophecies as to what is going to happen. In the second place, we not only know what is going to happen but we know within limits whether if a certain measure is instituted it is going to change what is otherwise going to happen.

Now obviously any such information ought to be very, very useful. It is information which is, of course, being used by courts all over the country. I was a little surprised that there was not more discussion this afternoon in the face of the rapid extension of psychiatry in the courts of Boston, Chicago, Cleveland, in Baltimore and New York, in Kings County, and in Massachusetts where psychiatric examination is compulsory.

In view of the rapid extension of court psychiatric work it becomes more and more imperative to understand what the psychiatrist assumes, pretends, attempts, or promises. What does he assume or attempt to do? How does he proceed? By applying the technique of examination with which he is familiar, the same sort of serious examination he applies to all other people that have misbehavior problems or episodes (whether or not they have specifically crossed the legal specifications), by applying the same technique, which includes a comprehensive historical study of the individual, a comprehensive study of the hereditary background, the personal background, the individual's developmental factors, medical factors, environmental factors, social, physical, chemical, X-ray factors, if you wish, all the factors that enter into the make-up of this kind of a personality. From this data the psychiatrist can tell you, and you are the one he wants to tell, what, on the basis of previous experience, is likely to be the outcome of this individual in his further struggles with life, treated or untreated. It is just as if you took your own sister or niece to a doctor and said, "Doctor, this girl has been ailing for the past six weeks, she has been moping around the house, complaining of headaches all the time, she is losing weight and strength, she doesn't eat, she feels feverish and coughs up blood. What is the matter with her? What have we got on our hands, and what have we got to do? Is she going to get better or worse? What will be the result? If you treat her will it make her better? How should we treat her?" That is precisely the sort of problem the doctor is constantly being faced with.

Now for another example. Suppose a man comes up before a judge charged with stealing an automobile or a tire. The psychiatrist could be asked to answer similar questions with regard to him, and may be perfectly capable of telling you after a study of the man that it is absolutely a hopeless problem from the standpoint of society, that as long as he lives he will be a very persistent stealer and that his propensities for theft are totally irremediable, that for various reasons which he would outline for you it is useless to expect that the usual sentence for stealing a tire is going to do that particular individual any good. He would therefore strongly recommend against the type of treatment which consists in giving this man six months or six weeks or six years of what is called punishment with the idea that that is going to reform him. Or it might be a case for which a specific type of treatment might, from medical experiences, be expected to produce more favorable results.

The same thing might be applied to the individual who is being considered for parole. The psychiatrist might say, "It is not wise to parole this man. He will go back to doing the same thing." As several of the speakers pointed out this afternoon, there are many repeaters where the same type of crime is manifest, and yet nothing was suggested for this particular class of offenders.

The psychiatrists I can assure you are not hunting for a job. If you try to get one for your own court you will find that out only too quickly. As a matter of fact it is a matter of anxiety at the present that we haven't anything like enough psychiatrists to fill the present demands for court positions. Furthermore, if any of you have any lingering ideas that the psychiatrists are interested in the ridiculous spectacle of partisan testifying on one side or the other in criminal cases as to sanity, please get that idea out and get the ideas in that I am about to read. Most important of all, get ready your criticisms and your corrections, your advice about the matter, because we believe, as I have said, that this is a legal problem for lawyers to solve.

The Committee on the Legal Aspects of Psychiatry has recommended to the American Psychiatric Association that it declare itself as holding the following opinions:

(1) *That* the psychiatrist's chief concern is with the understanding and evaluating of the social and individual factors entering into failures in human life adaptations.

(2) *That* crime is a designation for one group of such adaptation failures, and hence falls definitely within the focus of psychiatry, not excluding, of course, certain other branches of science.

(3) *That* crime as well as other behavior and characterologic aberrancies can be scientifically studied, interpreted, and controlled.

(4) *That* this study includes a consideration of the hereditary, physical, chemical, biological, social, and psychological factors entering into the personality concerned throughout his life as well as (merely) in the specific "criminal" situation.

(5) *That* from a study of such data we are enabled in many cases to direct an attack upon one or more of the factors found to be active in a specific case to effect an alteration of the behavior in a propitious direction; while in other cases where this is not possible we are able in the light of past experience and discovered laws to foresee the probabilities to a degree sufficient to make possible proper provision against subse-

quent (further) injuries to society. By the same experience and laws we are enabled in still other cases to detect and endeavor to prevent the development of potential criminality.

(6) *That* these studies can be made with proficiency only by those properly qualified, i.e., scientists who have made it their life interest and study to understand and treat behavior disorders.

(7) *That* this point of view requires certain radical changes in legal procedure and legislative enactment, insuring the following provisions:

(a) The court appointment, from a qualified list, of the psychiatrists testifying in regard to the mental status, mechanisms, or capabilities of a prisoner; with opportunity for thorough psychiatric examination using such aids as psychiatrists customarily use in practice, clinics, hospitals, etc.; with obligatory written reports, and remuneration from public funds.

(b) The elimination of the use of the hypothetical question and the terms "insane" and "insanity," "lunacy," etc.

(c) The exemption of the psychiatrist from the necessity of pronouncing upon intangible concepts of religious and legal tradition in which he has no interest, concern or experience, such as "responsibility," "punishment," and "justice."

(d) The development of machinery adequate to the requirements of the psychiatric point of view in criminal trials and hearings, including court clinics and psychiatrists, and ultimately a routine compulsory psychiatric examination of all offenders with latitude and authority in the recommendations made to the court as to the disposition and treatment of the prisoner.

(8) *That* this also entails certain radical changes in penal practice, including:

(a) The substitution of the idea of treatment, painful or otherwise, for the idea of retributive punishment.

(b) The release of prisoners upon parole or discharge only after complete and competent psychiatric examination with findings favorable for successful rehabilitation, to which end the desirability of resident psychiatrists in all penal institutions is obvious.

(c) The permanent legal detention of the incurably inadequate, incompetent, and antisocial, irrespective of the particular offense committed.

(d) The development of the assets of this permanently custodial group to the point of maximum usefulness within the prison milieu, industrializing those amenable to supervised employment, and applying their legitimate earnings to the reimbursement of the state for their care and maintenance, to the support of their dependent relatives, and to the reimbursement of the parties injured by their criminal activities.

(9) *That* effective preventive medicine is applicable in the field of psychiatry in the form of mental-health conferences and examinations, child-guidance clinics, mental-hygiene clinics, lectures and literature, and similar institutions and efforts.

(10) *That* the protection outlined provide an efficient and scientific solution to the problems of crime, viz.:

(a) The protection of society.

(b) The rehabilitation of the "criminal" if possible.

(c) His safe and useful disposition or detention if rehabilitation is impossible.

(d) The detection and the prevention or deflection of the development of criminality in those potentially predisposed.

The American Psychiatric Association is now considering this and other recommendations of its committee's report. We very sincerely hope that the American Bar Association will also consider and criticize it, and endorse it if they will, and cooperate with us in giving to the public and to those who are really interested in the crime problem such help as these sanitary engineers, as we have for the moment assumed the psychiatrists to be, can offer. I thank you, Mr. Chairman.

2. What Is Wrong with Our Prisons?

The fundamental idea back of the American methods for handling criminals is punishment. Ask the average man the purpose of prisons and he will reply, representatively and correctly, "punishment, of course." What does penitentiary mean but a place to be sorry and what does the word penology come from but a root meaning pain? If anyone has the slightest doubt about this let him spend one day at police headquarters of any city or let him spend one day in any prison or county jail. Let him read the daily papers in regard to the lawlessness on the part of the police everywhere.

No one not intimate with the details has any idea of the extent to which the victims of the police are bullied and beaten. Thirty-seven of the leading lawyers of Wichita, Kansas, recently organized to "de-Russianize" the police—but in most cities not even this gesture has been made against the brutalities and torture of the "officials." Ninety-nine per cent of the people of the United States have never been in a penitentiary. They know nothing of the real spirit pervading such places. They know little enough about their own county and city jails. For their peace of mind it is a good thing.

Punishment has had able defenders from Plato to Thomas Aquinas and Kant. And it has had other apologists. But does it do any good? It is supposed to reform the prisoner, to detain him, and to deter others. Let us analyze these briefly.

How is it supposed to reform him? He is supposed to "learn a

Reprinted from *Plain Talk*, 7:175–182, August 1930.

lesson" and resolve never to do it again. The great mockery of all this is the fact that in practically every prison where statistics have been carefully gathered, the considerable majority of all the prisoners are there for the second, third, or even the twentieth time.

The most of them are not detained for long. In the state of Kansas, for example, a life sentence means on the average about twelve years of servitude. Very few prisoners serve their sentences out. I do not mean to imply that I think they should; I merely mean to point out that the prison does not keep them from being a menace to society as it is supposed to do.

As to the spectacle of punishment's deterring other prisoners from committing crime, all we can say is that there is no proof of this. There is a good deal of proof to the contrary; it is an old story that in crowds gathered to watch the hanging of pickpockets in England many had their pockets picked while they watched. Those of us familiar with criminals have not much hope that the type of person who becomes a criminal will be deterred from crime by the punishment inflicted upon others.

Punishment does none of the things it is supposed to do. But it does accomplish something else. Psychiatrists feel that it is this something else which explains its persistence in spite of the general knowledge among all serious students of the subject that it is inadequate and unscientific. What is this something else that it does?

The one thing that the punishment of criminals does and does satisfactorily, although very expensively, is to gratify our passion for revenge. It gratifies, it comforts, it gives pleasure and satisfaction and even delight to the general public. It does this regardless of its futility, its expensiveness, and the fact that it permits such things as prison riots, crime waves, and gang wars. Naturally, the reader will ask, how does it gratify us?

To answer this question the psychiatrist feels peculiarly competent. It is a phenomenon with which he is quite familiar in the course of his daily practice, where the underlying motives of strange acts of people are constantly being sought for and found.

The psychology of the vicarious gratification which the punishment of criminals affords the general public may be demonstrated somewhat as follows: On one hand it depends fundamentally on the process of repression, which simply means that the psychological processes which determine our gratification in the punishment of others are repressed back into the unconscious so that we are unaware of them. In spite of a great deal that has been written and spoken about the unconscious mind, it is not yet clear to the vast majority of people that most of our mental processes go on without our knowing about them. We can judge only by inferences and by certain sidelight glimpses that we get from the study of the broken mind.

In the case of punishment, the reader will ask, what is it that we have repressed? What is this thing which dominates us, of which we are unconscious? What evidence have we that such propensities exist in us?

It is probable that most of us have a guilt complex. The guilt complex is a sense of sin about which philosophers, theologians, psychologists, and others have argued for many centuries. Psychoanalysts think it can be traced back to the violation in childhood of certain taboos. For the purposes of this discussion, it makes little difference if they be right or wrong. Most people know that there is such a thing as a guilt complex whether they call it by that name or not. Now, a guilt complex is not simply a guilty conscience. But a guilty conscience may cover up a guilt complex. A guilty conscience occurs more easily in those who have a painful guilt complex, or, perhaps I should say, people with an obstreperous guilt complex are particularly prone to suffer from conscience.

Sooner or later, a child does certain things which he has been forbidden to do. To an extent he realizes his offense and is apprehensive in consequence. Technically speaking, this fear of consequences is a separate thing, but so closely is it associated with a guilt complex that for practical purposes we may consider them as going together. The child does something that he knows he should not do. The parent discovers it and is angry. He punishes the child for having done it. The parent has recovered from his anger and the child from his punishment; the matter is considered closed. From this the child derives a certain emotional pattern for reacting to offenses. He does something he knows he should not; he is punished; the punishment neutralizes the event, then all is well again. Not only does the child think this, but most adults think it.

The next step in the program is the assumption of the prerogative of punishment by the child itself. Dr. A. A. Brill recently cited a case he had observed of a 4½-year-old child who, whenever she ate chocolates which had been forbidden her, struck herself a smart blow on her hand. In this way she felt entitled to eat as much candy as she liked, providing she punished herself appropriately. In my book *The Human Mind,* where I have cited several cases of this sort, there is one newspaper clipping about a boy of 12 who was so "conscience-stricken" after having killed a redbird that he hanged himself.

One of the most extraordinary cases of this sort I have ever seen was a carpenter, 35 years old, who suffered as a child of 12 or 14 with a twitching and jerking of his arms which was called "St. Vitus Dance." That this was probably not the correct diagnosis appears from the fact that it had continued for the next ten years, growing steadily worse. He had developed a great number and variety of sudden jerks, twists, lunges, grimaces, kicks, waggles, and even barks and whoops. For a few moments he would be at rest, and begin an intelligent conversation, only to be insufferably interrupted by the unexpected misbehavior of various groups of muscles. His arm would fly up, his legs would kick out, his head would twist halfway round, his diaphragm would contract sharply, and he would gasp or shout. In spite of it he could pursue an intelligent conversation—and he held the position of head carpenter in a sizable shop in another city. Furthermore, as he frankly told us, he was active both socially and sexually.

It now remains to specify more particularly the nature of his involuntary movements. As he had long since recognized, they all seemed directed against himself. His arm jerks nearly all turned into body blows; often he would jab his own face with his thumb; there was a large sore on his forehead, "and seems like if I get a sore started I pester it nearly to death." He kept pecking and knocking and scratching this sore. Three of his front teeth were missing, which, he said, he had knocked out in these maneuvers with his hammer. His hands were covered with the scars of minor injuries. "If I get a knife in my hand," he said, "I invariably cut myself, it never fails."

Some light is shed on the motivation of these involuntary acts by a few sentences. "My mother and I had a little friction," he said. "You see, she's always ablaming something on somebody. She says I'm gettin' my desserts—that I'd never been this way *if I hadn't run around so much*. With women, I mean. She says that—but I know that ain't it." But what mother says is apt to be what son believes, whether he knows it or not.

The extreme forms of self-punishment concentrate so much pleasure and satisfaction upon the propitiation that they are apt to drown out all other considerations. We see only the strange spectacle of delight in suffering. This is what is called *masochism* and is ordinarily although somewhat ambiguously described as a kind of sexual perversion.

And when the suffering is inflicted upon someone else, this enjoyment of pain is, in the extreme degree, called *sadism*. And it is directly related to the preceding, because the punishment of self leads to the punishment of others. This extraordinary step is accomplished by another psychological mechanism known as *projection*. You can read about projection in any of the books on abnormal psychology or psychiatry. It is what we do when we criticize others for something which really applies more correctly to ourselves, but which, rather than endure, we direct toward some innocent person. Sometimes instead of an innocent person it is a guilty person who is, however, not guilty to the extent or even in the way in which we allege. This is I think what Jesus meant when He said, "Judge not that ye be not judged." He meant that the woman who bitterly denounces her neighbor for having such a wicked tongue is really thereby exemplifying the fact that it is she herself who has the bitter tongue, whatever her neighbor may have. A mother who spanks her child because he gets mud on the floor or breaks a dish when she herself has just carelessly lost a ten-dollar bill out of her pocketbook is really projecting on the child her own guilt. She is also displacing the emotion from its proper place to an innocent object.

I have recently obtained evidence that projection of the type just mentioned, that is, projection of the guilt feelings of the parents onto the child and a corresponding severity in the punishment of the child, is extraordinarily common. The mental-health department of *The Household Magazine* recently conducted a series of contests offering prizes for the best letters answering such questions as "How I Cured My Child of Lying," "How I Cured My Child of Stealing," etc. There were literally thousands of contestants—each mother telling proudly how she had effected a cure of a particular defection. The extraordinary thing about it was that seventy-five per cent or more of these replies indicated the use of methods which sacrificed all other considerations to the end of immediate effectiveness. The extreme to which parents go in the name of correction and the frequency with which cruelty, intimidation, terrorization, and similar methods were proudly reported passes belief.

I cannot expect my readers to believe what I myself would not have believed had I not read these letters—many hundreds of them—with my own eyes. For example, one mother actually engaged some Chinese laborers to kidnap her 4-year-old boy and drive wildly through the streets of her town for half an hour, with the child screaming in the rear seat, as a method of curing him. Another had her son jailed and then came each day with sham tears to the judge pleading for his release.

Several letters described with great gusto how the parents had gone through the motion of hanging their own child to the limb of a tree or to the rafters in the attic to cure him of the crime of running away. And this is to say nothing of hundreds of letters which advised whipping, ducking in water, tying in a sack, tying up with ropes, locking in dark closets, turning a child out of the home and sending him down the street with a suitcase with the idea that he was never to return, telling him that he would turn black, that God would strike him dead, that the guardian angels would turn their backs upon him and desert him. Threats of all sorts such as poison, being eaten alive by rats, and other things were used as cures.

Characteristic of many of the letters of the sort just quoted was the tense emotionalism of the writer. The varied language which showed the fear, the hate, the emotional surcharge of the parent who was seeking purification of her own unconscious guilt in these sadistic attacks in the name of righteousness upon helpless little children, children who were undoubtedly reacting in precisely the way in which they could be expected to react considering the training they had had and the opportunities presented them.

Similarly, no doubt, we all take out our feelings for the need of punishment on scapegoats of various kinds. The Jews established the scapegoat several thousand years ago, and a very commendable plan this was. For surely it is much better to kill a goat or to turn a sheep loose in the desert than to beat a child to death or to start a street brawl or lynch a Negro. But from the standpoint of the protection of the ego it is better to do even these terrible things than to visit the same punishment upon ourselves, the ones whom we unconsciously feel to be the most guilty. The old idea which we continue to support was that just so somebody got punished for the evil done everything was all right. I understand that it is still possible in China to buy a substitute for prisoners sentenced to be executed.

But taking it out on criminals is by all odds the most satisfactory method. It is perfectly proper and ethical and legal and highly moral to do so. That is why we say that the prison system of the present time is one dictated entirely on an emotional basis. The men in charge of prisons, and the people entirely familiar with criminals have denounced the present system for a long time but the public pays no attention to them. It pays no attention to them because it cannot give up the enormous satisfaction which it is now getting out of what its more intelligent leaders deplore. This is clearly apparent in the arguments urged against any effort to improve this. There is always a great outcry about coddling prisoners. I think no one has any great desire to coddle prisoners, but for that matter why shouldn't they? Why shouldn't prisoners be coddled so long as they are kept from hurting us? Let them live on the fat of the land so far as I am concerned, if they can only be kept away from my home and my family and my neighbors' homes and families.

Another way of phrasing the objection is that the prison reformers are letting sentiment dictate their policy instead of cold fact. This is a typical example of the mechanism of projection which I discussed above. As a matter of fact it is the prison reformers who are the unsentimental cold-blooded scientists. They haven't a great concern about the welfare of the prisoner, if they are truly scientific. What they are concerned about is the most expedient way of protecting society. Now this is not sentimental, it shows an *absence* of sentiment. It is much more human to be sentimental and be angry at the criminals for being so mean or on the other hand to be very sorry for them for being so unfortunate. I daresay there are prison reformers who have this attitude, but it is not true of most of them and it is not at all true of psychiatrists.

It is a curious thing to me that psychiatrists are so frequently attacked on the issue of capital punishment. Officially, psychiatrists have no opinion on the matter. Killing people is not a psychiatric function. We recognize that the people who like to kill other people are more or less sadistic whether they do it in the name of the law or in the romantic tradition of vengeance. We also recognize that the sadistic impulses of millions of people are incited and gratified by the lurid press reports of executions.

Some psychiatrists, most of them I believe, oppose capital punishment—not so much because they pity any particular criminals and want them to continue to enjoy the sweets of life as because they feel that it creates a false sense of security. A spectacular murder case which attracts a disproportionate amount of public attention and then ends in an execution has a tendency to reassure the public and encourage them to believe in the absurd doctrine that criminals are getting their desserts. In the first place it isn't at all clear just what they deserve and in the second place it is very certain that whatever it is they are not getting it.

My own objection to capital punishment is very simply explained. I think it is a terrible waste of good guinea pigs. We don't know much about the manner of man that kills. Until we do, we are not going to get far in reducing the homicide rate, and so long as we kill off our perfectly good laboratory material, we can't expect to find out much about it. I think our chief interest in any particular murder case should be in finding out something about the fellow that does the killing so that we can further safeguard ourselves, our families, and our neighbors. And this can't be done if they are dead.

John Oliver in his excellent book *Foursquare* raises a very curious objection to capital punishment, it seems to me. He says, in substance as I recall it, that he is in favor of capital punishment as good riddance of bad rubbish in certain cases, but he deplores the unforgivable bungling with which so many of the executions are performed.

I admire Dr. Oliver and his book, but I think he ignores the real reason for the continuation of capital punishment. Capital punishment does not exist for the purpose of getting rid of the "bad rubbish." Dr. Oliver's reason is sound scientifically but it is not sound socially. Society has never approved of self-purification in this or any other form. Euthanasia has never had a chance.

The real reason for capital punishment is that it gratifies the sadism and the revengeful feelings of many people who project their guilt upon the scapegoat. Now, in order for them to get the utmost satisfaction out of the spectacle, it ought to be made as horrible as possible. The more bungling, the more barbaric, the more butcherous the performance, the more are the tired but anxious Babbitts going to lean back in their armchairs with the evening paper, heave a sigh of relief, and say, "Well, thank God that fellow got what's coming to him; that ought to teach them all a lesson."

If there were any soundness to the reason implied by Dr. Oliver for capital punishment, and to his objection to it, execution by a large dose of morphine or a small drink of prussic acid would long since have come to be the universal vogue. Dr. Oliver has fallen into a common fallacy of the psychiatrists; not that they think that everyone is like their patients, but just the reverse: they are apt to get into the way of thinking that only their poor patients suffer from mental pathology and that the rest of the world is made up of "normals."

As I have said in *The Human Mind,* I do not think there are any normals.

A rational penology must gradually evolve which will aim not at the executing or punishing of prisoners but at the protecting of society. It will further recognize that protecting society can only be accomplished when society ceases to seek to have prisoners punished. The very fact that the public expects the prisoner to be punished militates against the successful protection of society. This proposition seems extraordinarily simple to those of us who are familiar with the workings of the human mind. It seems extraordinarily absurd and far-fetched to the average reader who picks up his journal and reads that psychiatrists are opposed to punishment. And it has been my aim to clarify this paradox.

Five times in 1929 there occurred bloody riots among the prisoners of large penal institutions of this country—at Dannemora, New York, at Canon City, Colorado, at Leavenworth, Kansas, and twice at Auburn, New York, the oldest prison in the United States. Reduced to its simplest terms, a prison riot is a desperate uprising of desperate criminals to whom liberty or death seems dearer than life under existing circumstances. The official investigations have shown deplorable conditions which everyone with intelligence knew about, in a general way, already. Now, however, we have the official record that at Auburn, for example, there was oppression, overcrowding, wretched food, the use of torture methods under the guise of "punishment," wages of a dollar and a half a month for those few prisoners who were permitted to do anything, and a vast idleness. To all this must be added the fact that the repeal of the statutes making it possible for a convict to earn a diminution of his sentence by good behavior, the reduction in the number of paroles, the lengthening of sentences and the Baumes Laws, which fixed a life sentence for a felony committed by a fourth offender, have brought about a spirit of hopelessness and hatred which make any risk worth taking.

"The prisons of the United States," states the *Encyclopaedia Britannica*—to cite an impartial judgment—"are today [1929] substantially what they were in 1830, as regards both architecture and disciplinary methods. There have been some improvements in construction and sanitation, but the old punitive system remains almost unimpaired, and any attempt to improve or mitigate it is attacked by the conservative judges and lawyers as a sentimental effort to coddle prisoners." [1]

Now it is a curious and a significant thing that the state of New York has been foremost in stringent dealings with criminals. New York was the first state to enact the Baumes Laws, and for all the scientific work that has been going on in New York State, more perhaps than in any other state, its prisons are still among the most antiquated in the country. And it is in New York State that the most prison riots have occurred.

Governor Roosevelt of New York acted promptly in the matter of the second prison riot at Auburn. He acted promptly to do two stupid things. In the first place, he announced that the seven convicts at Auburn who attempted the desperate break were to be tried for murder and "dealt with with immediate and drastic severity"; in the second, he proposed as the one solution of the prison problems a thirty-million-dollar building appropriation to be spread over a good many years to come.

These two acts of Governor Roosevelt were stupid because they show complete lack of vision. They are wholly incapable of changing the situation. Governor Roosevelt is so brilliant a man that it is the more disappointing to have the mountain labor to bring forth such a mouse.

Governor Roosevelt had a wonderful opportunity to lead the way in the reform of our intolerable, medieval prison conditions. He had an opportunity to tell his state and the people of the United States what scientific students of the problem have been telling them for a long time, i.e., "the whole treatment of prisoners is wrong, utterly out of date, contrary to science, contrary to decency, without reforming value, and actuated only by an abominable spirit of vengeance." [2] He should have told them that "as long as our penal system is based on the vindictive and unscientific theory that punishment is the remedy for crime, the reason for these outbreaks will continue to exist no matter how many millions of dollars are poured into new and larger prisons. The only permanent solution lies in the adoption of scientific methods of dealing with crime." [3] If New York State were hit by a smallpox epidemic, Governor Roosevelt would not recommend a few million dollars be spent for graveyards for the victims.

Parenthetically, I may say that Germany and Mexico have already made radical revision of their criminal and penal procedures along lines we might pay heed to. The Soviet Union of Russia is also attempting to make such a change.

The substance of these changes is that the sentencing power is withdrawn from judges and invested in commissions or sentencing boards which, after considering the whole history and personality, the assets and the liabilities of the offender, decide what to do with him. The courts remain for the purpose of discovering guilt or innocence. An innocent prisoner is discharged; a guilty one is referred to the sentencing board or commission.

This board has at its disposal a diversified system of correctional institutions designed to meet the personality needs of the different types of prisoners. This is precisely what Governor Alfred E. Smith urged so long ago as January 1928 and which many of us believe to be the best proposed solution of the problem of disposing of social offenders. So long as criminals are sentenced according to the prescriptions written down in a book hundreds of years ago without regard to their individual peculiarities and without regard to the changing fabric of society, we can scarcely expect to be protected efficiently against assaults upon the social order.

Prison riots express the intolerableness of a solution of the crime problem which expensively gratifies unconscious feelings of guilt on the part of a society which consciously believes it wants protection. It is defended by rationalizations about "exemplary deterrence" and prattle about concepts of "justice" and "responsibility" which no one understands. What is needed is a coldly calculated system for segregating and detaining the socially impossible in such a way that riots are not provoked nor money wasted, nor sadists gratified, nor the public endangered, nor parole boards expected to do miracles.

3. Are Policemen Supermen?

It should not be very hard to persuade a policeman to agree that his job requires him to have the ability of a superman. As a matter of fact, in choosing his profession he has elected to be a superman. What he has said is that he wishes to announce himself ready to act more forcefully, more wisely, more calmly, more bravely, and more law-abidingly than the average man.

But can he? Is he really a superman?

In some cases he can prove it—by physical tests, for example. Furthermore, a study conducted at the Menninger Clinic a few years ago showed that our Kansas police officers, at least, are also well above the average in intelligence.

But intelligence and physique are not the only factors to be considered in the selection of competent police officers. Motives and emotions are important as well as brains and muscles. Why does an applicant want to be a police officer in the first place? What concept has he of the profession he is about to join? What ideals does he have and what sacrifices is he willing to make in order to fill his uniform with competence and pride? Does the young candidate aspire to his job because he wants to look important? Because he wants to bully people? Because he wants to have an excuse to get away from his wife a little more often? Sometimes these secret motives are the real ones.

The man who has secret inferiority feelings, the man with an

Reprinted from the *Kansas State Peace Officer's Magazine,* 15:2, December 1950.

over-strong, vengeful conscience, the man who lacks self-respect, the man with burning resentment against authority of any kind—such a man will become a bad police officer. He is not a superman, except in authority—and he promotes public danger rather than public safety. Such individuals, given the authority of the law, become the destroyer of the law. They think that to insure respect they must inspire fear.

All of us, whether we are doctors, poets, grocery clerks, politicians, racketeers, drunkards, gangsters, scientists, priests, or police officers, have within us aggressive, destructive, lawless, cruel, selfish, ruthless tendencies which are capable of coming to the surface under the right conditions.

All the things that we call civilization—the radios, bathtubs, neckties, automobiles, books, paintings, cosmetics—are really just a thin veneer over the basic biological nature of the people who drive the automobiles, use the cosmetics, read the books, and listen to the radio.

I call these aggressive drives "tendencies" to indicate that while they may rarely come to full expression they are always there. Civilization is nothing more than the development of a program for controlling these aggressive impulses. We are constantly losing partial control of these tendencies and requiring help from our neighbors or our police officers or our wives.

Policemen have these destructive tendencies just like everyone else. And they must learn to master them in themselves before they can efficiently master them in others. In this respect, if in no other, a competent policeman would deserve the title of "superman."

A police officer is a personification of conscience. This may either be a conscience of ideals or a conscience of vengeance. The police officer has many temptations, and one of them is to use his power and authority vengefully and hence destructively instead of constructively. The possession of authority is a great burden. Few can bear it and still fewer can be trusted to employ it constructively.

One aid in the control of aggressiveness is good manners. Sometimes a police officer gets the idea that good manners are not very important. We know he is mistaken. After all, the customs and laws of the country are merely some rules about good manners. It simply is not good manners to take another fellow's property or to risk another fellow's life in a speeding car. It used to be, but it isn't now and it is written down in a book so it is called a law.

Good manners help. So does education. So does religion. So do work and play. In work one has to destroy something; it is certainly better to cut weeds than to cut throats—it takes the same kind of energy, psychological and physical. It is better to beat a golf ball around the links or to beat someone at tennis than to use this same energy in a fist fight or driving a hot-rod at ninety miles an hour.

In the list of things that help in the control of destructive impulses, I give a prominent place to the "umpire." This is my conception of the police officer of the new type—an umpire or linesman, whose primary duty is not to arrest people but to enable people to avoid the necessity of being arrested.

People need policemen. People are most comfortable when they feel there are rules and regulations regarding such things as driving, for example—when these exist for a reason (the reason of safety, in this case) and which it is not the privilege of any individual to break.

They are more comfortable when they feel that such rules and regulations are enforced by umpires who are not inverted footpads but who are friends of the driver, not of one driver but of all drivers.

If such a policeman must make arrests, he does it in a very different way from the cartoon character, the little-man-in-big-blue-pants who exploits his authority to the discomfiture of an occasional offender but who in the long run encourages lawbreaking.

Every police officer has to remember that people are not only animals, they are also children. This is true no matter how old they are and it is one reason why the man behind the wheel of a high-powered automobile is often such a different individual from that same man as a pedestrian. A child is small and weak and knows it, but he thinks that when he grows up he will be big and strong. When he grows up he finds he is not very big and not very strong compared to all the forces in the world.

Hence, all people continue to suffer from a feeling of inferiority.

And if one give such a person who has allowed this feeling to dominate him a 160-horse-power engine that will run many times faster than the most vicious stepmother or the most irate uncle or the most domineering father—give such a grown-up child a machine like this and what does he care for little blue-coated policemen or little printed signs that say "Slow" or little marks in a book that say "30 miles an hour"? The child in him is always tempted to forget the rules and penalties and all the realities of social existence.

But our superman, the police officer, has to remember them and has to remember the child in every man—even in himself. And if the child or the beast in the man should become dominant, the police officer can no longer stand as a symbol, a reminder, a warning.

He must act. Powered by his authority, he must oppose the irrational childishness or the ruthless beastliness of the driver. He must put himself on the side of the driver's better self, his adult self, his mature self. And the police officer should never forget there is such a self.

Even the worst man has his ideals and it is on the side of these ideals, on the side of his offenders' intelligence, conscience, knowledge, and better judgment that the policeman must align himself. This is the part of the offender which must not be frightened by the policeman but strengthened. It needs help from the police officer in suppressing the rebellious elements of the personality.

Some people have great difficulty, even with the very best of help, in suppressing the childishness within them. These are the habitual offenders, and they include both those who seem to have no respect for the law whatever and those who seem to respect it and try to keep it but are always getting into trouble of some kind through "someone else's fault." The National Safety Council has said that ninety per cent of the traffic accidents are caused by ten per cent of the drivers. People who have so little esteem for themselves that, consciously or unconsciously, they drive as though they were seeking to destroy themselves (not to mention others)—and do it again and again—these "accident-prone" people are just as sick as if they had cancer or polio or heart disease, and they need help just as badly.

Many of these people would benefit more by seeing a psychiatrist than by seeing a judge.

To be a policeman takes intelligence, understanding, warmth, kindness, patience, tact, and an immeasurable amount of self-control. It takes, in fact, the abilities of a "superman." Are these qualities appreciated by the public? Most certainly not. But let me ask you, too, if they are appreciated by the policemen themselves? When police officers come to have a higher opinion of themselves, to recognize that they are leaders in the community (the conscience of the community, as it were), umpires in the great game of semi-domesticated human beings trying to live peaceably with one another in a complicated world, they will inspire similar respect, support, and admiration from the public at large.

4. A Letter to Men in Prison

Once I was asked to contribute an article for a newspaper edited, published, and distributed by the prisoners in a penitentiary. I never learned subsequently if what I sent was published,* but this is what I wrote:

Three groups of people know that the modern prison system is an utter failure. The wardens and law-enforcement people know it, psychiatrists know it, and prisoners know it. These three groups of people, strangely assorted though they may sound, would all agree, I believe, on the following points:

1. There is evil in the hearts of all men, and life is a constant struggle to control it.

2. For various reasons certain individuals fail to control it—too often, too consistently, or too extremely.

3. Some of these individuals go off the deep end so far that they are regarded as crazy. Others are not any more crazy than the average person, and not any less. And so when they go too far they get caught in a system the theory of operation of which is that man must be shut away from the rest of the people for a while in order to show them that crime does not pay and to keep them out of other people's hair.

Reprinted from the *Menninger Quarterly,* 9:8–9, Fall 1955.

* The article was printed in *The Inside Story* (Tennessee State Penitentiary), Fall 1953, pp. 13–15.

4. But the result of the system is that they learn that if they are smart enough, crime *does* pay. "Look at so-and-so and so-and-so in high places and low places." Furthermore, those particular fellows who have done the most damage, such as little-girl molesters and a few others who ought to stay in jail a long time, generally get out in a few years and go back to their old tricks. So the jail that is supposed to protect society doesn't do it, and the jail that is supposed to reform the offender merely embitters him and teaches him some new tricks, ruins his chances to get a job, and costs the state a lot of money.

Now, as I say, some of us well know these facts, but we don't know what to do about changing the system. What is the intelligent, constructive, sensible thing to do with offenders? What could be done that will really protect society from those that can't be reformed and which will accomplish some kind of reformation for those who can be? I'm asking *you*.

In the long run prisoners know more about this than anyone else, and ought to come up with the best ideas. The law-enforcement people all know the present system isn't working, but they don't know what to do. Furthermore, they are hounded by a public that doesn't realize their problems or the prisoners' problems, but expects the traditional practices to continue, chiefly out of fear. We psychiatrists are overwhelmed with our clinical problems, because there are far more mentally sick people than we have any sort of decent provision for. We know the futility of the prison system, too, but, to tell the truth, we can't put our minds to it. We haven't time. Nor do we really know enough about it, because most of the people *we* study are obviously sicker than most prisoners. Incidentally, the improvement in the humane care and treatment of the mentally ill and the change in public attitude toward it sprang very largely from the suggestions, recommendations, and reports of former *patients,* such as Clifford Beers, Harold Maine, and Mary Ward.

So I come back to the point that progressive ideas about the control of social offenses and the wisest handling of offenders for their good and society's protection are likely to spring from the constructive thinking of some who have had personal, bitter experience, and

who are able to rise above that experience and devote themselves to
the solution of a problem which baffles us all, and the solving of
which will be a magnificent life expression for some of those who
have suffered.

5. Verdict Guilty—Now What?

Many times a day, all over the land, a thoughtful legally empowered representative of society faces an accused man, reflecting thus: "Verdict guilty—now what?"

The judges know the statutes. They know what the law says. But judges also know that the criminal law is under fire and that they themselves are under fire in their interpretations of it as applied to misbehavior. For the law was created to protect society, and there are reasons to think that the traditional practices are not accomplishing the intended result. The judges know this, too, and are concerned about it. They have even asked us psychiatrists about it!

Since ancient times criminal law and penology have been based upon what is called in psychology the pain-pleasure principle. Human beings, like all animals, tend to move away from pain and toward pleasure. Hence the way to control behavior is to reward what is "good" and to punish what is "bad." This formula pervades our programs of child rearing, education, and the social control of behavior. The present discussion, however, will be limited to the latter approach.

Law and science agree that we are all tempted, that "it must needs be that offenses come." But what about the woe for them through whom the offenses come? They have not been deterred by

A contribution to a symposium in the criminal law section of the American Bar Association at its annual meeting on Aug. 26, 1958, held in Los Angeles. Reprinted from *Harper's Magazine*, August 1959.

threat; they must be punished. Only if the promised pain is inflicted on some does the threat have any deterrent influence on them, or upon others.

With all this three out of four readers will no doubt promptly concur! "Why, of course," they will say to themselves. "Only common sense. Take me, for example. I knew what the speed limit was and I knew what the penalty was. Usually I drove moderately because I didn't want to get a ticket. But that afternoon I was in a hurry. I had an appointment. I didn't heed the signs. I did what I knew was forbidden and I got caught and received the punishment I deserved. Fair enough. Since then I have always driven more slowly in that area. The punishment made me even more amenable to the threat. Surely many people are deterred from cheating on their income taxes, robbing banks, and committing rape by the fear of punishment. They know what to expect and they know what they will probably get. These things are necessary to control us all."

This sounds reasonable enough and describes what most people think—*part of the time*. One can easily talk oneself into believing that this demonstrates how the deterrence theory of criminal law prevents crime. Of course all the reader has done is to say what deters *him* from certain forbidden actions. He knows this doesn't deter every one. He knows that the same principle doesn't deter even him from doing certain forbidden things. He knows too, if he reflects, that the threat of punishment in jail does not deter him really so much as his own conscience, his self-respect, and his wish for the good opinion of his neighbors. Exceeding the speed limit is not really regarded as criminal behavior by most people for all that it is dangerous, heinous, and self-destuctive. But it is the kind of a "crime" which respectable members of society—I apologize for the expression—commit and condone. This is not the case with rape, bank robbing, check forging, vandalism, and the vast multitude of offenses for which the penalty system primarily exists. And from these offenses the average citizen, including the reader, is deterred by quite different restraints.

Today it is no secret from anyone that our official threat-penalty theory is an utter failure in the control of this latter kind of misbehavior. Criminologists and penologists have known this for years. When pocket-picking was punishable by hanging, in England, the crowds that gathered about the gallows to enjoy the spectacle of an execution were particularly likely to have their pockets picked by skillful operators who, to say the least, were not deterred. We have long known that the perpetrators of most offenses are never detected; of those detected, a small percentage are found guilty and a very small fraction serve a sentence. Most significant of all, we are quite certain now that of those who do receive the official punishment of the law, many become firmly committed to a continuing life of crime and a continuing feud with law-enforcement officers.

The science of human behavior has gone far beyond the common-sense rubrics which dictated the early legal statutes. We know now that one cannot describe rape or bank robbing or income-tax fraud simply as pleasure. Nor, on the other hand, can we describe imprisonment merely as pain. Slapping the hand of a beloved child as he reaches to do a forbidden act is utterly different from the institutionalized process of official punishment. The offenders who are chucked into our county and state and federal prisons are not beloved erring children for whom someone is anxious that they not get into further trouble, endangering their future. The prisoners we chain and choke and play legal games with are not anyone's beloved children. They are usually unloved children, grown-up and still unloved, but none the less hungry for human concern which they never get in normal ways. So they pursue it in abnormal ways— abnormal, that is, from *our* standpoint.

Society at large is not a small, compact family or even a schoolroom. It is a great mass of people, each one of whom comes from a family, some of them from families where character structure is fostered and some from families where cruelty, misery, hopelessness, dishonesty, and meanness are the rule. Now I am not bespeaking pity for the product of such homes, much as I think they deserve it. I am only making the point that what might deter the gentle reader from a course of conduct which his neighbors would not like does not necessarily deter the grown-up child of vastly different background. The latter's experiences may have conditioned him to believe that the chances of winning by cheating are vastly greater than the probabilities of fair treatment and opportunity. He knows about the official threats and the social disapproval of such acts. He knows about the hazards and the risks. But despite all this "knowledge," he becomes involved in waves of discouragement or cupidity or excitement or resentment leading to episodes or programs of social offensiveness.

These episodes may prove vastly expensive both to him and to society. But sometimes they will have an aura of success. Our periodicals have only recently described the wealth and prominence for a time of a man described as a murderer and many other things. Konrad Lorenz, the great psychiatrist and animal psychologist, has beautifully described in geese what he calls a "triumph reaction." It is a sticking out of the chest and flapping of the wings after an encounter with a rival. Certainly all of us have seen this primitive biological triumph reaction—in some roosters, for example, and in some criminals.

In general, the gains and goals of the social offender are not those which most men seek. Most offenders whom we belabor are not very wise, not very smart, not even very "lucky." It is not the successful criminal upon whom we inflict our antiquated penal system. It is the unsuccessful criminal, the criminal who really doesn't know how to commit crimes, or fails when he attempts it, and gets caught. Indeed, until he is caught and convicted a man is technically not even called a criminal. But the clumsy, the desperate, the obscure, the friendless, the defective, the diseased—these men who commit crimes that do not come off, bad actors they are, indeed. But they are not the professional criminals, many of whom occupy high places. In some instances the crime is the merest accident or incident or impulse, expressed under stress of unbearable intensity or suddenness. More often the offender is a persistently perverse, embittered, lonely, and resentful individual who has joined the only group to which he is eligible—a group of the outcast and the antisocial.

And what do we do with such offenders? After a solemn ceremony we publicly announce them to be enemies of the people, and on the basis of laws written many years ago we consign them for arbitrary periods to institutional confinement. Here they languish until time has ground out so many weary months and years, and then with a planlessness and stupidity surpassed only by that of their original incarceration they are dumped back upon society, regardless of whether any change has taken place in them for the better and with every assurance that changes have taken place in them for the worse. Once more they enter the unequal tussle with society! Proscribed for employment by most concerns, they are expected to invent a new way to make a living and to survive without any further help from society.

Intelligent members of society are well aware that the present system of dealing with this problem is antiquated, expensive, and disappointing. There is a great deal of evidence that we are wasting vast quantities of manpower through primitive methods of dealing with those who transgress the law.

In 1917 the famous Wickersham report of the New York State Prison Survey Committee recommended the abolition of jails, the institution of diagnostic clearing houses or classification centers, the development of a diversified institutional system and treatment program, and the use of indeterminate sentences. *Forty-one years have passed!* How little progress we have made!

Twenty-five years ago the American Psychiatric Association, the American Bar Association and the American Medical Association, officially agreed separately (and together) upon five principles to recommend:

1. That there be available to every criminal and juvenile court a psychiatric service to assist the court in the disposition of offenders.

2. That no criminal be sentenced for any felony in any case in which the judge has any discretion as to the sentence until there be filed as part of the record a psychiatric report.

3. That there be a psychiatric service available to each penal and correctional institution.

4. That there be a psychiatric report on every prisoner convicted of a felony before he is released.

5. That there be established in each state a complete system of administrative transfer and parole and that there be no decision for or

against any parole or any transfer from one institution to another without a psychiatric report.

That was twenty-five years ago! Have these recommendations been carried out anywhere in the United States? * Offenders continue to be dealt with according to old-time instructions, the authors of which, now dead, knew nothing about the present specific instance, nothing about the offender, nothing about the circumstances, nothing about the previous events in his life, nothing about the misunderstandings accumulated by him, or the provocation given to him.

The logical, sensible, scientific question then would be: What kind of management, what kind of handling, what kind of treatment could be instituted that would deter him or be most likely to deter him? Some of these methods are well known, for some offenders have the money or the skillful legal counsel or the good luck of facing a wise judge so that they go a different route from the prescribed routine. Instead of jailing and deterioration, they get the sort of re-education and redirection associated with psychiatric institutions and the psychiatric profession. Let me remind you that relatively few wealthy offenders get their "treatment" in jail. This is not meant as a cynical comment, uncomfortable as it may make us. It does not mean that justice is to be bought, or bought off. It means that some offenders have relatives and friends who *care,* and who try to find the best possible solution to the problem of persistent misbehavior, which is *not* the good old jail-and-penitentiary and make-'em-sorry treatment. I am sure the lawyers understand me. I have personally participated in the treatment of too many lawyers' and judges' sons (psychiatrists' sons, too; no one is exempt!) to have any doubt that lawyers believe there are better ways to treat offenders than those of the system which we continue to use officially. But it is a reflection on the democratic ideals of our country that these better ways are so often—indeed, *usually*—denied to the poor, the friendless, and the ignorant.

---

* The nearest to it are the efforts made by the federal and the California systems for psychiatric assistance in the examining of the prisoner after the trial relative to his most expedient management, and before the trial in Massachusetts.

If we were to follow scientific methods, following the verdict of guilty, the offender would be detained indefinitely pending a decision as to whether or how to reintroduce him successfully into the society with which he has come into conflict. He would be painstakingly and thoroughly examined, with all the skill and knowledge of modern behavioral science, regarding his personality assets, his liabilities, and his potentialities. The nature of the environment from which he came and its effects upon him and his effects upon it likewise constitute a part of such an examination.

Having arrived at some diagnostic grasp of the nature of the personality of the offender, those in charge can decide whether there is a chance that he can be redirected into an adaptation to the world he will live in which will prove to be mutually satisfactory. If so, the most suitable techniques in education, industrial training, group administration, and psychotherapy should be selectively applied. All this may be best done extramurally or intramurally. It may require maximum "security" or only minimum "security." If, in due time, perceptible change occurs in the subject, if he responds to the program, the process should be expedited as much as possible by finding a suitable spot in society and industry for him, and getting him out of prison control and into civil status (with parole control) as quickly as possible.

The desirability of moving patients out of institutional control swiftly is something which we psychiatrists learned the hard way, and recently. Ten years ago, in the state hospital I know best, the average length of stay was five years; today it is three months. Ten years ago few patients were discharged under two years; today ninety per cent are discharged within the first year. Ten years ago the hospital was overcrowded; today it has eight times the turnover it used to have; there are empty beds and there is no waiting list.

But some patients do not respond to our efforts, and they have to remain in the hospital, or return to it promptly after a trial home visit. And if the *prisoner,* like some of our psychiatric patients, cannot be changed by genuine efforts to rehabilitate him, we must look *our* failure in the face, and provide for his indefinitely continued confinement, regardless of the technical reasons for his assignment to us. This we owe society for its protection.

There will be some offenders about whom the most experienced workers are mistaken, both ways. And there will be some concerning whom no one knows what is best. There will be mistakes, and there are many problems for research. But what I have outlined is, I believe, the program of modern penology, the program now being carried out in some degree in California and a few other states, and in some of the federal prisons.

This intelligent, civilized, scientific program, which would save the people of every state so much now wasted money, so much unused manpower, and so much injustice and suffering, is slow to spread across our country. Any intelligent and thoughtful person can see its wisdom, and even the less reflective ones can appreciate its economy. But it is held back by many things. It is handicapped by the continued use of fixed sentences in many places. It is handicapped by unenlightened community attitudes toward the offender whom some want tortured. It is handicapped by the prevalent popular assumption that burying a frustrated individual in a hole for a short time will change his warped mind, and then, when he is certainly worse, he should be released because his "time" has been served. It is handicapped by the persistent failure of the law to distinguish between crime as an accidental, incidental, explosive event, crime as a behavior pattern expressive of chronic unutterable rage and frustration, and crime as a business, the use of fraud as an elected way of life. The program is further handicapped by the lack of interest in the subject on the part of lawyers, most of whom are proud to say that they are not concerned with criminal law. It is handicapped by the lack of interest on the part of members of my own profession. It is handicapped by the mutual distrust of lawyers and psychiatrists. To quote from a recent statement, lawyers

. . . are skeptical of psychiatry because of the immodesty of some psychiatrists which has allowed them to make extravagant claims regarding their power of diagnosing and solving not only of individual, but of social problems. They are skeptical because of what they have been able to learn regarding the unreliability of psychiatric diagnosis and the uncertainty thereof. They are skeptical because of the fantastic character of the testimony which psychiatrists give in the courts. They are skeptical because of the widespread disagreement among medical psychologists about the fundamental problems both in theory and practice. They do not understand how scientists can differ so radically among themselves about matters of science, and they are forced to conclude either that those who disagree are not scientists, or that that about which they disagree is not science, but rather opinions of greater or less validity.[1]

On the other hand, most members of the legal profession have no clear idea of the way in which a psychiatrist functions or of the basic concepts to which he adheres. They really cannot understand, for example, why there is no such thing for psychiatrists as "insanity." Most lawyers have no conception of psychiatric case study. They do not understand the nature of psychiatric diagnosis. They seem to think that psychiatrists could take a quick look at a suspect, listen to a few anecdotes about him, and thereupon know and be able to say, definitely, that the awful "it"—the dreadful, soul-pervading miasma of madness, the loathsome affliction of "insanity"—that this was present or absent. (Because we all like to please, some timid psychiatrists fall in with this fallacy of the lawyers and go through precisely these preposterous antics.)

This infestation or devil-possession theory, this ontologic conception of mental disease as a *thing* present or not present in an individual, is an outmoded, erroneous, medieval and premedieval concept. It has been largely abandoned by psychiatry but it steadfastly persists in the minds of many, if not most, laymen, including, unfortunately, many lawyers.

It is true that almost any offender—like any other human being—when questioned for a short time, even by the most skillful psychiatrist, can make responses and display behavior patterns which will indicate that he is enough like the rest of us to be called "sane." But a barrage of questions is not a psychiatric examination. Modern scientific personality study depends upon numerous approaches made by various specialists—physical, clinical, and sociological as well as psychological. It takes into consideration not only static and presently observable factors, but dynamic factors, historical factors, and factors of environmental interaction and change. It also looks into the future for correction, re-education, and prevention.

Hence, the same individuals who appear so normal to superficial observation are frequently discovered in the course of prolonged, intensive scientific study to have tendencies regarded as "deviant," "peculiar," "unhealthy," "sick," "crazy," "senseless," "irrational," "insane."

But now you may ask, "Is it not possible to find such tendencies in any individual if one looks for them enough? And if this is so, if we are all a little crazy or potentially so, what is the essence of your psychiatric distinctions? Who is it that you want excused?"

And here is the crux of it all. We psychiatrists don't want *anyone* excused. Nor, on the other hand, do we want any one senselessly detained or prematurely released!

What we believe about this matter of everyone's potentialities for antisocial behavior is this: Of course, we all have them. The law exists to remind us of the universality of such propensities, and of the unanimous social disapproval of them. The hypothetical "normal" person is one who is more successful at all times in controlling and covering up his tendencies toward aggressive, antisocial tendencies than the one we call mentally ill. And cover them up we *should* —or else redirect them, or get some help with them. We "normals" control our criminal impulses. The offender, on the other hand, has already broken down in the effort to cover up and control himself and present a clean façade to the eyes of the world. He hasn't had the success or the help or the good luck you and I and other saints have had. Nor has he, on the other hand, become so completely demoralized and disorganized as to *look* "crazy" and run wildly into psychiatric asylum.

The man who does criminal things is less convincingly disorganized than the patient who looks sick. Just because the former more nearly resembles the rest of us, and seems to be indulging himself in acts that we have struggled with and controlled, we get hot under the collar about the one we call "criminal" whereas we can pityingly forgive him whom we call "lunatic." But a surgeon uses the same principles of surgery whether he is dealing with a "clean" case, say some cosmetic surgery on a face, or a "dirty" case which is foul-smelling, offensive, and disagreeable to a high degree. What we are after is results, and the emotions of the operator must be under control. Words such as "criminal" and "insane" have no place in the scientific vocabulary any more than pejorative adjectives such as "vicious," "psychopathic," "bloodthirsty," etc. On the other hand, descriptive adjectives may well describe the man whether he is crazy, criminal, or "perfectly well." The thing is to get all the descriptive adjectives that apply to the case, and this is a scientific job—not a popular exercise in name-calling. Nobody's insides are very beautiful, and in the cases that require social control, whatever they be called, there has been a great wound and some of the insides are showing.

Intelligent judges all over the country are increasingly surrendering the onerous and presumptuous responsibility of deciding in advance what a man's conduct will be in a prison and how rapidly his wicked impulses will evaporate there. With increasing use of the indeterminate sentence and the establishment of scientific diagnostic (classificatory) centers, we shall be in a position to make progress in the science of *treating* (correcting) antisocial trends. Furthermore, we shall get away from the present legal smog that hangs over the prisons, which lets us detain with heartbreaking futility some prisoners fully rehabilitated and able to be useful citizens, while others, whom the prison officials know full well to be dangerous and unemployable, must be released, *against our judgment,* because a judge far away (who has by this time forgotten all about it), said that five years was enough. In my frequent visits to prisons I am always astonished at the infrequency with which the judges who have prescribed the "treatment" have come to see whether or not it was effective. What if doctors who sent their seriously ill patients to hospitals never called to see them!

As more and more states adopt diagnostic centers directed toward getting the prisoners *out* of jail and back to work, under modern, well-structured parole systems, the taboo of jail and prison will begin to diminish just as the taboo on state hospitals has diminished. Once it was a lifelong disgrace to have been in either. Lunatics, as they

were cruelly called, were feared and avoided. Today only the ignorant retain this phobia. Cancer was once considered a *shameful*
thing to have, and victims of it were afraid to mention it, or have
it correctly treated, because they did not want to be disgraced! The
time will come when offenders, much as we disapprove of their
offenses, will no longer be unemployable untouchables and un-
speakables. They are our unfortunate brothers and children, and we
who are stronger and more fortunate have the responsibility of helping and guiding them, detaining them indefinitely only if they
are incurable.

To a physician it seems hardly necessary to conclude an article on
the bitter treatment of our fellow men with a coda declaring that
under no circumstances should we kill them. It was never considered
proper for doctors to kill their patients, no matter how hopeless their
condition seemed to be. True, some patients in state institutions have
undoubtedly been executed without benefit of sentence. They were
a nuisance, expensive to keep and dangerous to release. Various people took it upon themselves to put an end to the matter, and I have
even heard them boast of it. The Hitler regime had the same philosophy.

But in most civilized countries today we have a higher opinion of
the dignity and the rights of the individual and of the limits to the
power of the state. We know, too, that for the most part the death
penalty is inflicted upon obscure, impoverished, defective, and
friendless individuals. We know that it intimidates juries in their
efforts to determine without prejudice the guiltiness of a suspect.
We know that it is being eliminated in one state after another, most
recently Delaware. We know that in practice it has almost disappeared—for over seven thousand capital crimes last year there
were less than one hundred executions. But vast sums of money are
spent—let us say wasted—in legal contests to determine whether or
not an individual, even one known to have been mentally ill, is now
healthy enough for the state to hang him. (I am informed that such
a case has recently cost the state of California $400,000!)

Most of all, we know that no state employees—except perhaps
some that ought to be patients themselves—want a job on the killing

squad, and few wardens can stomach this piece of medievalism in their own prisons. I recently knew intimately of a quarrel between two officials, each of whom wished the other to have the hanging of a prisoner carried out on the other's premises.

Capital punishment is, in my opinion, morally wrong. It has a bad effect on everyone, especially those involved in it. It gives a false sense of security to the public. It is vastly expensive. But over and beyond all these things it beclouds the entire issue of motivation in crime, which is so importantly relevant to the question of what to do for and with the criminal that will be most constructive to society as a whole. Punishing—and even killing—criminals may yield a kind of grim gratification, and secretly, let us all admit, there are times when we are so shocked at the depredations of an offender that we persuade ourselves that this man the Creator didn't intend to create, and that we had better help correct the mistake. Playing God in this way in deciding to exterminate some human being whose behavior we don't like has no conceivable moral or scientific justification.

Let us return in conclusion to the initial question: "Verdict guilty —now what?" My answer is that now we, the designated representatives of the society which hurt this man and was hurt by him, must take over. It is *our* move. And our move must be a constructive one, an intelligent one, a purposeful one—not a primitive, retaliatory, offensive move. We, the agents of society, must move to end the cycle of tit-for-tat and blow-for-blow in which the offender has foolishly, desperately, and futilely engaged himself and us. We are not driven, as he is, to wild and impulsive actions. With knowledge comes power, and with power there is no need for the frightened vengeance of the old penology. In its place should go a quiet, dignified, therapeutic program for the rehabilitation of the disorganized one, if possible, the protection of society during his treatment period, and his guided return to useful citizenship as soon as this can be effected.

SCHOOLS

6. Citizens and Schools

The National Citizens Commission for the Public Schools, of which I have the honor to be a member, has at various meetings and in various special studies gathered many facts in connection with public-school education in the United States. Some of these facts would seem to indicate that in spite of the universal acclaim and prestige of education, and in spite of 150 years of experience, it is still far from our ideals.

There is not even very general agreement as to why education is a good thing. The conclusion of Charles Beard, which was essentially the same as that of Luther, to the effect that it helps to sustain democratic government is certainly not the *popular* notion of its chief function. Self-realization, training in human relations, and the development of economic efficiency are also important functions of education in addition to training for civic responsibility. How well these are accomplished for today's children can be judged, to some degree, by our national statistics regarding crime, delinquency, political corruption, divorce, mental illness, and poverty. I do not imply that education should be expected to cure these evils, but it is implicit in the definition of function that education aims to prevent them.

Even the simplest element in education, that of acquiring a knowl-

Presented at the annual meeting of the National Citizens Commission for the Public Schools, Jan. 26, 1952, in St. Louis, Missouri. Reprinted from the *Menninger Quarterly*, 6:7–10, December 1952.

edge of useful facts, would appear to be defective in the experience of many children, if such surveys as the recently publicized one of Maurice G. Blair, associate superintendent of the Los Angeles schools, is indicative. Report of this survey, published in *Time* magazine, December 10, 1951, shows the dramatic defects in the body of factual knowledge accumulated by school children both in the elementary grades and in high school. For instance, "Among the eleventh graders (aged 16 to 18), 3 per cent could not tell the time shown on a drawing of a clock, 8 per cent did not know how many feet there are in a yard, 4 per cent could not say what letter comes before M, and 14 per cent could not give the answer to: 'What is 50 per cent of 36?'"

My own opinions of the school program are based upon facts that have come to my attention, as a psychiatrist, from four main sources: (1) From the observation of school failures whom I have seen as patients—either as children or as adults—whose educational defects show up in their illness. (2) From contacts with teachers themselves, as informants, friends, acquaintances, or patients. (3) From my observation of the educational defects in the doctors whom I teach. (4) From reading and hearing facts collected by individuals and organizations such as this.

I have been asked what parts of the school program seem to me *most* in need of study and action by citizens, what elements in the incomplete success of the educational program seem *to me* most serious and most likely to be benefited by popular interest. I can state my opinion clearly and simply. I think the part of the school program most needing study and action by citizens is the individual schoolteacher, specifically, the character and personality qualities of the schoolteacher.

I once took my life in my hands and wrote a book. In that book, *Love Against Hate,* I discussed some of the things in our civilization which made it hard for people to live, looking at this question again from the point of view of a psychiatrist. In it I said several things which I am prepared to repeat now, in support of the opinion just expressed.

I said that I thought the techniques of education were overstressed and the effects of teacher personality on the children were underestimated. I said that just as the professional peculiarity of doctors is that they will not take their own medicine, so the professional peculiarity of some *educators* (not teachers, but those who teach teachers) seem to be that they will not learn. I did not refer to such progressive, open-minded educators as come to such meetings as this; I am speaking rather of those who formulate educational policy officially, and the learning I specially have in mind is learning psychological facts.

I said that education in an official sense continues to regard itself as something intellectual, denies the contribution of emotion to human life and learning, and fails to require of its teachers any preparation or qualification for this aspect of teaching. I said that I distrusted the objectives of contemporary education, the hypocritical sanctification of educational theory which prevails in the popular mind and in the writing of many educators. "When I read that education exists 'to enable us to live and live more abundantly,' I think of some of my illiterate friends on western farms or in the northern wildernesses, and compare the richness and fullness of their lives with the sterility, emptiness, and frustration of the lives of many so-called 'educated' people. It almost seems to me sometimes that education is something we force children to undergo in order to prevent them from enjoying life. I am sure many a child has the same sentiments."

Finally, I said that *what the teacher is* and *what motivates her in teaching* are far more important than what or how she teaches. What a teacher is depends upon her own personality development—the value system she has established for herself, her ideals, her emphases, her attitudes, her manners, i.e., her techniques of human interrelationship, and her pattern of love and hate; her motives—whether she is teaching because she loves children and wants to give, or hates children and wants to make them learn.

You will notice I have said nothing about teaching methods or curriculum or discipline. I think none of these are very important, *relatively*.

Does our educational system attract the superior young woman?

Does it keep her? Does it cultivate her? Does it reward such teachers? Does it frustrate and alienate such teachers? Does it encourage him or her to get married and have a family and live a normal life? Does it injure such teachers? Does it really *want* such teachers?

How much consideration does the average citizen give for the teachers of his children? Does he know where they live? Or how? Does he know what clubs and organizations they belong to, what working conditions they have, what recreation is available for them? Does he know what they are paid? Why should not the teacher's prestige be as high as that of the doctor? And why should we pay her less than the plasterer, the dentist, or the physician? Isn't there a certain smell of hypocrisy about our pious praise of education? Do we really mean it? I should think the teaching profession might well wonder. And it seems to me not at all difficult to explain the national teacher shortage.

We psychiatrists believe that the mental health of the next generation will depend upon the proper inspiration and guidance of the children of this generation. Next to the parents themselves, no one has an influence comparable to that of the teacher. *Do we really want mental health? Do we really want mentally healthy children? Do we really want mentally healthy teachers?* If we do, what are we willing to pay for it?

In summary, there are weak, sick teachers; there are certainly many overworked, frustrated, discouraged teachers; there are a few outstanding teachers. There are many vacancies for teachers. For the most part, the public takes too little interest in the teacher. The paradox remains: "Education" has high honor, on our lips; teaching has low prestige, reflected in our behavior. So perhaps I should revise my opinion and say, not that we should look into our teachers, but that we should look into ourselves.

RELIGION

7. *Religio Psychiatrici*

Like most other human beings, psychiatrists are busy with their daily work, giving too little time, perhaps, to reflections regarding the name and nature of God or the proper form of worship. The adjuration of Alexander Pope is quite generally our guiding motto:

> Know then thyself, presume not God to scan;
> The proper study of Mankind is Man.

As individuals, we psychiatrists grew up in various religious traditions, and we tend to continue in them, reared by parents of differing origins, who taught us *their* forms of acknowledging the great mysteries as well as they could—as well as they could repeat and restate and perhaps extend the instructions they had received from *their* parents, and so on back. Thus we carry on in various forms of worship the acknowledgment of our reverence. The forms vary greatly, as we all know; and for some this very variance is distressing and improper; they conceive of a standard and universal form, "the one true church." For others, this idea itself is absurd and unsatisfying. I am often reminded of a remark made to me by a devout Catholic colleague as we were listening to a patient singing at a

This is substantially the second of three lectures that Dr. Menninger gave under the general title "The Relation of Religion and Psychiatry" on the Alden-Tuthill Lectureship at the Chicago Theological Seminary. The lectures were given Jan. 23, 24, and 25, 1951. Reprinted from the *Chicago Theological Seminary Register*, 41:1-9, March 1951.

recital in the wards of a psychiatric hospital. "In how *many* different ways people pray!" he remarked, quietly, as we walked back to my office.

Prayer might be defined as the issuance of communication directed to God. If one believes in the existence of God, the question of communication between Him and His creations, or between them and Him, becomes an issue. The existence of a God does not imply the existence of such communications, but it seems to be assumed in most formalized beliefs. But if I were asked, for example, as a sample scientist and psychiatrist, whether or not I believe in prayer, I could not make a conscientious answer without stipulating that the question be resolved into various parts. If I were asked, "Do you believe that prayer exists?" I could answer easily, "Yes"—for me, and for many others. If I were then asked, "Do you believe that the prayers of men are heard by God?" I could answer in the affirmative because my conception of God is such that *everything* reaches Him. If I were asked, "Do you believe that God answers prayers?" I could answer affirmatively, but my affirmative answer would not necessarily mean that I agree with what is in the mind of the questioner.

The effect of prayer upon God is scarcely subject to investigation, but the effect of prayer upon those who offer it could well be made a matter of scientific research. A psychiatrist, Samuel W. Hartwell, suggested that prayer may be a very hygienic and even therapeutic experience, because it enables people to verbalize certain introspective reflections and half-conscious wishes under circumstances of intimacy and trust which rarely prevail in interpersonal relationships.

I once asked Chaplain Robert Preston of our Winter VA Hospital to tell me, from his long observation of hundreds of psychiatrists at work, what he could conclude in general terms about our religiousness. "What do psychiatrists believe?" I asked him. "We don't come to your services very often; you don't hear our devotions. What do our lives seem to you to indicate?"

He thought about it for a while and then wrote me this:

> You psychiatrists seem to believe that some people can be understood and, by understanding, be helped. Behind this belief there seems to be a belief that many people need help. The facts seem to justify these beliefs.

Furthermore, you seem to believe that in re-examining your efforts constantly in the light of the results obtained you can discover and affirm a principle of workability. You seem to have concluded that long-term results are more important than immediate results. This brings you into the field of social relationships, which I shall mention further in a moment.

You seem to have a belief in the importance and the dignity of the individual human being. It is an assumption, of course, which you seem to make with a dedicated faith, that every individual is worth helping. You seem to believe that each individual has capacities for being destructive and capacities for being constructive and creative. You seem to feel that it is possible for another human being like yourselves, granted an understanding of the particular problems and mechanisms of this individual, to guide him in the direction of constructiveness and away from destructiveness. You have demonstrated that it is possible to regain strength from the beneficial positive factors in the case of severe conflict and to restore people to an inner equilibrium. This requires a disciplined honesty in seeking the real sources of trouble and implies that health demands truthfulness within the self.

Concerning society you seem to believe that human beings are interdependent more deeply and crucially than most people realize. The measure of an individual's health is linked in your concept with his level of usefulness in carrying out his own responsibilities and contributing to the welfare of others. Hence, you contend, tendencies which are harmful to others are a mark of disorder within the person and arouse your feeling of responsibility for the use and techniques of modification.

You are more keenly aware than most people of the influence of groups upon the individual because you see in the mental hospital the persons who have been broken by, or at least not helped by, social institutions—domestic, economic, educational, and religious. Sometimes you observe that the teaching of religion has affected individuals in ways which were not intended by the teacher or by the religious leader. Surrounded by the extremes of tragedy, dwelling with the victims of disillusionment and self-destructiveness, you are constantly impressed with the deceptiveness of superficial explanations. It leads you to a feeling that there may be praise with the lips while the heart is far away and, hence, that if "faith is the substance of things hoped for, the evidence of things not seen," it must be made as substantial as possible.

In this beautiful and I trust truthful appraisal of the work of the psychiatrist, you will note that Chaplain Preston says "you *seem to believe.*" He means that psychiatrists *act* in certain ways which imply (to him) that they possess such beliefs. "By their fruits ye shall know them."

Such behavior could be considered in two categories: behavior with reference to fellow creatures, which involves "morals," and behavior with reference to God, which is subsumed under "worship."

Worship may be private or public, or both. Perhaps we should agree that it must be consciously and thoughtfully done to be considered worship, whether public or private. There are certainly psychiatrists who do not formally worship in any way. There are others who feel that their attitude toward their God, in whatever form they envisage Him, is a matter for private and intimate contemplation only. Still others—and here I include myself—see value in group assemblage and some kind of formal ritual. As a Presbyterian I am not a genuflector but I respect genuflection as one of several simple maneuvers which have the same meaning of reverence, enhanced for any particular individual by the conditioning of childhood training and the example of loved ones, companions, and friends. The mutual stimulation, reinforcement, and encouragement that the individuals of a group receive from one another are well known to psychology, and the effect of a common relationship to a leader—pastor, rabbi, or priest—has been carefully examined by many scientists, including Freud.

Alfred B. Haas, professor of practical theology at Drew University, has contributed a valuable comment on the therapeutic value of hymns. In it he points out that, because of their emotional associations, hymns reduce anxiety, alleviate a sense of guilt, strengthen inner resolves, bring comfort, and divert self-preoccupation. Of course, not all hymns do this. Nor would I minimize the value of other forms of church music in arousing religious sentiments.

Going to church is not equivalent to religion—perhaps not even essential—but it is a form of religious activity which comforts, encourages, and supports those for whom its forms and its fellowship are acceptable. It, too, arouses the religious feeling. In this sense it appeals to many psychiatrists as a prescription for patients, if not for themselves. No one need be reminded of its abuses, but it is characteristic of this world that any good thing may be turned into evil.

If we take literally the words of Jesus, "If ye do it unto one of the least of these my brethren, ye do it unto me," we do not leave the question of behavior toward God when we turn to consider more specifically behavior toward our fellow men. And, for the psychiatrist, fellow men are chiefly patients. In what ways and in what spirit does the psychiatrist minister to his patients?

"Psychiatrists are wicked men," we are told. "They persuade their patients to a godless, immoral philosophy. They repudiate the conscience; they advocate irresponsible self-expression to the disregard of moral law. They attempt to thwart the design of the Creator, whom they deny while they themselves play God. They order and reorder human life and arrogate to themselves the molding of the conscience."

This misunderstanding stems from the fact that mental illness has long been a mystery. It is enormously prevalent—more abundant than all other forms of illness put together. It exists in myriad forms. Every priest, pastor, and rabbi spends a considerable amount of his time, I am sure, listening to parishioners who are in distress because of recognized or unrecognized mental illness. Clergymen more than most people are aware of the vast extent of misery and suffering in the world. They and the psychiatrists are together on this. Like the psychiatrist, the minister feels impelled to do something to diminish this suffering, not only by advice to the individual, but by proclamation of principles of living. In their sermons they endeavor—most of them—to hold out hope, comfort, encouragement, and reassurance to congregations in which there are many who need this help. Meanwhile, the psychiatrists are spending *their* days listening, comforting, correcting, and reassuring.

For the mystery of mental illness has begun to yield to science. It began with Freud's discovery that most psychological processes are not conscious ones—that there is a vast organization of mental functioning of which our conscious experiences are only a small part. This is actually no more novel than the discovery made many centuries ago that there were internal organs and internal physiological processes not visible in the intact human body. But just as the dissecting scalpel, the microscope, the X-ray, the sphygmomanometer, the electroencephalogram, and many other technical devices have now enabled us to look behind the bloodshot eye, the pallid skin, and the wasting flesh to determine what preserves or destroys these structures from within, so we now have methods for looking behind the surface of conscious thinking and overt behavior, there to see undreamed-of intricacies, forces, functions, and processes. And these methods of looking have provided us with methods of changing the patterns.

The study of personality on this grander and more inclusive scale is really the basic content of modern psychoanalysis and modern psychiatry. It is the basis of our therapeutic program. This function of the psychiatrists understandably alarms some clergymen, for it seems to put too much responsibility for personality-molding in the hands of the psychiatrists. We have long since accustomed ourselves to relinquishing the personality-molding of our children to underpaid, poorly trained grade-school teachers; we have no doubts about qualifications for surgeons to whom we resign ourselves for modifications of the structural aspects of our personalities. But psychiatrists remain suspect. This is particularly true in the case of psychoanalytic therapy used by the psychiatrists, but is the one which is based on the principle that full self-knowledge permits better self-realization. "Ye shall know the truth and the truth shall make you free." Some clergymen, some theologies, view such individual freedom, such greater knowledge, as dangerous.

The technique of psychoanalysis is highly specialized, and it is no wonder many people misunderstand it. Some seem morbidly anxious to misunderstand it and to turn a penny publishing their ignorant defamations.

In the contrary direction I commend a most excellent article by Lois Perry Jones in a little magazine called *Life Today* (December

1950). Mrs. Jones accurately points out "what a psychoanalyst *doesn't* do!" Thus:

1. He doesn't use bristling Freudian terms in talking to his patient.
2. He doesn't dispense sympathy in the form of sympathizing.
3. He doesn't insist on changes in the patient's environment or habits; indeed, he does insist that until the analysis is completed no radical changes be made.
4. He doesn't make decisions for his patient.
5. He doesn't remove his patient's conflicts.
6. He doesn't make his patients perfect.
7. He doesn't make his patients happy.
8. Indeed, strictly speaking, the analyst doesn't cure his patients; he helps them to cure themselves.

What he does do is this: By helping his patients to understand the truth about themselves and their environment, he enables them to choose more wisely and hence more nearly determine their own destiny, to decide what they really most desire, and hence what their life shall be like—within limits—achieving through love and work and play a desired goal.

I should like to illustrate some of the pronouncements which seem to impugn psychiatry but which actually serve rather to demonstrate the speaker's ignorance. One is quoted as saying, for example, that psychoanalysis is a form of escapism. This is a correct statement, if the verb *is* be changed to *may be*. Some patients undoubtedly seek psychoanalytic treatment to escape from realities, or even unrealities, which they cannot bear or which they think they cannot bear, and it is the duty, the custom, and the proper procedure for the psychoanalyst to point this out to the patient, at the right time. In this way he can be helped to cease "escaping." But many persons find their own necessary and quite satisfactory escapes. Playing golf may be escapism; likewise taking a vacation or going to sleep. Escapism in itself is not an evil; it is a phenomenon. It may be useful; it may be harmful. Of course it is true that from certain things there is no escape, but a good psychoanalyst is going to point that out to his patient with just as much honesty and deftness and clarity as the priest or the minister will.

Another quoted charge against psychoanalysis is that it "fails to relieve the unresolved sense of guilt of sin." As it stands, this statement doesn't add up to any charge at all. I see no reason why psychoanalysis or surgery or cosmetology should relieve anybody from feeling guilty about a sin.

If *just the opposite charge* had been made—namely, that the psychoanalysts *did* undertake to resolve a sense of guilt for sin, it would have been a stronger point. Some patients (and others) get the impression that some psychoanalysts have taken upon themselves the responsibility for absolving people from a sense of guilt and that this is against public policy, against theological concept, and against moral principles in general—that it is the business either of the state or of the church to do something about guilt, and certainly not the function of a physician.

But such pat assignments fail to distinguish between *guilt* and a *sense of guilt,* and between a sense of guilt related to *actual* offenses and a sense of guilt related to *imaginary* offenses.

To approach the matter immediately from a clinical standpoint, I would remind you that every psychiatrist sees patients every day who feel extremely guilty *about something they have not done.* If such individuals were to go to a judge and ask to be sentenced for this sin, the judge would be astonished; if they were to go to a priest, he would no doubt assure them that they had never done anything and therefore had no guiltiness and therefore *should* not have any *sense* of guilt. But if they insist on having a sense of guilt even when they have no actual guilt, there is nothing the priest can do about it except to send them to a psychiatrist! For, on the other hand, there *is* something that a psychiatrist can do about it. A psychiatrist can, with the scientific tools now at his disposal, ascertain the unconscious, invisible reason for the false sense of guilt, attached to a nonexistent sinful or criminal act. This is not the place to go into an extended discussion of the psychological mechanics of forming or relieving a sense of guilt attached to nonexistent crimes. It is a very, very common clinical symptom with which every skillful psychiatrist is constantly faced. One could go so far as to say that in almost every mental illness or nervous illness there is a very strong component of this. For such a symptom, psychoanalysis offers relief, and the church does not offer any relief. If a man has horse-whipped his children, I am sure that no psychoanalyst would want to see him absolved or relieved from a sense of guilt about it in any other way than that prescribed by law and concurred in by the church. On the other hand, if a man imagines that he has caused the death of someone in China through remote control, or if someone feels guilty to the point of suicide because he feels that he wasted too much water washing his face in the morning or because he stepped over the threshold on the right foot instead of the left foot, then I think there would not be any doubt as to whether he should be offered relief by a priest or a psychoanalyst.

There is a common assumption that psychoanalysts favor sexual promiscuity and that they encourage people not to have any sense of guilt about it. This assumption is false, and its reiteration is a lie, a slander, a canard, and a misrepresentation of facts. Freud refuted this charge nearly fifty years ago, and no honest, intelligent, informed person can allege it. Psychoanalysts do not favor promiscuity, do not encourage it, do not attempt to relieve any patient's guilt about it, and, in short, are no more to be considered immoral exciters to crime than anyone else who is doing his best to diminish the errors of mankind. Quite the reverse, most of them spend hours and hours attempting to relieve patients from the compulsive feeling of need for these very "immoralities."

One might ask, "What keeps alive this common, but vicious, misconception?" I think it is very easy to say. Parents necessarily constantly restrict the sexual life of their children and sometimes in most crude and harmful ways. Sooner or later the instincts of the growing child bring him into conflict with the code of society, and he reacts to his parental experience in one of several ways. One way is by complete inhibition of his sexuality, which, if continued throughout life, means that he develops an abnormal personality. Neuroticism, impotence, homosexual propensities, and other sexual irregularities may be substituted for normal sexual adjustment. Many people come to psychiatrists because of a certain degree of inhibition in their sexual life which results from a feeling that any kind of sexual activity is wrong, including normal sexual relations with the spouse. Now it is not sufficient to *tell* such individuals that this is incorrect; they have been told so in a thousand ways, but they cannot believe it. In psychoanalysis they *do* lose an inappropriate and abnormal sense of guilt which had attached itself to sex in general; they discover that sex is not the evil thing which they have considered it to be but a purposive life function. In their sudden joy in such a discovery, such individuals by word of mouth or even sometimes by deed try to indicate that they no longer have the crippling inhibitions that have ruined their lives. But the errors of such individuals no more indicate the sinfulness of psychoanalysis than do the sins of certain Catholics indicate the wickedness of Catholicism or the offenses of certain Protestants the failure of Christianity.

I have made use of some of these recent accusations as to the immorality of psychiatry and psychiatrists to indicate how some of the charges against our "works" are made in ignorance. For I do think that psychiatry has a morality, and I do think that beliefs which must in the last analysis be described as religious are implicit in the theory and practice of psychiatry.

Consider, for a moment, what the daily work of the psychiatrist is. Consider his ministry of care to the most miserable, the most unloved, the most pitiable, and at times the most offensive and even dangerous of human beings. Consider the psychiatrist's role, properly conceived, as that of the friend, the guide, the protector, the helper, the lover of these unhappy people. "Passing through the valley of weeping, they make it a place of springs" (Psalm 84).

Consider what *you* call his tolerance, his forbearance, his patience with stubbornness, anger, spitefulness, silliness, sulkiness, belligerency, desperateness, unreasonableness, maliciousness—all the manifestations of hate. These he meets, if he is a good psychiatrist, with an attitude he is not ashamed to call love. We can live, he tells them, if we can love.

"You can be angry with me, if you must," the psychiatrist tells his patients (by his behavior); "I know you have had good cause to be angry at someone, so angry you became afraid of it. But you need not be afraid here—not afraid of me, not afraid of your own anger, or

of your own self-punishing conscience. You needn't be afraid that
your anger will arouse my anger and bring you pain again, and
make you feel wronged and disappointed and rejected and desperate
and driven mad once more! For I'm not angry, and I won't get
angry, and after a while you won't be angry, either. These people
all about you whom you can't look at now—you will find that they
are your friends. We are all your friends. We all love you, in spite of
the unlovableness you feel. Presently you will begin to realize that,
and relax a little, and then more and more. And as you come to
understand us better, and we you, the warmth of love will begin
to replace your present anguish, and you will find yourself helping
us and getting well!"

This is what the psychiatrist must say in every gesture, every act,
every order, every word. This, in modified forms, is what he must say
to every patient. Does it sound ungodly?

The psychiatrist dedicates his life to the furtherance of the welfare,
the life-betterment of those whose capacities for adjustment have
been overtaxed. So, of course, in a specific way do the shoemaker and
the dentist. But the overtaxing that brings patients to the psychiatrist
reveals itself in pain, in queerness, in isolation, in discouragement,
in ineffectiveness, in disagreeableness, in idleness and isolation, in
despoliation and defilement. These are unlovely pictures, and it is
the goal of the psychiatrist to inspire and guide and effect their
change. By the grace of God he is *usually* rewarded with success—
not *his* success, but the patients'! *Most* psychiatric patients get well.
Hence it is that the chief prayer of every psychiatrist should be:
"Keep back thy servant also from presumptuous sins; let them not
have dominion over me."

8. Moses and Monotheism

If, in some magical way, Plato or Galileo were to reappear on this earth, and to remain silent for six years, the announcement of a book expressing his most recent ideas would justly be an event of surpassing importance. Every newspaper and magazine in the civilized world would be endeavoring to obtain the privilege of reprinting, and columns would be filled with interviews, comments, analyses, discussions, perhaps even refutations. And yet in June 1939 there appeared the first book in six years from the pen of a man whose intrepidity and originality of thought, whose intuitive brilliance, whose fruitful adventures into the unknown have already given him a place in history comparable to that of such notable predecessors as those mentioned. And if there have been no headlines (which is not entirely the case) and as yet no reprinting, no interviews, no front-paging, it must be ascribed in part to the blindspots which always afflict us with respect to a contemporary genius, in part to the modest and retiring nature of this particular genius, and in part to the curious fear and taboos attaching to every revolution in the established conceptions of organized society.

For fifty years Sigmund Freud has devoted himself to the study of human life. But he has directed his attentions not to those aspects of life which were the most obvious, not to the external manifestations, but to the internal operations, the machinery of the soul. In

A review of the book *Moses and Monotheism* by Sigmund Freud (New York: Knopf, 1939). Reprinted from *The New Republic*, 100:23-25, Aug. 9, 1939.

the modern concept of the word, Freud discovered psychology. More accurately, he discovered the technique for studying subsurface psychology, and he has used this instrument with indefatigable patience and incredible courage. He made no secret of his method or of his findings, and he built his theories, and modified them from time to time, on the basis of what he and his followers learned from clinical experience.

Some twenty years ago, in the ripeness of middle life, he gave still further evidence of his temerity by going beyond his facts in the construction of theories to explain the data which he had accumulated and to anticipate the discovery of new facts and the correction of old prejudices. In a sense, these theories were but the extension of conclusions about human psychology drawn from his empirical observations, conclusions which can no longer be called hypotheses because they have been so amply supported and verified by the observations of many other scientists. Each new pronouncement of this great genius has been met by storms of objection, refutation, ridicule, and skepticism. And time after time, following the initial storm, the reaction against his quiet proposals has died down and their authority become established. I would not give the impression that every postulation of Freud's has been substantiated, because this is far from being the case. Freud has altered and revised many of his original propositions and conclusions, some of them several times. Although he still retains his originality of thought and his courage to venture into unknown territories armed only with the knowledge that he has acquired in the investigation of the human mind, he still records his ideas with a diffidence and tenuousness which are in sharp contrast to the arrogant positivism of some of his skeptics.

Moses and Monotheism has already been reviewed so frequently that its essential content is probably well known to most readers of this journal. In substance Freud turns his attention to the psychological implications of the religious concepts which dominate the Occidental world. He does not explicitly say so, but he is obviously intrigued with the contemporary illustrations of the ancient quip that half the world worships the Jew and the other half hates him. Of course, the Jew is the same half that hates him. But Freud's book is not primarily a study of anti-Semitism, having only an indirect bearing on that problem, although he does come to the conclusion that "hatred for Judaism is at bottom hatred for Christianity."

Freud's thesis is that there is support in psychology, anthropology, biblical exegesis, and history that Moses was born an Egyptian, that he "chose" a group of Semitic captives to be his special wards, and, inspired by the ideas of Amenhotep IV, instructed these Semites with regard to monotheistic conceptions and what was later called the Elohim religion; that he likewise taught them the Egyptian custom of circumcision, and that he led them toward Palestine. The theory continues to the effect that these semicivilized nomads reacted first positively and then negatively toward the idealistic "Moses religion," fluctuating constantly between it and a return to a polytheistic worship, absorbed Jahve (Jove) elements into their Midianite Elohim concepts, and thus became sufficiently bellicose to kill their idealistic leader and to conquer and displace the Canaanite tribes. Thereafter, Freud assumes, a second and false Moses was set up as their leader. But the blood guilt for the murder of their emancipator continued to obsess them so that their religion became dominated by ceremonials of atonement, sacrifice, and purification. In spite of these, or perhaps because of them, the Jews continued to oscillate between monotheism and polytheism, fleeing centrifugally from the Moses concept to the polytheistic faiths and practices of surrounding tribes and then centripetally back again to rigorous monotheism and nationalism. Anyone familiar with the historical books of the Old Testament must recall the monotonous repetitiousness of the good kings and bad kings, of the idolators and the prophets.

Freud agrees with Christian theology that, although Jesus was killed, he let himself be killed as a voluntary sacrifice—innocent himself, but representing those who had "sinned." By thus taking upon himself the guilt of the others—the guilt for the "original sin," which was the murder of the primeval father (Moses)—he set free those "sons" who could identify themselves with him. These theological principles were worked out and generalized by the brilliant Jewish theologian, Paul of Tarsus, so that Christianity became the successor to Judaism, the latter becoming a "fossil" religion. The

Christians, then, were those Jews who could say, "Yes, you and we killed our God, but we have admitted it and atoned for it and are cleansed from the guilt of it, but you (other Jews) will not admit it. You will not allow yourselves to be represented by the sacrifice of Jesus as we have, and so you must go on suffering and feeling guilty." But in elaborating this extension of Judaism, primitive Christianity receded from the austere heights of the Moses religion, Freud says, and became patently polytheistic, absorbing elements from Greek and Roman ideologies.

This is the thesis of "Moses." The questionable validity of the exegetical and historical proof Freud frankly concedes, but its psychological soundness he defends, and he is fully justified in doing so. It might be in order to indicate what is meant by psychological validity in contrast to historical validity. For example, the proposition that Moses had been killed by the children of Israel in the desert has been advanced and believed by others, but many historians will probably continue to declare that the evidence for it is entirely unsubstantial, that it has, therefore, no historical validity. Freud admits this possibility, but maintains correctly that it does have psychological validity. The consequences, the succeeding events, were precisely what one could have predicted had the murder occurred. As a matter of fact, it need not have actually occurred, provided it were generally desired, for in the depths of the human mind the intention or wish to perform an act is, as every psychiatrist and psychoanalyst knows, burdened with a sense of guilt scarcely less intense than that caused by the actual act itself. That the Jews rebelled against Moses, fought his leadership, disobeyed his regulations, "murmured against" him, is abundantly attested in the Bible, and there can be little doubt that they *wanted* to kill him.

Therefore, Freud does not have to prove that the Jews killed Moses; he needs only to prove that they wanted to, and felt as if they had done so. He points out that the Jews are a people burdened with a tremendous sense of guilt which drives them constantly on the one hand to make atonements and propitiations to God and to their consciences, and on the other hand (a point which Freud does not mention specifically) to indulge in provocative behavior, behavior that is sometimes described as masochistic.

Psychological validity is further to be found in the illustration of the cyclic pattern of disadvantageous behavior, which in an earlier essay Freud described as due to the "repetition compulsion." The Jews did kill Jesus and, so far as we know, Jesus, like Moses, had committed no worse crime than that of having exhorted his people to worship a single, living God and to give decent treatment to one another. It is to Freud's frank admission that the Jews killed Jesus that some Jewish critics of the book object. In the first place, they say, it is not true; it was the Roman soldiers who killed Jesus, not the Jews. In the second place, even if it were true, one should not mention it just now.

Such objections on the part of the Jews are eloquent testimony to the soundness of Freud's main thesis. To evade the issue on a technical basis, to say, "Yes, of course, the Jews wanted to get rid of Jesus and had him tried in a Roman court, but it was not actually they who stuck the cross in the ground," is a kind of legalistic sophistry which only places those who use it in a bad light. It is as if they would say that the Jews wanted to kill Jesus, but sought a way to accomplish it without assuming the responsibility. Freud does not evade the responsibility or the accusation; he interprets it. One such honest scientific effort to get at the truth, as Freud makes in this book, does more to combat anti-Semitic prejudice than do a dozen eulogies of Jewish accomplishment or a hundred denials of Jewish wickedness or a thousand schemes for attempting to suppress (for supposedly strategic reasons) the abilities or opinions of brilliant men who happen to be Jews.

In pursuance of our thesis as to the psychological validity of the theory, it may be pointed out that whether the Jews were unanimous in their condemnation of Jesus (which they were not) or whether Jesus was killed through the machinations of a few leaders who felt imperiled by his doctrines, is not important. The important fact is that the Jewish conscience acts repeatedly in denial of the accusation of murder. This is intertwined with the tendency of the

Christians, or I should say some Christians, to unload their own sense of guilt onto the Jews instead of onto Jesus. Who was actually responsible for the death of Jesus is a moral question and one in which psychology is not interested. What is psychologically important is that Christians and Jews react to guilt feelings, and react to them in ways which are superficially different but actually, in the last analysis, the same—by denial, by atonement, by ritualistic sacrifice.

It would be a narrow interpretation to regard *Moses and Monotheism* only as an analytic interpretation of the Jewish people and their peculiar history. The real importance of the theories elaborated in this book depends upon their universality. For what the Jews did and what the Jews do are what all people do. Someone has said that the Jews are like everyone else, only more so, and Freud has taken advantage of this acute observation to show that certain ideals of self-importance and separation inculcated in the early demarcation of this group enable us to study the application of the psychology of the individual to the psychology of a larger group. And just as Freud is able to interpret the history of the Jews in the light of his knowledge of the psychological history of the individual, so in this Jewish group pattern one can see certain world patterns. Yet it would be carrying the implications too far to say that the American people still punish themselves for their burden of guilt in the enslavement of the Africans, or that the British people must still atone for the rape of India and South Africa, and so with France and Spain. It would be a false extension of Freud's theory to think in these terms, because the crimes of these countries were not the crimes of the whole people, as in the case of Freud's illustration. Society has emerged from the tribal group to larger and more complicated units, the mass psychology of which we do not fully understand. But toward an ultimate understanding of them this masterful contribution of Freud's to the psychology of one clear-cut group of people, whose detailed history is a part of our intellectual and social heritage, must be regarded as fundamental.

It is a pity that Freud did not continue the application of his theory of the oscillations of religious interest between monotheism and polytheism, between Elohim and Jahve-Baal, one step farther. His failure to do so stems in part from a curious Viennese provincialism with which he has always been afflicted. For, just as the early church theology and its subsequent Roman development represented another swing away from monotheism into a more or less militant polytheism, so the Protestant Reformation represented a swing back to the monotheistic Elohim religion of Moses. In essence Protestant Christianity, the Moses religion of Elohim, and the Ikhnaton worship of Aton are analogous and in a sense continuous. Hence, it is no mere accident of geography that the Protestant Christians of England and the United States should have been the defenders and friends of the persecuted Jews of Germany and Austria, or that the Catholics, on the other hand, in spite of the possibility that they may meet the same fate as the Jews, should have stubbornly defended the fascist regimes of Franco and Mussolini and, indirectly, of Hitler. It is true that most of the Nazis of Austria and Germany are, or were, nominally Protestants, but it is also significant that under the Nazi regime they are being compelled to relinquish this Judaic faith. If one finds no Catholic figure in Europe corresponding to the Protestant Niemöller, it is not because Catholics are not brave and willing to suffer and die for their faith. It is because Hitler is exactly right when he says that Christianity, meaning Protestant Christianity, is Jewish, that is to say, a monotheistic Moses religion; Catholicism, on the other hand, as Freud says, is polytheistic and in this sense non-Jewish. Freud neglects to make this exceedingly important distinction, but throughout his book refers to Christianity as if it were synonymous with Catholicism.

Similarly, Freud neglects the fact that reformed Judaism is also a return to the spirit of the Elohim religion, with far less emphasis upon rituals of atonement and propitiation and far more upon the improvement of the interpersonal relationships between human beings. It no longer struggles with the temptation to return to the many gods, subtly implied in that clarion cry of orthodox Judaism, *"Schma, Israel, adonoi elohainu, adonoi echad!"* "Hear, O Israel, the Lord is our *Gods* [*sic*], the Lord is one!" On a psychological basis Protestant Christianity and reformed Judaism should long since have become amalgamated, since both in theory and in practice they represent one great religious Catholicism. It is not our function to evaluate these any more than does the author of *Moses and Monotheism* and it may be that the Jahve system can better serve the needs of some human beings than the monotheistic system. There is much to indicate that it better serves the uses of autocracy and tyranny. But there should be no shutting of one's eyes to the fact that this is the real distinction between these world religions, and not the many trivia which are advanced to maintain secular separatism.

This is the great social message of Freud's book. Superstitious religion stems from the neurosis of the individuals that compose society and serves regularly to cloak the actions of hate in a pious disguise. Such religion is based on the theory that men were made by "the gods" in their image. Religious concepts which recognize that man created God, that he is an ideal constructed from unconscious memories of a benign father with the highest aspirations of human thought, that he represents not some shibboleth for the entrance into a future life, but the index of an increased regard for the dignity of present-day human life—this is the spirit of a civilized, intelligent religion. But, like the Aton religion, the Moses religion, the Elohim religion, the Jesus religion, it is not one which lends itself to vigorous exploitation. In this sense it suffers the weakness of democracy as compared to the strength of autocracy. Its strength is internal rather than external. The ultimate victory of this kind of religion would be marked by its official disappearance; man will have achieved the social wisdom that would make religious idealism no longer necessary.

9. Psychiatry Looks at Religion

On the train this afternoon I read a book by a friend of mine in New York, Rabbi Louis Finkelstein, who has collected the spiritual biographies of a number of men. And I was thinking a little bit about my own spiritual biography. I remember the impression I got from my mother, who was a great teacher and Bible student. I remember how shocked I was when I went away to the university—and I blush a little at the naïveté of my youth—how shocked I was when for the first time I met people who called themselves Jews and were called Jews by other people. I had never met any Jews before, and I was shocked to learn that they believed only half of the Bible. I was still more shocked when I found that some of my professors did not believe any part of the Bible. I finally decided I really belonged with the Jews, as I could not go as far as some of my professors and throw it all out. I thought maybe I could believe about half of it.

For every adolescent there comes some kind of absorbing interest. He gets an inspiration from intellectual enlightenment in some field. Sometimes it is chemistry, sometimes it is literature, and sometimes it is poetry, or mathematics. I think that the great enthusiasms of youth are often much better guided in these directions than they have been in the direction of religious thinking. We try to catch up with the new things that are being discovered. Matters of religion

Transcript of a talk given in St. Louis, April 14, 1953, at a public meeting sponsored by the Central Conference of American Rabbis. Previously unpublished.

for a long time seemed to me to be relatively unimportant. Religion, I thought, was nothing new. I have a different view of things now.

If one is interested in psychiatry, he cannot exclude anything that pertains to human beings. And certainly religious faith pertains to human beings. What has been more characteristic of human beings for six or eight thousand years than the way in which they conceived of the world and the Creator, and the way in which they conceived of themselves and of one another?

Actually, the conflict between psychiatry and religion—perhaps I ought to say between the opinions of some psychiatrists and the opinions of some religionists—is a kind of personal conflict relating to fears of impaired authority. Both of them are actually dedicated to the same purpose and, to a considerable extent, use the same methods insofar as both appeal to the intelligence of suppliants. Both of us combat trouble in the individual. Our approach is different, but we are both endeavoring to cope with something which gives him or those about him pain. And comparable to sibling rivalry, hostility between children of nearly the same age in one family, it is natural to see psychiatry and religion a little bit suspicious of each other.

Dr. Gordon pointed out—he did not exactly put it this way, but let me put it this way—that religionists are frequently reminding psychiatrists that one of their great prophets, Freud, called religion an illusion. That is how the name-calling started. In the first place, as Dr. Gordon pointed out, an illusion is not a delusion. There are a great many necessary things which must, in a sense, be classified as illusions—art and music, for example. I am sure, as Dr. Gordon said, that Freud did not mean to say that the religious experience was negligible or that it was false, or that it was nonexistent.

I think Freud did feel that certain forms developed in the name of religion were harmful. But Isaiah thought that; and Jeremiah thought that; and Micah thought that; and Hosea thought that; and Jesus thought that. The conclusion was not original with Freud. Empty forms of religion have been criticized over and over again. Perhaps constant criticism of the forms of religion is necessary, just as we scientists feel that it is constantly necessary for us to criticize, correct, alter, and hold in suspicion the hypotheses that we assume at the present time to be basic. Every postulate of science is, by definition, capable of being completely overthrown and replaced by a better one. That is the attitude of science. Now there is a difference between religion and science in this respect. But I do not think it is different in regard to forms. Religious forms have changed vastly, and it is not so much the religious form itself that needs revision as the way the form is exploited or abused or caricatured by the people who are observing it. I am sure that you know this, and I am only reviewing something with which you are familiar.

You know our criticisms about religion as well as I. You know that form can replace content; you know that faith can become superstition; you know that ritual can become compulsive and obsessional; you know that Baal can become more attractive than Jahve; you know that prayers can be said to be heard by men instead of the One they were supposed to be heard by; you know that prayers can be used to ward off witchcraft instead of expressing praise. You know that religion can be used to exploit people. But so can law, and so can science, and so, I am sorry to say, can psychiatry.

Is it not possible for religionists and psychiatrists to agree that the good life requires of us "to do justice, to love mercy, and to walk humbly with God"? Could we not all agree that, if there were one maxim to be acted upon throughout one's whole life, it would be the Biblical precept, "Thou shalt love thy neighbor as thyself"? This can also be put in the negative, "What is hurtful to yourself, do not to your fellow man; that is the whole of the Torah, and the remainder is but commentary." I do not need to identify that, for you will recognize it as the teaching of Hillel. "Do not unto others what you would not they should do unto you"—that was the teaching of Confucius. "That is the sum of duty: Do naught to others which if done to thee would cause thee pain"—that is Hinduism. "No one of you is a believer until he loves for his brother what he loves for himself"—that was written by Mohammed. "In happiness and suffering, in joy and grief, we should regard all creatures as we regard our own self, and therefore should refrain from inflicting upon others such injury as would appear undesirable to us if inflicted upon ourselves." This somewhat more verbose form is Jainism.

The Sikhs are the briefest. They say: "As thou deemest thyself, so deem others." In Taoism, it is worded this way: "Regard your neighbor's gain as your own gain: and regard your neighbor's loss as your own loss." And the Zoroastrians (you know Judaism and Christianity owe much to their theological formulations, and so does psychoanalysis) put it like this: "That nature is good only when it shall not do to another what is not good for its own self."

Well, are these all the same? The thought is the same in all. But just as we live in different states and cities, just as we grow up with slightly different customs and speak different languages throughout the world, so do we naturally worship and believe and express our beliefs in different forms. Every thoughtful person must conclude that the most eloquent, the most magnificent conceptualizations that we can arrive at in our feeble human powers must be, in a sense, only a shallow approximation of what we feel and not a description of something that exists. If I were to look at the world assembly of those who believe in something which they call religious belief, and if I were to look at the various psychiatrists and the psychiatrists' helpers who hold up our hands, psychiatric social workers, psychiatric nurses and psychiatric aides, therapists and psychologists, I would say: These are two bodies of people, both dedicated to the kind of work in which the importance of the other person is greater than it is natural for that importance to be in a normal person.

Mental sicknesses can be described as of two kinds. First, there are those afflictions which cause anguish and pain primarily in the persons who suffer them. They suffer depression or fear, uncontrollable anger or bitterness, and sometimes this anguish drives them frantic or drives them to drink or drives them to the doctor and he drives them to the hospital. That is the kind of mental illness that you know about. There is a second kind of mental illness from which individuals may suffer but the people around them suffer a great deal more. Whether one calls it vandalism or psychopathy or criminality, we know some people whose mental abnormality results in *our* suffering. We are very much concerned about having them treated. There are two obvious forms in which the strange behavior representative of mental sickness commonly occurs. One kind is a recognized field for psychiatry; the other is coming to be. As yet psychiatry does not know what to think about certain strange forms of group behavior which may affect whole counties or whole countries. What, for example, should we call those strange things that occurred in the Middle Ages? Whole city populations began to dance out in the streets all day long until they dropped down exhausted. Would you call that a kind of mental illness? Maybe that is too simple to say. It may be that we would have some argument on our hands as to where to draw the line between something that is contagious in a mob and something that is individually disturbing. But to reverse all the ordinary formulas, to say that what you and I think of as truth is not truth, this kind of reversal of the ordinary interpretations of reality, this idea that all kinds of means are justified by a certain Utopian end, all this in an individual patient would certainly be considered a mental sickness because it is such a complete repudiation of reality.

Some have described Communism as more of a religion than a disease, a godless religion and hence not really a religion but a kind of faith. The politicians and the press and the public seem to think that communistic affiliation is all a matter of expediency or trickery or politics to be combated by free state techniques. But whether it is considered a religion, a disease, or a form of behavior, it is subject to scientific study. A little sociological and psychiatric research might discover better ways to control such mass infections with wrong ideas than a dozen orators or scores of loyalty tests or hysterical inquisitions and various other intimidations.

Thus, in our own country, we cannot but be aware of some kind of mass reaction to certain fears, and this reaction is not altogether healthy either. The general uneasiness gets widespread and the number of proposed remedies increases. Russian propaganda is alarming, and the antics and devices of some of our fellow citizens alarm us, too. Chauvinism becomes more strident in high places, and we begin to have doubt about our invincibility and self-sufficiency.

Is this another kind of mental illness, or symptom of it? Let us reflect. It is painful, it is destructive, it is aberrant, it is irrational, and, sometimes we call it hysterical. But nations and groups of people cannot really be said to have diseases, except as a figure of speech, though some authorities have played with the idea. It certainly does indicate, I think, the existence of a large number of people who are susceptible to contagious excitation of apprehensiveness which arouses abnormal reactions of fear and prejudice. Such individuals become highly susceptible to the hypnotic suggestions of the wrong kind of leaders. This represents a partial repudiation of reality and reason.

Such reactions have been studied scientifically at great length, in groups of various kinds, but particularly in the Army. The Army, like civilization in general, requires renunciation and organization. Both of these, to be effective, require leadership. Leaders capable of renunciation and vision preside over our increasingly high units of society: this temple, for example, this county, this city, this state, our nation, the Western Hemisphere, and the United Nations. Leaders capable of renunciation and vision and therefore capable of presiding over increasingly large units of society are rare and precious individuals.

During the war, my brother (then Brigadier General) William Menninger, was in charge of psychiatry in the Army. He and his associates in the Army studied the military situation at great length. It was noted repeatedly that where there was a good sergeant, or a good captain, or a good colonel, the morale of the unit was good, its effectiveness was high, and its mental breakdowns were at a minimum. The opposite was also true. A poor leader of a small unit would have half a dozen mental breakdowns in his unit, whereas a good leader of the same-sized unit, and with the same experience, would have only one or two. This showed how organization and leadership had much to do with the personal functioning of the individual.

It is safe to say that good leaders are rare and that bad leaders are more numerous, because anyone who is positive in his precepts, who will make promises and dogmatic assertions, will be believed by large numbers, whether these pronouncements are true or not. It is a somewhat startling experience to see group hypnosis. By the use of certain techniques, almost any articulate person with a little coaching can have a good part of a roomful of people believing absurdities within thirty minutes. Many can be convinced, for example, that they cannot unclasp their own hands. They sit there and struggle and try to do it without success. This seems weird, and you will probably not believe it, but please take my word for it.

What does it really mean? It means that the power of the positive statement uttered repetitiously is far more influential than the average person realizes. We know that this technique has been exploited. It has been used by Hitler. It has been used by all demagogues without being called hypnosis, and without the formal setting of hypnosis, but involving the same device of excessive suggestibility and certain conditions of expectation and need. Even in medicine, the greatest frauds and charlatans have always had loyal supporters and believers, among them some very intelligent people. You may have seen an article in a national magazine lately describing some strange activities of a healer in Italy who attracts large numbers of very important people there. His treatment consists of a kind of mumbo-jumbo. Such techniques will always attract some people.

Our greatest fear should concern our own susceptibilities to the seduction of false ideas. And our greatest need is for good leaders who will not depend upon mumbo-jumbo. We need not despair of the mental health of this country, for we are not without good leaders. By good leaders I mean men of vision and intellectual honesty, of perceptiveness and courage and personal uprightness. The title of a chief of a certain South American tribe may be translated as "He who walks ahead." The leader must walk ahead and see ahead and control his temptation for the exploitation of power and for compromise with truth.

The question often arises in academic discussions as to whether such rare individuals can be called abnormal. They certainly are supernormal. This term implies that there is some kind of a norm or average. What is the average? We can imagine a man, a quiet fellow, doing his work in the world as well as possible, knowing what he wants and going after it consistently, according to the rules, with a minimum of aggression. He is satisfied when he achieves a few of his goals. He takes pride in his labor, hoes in his garden, and reads his evening paper. He is sorry if he stops to think about some people having a hard time, and there is not much he can do about it. He contributes if he is asked to for the widow McPherson's funeral, and he donates to the Red Cross. He stays away from trouble, minds his own business, and lives his own life as he is permitted to live it. Now, such a man is not likely to concern himself with the problem of mental illness in the state, or with the conflict of psychiatry and religion. He is sorry about ill people, but he thinks it is a queer interest for anyone to have. He is apt to say to his neighbor that some people are crazy enough to think that crazy people are important and that criminals ought to be helped. He is sorry for them, but their plight is none of his doing and, after all, he pays his taxes.

Do I need to remind you how difficult it is to get financial support for psychiatry and for psychiatric research? Not even pennies, a few fractions of a mill on every dollar, go for this sort of thing. The enormous effect of a substantial investment in research pertaining to mental disease is like a dream of Aladdin's lamp. We cannot even guess what the results would be if the amount of money that has been spent for industrial research had been applied to psychiatric research. Do I have to remind you how few people spontaneously join mental-hygiene societies, or how cautious legislators are in attempting to judge the sentiment in their communities regarding decent appropriations for the care of the mentally ill? This is so not because people are hardhearted. It is because they put these things out of their minds. They consider an interest in them abnormal— and maybe it is. But there are some individuals who cannot get these things from their minds. For them the troubles of the world are their troubles, too. The simple expedient of seeing no evil, hearing no evil, and speaking no evil does not operate for them.

Anyone will respond if he sees a suffering or mangled child. But for the sensitive man, the very knowledge of so many suffering children in this world leaves him no peace. He cannot ignore the less obvious form of human suffering. He cannot hide behind the comfort of ignorance. He does not have to see a Negro lynched to be concerned about the inconsistency in our democratic practice. He need only visualize a colored citizen leaving the back door of a restaurant with food in a humiliating paper sack. When the members of his club shelve the application of an outstanding community leader for the categorical reason that his ancestors lived in Palestine, that kind of man is sad and angry and ashamed and hurt, more so than his rejected fellow citizen. The knowledge that more than half the people in the world go to bed hungry every night subtracts from his joy in eating. The helpless, suffering, sick people that are being treated poorly or inadequately in the state public hospitals is saddening to him, and a spur to action. That there are thousands of homeless, heartsick children in every state of the country, and thousands of lonely, dreary, miserable aged people everywhere, that these things exist are not mere matters of fact to such a man—they are matters of deep concern. He cannot persuade himself that they do not exist or that they do not disturb him.

On the other hand, he is not thrown into a futile depression because of this knowledge, beating his breast and deploring that God is so forgetful. He does not retreat into a mysterious world of schizophrenic fantasy. He does not go berserk and stab offending neighbors or shout defamations of character from the housetops. He does not deceive himself with dreams of revolutionary reform. He does not drown his troubles in alcohol. No, he reacts to the suffering caused by his identification with the universe in quite another way. He tries to do something about it. He directs intelligent efforts to alter it, and to enlist help in doing so. He sacrifices his own pleasure for his duty. He refutes the alleged first principle of life—he gives his life for his friends. He does not ask who are my friends or who is my neighbor. He remembers that there was such a man from Samaria who went on a journey.

There are really many such men and women. They will probably always be in the minority and probably they will always be regarded by some as abnormal, a little crazy. That is not an official psychiatric diagnosis. Jesus said, "Whosoever shall seek to save his life shall lose it; and whosoever shall lose his life shall preserve it." And, of course, he too has often been called crazy.

No, by none of our standards is this a correct designation. For while such individuals have risen above the norm, they have also risen above themselves. They have reached out and included within their own personality as much of the whole universe as they could touch or learn about. They love their neighbor not as their own selves, but as the more correct original Hebrew has it: "Thou shalt love thy neighbor; he *is* thyself."

The public does not always understand such people, but it respects them, and it is grateful to them. In the very designations applied to them, there is mixed with some envy and guilt feelings a deference, a clumsy, inarticulate attitude of admiration for the gifts of vision, understanding, sensitivity, and love which enable them to be so great a blessing to their fellow citizens. And when, in addition, such individuals of outstanding intelligence, courage, and honesty, are able to reject the temptation to use the unjustified or the implied promise to gain the support of unthinking followers, there emerges the highest type of natural leadership. It is the type of leadership we had in the prophets. It is the type of leadership we have in some American prophets, though they would demur to the title of prophet. They occupy this and similar pulpits week after week, doing the best they can, making no promises except that God is good. Religious leaders of this type can be regarded by psychiatrists only as allies and friends.

10. Freedom

Humility is said to be a virtue which vanishes as soon as one announces his possession of it. Somewhat similarly, freedom is a condition of existence which tends to disappear when one attempts to define it.

Probably no one past the age of childhood imagines a state of complete freedom, some vague ethereal anarchy in which nothing depends on anything. But the noun "freedom" continues to have high honor, and the adjective "free" is ubiquitously useful. Even the abridged Webster assigns it over a score of meanings. It is opposed by such ogres as *enslaved, restricted, bound, confined, rigid, costly,* and the like. Freedom seems, then, to imply a condition or place of greater comfort than the place and conditions in which one is, although we are often reminded that with more freedom (i.e., more *of* freedom) there is more responsibility and more danger. Hence the very word freedom is often used with restrictions! We speak of freedom *from* certain things (i.e., not from everything) and freedom *for* or *toward* certain things.

The aspects of freedom usually referred to in everyday discourse relate to restrictions imposed by the laws of physics, the laws of time and space, and the laws of the land, plus less frequent reference to moral obligations. But theoretical discussions of freedom soon reduce themselves to the problem of psychological freedom. We all concede that physical and statutory laws restrict us, and that some can be

Reprinted from the *Bulletin of the Menninger Clinic,* 19:240–243, November 1955.

violated with a penalty, while some cannot be breached. Our bodies function by unchanging physiological laws. But how about our minds? Are not our minds "us," and do we not make some of the laws of our own behavior for ourselves? Are we altogether the products of our heredity and our environment? Are psychological laws like those of physics or like those of the state? Are our mental processes orderly or anarchic?

Actually the word freedom has always been something of a shibboleth. C. D. Broad, the British psychologist, speaks for many scientists when he describes freedom as an illusion. At the other pole are those who consider it heresy to deny freedom of the will (although the phrase itself is awkwardly tautological). One's group membership determines in part and is likewise determined by one's view of freedom. As a scientist, I cannot imagine or concede the existence of a state of unordered organization, a negation of natural law. As a Presbyterian, I am, like Calvin (and also Luther, Aquinas, and Augustine) committed to a belief in God's omnipotence and divine plan for the universe. But *some* people are neither scientists nor Presbyterians! And perhaps there is that assigned divinity within each of us such that we each have some original law-making or at least law-interpreting to do. Can this be "allowed for" in a rigorous scientific description of psychological functioning or in a strict deterministic theology?

To psychiatrists and psychologists, the great importance of the concept of freedom to some people and the fear it inspires in others, make a good place to begin to study it. What kind of childhood, we ask ourselves, what early experiences have made freedom so critical for this individual? Why is escape so "pleasurized" or terrorized for him? Emergence from the uterus at birth might be called an escape, a freeing; the severance of the cord and the institution of respiration and alimentation complete the physical freeing of the baby from the mother. But are those so desired or welcomed by the infant? Is his emancipation thereafter progressive and continuous or is one dependency merely exchanged for another? When does the child first recognize himself as an independent agent—is it when he first pulls himself erect in his crib, or when he takes his first proud steps across the room to his waiting mother? Is it when he first gains control of his sphincteric functions and assumes the authorship of a "created" product, or when he first discovers that he can successfully pit his will against those of his parents in this function?

You can see from the questions I raise how we psychiatrists and psychologists have our own peculiar concept of the *sense* of freedom. We believe it does develop from some of these early childhood experiences, and we are reminded of this many times in our clinical work. Many, perhaps most, patients come to us with an impairment of this cherished feeling, often ascribed in part to something outside of themselves, physical, political, economic, or sociological. They cannot do what they want to do, or refrain from doing what they don't want to do. They feel that they have *no* choice, that their external freedom is restricted because of a restricted internal freedom.

All objective scientific evidence is against the existence of psychological freedom in the sense of an entirely capricious, undetermined, independent program of action unrelated to the past. At the same time, subjectively we all *feel* with a high degree of certainty that there *is* such a thing as psychological freedom—for us and for others. While we are prepared to believe "science" that we are all the "product of our environment and heredity," we all speak and think and act as if we believed that each of us constantly chooses in some autonomous way just what he will do with his circumstances—at the present moment and, likewise, in the moments to come. We weigh the pressures and "decide" which way we are going. We can remember, we can reflect, we can think. No one else can stop us from thinking; if I am stopped from thinking I must conclude that there is a part of me which is relatively free to act with reference to another part of me, which is the unfree part.

Psychiatry conceives of the human organism as having acquired numerous devices for accommodating itself to a constantly changing environment. The organism wants to make use of some features of that environment and to avoid other features. Each individual may be thought of as a center or epicenter, set about, pressed upon, and pressing against forces coming from many different directions, from other epicenters and also from within. There are those mysterious instincts that compel us to act other than as inert fragments of dust. *Something* seems to make us go, and as a matter of observation, seems to make us go in two opposite directions: we build and we destroy; we grow and we involute; we love and we hate. If there were no other forces in the world, freedom might consist in the fulfillment or gratification of these instinctual drives. Their existence sets up one limitation on our theoretical freedom, but also sets a goal, the attainment of which represents a "freedom" for us.

However, we may not forget that there *are* other forces. There are other people! There are all the phenomena which we call "external reality." Not everything outside the human organism favors our purposes; not everything is edible, not everything is comfortable, not everything is usable, not everything is friendly. To live is to be beset with ceaseless threats, obstacles, and challenges as well as opportunities. There are physical realities, social realities, and other kinds of realities, all of which act as forces and facts which definitely restrict the expression of the instincts of the individual. But there is still the possibility, indeed the necessity of some choice in these matters, and the sense of unfreedom develops when our preference is blocked by an unexplained, or, as it seems to us, unjustified and unnecessary restriction. But are our preferences spontaneously developed by us?

In the third place, the human organism is boxed in by the fixed structure and function of the soma, the clay house in which the spirit dwells. Theoretically the governing apparatus, the psychological system, cannot be separated from the somatic structure; "mind and body are one." But to the individual it always *seems* as if *he* were something over and beyond his *body,* that "baneful corpse to which [the soul] is tied." (Plato, quoted by Philo in *Gorgias;* see also Romans 7:24.)

Finally, there is pressure, and hence a block to freedom, in the peculiarly human institution which has puzzled philosophers since long before Kant and his "categorical imperative." This moral force of conscience represents a form of self-regulation which psychiatrists, following Freud, call the super-ego. This word has come to have a definite meaning for those of us who work with a particular purpose in a particular way with a particular kind of human being. Whatever it be called, it is a powerful force impinging upon our freedom, a force which is neither instinctual, nor somatic, nor (any more) external reality.

Psychiatry thus conceives of the human organism as impelled in certain directions but hedged about by limitations and restrictions, and impeded further by conflicts in the very nature of its basic impulses. Now the theoretical question is whether these various pressures automatically balance one another off, as it were, and effect some kind of mechanical resultant, or whether something within us can operate to effect an alteration in the reconciliation of these forces and events. In other words, are the functions of the ego in any degree autonomous, or are they merely the expression of memory, learning, experience, example, and pressure? Or is there any difference? Is the ego *more* than a collection of integrated and integrating functions? Has it some autonomy or "energies" or creativity ("divinity") of its own?

Perhaps this is only a word problem, a "semantic" difficulty complicated by our still great ignorance about the human mind. We do know, though, that every individual is constantly sustaining frustrations and encountering emergencies, great and small, and occasionally has to resort to extraordinary measures in order to survive. These measures may not prevent him pain and even failure, impairing both his objective freedom and his subjective sense of freedom. It is for this reason that the measures used are often called "symptoms" and the total picture "illness."

Psychiatrists have learned some techniques for helping (some) people to relinquish some of these emergency devices, these cumbersome life-preservers, and resume or achieve a less entrammeled way of life. Thus treatment in psychiatry consists essentially in setting people free, or at least free-er. This is done chiefly by the patient himself, who is helped to find or see the truth about himself. This "truth" may be the need of a different kind of restraint or the possibility of a different kind of freedom. It may depend upon new facts or it may depend upon a new view of old facts. It may be the possibility of a choice of alternatives, one previously invisible. In any case it involves changed attitudes, and, though freedom be considered an illusion, our attitudes toward it are facts.

PART SIX

The Historian of Psychiatry

"I wish to show what has happened in these forty years as I have seen it, for during this time all the great developments in this field of medicine have taken place and I have seen them unfold before my eyes, and in many instances I have taken an active part in what has happened." William Alanson White thus stated the objective he had in writing *Forty Years of Psychiatry*. When Karl Menninger wrote a review of this book in 1936, he began to write about the history of psychiatry, a subject that came to interest him more and more.

Karl Menninger could well use Dr. White's objective as an introduction to every one of his own papers written about the history of psychiatry. For he, like White, has been a part of many of the advances in psychiatry, has watched them unfold, and, in numerous instances, has influenced what has happened. White disclaims in his book any attempt to be autobiographical, but concludes that necessarily he has to be because his life has been so intertwined with the development of psychiatry during the forty years he is writing about. Nor does Karl Menninger attempt to be autobiographical in his papers about the history of psychiatry, but necessarily he is so. And, in many instances, by emphasizing the autobiographical features he brings to life the dramatic developments of psychiatry in his time.

When he reviewed Dr. White's book, he paid tribute to a man he deeply admired and respected. White was a distinguished American psychiatrist who dared professional ostracism by studying and defending psychoanalytic insights. White must have given Karl Menninger courage to do the same thing.

In addition to his father, Dr. C. F. Menninger, and to Elmer Ernest Southard, Karl Menninger was inspired by many others—Smith Ely

Jelliffe, A. A. Brill, Sigmund Freud, and Albert Schweitzer. Some of these great men have died, and, as he has grown older himself, he has been asked to pay tribute to the passing of some of these leaders. Included here are several such memorials. Not only do they stand as appropriate citations for the person being commemorated, but in each instance he places their work in a historical perspective.

As a young man, he dared at considerable professional risk to be a psychiatrist and to be a private practitioner of it. Later he dared even more to become a psychoanalyst. In the later papers in this section, he stands at the vantage point of seniority and professional security which allows him to look back on his own development as a psychiatrist and the development of American psychiatry in general. Having traversed the path from alienist to neuropsychiatrist to psychiatrist to psychoanalyst, he has often been asked to lecture and to write about the development of psychoanalysis in the United States and its impact upon American psychiatry.

In the last paper in this collection, he speaks, more than in any other that he has written, about his own footprints in the history of psychiatry. He neglects to discuss his plans for assisting in the future development of psychiatry. But he is already busy at the task. Despite his abiding interest in history, his outlook on life is a visionary one, and his engagement with life is with the future. His own participation in the future of psychiatry is a fascinating matter of conjecture. The world in which Karl Menninger lives is a busy and exciting one, for it is filled with many people and many things.   —B. H. H.

1. Forty Years of Psychiatry

No one is better qualified to record a history of the dynamics of American psychiatry than Dr. White, our revered leader and colleague. Gifted with a clear vision of the deeper meaning of movements and events, a gift which undoubtedly participated in his election of psychiatry as a career, and endowed also with the capacity of expressing himself clearly and convincingly, he has summarized in this small volume the growth of psychiatric conceptions in his own mind and, what is almost the same, in his native land.

For what Dr. White was able to see he gladly passed on to others, and this made him one of the leaders of the profession, both scientifically and politically. That he has never lacked the courage of his convictions is well known, and perhaps it is because of this rather than in spite of it that he has stood at the head of the profession notwithstanding his early espousal of the unpopular cause of psychoanalysis. Later, when the administrative functions of the "old-fashioned" hospital superintendent were exciting the contempt or at least the disavowal of those who felt that psychiatry should concern itself only with the clinical minutiae of hospital patients, he likewise came to the defense of "these sturdy gentlemen" and in one of his most felicitous passages pointed out that skillful provisions for the care of the mentally sick were intimately and inseparably

A review of William Alanson White's book *Forty Years of Psychiatry* (New York: Nervous and Mental Disease Publishing Company, 1933). Reprinted from the *Psychoanalytic Quarterly,* 2:619–620, July–October, 1933.

related to the scientific understanding of their condition, and that the administration of a hospital for the mentally sick is no less a special division of psychiatry than the examination of the spinal fluid or the interpretation of a dream.

Psychoanalysts in particular will admire the courage of his defense of psychoanalysis at the meeting of the American Medical Association in 1914, when the opposition to psychoanalysis was led by an exceedingly powerful and respected psychiatrist, Dr. Carlos McDonald, president of the Association, and also president of the Lunacy Commission of New York State. The well-known Philadelphians, Burr and Dercum, led a vigorous attack on psychoanalysis to which Dr. White replied with words which it is difficult to realize were quite radical and bold nineteen years ago.

The book is a survey and not a critical study of the development of new ideas in psychiatry, and naturally on account of the author's viewpoint it has a tendency to put more emphasis on public institutional psychiatry than upon the more individual applications. Indeed, if a criticism were to be offered, it might be that the book has a tendency to think of psychiatry in terms of theories and mass applications rather than in terms of the practical application to the individual. The great public institutions for the indigent insane are directed, on the whole, very sagaciously, but the fact remains that, aside from the work in the author's own institution and one or two others, most of the progress in psychiatry has come not from these asylums but from the painstaking work of individual psychiatrists with individual patients.

Another critical comment might be that in one or two places Dr. White perhaps assumes too great a familiarity on the part of psychiatrists with the origin of Freudian theories.

This is a book which every psychiatrist will want to possess, not alone because of its interesting, well-turned contents, but because William Alanson White wrote it.

2. Elmer Ernest Southard
1876–1920

In the early years of this century there flashed across the horizon a bright star in the field of psychiatry, a star that blazed brilliantly, briefly, and disappeared as suddenly as it had come. The light of the star went out in 1920 when Elmer Ernest Southard, one of the youngest professors in the three hundred years of Harvard history, died at the age of 43.

It was a brave and ambitious task that Professor Frederick Gay of Columbia University set himself when he essayed to write the life of his friend. Yet he has done it faithfully and accurately. If his compilation of facts lacks something of the scintillating spirit or the warmth of feeling characteristic of the man whose life is recorded, this must be charged up to the inevitable difficulties of describing the soul of a genius.

There can be no doubt of Southard's greatness measured by his breadth of vision, by his capacity for stimulating and inspiring his students and colleagues, and by the amazing fertility of his investigatory curiosity. The man who was not only a pathologist, a psychiatrist, a hospital executive, and a teaching professor, but a philosopher, a philologist, a psychologist, a poet, a chess champion, a sociologist and, above all, a charming, gracious human being is a personality too rare and precious and extraordinary to be registered in the cold

From a review of *The Open Mind* by Frederick P. Gay (Chicago: Normandie House, 1938). Reprinted from the *Psychoanalytic Quarterly,* 8:544–546, 1939.

lines of print of a formal biography. In his few brief years Southard attracted to himself and inspired a large number of disciples with whom he dealt with a never-failing kindliness, with that extraordinary technique which so few professors have of making subordinates feel that their ideas are brilliant and important. Often he would take an idea diffidently tendered by one of them and perhaps almost valueless at the beginning, mold or polish it into something of worth, and give it back to the author without the slightest intimation that anyone but that author deserved credit for the project.

The innumerable facets of his personality as seen by his intimate friends, his colleagues, his students, have been patiently collected and recorded by Professor Gay in a book which every man who knew Southard will want to possess, and which every man who would know the determining personalities of American psychiatry will feel obliged to read.

To readers of the *Psychoanalytic Quarterly* it is an interesting speculation as to why those two leaders, Southard and Freud, never met, and what would have happened if they had. In spite of Southard's nominal rejection of psychoanalysis, one of the reviewer's friends is convinced that although he had not publicly acknowledged his intellectual acceptance of psychoanalytic principles, he had long recognized their validity. I knew him very well, and I do not quite believe this; for it must be said that strictly speaking the title Professor Gay has given this book is not accurately descriptive of Southard. Southard had a brilliant, a versatile, a profound, a cultivated, and a productive mind, but not an open mind—an open heart, but not an open mind. This is one of many ways in which he resembled Freud. They also shared the same personal charm and graciousness, the same self-effacement, the same joy in the discovery and elaboration of new ideas, and the same prejudice against foreigners. And just as Professor Freud has never been able to bring himself to feel quite right about America and Americans, so Professor Southard had a definite prejudice against Europeans and against ideas originating and developing in Europe. He would have pointed to the present political developments there as evidence for the justifiability of his prejudices. Psychoanalysis was one of these European ideas, and Southard rejected it instinctively (I use the word in its conventional, not its scientific, sense). Furthermore, I do not feel it is disloyal for me to say that Southard was essentially a "superficialist" in the sense that he felt that the nature of things was patently apparent even on the surface if one but looked carefully. He regarded the tendency to sneer at the obvious as a kind of blindness. It required courage for him to say that he could detect pathological changes by the manual palpation of the gross naked brain, and it required courage for him to say that one could see from the very reasons alleged by employers for the discharge of certain employees that the latter were sick. Freud too bespoke the significance of the obvious; for example, the psychopathology apparent in everyday life. But where Freud depended upon deep subsurface analysis, Southard depended more directly upon deductive logic and philosophical extensions, especially by analogy. In this sense Freud is, of course, much the greater scientist; but whereas Freud nominally rejects philosophy and exalts empiricism, Southard, although trained in the mechanics of empirical science to a far greater degree than Freud, preferred the philosophical disciplines to those in which he was trained.

And it is extremely interesting that Southard, who sparkled with life, whose whole career was characterized by an optimistic vivacity, should have died so young, while Freud, whose sober realism led the optimistic Southard to describe him as a pessimist, Freud, who wrote of death, who gave us that magnificent conception of the death instinct, lived, in spite of suffering and sorrow far beyond that to which the average man is exposed, to almost twice the age at which Southard died.

3. Havelock Ellis
1859–1939

Havelock Ellis died in England on July 10 at the age of 80. He was described by the New York *Herald Tribune* as a psychologist and sociologist, by the *Times* as an essayist and philosopher, and by *Time* as an editor and sexologist. Perhaps in other journals it will be recorded that he was a poet, an artist, a physician, a psychiatrist. Such designations are correct, but even taken all together they are inadequate, for Havelock Ellis had the versatility that is the blessing of genius.

Most of those to whom his name is familiar know only about one or two aspects of his life. Some think of him correctly as a pioneer in the study of sex; others esteem him for his literary grace and his gift as a critic; few remember that he was a successful editor and still fewer that he was a physician and a psychiatrist; only his intimates knew that he was an excellent cook as well as a charming host. He himself might have put first among his attainments that he led a full, a rich, and a happy life. He believed, in the words of the Numidian Bishop of Hippo, that one should "love and do what you like," and he practiced this.

As a thoughtful boy of 16, Ellis dedicated himself to the study of sex at the period in life when other youths are solving their adolescent struggles by indulgence in political and religious fervor or by ostentatious rebellion against custom and social orthodoxy. He

Reprinted from *The Nation*, 149:103–104, July 22, 1939.

pursued this idea with scientific detachment and with unfaltering courage in the face of bitter and slanderous opposition, indifferent alike to applause and praise on the one hand and abuse and criticism on the other. Substantially, Ellis did three things. In the first place, he made a careful, thorough, and honest collection of data relating to a phase of biology which the hypocrisy and prudery of medical science had, until Ellis, caused to be ignored for the most part. In the second place, he evolved and advocated a hedonistic philosophy of life tempered if not determined by the sane, scientific attitude toward sex which his studies engendered. In the third place, he presented his scientific findings and philosophical beliefs to the world with that artistic combination of directness and delicacy which made them acceptable to nonscientific readers.

It is inevitable that Havelock Ellis should be compared with Freud. Like Freud, Ellis was scientist, physician, psychiatrist, psychologist, philosopher, and essayist. Like Freud, he bravely but modestly stuck to his principles in the face of persecution. Like Freud, he was vastly and widely misunderstood. Like Freud, he recognized the importance of sex. While Ellis was saying that sex was the center of life, Freud was saying that the sex instinct should be called the life instinct. Freud has acknowledged his indebtedness to Ellis for several ideas and terms. But their ways parted, for Freud is primarily a clinician, and this Ellis never was. While Freud worked with patients, Ellis worked with ideas. Both had the ideal scientific attitude, but of the two only Freud used the traditional scientific method. Even Ellis's celebrated *Studies in the Psychology of Sex* was chiefly a collection of data. They had no practical applications, no therapeutic usefulness. Freud looked at the same data, not in large collections but in individual instances, and asked, "Why should these things exist in this person? Why does he feel or act as he does?" And then he proceeded to find out. What Freud did was to explain the why and the how of the facts which Ellis tabulated. On the other hand, while the work of Ellis supplied no means for understanding or relieving the individual, it formed the basis for a philosophy of life which benefited and enlightened the entire world, and thus prepared the way for Freud's work with individuals.

It seems extraordinary today that the leading British medical journal, the *Lancet,* refused to review a scientific study of homosexuality by a medical man (Ellis) and explained this in an editorial entitled "The Question of Indecent Literature," declaring that it had not been published under the proper auspices. To this Ellis made reply that none of the medical publishers whom he had approached were interested in the publication of such a book. By others than the medical press the first volume was called "a wicked, bawdy, scandalous, and obscene book." Even *The Nation* of those days commented rather haughtily if not contemptuously that frequently in the volume "one comes upon remarks that suggest a paean upon sex, scientifically, philosophically, and poetically."

How does it come about that some individuals, such as Ellis and Freud, can have so completely escaped those psychological fetters which bind all of us? The answer is not easy to give. This much one can say, however, that there certainly was in Ellis a highly developed sensitiveness to the principles of dialectics, to the recognition of truth in the opposite. Early in his life he wrote that there were few questions about which, after a study of both sides, he did not come to a conclusion "totally opposite to the orthodox one which I have always been taught to believe true." Discussing this further, Ellis said that he felt sure that he was not actuated by any spirit of perversity, but on the contrary was frequently "convicted" in spite of himself and "made miserable." To one psychoanalytically oriented this accidental substitution of the word "convicted" when he obviously meant to write "convinced" suggests how strongly determined this attitude was by emotional factors. It is significant that Ellis, who led a most idealistic sexual life, should have written the world's greatest treatise on the abnormalities of sex. Olive Schreiner once wrote that Ellis was like a cross between a Christ and a faun. But all this does not explain him; it only indicates that it was out of vast internal contradictions that there grew an outer life characterized by a magnificent unity of purpose and spirit.

4. Sigmund Freud
1856–1939

I

At midnight, September 23–24, 1939, Sigmund Freud died in London in his eighty-fourth year. His death came as a great relief to those who knew how the cancer which had afflicted him for sixteen years and which had necessitated operation after operation and caused him constant unalleviated pain had within recent months extended beyond the reach of surgical or radiological relief. It is an eloquent, though incidental, testimony to the heroic qualities of the man that during all this period his only medication was an occasional tablet of aspirin. Only within the last few hours of his life was any morphine administered, and despite incredible suffering, to which was added the sorrow of exile and the loss of many friends, he had continued to see his patients and to work on his manuscripts until a few weeks before his death.

The solemn magnificence of this brave and losing battle of an indomitable spirit with an inexorable physical process reflects at the same time the theme and the vitality of his life work. His greatest concept was that of the instinctual conflict between the will to live and the wish to die, the life forces and the death forces. In his early years he passed productively and brilliantly through the phase of laboratory interests and then through that of clinical med-

Dr. Menninger has written tributes to Sigmund Freud on three occasions. These are presented here in order of their appearance. The first is reprinted from *The Nation,* 149:373–374, Oct. 7, 1939. The second and third were introductions to special Freud memorial issues of the *Bulletin of the Menninger Clinic* in September 1949 and May 1956, respectively.

icine (neurology), and made great and lasting discoveries in each
of these fields. But he was not satisfied with these; he became interested in the more fundamental factors that served to determine
not only disease but health, not only symptoms but behavior, not
only pain but sorrow. And for the next three decades of his life he
studied the phenomena of what he later called the life instinct,
which shows itself most directly in the impulse to love and to reproduce. For this he was reproached and ridiculed by those many
for whom the conventional attitudes of hypocrisy, prudery, and
salaciousness impelled the relegation of sexuality to the role of a
dirty and inconsequential incident of unfortunate biological necessity.
When as the result of indefatigable patience and unflinching courage he had gained for his views the recognition and acceptance of
scientific leaders, he turned to the consideration of the malignant
force which battles against this life instinct. Man, he said, is his
own worst enemy; warring constantly against the instinct to live and
to let live, to love and to create, is an instinct which has as its object
the return to inorganic insensibility; it is this instinct in the direction of death from which arise our hates, our bitterness, our suffering, our sicknesses, and our demise. This concept of hate aroused the
same resistances and refutations as had his earlier concept of love,
despite such frightful confirmations of it as the activities of the Third
Reich.

It is a presumptuous thing to comment on the life of a genius
upon the occasion of his death. Freud is not a man about whom
one can write a few casual words, a few comments of praise, a
few notes of criticism, and feel that an appropriate gesture has been
made to his passing. For Freud was not an ordinary man; he was
not an ordinary scientist. He was so nearly unique an individual that
it is difficult to find anyone with whom to compare him. No one in
the field of psychology ever attained to a fraction of his stature.
Among medical scientists almost none can be said to have approached
him in brilliancy, originality, or influence upon medical practice.
Perhaps no other one individual in the field of science lived to see
the thinking of the entire world so profoundly modified by his
discoveries within his lifetime as did Freud. Galileo, Dalton, La-

voisier, Darwin, these and others contributed discoveries which greatly modified our thinking and our ways of living, but the effect was more gradual in its permeation. For not only medical science and psychological science and sociological science, but literature, art, anthropology, pedagogy, and even popular speech show the influence of Freud's discoveries and show them in unmistakable terms.

All that Freud did stems from one simple discovery, a discovery based on knowledge which many had possessed before him. This was the knowledge that beneath the surface manifestations of human life there are deeper motives and feelings and purposes which the individual conceals not only from others but even from himself. Freud discovered a method for ascertaining and eliciting this hidden material; he called this method psychoanalysis. By means of it he and many others working with him gradually accumulated a considerable body of systematic knowledge about the unconscious processes of the human personality; this body of knowledge is also called psychoanalysis. It is psychoanalysis in the former sense which trained physicians use for the relief of suffering and maladaptation in their patients, and for further reseach in the study of personality. It is psychoanalysis in the latter sense which has come to modify the trends of literature, science, and philosophy.

It was from the fruit of his methodological discovery that Freud learned to understand technically, and hence usefully, the concept of ambivalence—although as a matter of fact this particular word was not coined by him. He became able to understand and to help others to understand that just as back of life there is always death, so back of professed love there is always some hate and back of professed hate always some love. More clearly than anyone else he saw how stalwartly the human mind defends itself against the acceptance of unpleasant truth. This helped him to be tolerant in the face of the ridicule, the misrepresentation, the distortion, the bitter and unscientific refutation of his theories which they initially aroused throughout the world. He reminded himself and his students that all scientific discoveries which diminish the feeling of self-importance in mankind stimulate resentment and incredulity. And so, were he alive, he would not be dismayed by the astounding ambivalence revealed in some of the contemporary comments upon his life. It would neither surprise nor disturb him that a great newspaper (the New York *Times*) should have published—on September 25, 1939 —an editorial ostensibly commemorating his death but actually vilifying him, misrepresenting him, speaking of "his colossal self-satisfaction and his natural intellectual arrogance," declaring with pompous inaccuracy "that psychiatrists still dismiss him as unscientific," flagrantly misrepresenting the facts about his last published book, and ending with the awkward and dubious compliment that he "was the most effective disturber of complacency in our time."

It is true that Freud was never happy in his feeling toward America, and even his best friends, many of whom were Americans, were never able to fully understand it or to alter it. He felt that we were characterized by an "unthinking optimism and a shallow activity." He was always suspicious of the popularity his theories and techniques acquired in this country. It is an ironic paradox that America should today be the country in which his theories are best known and most widely accepted. This is true not only of the general public but of medical scientists.

Sigmund Freud finally succumbed to death after many years spent in deflecting it from others. He was subject to prejudices and complexes although he spent his life in eliminating them from others. But these things do not detract from his greatness; indeed, it can be fairly said that he gave evidence of fewer prejudices and fewer complexes than most men, just as he retained his grasp on life longer than most men. What cannot be conveyed in words is Freud's ineffable modesty and gentleness and essential sweetness of character, for he had the qualities of the true scientist, and he never for one moment forgot that he was only a passing observer. To the eternal blessing of the human race, his sharp eyes and his great mind made his observations uniquely effulgent.

II

Some centuries before Christ, it occurred to some wise Grecians that honor we do others is in part for our own sake, and Ben Jonson cast this thought in his romantic idyll:

> I sent thee late a rosy wreath,
> Not so much honoring thee
> As giving it a hope that there
> It could not withered be.

It is in this spirit that the editors of the *Bulletin* and the cooperating committee from the Topeka Psychoanalytic Society have dedicated this number to the memory of Sigmund Freud. The honor we can offer him is nothing compared to the support which his eternal spirit gives to our own work, our thinking, and our ideals.

It is for our own sakes, not in a ritualistic compulsion, that we call to mind in thoughtful reflection the solemn events of ten years ago. On March 13, 1938, a cable was sent to Professor Freud inviting him and his family to become our permanent guests and to continue his work here in whatever way he desired. All the world knows how he was able soon after this to get out of Austria and spend a little over a year of refuge among friends in London. In May of 1939 one of us, representing the American Psychiatric Association, cabled him this: "Your fellow members assembled here in convention unanimously express their gratification at your safe arrival in London and send best wishes." Four months later he was dead.

Few of us realized the physical suffering that accompanied the distress of those later years of his life. Dr. Max Schur has written a note to the *Bulletin of the American Psychoanalytic Association* incident to the death of Dr. Hans Pichler, who died in Vienna in February 1949. The last of the twenty-eight operations by Doctor Pichler was performed in London in September 1938.

At the time of Freud's death, there appeared an editorial in the New York *Times* (September 25, 1939) which seemed to many of us to be misrepresentative, demeaning, and patronizing. "Psychiatrists," it said, "still dismiss him as unscientific." The editorial ended with the awkward and dubious compliment that "Freud was the most effective disturber of complacency in our time." This editorial angered many of us. It was answered in a spirited and eloquent way by Dr. Smith Ely Jelliffe and of course it was eclipsed by many other memorial notices far more complimentary.

But as the years have passed and the world has grown more

troubled rather than less, that description of Freud as "the most effective disturber of complacency" seems—to the writer, at least—to have taken on a new and stronger significance. For perhaps, of all the deadly sins in a sinful world, complacency is the greatest. The complacency which springs from the assumption that man is a rational creature and that science is the answer to everything (or else that religion is), the complacency of intellectual arrogance, the complacency of emotional isolation and social indifference—these are complacencies which need disturbing and which Freud did disturb profoundly and, let us hope, irrevocably.

In these days when peace of mind and peace of soul are held up as desiderata of the highest order at the very moment that millions are homeless and millions are hungry and millions are in slavery and millions in fear—surely we need to fear the dreadful disease of smug complacency and restless pursuit of an illusory peace. Freud did much more than disturb our complacency. But that alone is a great heritage.

III

One hundred years ago now a child was born in a humble home in the hinterlands of central Europe who grew up and became a doctor and a research scientist. His discoveries and proposals changed the thinking of the whole world within his lifetime. This did not make him less humble; he bowed his head lower and through suffering and exile worked all the harder. Not to Isaiah nor to Jesus nor to Plato, not to Empedocles nor to Galileo nor to Newton was it given that they should live to see the effects of their discoveries and their teachings. But Freud may have thought of Moses who changed his world but lay down in a lonely foreign grave, or of Alexander, who conquered everyone except himself and died in disappointment and defeat far from home, or of Columbus, who found a new world but died in chains in the old one.

But revolutionary and world-shaking as were his discoveries and postulations, perhaps Freud's most long-lasting influence upon those of us who follow him lay in his character. His persistence in the pursuit of enigmatic and mysterious data, his conviction regarding the reality and lawfulness of psychic phenomena, his belief in the curability of the "hopeless" neuroses, his humility in the midst of renown, his courage in the face of disaster, his patience in the grip of suffering—it is these which now three generations of followers have consciously and unconsciously taken unto themselves and into themselves as ideals. If we are less assiduous than he in the pursuit of truth, less modest in the proclaiming of it, or less effective in its application, count it our lesser stature, not our lesser aspiration.

We are a sentimental species, and proud of our time-binding faculty. So we "celebrate," as we say, in our quaint human fashion, the double decimal of the circuits of our planet about the sun since the mother of Sigmund Freud first gazed at her newborn child and wondered, as mothers do, what he and the world might do to one another. More than anyone who ever lived, that child was to show us how "as the twig is bent the tree's inclined." And so on this anniversary we honor a great tree of many leaves but we honor also that mother and the father and the others who together bent that twig in that village in another part of our planet, one hundred years ago.

5. Smith Ely Jelliffe and Peter Bassoe
1866–1945 and 1874–1945

I should like to write a very personal memorial notice concerning two great men in our field of medicine, both of whom contributed much to it and both of whom greatly influenced my life and therefore had a direct connection with the institutions and organizations with which I am connected.

My teacher, Ernest Southard, died in 1919. His brilliant and catholic mind was nonetheless capable of stubborn prejudices, and one of these prejudices was against psychoanalysis. Yet it was through him that I had met Smith Ely Jelliffe of New York, one of the most vigorous and most gifted of the protagonists of psychoanalysis at that time. Dr. Jelliffe was like Dr. Southard in his catholicity of mind and in his brilliance; he was less philosophical than Southard but more erudite and far more experienced clinically. I remember with deep gratitude how he took me under his wing after Southard died—me, a youngster fresh out of my hospital training, unknown to anyone in the field. Dr. Jelliffe introduced me to people, to experiences, and, above all, to ideas. He took me into his home, where I was impressed no less by the thousands of volumes of neurologic and psychiatric wisdom than by the infinite variety of home-made wines and liqueurs and the enormous collections of fungi, mosses, and pressed botanical specimens.

It was Jelliffe who introduced me to clinical psychoanalysis; prior

Reprinted from the *Bulletin of the Menninger Clinic*, 9:177–179, November 1945.

to that time I had known only the published material of Freud, Jones, Brill, Frink, and others. In those days a personal analysis was not regarded as a necessary prerequisite to the clinical practice of psychoanalysis, and it was Jelliffe who first encouraged me to try the experiment of listening for a time to free associations and judging for myself whether or not they had any clinical meaning. I recall a private meeting of a few psychoanalysts in New York to which Dr. Jelliffe took me, at which one of the members of the group described in considerable detail his own personal experiences in analysis with Professor Freud, subsequently discussed by all those present as if it were an ordinary clinical case.

In those early days of psychoanalysis Jelliffe always stood for an open-minded consideration of the theories and findings of all workers. He was regarded by some as being Adlerian and by others as being Jungian. I think he did give considerable weight to the ideas of these men, particularly Jung, but basically he was Freudian in the best sense of that word. As he grew older he became more and more definitely so. In fact I recall very clearly his angry reaction to an article of Jung's which we read together; what he objected to were certain claims of Jung for priority which he said actually belonged to Freud.

Dr. Jelliffe saw no borderline between medicine, neurology, psychiatry, and psychoanalysis. This seems obvious enough today, but in 1920 this was more than heresy; it was either "dilettantism" or "psychosis." I have heard Jelliffe described by envious and hostile critics as belonging in both categories. Nothing could be more inaccurate. The profundity and orderliness of Jelliffe's investigations were evident in whatever field or aspect he wrote about. He was an exceptionally fine neurologist and an exceptionally fine psychiatrist and an exceptionally fine internist. He knew all these fields just as he knew the fields of mycology, botany, geography, chemistry, and many others. He knew the essential contribution of every European worker in neurology and psychiatry, and knew most of the leaders personally. His reading was prodigious and his memory equal to his voracious reading.

It is apt to be forgotten in these days of "psychosomatic medicine" that Jelliffe was writing about the emotional factors in physical disease thirty years ago. When he suggested (1916) that psoriasis might be a "hysterical conversion syndrome," or that tuberculosis was in some degree amenable to psychotherapy (1919), or that psychogenic factors were present in multiple sclerosis (1921), bone disease (1923), hypertension, urinary-system disorders, and many other "somatic" conditions (1925–1935), he was laughed at; he was maligned; he was ignored. But he was also respected, listened to, and imitated. Psychiatrists began to think about the possibility that their field extended beyond the description of delusions and hallucinations. He and his longtime associate, William Alanson White, and their mutual friend, A. A. Brill, were the real fathers of psychoanalysis in this country; and Jelliffe should be regarded as the founder of psychosomatic medicine and credited with the introduction of the term.

Dr. Jelliffe died on September 25, 1945, after a long illness against which he battled with great courage. His funeral was held in his home at Hulett's Landing on Lake George, and he was buried near there in the forest, among the trees he had seen grow from sprouts. In this quiet spot (his wife writes) "the winds alone will move the trees to sound, and summer rain will fall and winter snow; the small animals he loved will scamper over him. His frantic seeking for knowledge, his bright spirit will rest. Surely he will now know all that he sought."

Only a few weeks after this one great tree had fallen, the thin forest of our medical leaders was depleted by the fall of another giant.

Peter Bassoe, who died in Chicago on November 5, 1945, was a man very different in type from Smith Ely Jelliffe but similar in being a great leader, teacher, and friend. Dr. Bassoe was a neurologist, pure and simple. He never laid claim to any considerable knowledge of psychiatry although he was always interested in it and never displayed the depreciatory attitude toward it which used to prevail in some neurological centers. For many years he edited the *Yearbook of Neurology and Psychiatry* with eminent fairness to the latter field. Thousands of medical students learned clinical neurology under his tutelage. He contributed many original articles of significant scientific value. But in my own opinion, his greatest contribution was the inspiration given to his many colleagues by the strength and beauty of his personal character.

My personal association with Dr. Bassoe began shortly after I had met Dr. Jelliffe. In the winter of 1921 I called upon him in Chicago and was most hospitably received. He showed me his work in the Rush Medical College and the Presbyterian Hospital, with which he was long associated, and took me to his home in Evanston where I became well acquainted with his wife, herself a physician, their son, and their four daughters. Dr. Bassoe and I talked about the formation of an organization of neurologists and psychiatrists practicing in the Middle West. He endorsed the idea heartily and suggested a list of men who might form the nucleus of such a body. At our first informal meeting in St. Louis in 1922 he presided and was unanimously chosen temporary chairman and later elected our first president.

The Central Neuropsychiatric Association thus born grew to be a sizable body; I have often heard it described as the liveliest neuropsychiatric organization in the world. Whatever success it has achieved is certainly to be ascribed in large part to Peter Bassoe, who was present at every meeting since its formation, served on almost every committee, counseled every president and secretary. All of us will remember him as a kindly, wise, gentle, fatherly man who was fair to everyone, considerate of everyone, friendly to everyone, a man who never did a mean or selfish thing in his life, who never expressed an ungenerous or bitter sentiment. He was able to do this without swerving for a moment from his scientific ideals and his professional work.

This is what we shall remember.

6. Contributions of A. A. Brill
to Psychiatry

Because I knew him for many years, and sat with him at many meetings of the American Psychiatric Association and the American Psychoanalytic Association, I feel qualified as well as honored to fulfill a request to speak a few words at this annual meeting of the American Psychoanalytic Association about the scientific work of our long-time "permanent president."

Let us remind ourselves today, and let us often remind our children and grandchildren and great-grandchildren hereafter, how much we owe to Abraham Arden Brill. Let us remind them that it was this little doctor with a big heart—born in Austria, an immigrant to America, a boy who arrived with three cents in his pocket, a student who put himself through school and through medical school—that it was this real American who perceived the greatness of Freud's discovery and brought it to America.

Let us remind them that it was he, this indomitable, irresistible, uncompromising little doctor, who gave life and being to psychoanalysis in this country—who first translated Bleuler and Jung and Freud for Americans to read; who fathered the New York Psychoanalytic Society and mothered the American Psychoanalytic Association; who faced with intrepidity and good humor the sneers

Delivered at a tribute meeting to Dr. Brill, annual meeting of the American Psychoanalytic Association, Washington D.C., May 15, 1948. Reprinted from the *Bulletin of the Menninger Clinic*, 13:185–187, September 1949.

and jeers, the scorn and calumny of his colleagues to speak out for what he believed, to speak the truth he saw and hoped they might sometime see.

Let us remind ourselves and our successors that the great edifice of psychoanalysis and psychoanalytic psychiatry which today we eagerly and proudly help to build still greater, was established for us here, with his life blood, by A. A. Brill. He taught Americans such everyday words as repression, displacement, transference, abreaction, and the unconscious. He wrote the first English treatise on psychoanalysis, plus 140-odd other books and articles. For many of us in this Association, as we look around each year at the ever-increasing multitudes that flock to these meetings, once so pitiably small and esoteric, the figure of a plump, cheery, energetic "permanent president" will always be visible—sitting at sessions or chatting in corridors, nodding, listening, smiling at us, and ill concealing his pride in the evidence of the rich fruit of his many labors.

If some of his earlier contributions now seem elementary, if some of his presentations and translations have now been superseded, let us never forget that it was with these as an entering wedge that he taught the present teachers of American psychiatry, and thus helped to develop the dynamic psychoanalytic psychiatry of today. Let us not forget also that many of his contributions were keen, novel, original, and of basic importance. With these stimulating, variegated studies, Dr. Brill continued to be engaged up to the day of his death, and they remain for the enrichment of our knowledge.

But the greatest contribution Dr. Brill made to us may well be something beyond these shining landmarks, these patriarchal milestones. I suspect that it may seem to many (as it does to me) that his greatest bequest to us was the example of his indomitably optimistic, honest, and courageous spirit. Death itself had no alarm for Brill. A little over a year before he died he addressed his beloved Vidonian Club on the topic "Thoughts on Life and Death." It is a charming and characteristic essay. In it he described in his fresh lively style a flight of *Ephemeridae* which he had once observed, and added, "We who, to our minds, belong to a much higher stage

of evolution tarry on this earth much longer; everything being equal
for three score years and ten, but in the end the

> ". . . Earth, that nourished thee, shall claim
> Thy growth, to be resolved to earth again,
> And, lost each human trace, surrendering up
> Thine individual being, shalt thou go
> To mix forever with the elements,
> To be a brother to the insensible rock. . .

"Thus spake a young man when he was only about sixteen years old,
in his *Thanatopsis,* in his reflections on death. I have always considered this summation of our seemingly complicated self by
William Cullen Bryant the most beautiful and most consoling description of the end-in-view. What could be nicer than 'to be a
brother to the insensible rock'?

"As to what happens after we stop breathing, I agreed with one
of my favorite authors, Samuel Butler, who said: 'Still, the life we
have beyond the grave is our truest life, and our happiest, for we
pass it in the profoundest sleep, as though we were children in our
cradles. If we are wronged it hurt us not; if we wrong others we do
not suffer for it; and if we die, as even the Handels and Bellinis
and Shakespeares soon or later do, we die easily, know neither fear
nor pain, and live anew in the lives of those who have been begotten
of our work and who have for the time come up into our room.'
Samuel Butler repeats here what Cicero said long ago and what
our own Herman Melville said somewhat differently: 'Since death
is the last evening of all, valiant souls will taunt him while they
may. Yet rather, should the wise regard him as the inflexible friend,
who even against our own wills, from life's evils triumphantly relieves us.' In old Greece it was customary to sacrifice a rooster to
Aesculapius when a person recovered from a disease, but when
Socrates was about to drink the hemlock he asked his friends and
pupils who were with him to sacrifice a rooster when he died,
'Because,' said he, 'I look upon the end of life as a recovery.' . . .

"And so," said Brill, with his famous chuckle, "whether we have
passed through life as Vidonians or as criminals, we have all done

our best with the means at our disposal. For whatever we did depended, not, as we think, on ourselves, but on accidental factors which we ourselves did not control.

"As you know I have always been deeply influenced by the monistic philosophy of Spinoza, who posits a single substance which he calls God and maintains that everything here is nothing but an accident of the divine substance itself. Man, as an individual thing, Spinoza conceives as an accident or a mode. The modes of Spinoza are to the substance as the rippling *waves* of the sea to the *water* of the sea. . . . Hence when I consider our departed founders"— and here he cites several, mentioning "especially my close friend Jelliffe, that brilliant and versatile mind who was the last of them to leave us; when I think of all these students of the mind I cannot help but return to the closing words of *Thanatopsis:* *

> "So live, that when my summons comes to join
> The innumerable caravan, which moves
> To that mysterious realm, where each shall take
> His chamber in the silent halls of death,
> I go not, like the quarry-slave at night,
> Scourged to his dungeon, but, sustained and soothed
> By an unfaltering trust, approach my grave,
> Like one who wraps the drapery of his couch
> About him, and lies down to pleasant dreams."

---

* The writer (K.M.) has altered the personal pronouns in the quotation from second to first person.

7. The Contribution of Psychoanalysis to American Psychiatry

I have been asked for a statement regarding the influence of psychoanalysis upon American psychiatry since I came into the field as a young physician in 1917.

At that time psychiatry in the United States was an institutional discipline, relating to the care and to some extent the diagnosis, but almost never the treatment, of various colonies of committed patients. Adolf Meyer, who had come to our country from Switzerland and begun work as a neuropathologist, had introduced the descriptive approach and ponderous attempts at classification made by Kraepelin in Europe. These were enthusiastically adopted by the state-hospital psychiatrists of America, with great unanimity. In the meantime, however, Adolf Meyer began devoting himself increasingly to clinical psychiatry and began to deplore the results of opening the Pandora's Box of Kraepelinian name-calling and therapeutic nihilism. Outpatient psychiatry in the modern sense was unknown, although "nervous patients" of various kinds were, of course, being handled by general practitioners, internists, and neurologists. The American Neurological Association was pre-eminent in prestige and scientific influence, reflecting an era of neurologic ascendancy which is said to have had its incipiency in the experience

Presented under the Maudsley Bequest before the Royal Medico-Psychologic Association at the Royal Society of Medicine, London, on July 31, 1953. Reprinted from the *Bulletin of the Menninger Clinic*, 18:85-91, May 1954.

of military surgeons during the Civil War in the United States and the Franco-Prussian war in Europe. The lesions caused by large- and small-caliber projectiles had attracted attention to the intricacy and importance of nerve-fiber connections, with a corresponding development of interest on the part of numerous internists who found interest and pleasure in precise localization and description.

These neurologists often found their "nervous patients" an irritation and a distraction from their main interest, but at the same time an indispensable source of income. Several of them, notably Weir Mitchell and his followers, had introduced proposals for more systematic therapy for the more severe cases, but most patients were treated by counsel, encouragement, sedatives, and/or placebos. Why hypnosis, Du Bois' persuasion therapy, and other forms of treatment were never more popular remains a mystery.

Definite and effective therapy for psychiatric cases began (about 1916) with the introduction of arsphenamine by Ehrlich. In spite of the discouraging results from the small doses which were effective with primary syphilis, both neurologists and psychiatrists persisted in efforts to treat general paresis and other manifestations of brain syphilis with various forms of arsenic variously introduced. The results were sufficiently encouraging in an area which had previously been so hopeless that for the first time psychiatrists and neurologists began to think in terms of treatment for psychiatric patients instead of merely in terms of diagnosis.

The simplification of psychiatric nosology by Ernest Southard in 1918 was a classification based not on therapeutic responsiveness but on diagnostic definiteness, although Southard himself was a great believer in the possibility of *treatment,* by education (as in the case of feeble-minded); by arsphenamine (in the case of the syphilitic), and by social adjustment (as in the case of the neuroses). It was Ernest Southard who first established a psychiatric outpatient department, and the notion of ambulatory treatment of severe mental illness. By some (e.g., Gay) he is credited with having first introduced the psychiatric social worker, although Meyer is also credited with this by others.[1]

The name of Adolf Meyer is more often associated with diagnosis and concept revision than with treatment, but his concept of total personality study implied treatment by assisted social adjustment and by psychotherapy. Furthermore, Meyer followed the example of George Zeller of Illinois and a few other far-sighted psychiatrists of the day in introducing folk dancing and variegated activities in place of the "menial work of making beds and running the floor polisher." [2]

Meyer was disturbed by the wholesale, uncritical acceptance of the Kraepelinian concepts which he had introduced in America, and spent much of the latter part of his life combating these static concepts with his more dynamic ones. Despite the great advance over Kraepelinian concepts represented by his "ergasia" formulations, this approach was never fully appreciated or extensively used in America, partly because of its strange terminology, partly because it was not specifically directed toward treatment, and partly because of the inertia involved in a revolution of concepts.

Just about the time that Adolf Meyer was proposing the concept of psychobiology, Freud's disciples—Brill, Jelliffe, White, and others —were introducing psychoanalysis, not only as a method of investigation and treatment but as a theory of personality function. While it is true that Freud later came to realize that the psychoanalytic method was more important for research and theory than for treatment, he was at first struck by the fact that he could effect cures in patients considered hopeless by all existing standards and methods. He was not the first discoverer to be buoyed up and carried further in his researches by the enthusiasm implicit in the belief that he had found a new and revolutionary treatment method. Certainly this idea caught the imagination of many doctors, including psychiatrists and neurologists, whose discouragement and dissatisfaction with the existing methods had developed in them a sense of futility and therapeutic nihilism.

Freud, following upon his experiences in France with Charcot and Liebault, developed a theory of the unconscious which gave full weight to the dramatic interplay of forces within the individual which ruled his behavior. Meyer, influenced by Dewey's pragmatic "functionalism," developed a more behavioristic conception of the

person, stressing the importance of life experiences for the development of a mental illness.

It was inevitable that these two concepts, psychobiology and
psychoanalysis, although actually reciprocal and synergistic, should
seem to be in opposition, and both of them appeared to the established Kraepelin-psychiatrists and Oppenheim-neurologists as expressions of new-fangled faddism. Human nature being what it is,
these four groups imagined themselves to be in great conflict with
each other. Meyer himself repeatedly declared that there was no
such conflict, but, while he spoke these words with his lips, he
showed in practice that he had great reluctance about an unequivocal
commitment to psychoanalytic methods and theories of personality.
Nevertheless the Freudians, in spite of initial ridicule and even professional persecution, rapidly gained increasing allegiance from new
members of the profession and even from many of the older ones.
The support of such leaders as J. J. Putnam, A. A. Brill, W. A.
White, Smith Ely Jelliffe, Albert Barrett, Richard Hutchings, A. P.
Noyes, Arthur Ruggles, and others clearly improved the prestige
of psychoanalysis and the conscientious, thorough, scholarly training standards and methods which were introduced by the psychoanalytic training institutes commanded universal respect.

Gradually the dynamic concepts have gained complete supremacy.
Almost nowhere in America today (1953) are the old Kraepelinian
methods and concepts practiced or defended. The Meyerian terms,
as such, were never widely used, but Meyer's ideas, translated by
W. A. White, dovetailed into those of Freud, the one for diagnosis,
the other for treatment, and both for a new personality theory.
The pseudo-conflict has thus been resolved. Historic vestiges remain;
some psychiatrists emphasize adaptation, and some adjustment, and
some repression. Some speak of the "total personality" and some
of the "character structure." But regardless of how they *speak,* most
psychiatrists now *think* in terms which express the combined
ideology of Freud, Southard, and Meyer. The Kraepelinian influence
remains visible chiefly in psychiatric case records and in official
nomenclature. Vigorous efforts are being made at the present time
to correct both of these.

It would be impractical to outline here the specific contributions of Freud to the theories and practices of American psychiatry. It is perhaps more representative to point to certain political and certain practical changes that have occurred as a result. From the political side, psychiatry, an unpopular and almost unknown specialty in 1918, has soared to heights of great importance. Membership in the American Psychiatric Association has jumped from less than three thousand to more than seven thousand. The governors of the forty-eight states in their recent annual conventions have focused their attention upon the fact that the maintenance and administration of the hospitals for the mentally ill is the greatest single problem of each and every governor. In many states this is now regularly the largest item in the annual budget of state expenditure. Medical schools quite generally have revamped their curricula so that psychiatry, instead of being totally ignored or relegated to a few Saturday-afternoon sessions in the fourth year, has become a subject of didactic and clinical instruction during each of the four years, and in some schools it is said to occupy as much teaching time as does surgery!

Psychoanalysis as a technique is still taught only in psychoanalytic institutes; candidates become eligible for admission only after at least two years of graduate psychiatric training and experience. But the theory of psychoanalysis, the psychoanalytically derived concepts of personality structure and of psychodynamics, are taught in practically every medical school and residency training center. And, whereas it was formerly impossible for any psychiatrist contaminated with psychoanalytic ideas to be offered a university appointment, today the medical schools are choosing as professors and heads of psychiatric departments men who have had psychoanalytic training. This would indicate that psychoanalytic training, originally undertaken only for the purpose of psychoanalytic practice, has now become a recognized part of the education equipment of the well-trained psychiatrist, particularly those who are going to teach.

Freud, it will be recalled, always had grave misgivings about the overpopularity of psychoanalysis in America. He was afraid that its essential principles would become diluted and compromised. Many of those of us who do both psychiatric and psychoanalytic teaching have shared his concern in recent years, although for somewhat different reasons than those of Freud. For there is no doubting its popularity. Thus, although there is a great shortage of psychiatrists in America, there are approximately one thousand candidates now registered as undergoing psychoanalytic training. This is almost as many as the total number of doctors currently receiving basic psychiatric training. This does not mean that all residents are undergoing psychoanalytic training, although many are; many of those receiving psychoanalytic training have completed their psychiatric residency training (which as a matter of fact is required by all our American psychoanalytic institutes). What happens is that after completing a residency in psychiatry those residents who can get staff positions in the hospital or in the medical school then begin their psychoanalytic training, and, as soon as they have finished this, the trend is for them to leave the medical school or the public hospital and go into private practice, limiting themselves to psychoanalytic treatment.

The reasons for this are numerous; it is indeed a fascinatingly interesting subject; it is more remunerative than public hospital service; it requires less exertion; it has fewer frustrations; it is more fashionable; it enlists one in a closely linked group of scientific workers concentrating upon a specialization within a specialty; and it makes for a kind of security and steadiness of income which is very appealing to young men entering private practice. But, nonetheless, it has serious drawbacks both for the physician and for the public. It restricts the experience of the physician to a very small number of patients; as one young doctor put it, "I hate to face the prospect of spending the rest of my life treating an average of four patients a year" (that is, eight patients a day seen daily for an average period of two years). It is a disadvantage for the public in that it makes for a situation in which a private patient is considered either a proper subject for psychoanalytic treatment or else a case for someone else; and that "someone else" is apt to be a colleague who similarly overspecializes and treats most of his patients with electroshock therapy. The psychiatrist who functions with catholicity as a counselor for troubled people is to be found less frequently in general practice than in the public psychiatric hospital and psychiatric clinics which, as I have intimated above, are woefully understaffed.

Happily, some of our young psychoanalytically trained psychiatrists are beginning to limit their psychoanalytic work to half time, reserving the other half of the day for examinations, consultations, hospital psychiatry, guidance clinic practice, teaching, and so on. This would seem to indicate that psychoanalysis as a private therapeutic specialty practice is assuming a more balanced and appropriate place in the total scheme.

But quite aside from these effects on distribution of psychiatric skills in the national community, the great success of psychoanalysis in America has had other negative effects. For one thing it has definitely impaired descriptive clinical observation. The young physician, intent on understanding and explaining symptoms on the basis of a hypothesis, is less inclined to be interested in learning to describe accurately what the patient seems to be experiencing and manifesting. An attitude of patronizing indifference toward the acquisition of systematic historical material, either biographic or pathographic, is justified by the glib excuse that since the patient has probably forgotten or repressed the most significant incidents in his life, it is a waste of time to collect conscious memories. All this makes the task of the psychiatric teacher, who believes in comprehensive case study and systematic case recording, enormously difficult. Insistence upon such fundamental procedures is apt to be interpreted by students as pedantry and "reactionaryism." Meanwhile, the general realization of the inadequacy of our nosologic concepts and designations plays into the hands of such objectors, who point out that we continue to describe the illnesses of our patients in one set of terms and record them in our records according to another set of terms.

However, in spite of these drawbacks, and notwithstanding the chauvinistic tendency toward a this-is-the-one-psychiatric-treatment-worth-doing attitude, there has been a renewed hope and interest in all psychiatric therapy stimulated by the "success" and by the "failures" of psychoanalysis. The very contrast of shock therapy, which has likewise had its successes and failures, has served as a stimulus to the more careful selection of cases for both of these therapies.

In addition, there has been a greatly extended use of the various adjunctive therapies—occupational therapy, recreational therapy, educational therapy, music therapy, physical therapy, athletic therapies, etc., in most American hospitals. Much is made of the concept of "milieu therapy"—the beneficial effects of a proper hospital atmosphere, routine, and personnel structure. Psychotherapy of types other than psychoanalysis has been greatly broadened, and the use of group therapy, as so beautifully developed in England, is another growing field. The status of surgical therapy (lobotomy) is as yet equivocal, with a few vigorous advocates.

Thus it may be said that psychoanalysis, by its optimistic attitude, its therapeutic devotion, and its revision of personality concepts, has vastly changed our psychiatric orientation, theory, and practice in America. Today the diagnostic preoccupation of the early part of this century seems childishly pedantic and irrelevant. The emphasis today is on treatment, on better treatment, on better methods of treatment, on new methods of treatment. (One might contrast this emphasis on treatment with the concept of care of the patient, which is much better done in England.) One frequently encounters the statement by authoritative persons in America today, that we are curing "only" about seventy-five per cent of our psychiatric patients, and that we should aim at curing ninety per cent of them. In the light of such goal-setting, overenthusiastic though it may be, it is indeed a startling experience to re-read the records of thirty-five years ago when a recovery rate of five per cent, eight per cent, and sometimes *even* twelve per cent was offered without apology or dismay.

Statisticians will be quick to point out that much here might depend upon our understanding of the word "cure," but the very fact that we now understand it differently is in itself an indication of changed attitudes and changed concepts.

This is not to overlook the scientific skepticism of such workers as Eysenk, whose statistics would seem to indicate that patients receiving psychotherapy (including psychoanalysis) are less likely to recover than if left to spontaneous readjustment. I think Eysenk's figures are incorrect, but I think his research effort is commendable. Before we can say how many of our patients recover and to what degree, and to what extent this is the result of our efforts, we must have a more definite agreement about our concepts of the nature of the disease process, and better ways in which to describe, define, and measure its manifestations. It is these topics which now particularly preoccupy some of us in America.

At the Menninger Clinic, one of our group research projects is an effort to simplify our nosologic concepts and our scales of measuring the severity of illness and the extent of recovery, thus affording us a basis of checking more specifically the actual results of psychotherapy. Similar research projects in various phases and from various points of view are being undertaken in other places. My own contribution to the International Congress of Psychoanalysis ("Regulatory Devices of the Ego under Major Stress" *) is related to this general endeavor.

The essence of my thesis was that the principle of homeostasis or steady state maintenance can be applied to psychological phenomena and psychoanalytic theory. The functions of the ego in receiving external and internal stimuli and in dealing with them for the best interests of the organism can be viewed as those of a homeostatic effector. The constructive and destructive drives of the organism must be so directed and modified as to permit the maintenance of a level of tension which is both tolerable and conducive to safe, productive, and satisfying living and continued growth.

Events constantly occur which tend to disturb the adjustments and reconciliations achieved, and these stresses require the ego to improvise adaptive expedients for maintaining the integrity of the organism. Minor stresses are usually handled by relatively minor, "normal," "healthy" devices. Greater stresses or prolonged stress excite the ego to increasingly energetic and expensive activity in the interests of homeostatic maintenance.

---

* See supra, p. 497.

In its effort to control dangerous impulses under such circumstances and thereby prevent or retard the disintegrative process which threatens, the ego initiates emergency regulatory devices which fall into five hierarchically arranged and specifically characterized groups, representing increasingly greater degrees of failure in integration.

I believe that this conceptualization of the ego's regulatory function provides us with a broader frame of reference for understanding mental illness and will enable us to discard some of our vague, many-faceted, traditional terms in exchange for more definite and precise designations of process and stage. It also helps us to align our psychoanalytic concepts with general organismic-biologic theory.

8. Freud and American Psychiatry

When I was invited to join with Dr. Wälder in flanking the address of our distinguished visitor, I sought the counsel of friends regarding the most appropriate material for the occasion. It was their advice that inasmuch as I had been selected to speak for my American colleagues, I attempt to trace some of the peculiarly American developments of the work of Sigmund Freud whose centenary we celebrate. So I shall offer some reminiscences and observations, making no apology for the personal flavor that is bound to color such a report. To an audience of psychoanalysts I dare not stress either my humility or my pride.

I shall skip lightly over those troubled days of our Association's adolescence and concentrate rather—in good psychoanalytic style—on our childhood, and on our marriage. I shall emulate the anonymous author of the Second Book of Maccabees, who wistfully recorded that ". . . having in view the . . . difficulty which awaiteth them that would enter into the narratives of the history, by reason of the abundance of the matter, we . . . have taken upon us the painful labor of the abridgment [finding] the task . . . not easy, but a matter of sweat and watching. . . . Yet, for the sake of the gratitude of the many we [resolved to] gladly endure the painful

At the Freud Centenary Celebration of the American Psychoanalytic Association held in Chicago, papers were read on April 28, 1956 at the plenary session by Dr. Ernest Jones of London, Dr. Robert Wälder of New York, and Dr. Menninger. Reprinted from the *Journal of the American Psychoanalytic Association*, 4:614–625, October 1956.

labor, leaving to the historian the exact handling of every particular, [endeavoring] . . . to avoid a labored fullness in the treatment. . . . Here then let us begin . . . for it is a foolish thing to
make a long prologue to a history and to abridge the history itself."

Some of my colleagues will recall that I was in that little group
of worshipful disciples who sat at the feet of Ernest Southard.
His death in 1920 left us highly charged with the exciting notion
that the human mind could be an object of scientific study. This,
to be sure, had been given to psychologists by William James,
Josiah Royce, and others, but to the medical men it had not as yet
been given at all. There was no mention of the human mind or
any of its functions in the medical textbooks of the period in which
I went to medical school. Patients had no minds. Neither did employees, nor yet criminals, nor indeed anyone except psychology
students and their experimental subjects.

It was this anti-psychologism which Ernest Southard, pathologist
though he was, most vigorously combated. Psychological phenomena
were exciting and intriguing data, and data as considerable and
significant as cellular data and tissue data. He was fond of emphasizing the principle of *bonum ex nocentibus*—good arising from
evil, the sweet uses of adversity. "From the study of the mentally
ill," he used to say, "we shall learn about mental health; from the
study of the mentally retarded we may learn something about the
learning process." In the midst of a veritable shower of new ideas,
new projects, new contacts, and new honors, Southard died suddenly, at the age of 43.

This was psychiatry at its best in the area where, a few years
previously, Freud had brought psychoanalysis to America. Southard's disciples were shattered, and scattered, by his death. But
they continued his ideas. Harry Solomon went sturdily on with
the neurosyphilis researches, Lawson Lowrey developed the outpatient multidiscipline idea in the form of the child-guidance clinic,
Mary Jarrett and Marion Kenworthy developed psychiatric social
work, Myrtelle Cavanan continued neuropathological research,
Alvin Mathers turned to medical education (in Canada), Frank-

wood Williams became medical director of the National Committee for Mental Hygiene. I came West to Topeka to join my father,
who had known and admired Southard, and—later—my brother
Will. Working together, we tried to put into effect the things
Southard had taught us.

There were, of course, other foci of psychiatry than Boston in
America, and my father insisted that I travel about the country a
month each year to visit them. So in 1920 or 1921 I met Adolf
Meyer, Smith Ely Jelliffe, Adolf Stern, A. A. Brill, Philip Lehrman, C. P. Oberndorf, and many others. I recall that Meyer received me while he ate his lunch—a sandwich and a glass of milk.
When the lunch was over, so was the interview. Years later I came
to know Dr. Meyer better, and to realize how much he gave to
American psychiatry. But it was difficult for him to communicate
his thinking or his real friendliness. Consequently, his disciples
were fewer than his wisdom deserved.

Jelliffe, on the other hand, was extremely articulate, and gave
me a royal welcome. He and his wife invited me to dinner and
took me with them to the theater and a night club (quite an experience for a Kansas boy in 1920). They insisted on my canceling
my hotel reservation and staying with them. Jelliffe talked to me
incessantly about Freud and Jung and psychoanalysis and complexes and libido, always as if they were most respectable and
timely topics; this was most astonishing to me. It had not been so
in Boston. It was not so in Baltimore. But ah, New York!

This most erudite of American psychiatrists, definitely one of
our psychoanalytic patriarchs and the father of American psychosomatic medicine, thus became my second psychiatric guide, and
my first psychoanalytic mentor. Together with Brill, Lehrman,
Stern, Taneyhill, Kardiner, and others, we attended a meeting
of the American Psychoanalytic Association in Boston to hear
Horace Frink, just back from Vienna, recount behind closed doors
his personal experiences in analysis with Freud. All of us—including Freud—looked for great things from Frink, whose book, Morbid Fears and Compulsions,[1] was, and still is, one of the clearest
and best-written expositions of psychodynamics. His subsequent de-

cline was one of the early tragedies of American psychoanalytic development.

I never learned who Jelliffe's analyst was. Oberndorf recorded that he and Jelliffe had some hours with Paul Federn in May 1914, just before the War broke out, and I believe he had some more analysis in Europe. I myself had a few hours with Jelliffe and, subsequently, with Albert Polon, one of the early American workers and one who, like Southard, died in his youth.

In between these rather frequent excursions to Boston, Baltimore, Washington, and New York, I was in Kansas, and quite busy for a young doctor. We were all neurologists *or* neuropsychiatrists in those days, and I was the only "neuropsychiatrist" in a very wide area. Neurosyphilis was one of our most common diagnostic problems, and those of us who could detect it and knew something about the new "wonder drug," arsphenamine, had something useful to offer the general practitioner. Untreated syphilis was then very common, and hence acquired and congenital neurosyphilis were quite abundant. (Freud once remarked how many of his neurotic patients came from syphilitic fathers.[2])

Psychotherapy was almost unknown. In Philadelphia the Weir-Mitchell complete-rest-and-force-feeding treatment was still in use for the neuroses and mild depressions. A few colleagues used hypnosis or Dubois' re-education technique or various placebo procedures such as faradic or Geissler tube stimulation. The state hospitals were in a most pessimistic mood of therapeutic nihilism; no one was assumed to recover from mental illness of any kind except by accident or the grace of God. But pinpoint diagnosis, with the brilliant example of the prosperous and rather contemptuous neurologists before us, was earnestly striven for.

Each spring the meetings of the American Psychiatric (and each winter those of the Orthopsychiatric) brought me East again. More and more we heard from the obstreperous and preposterous Freudians. Fancy a sober scientific assemblage where the program was about "Hallucinations in Disseminated Sclerosis," "Alzheimer's Disease in a Woman of 30," "The Effect of Influenza upon Dementia Praecox," and fancy the impact of having "Pop" Brill pop up with some psychoanalytic interpretations! What was the world coming to when these New Yorkers could come to a dignified meeting and begin talking about sex—and *such* sex! (Remember, there was no sex in medicine at that time. Look for yourself. Look in Osler, look in Cecil, look in Oppenheim. You will find nothing. Sex didn't exist.)

This is a situation the flavor of which is very difficult to recapture without producing a caricature. Please believe that we were not complete fools, nor as prudish as this may sound. But everything *looked* different. George Harvey Robinson's *Mind in the Making* was literally *thrilling* to us; we were all reading it. And these psychoanalytic concepts—even the basic ones of an unconscious (we said subconscious) part of the mind, of symbolic values, of sexual development—all of these were controversial topics.

Gradually, of course, they began to sound a *little* less shocking, absurd, and unreasonable—especially to the younger men—and then the early ridicule gave way to scorn and angry moral denunciation. No doctor with academic or social aspirations could afford to be associated with psychoanalysis. This, of course, made it all the more attractive to some alert and independent and, we must add, rebellious souls who were involved in a contemporaneous wave of intellectual enlightenment which came with—not necessarily from —psychoanalysis. An element of martyrdom, which was more theoretical than actual, furthered the spirit of adventure.

William Alanson White, the lifelong friend of Jelliffe, and an eloquent leader of American psychiatrists, maintained an urbane optimism regarding the growth and integration of all things psychiatric—the psychiatry of Kraepelin, the psychiatry of Southard, the psychiatry of Adolf Meyer, the psychiatry of Jung, and even the psychiatry of Freud, Jelliffe, and Brill. His diplomacy and political leadership had much to do with the realization of this amalgamation. He was friendly with them all—the conservative hospital superintendents, the dignified neurologists, the effervescent and often provocative psychoanalysts, and the youngsters like myself who didn't know *what* we were. It was he who engineered the affiliation of the American Psychoanalytic and the American Psychiatric Associations and, with Brill, fathered the psychoanalytic section in the latter organization; it was he who proposed Sigmund Freud for the Nobel prize.

I can recall how exciting it all was. There were fireworks at every meeting. No one could answer Jelliffe; he bowled them all over with his greater knowledge, greater vocabulary, greater memory; but they couldn't always understand him. Brill could be understood, however, and answered—but not silenced. Sometimes he left himself wide open to counterattack, but never to refutation. The opponents of psychoanalysis sometimes managed to make some of the new theories look pretty ridiculous. Some remarks of White's [3] made in 1914 are rather refreshing to read even after the passage of all these years:

> The thing that psychoanalysis did for psychiatry was to open a door to the understanding of the patient which strangely had always heretofore been closed; and one reason that it had always been closed was that the physician had never paid very much, if any, attention to what the patient said, putting his remarks down as of no significance because they were crazy or incoherent. Much less did the physician in the old days ever have the slightest idea that these crazy, incoherent remarks might by any chance have a meaning. Psychoanalysis oriented the physician toward his patient in an entirely different way . . .
>
> Dr. B—— has presented certain cases, certain clinical records and dismissed the subject by saying the whole thing was absurd; he did not bring forth any specific argument. A society of this sort should be the proper arena where such things should be threshed out on scientific merits; prejudices should not enter into the question at all. I am a psychoanalyst; I want the truth and I am willing to welcome any light that may be thrown upon the situation . . . I have no doubt that many hypotheses will be laughed at in years to come as being in fault, perhaps some of them ridiculous, but what we want is their correction at this point; we want more light; we want more truth; it does not do any good to call them absurd and let the matter go at that . . . those facts must receive some interpretation; if our interpretation is wrong, there is a right interpretation, and I ask the people who criticize the movement to come

forward and tell us what all these things mean. We offer our explanation; we are willing to withdraw if we are wrong.

I trust this society will maintain an open attitude toward this subject.

I can remember my own conversion—that moment in which the forces of repression yielded to the mounting pressure of what we call reason. My critical-point case—my Dora—was intelligent and good-looking, but she was a persistent sleepwalker. I made a careful examination, and came to the conclusion that the diagnosis was either (1) epileptic equivalent, or (2) hysteria major.

I told her this. But she said she didn't care what the diagnosis was; she wanted treatment. She said it was very embarrassing to wake up prowling around in her parents' bedroom, looking for something—she didn't quite know what—that her father kept hidden and which would change her completely if she could acquire it. This reminded me of some of the "nonsense" I had read in psychoanalytic journals, so I wrote Jelliffe about her. I told him I had no couch but I could borrow a chaise longue. He wrote back for me to use anything, just get her to talk. This wasn't at all difficult, and I listened to her once a week. But soon I had heard enough to make me go out and buy all the books on psychoanalysis that I could find. (As I look back on my notes of this and some of the other "wild analysis" I did in those days, I wonder if I do as well now.)

All over the country physicians like myself were wondering where to obtain systematic training in this new method and whether it was true, as rumored, that a personal analysis was a prerequisite. We did not know then how the New York Psychoanalytic Society had been almost torn asunder over this very question in what Oberndorf describes as "one crisis after another for five years." A few of us could afford to go to Berlin or to Vienna; a few were victimized by the three-months analysis promised by Otto Rank. Formal training was begun in New York in 1929, and in 1930 Franz Alexander came to Chicago and offered didactic analysis to a group of us who subsequently (1932) assisted him with Lionel Blitzsten and Ralph Hamill and Tom French in organizing the second American Psychoanalytic Institute.

From here on it is unnecessary for me to recount to this audience how systematic psychoanalytic training developed throughout the country, *universitate nullo modo adjuvante* (without benefit of or help from the medical schools or universities). Gradually psychoanalytic concepts began to prevail more and more. In 1930, in the first edition of *The Human Mind,* which I wrote for the profession but which seemed to appeal even more to laymen, I said that "practically no intelligent and informed scientist today disputes the main thesis and findings of psychoanalysis." My whole book implied that psychoanalysis was even then the essence of American psychiatry. I was violently attacked for this by one of my old friends and colleagues, who sent out a questionnaire to members of the American Psychiatric Association to prove that most psychiatrists did *not* accept psychoanalysis. Nevertheless, today American psychiatry is one based on a psychoanalytic theory of personality. The old Kraepelinean terms have largely disappeared. The Meyerian *terms* were never widely used, but the Meyerian *ideas,* translated by W. A. White, "dovetailed into those of Freud, the one for diagnosis, the other for treatment, and both for a new personality theory. The pseudo-conflict was thus resolved. Historic vestiges remain; some psychiatrists emphasize adaptation, and some adjustment, and some relationships, and some repression. Some speak of the 'total personality' and some of the 'character structure.' But regardless of how they *speak,* most psychiatrists now *think* in terms which express the combined ideology of Freud, Southard, and Meyer!" [4]

In European countries one often hears reference to "depth psychology," and there is an emphasis upon the science of the unconscious, of symbolism, of symptomatic acts, and so on. *Here* the emphasis is more upon ego psychology, "defenses," relationships, and reactions. Instead of depth psychology we speak of dynamic psychiatry, an expression rarely heard, I believe, in Europe. This is related, I think, to an important influence of psychoanalysis upon American psychiatry which may seem at first paradoxical. For in spite of the chauvinistic, doctrinaire attitude of "psychoanalysis-is-the-only-worthwhile-treatment" assumed by a few very zealous leaders and very recent Institute graduates, one effect of psycho-analysis has been to renew hope and interest in all psychiatric therapy. The very "success" of psychoanalysis as well as its "failures" have inspired this. Shock therapy, drug therapy, and surgical therapy have likewise had their successes and failures, and all this has served as a stimulus to the more careful selection of cases for each of these therapies.

Moreover, there has been a greatly extended use of the various adjunctive therapies in psychiatry in most American hospitals. Much is made of the concept of "milieu therapy"—the beneficial effects of a proper hospital atmosphere, routine, and personnel structure. Psychotherapy of other types than psychoanalysis has been greatly broadened, and the use of group psychotherapy, as so beautifully developed in England, is another growing field. All these have developed from the impact of the optimism, the rational-ism, and the new concepts which psychoanalysis gave us.

Psychoanalysis has changed (American) psychiatry from a diag-nostic to a therapeutic science, not because so many patients are cured by psychoanalytic technique but because of the new under-standing of psychiatric patients it has given us, and the new and different concept of illness and health. Old names die slowly, but the essential namelessness of mental illness became palpable to us in the light of Freud's great discoveries. We know now that in the unconscious we are all mad, all capable of a madness which threat-ens constantly to emerge—sometimes does emerge, only to be tucked away again out of sight, if possible. To understand this in one's self and to improve one's methods of controlling one's own madness are essential to understanding it in others whom we essay to help.

Thus the prerequisite of a personal analysis, which so disturbed our psychoanalytic beginnings, has turned out to be the keystone of the psychoanalytic movement. More and more clearly we recognize that Freud's greatest achievement was his courageous self-examina-tion, his unparalleled self-psychoanalysis. More than anyone who ever lived, he followed those great historic adjurations, "Know thy-self" and "Physician, heal thyself." Because of what Freud discovered, no psychiatrist today can ever again be quite so much at the mercy of his own unconscious as in the days before Freud undertook this historic task and unveiled his revolutionary findings about the human personality for us all to see, and to test and to work from. All of the enormous influence that psychoanalysis has had upon America, upon our sociology, our anthropology, upon psychology, upon literature, upon art, and, above all, upon medicine— all of this stems from the new conception of the nature of man to which Freud introduced us.

The question remains as to why the American soil was so fertile in its reception of Freudian discoveries and hypotheses, contrary even to *his* expectation. We may not and would not forget, of course, that Americans are not only the sons of New Yorkers and Virginians, but of Englishmen and Dutchmen and Scots and Africans and Germans. We should not forget, also, that America has been the beneficiary of Europe's tragedies. To our shores there have come many teachers from the Old World who are now to be accounted Americans. They brought to us learning and wisdom; their idealism and scholarliness framed our psychoanalytic institute programs. In a hundred years of development, the medical schools and universities had not evolved a single systematic course of training in psychiatry until after the psychoanalytic institutes had shown the way, and it was upon the pattern of psychoanalytic training that courses of instruction for psychiatric residents were developed. For such fortuitous traits of open-mindedness, practicality, romance, adventure, optimism, ingenuity, or whatever it may have been (and others may judge this better than we) which permitted us to make such use as we have of Freud's great gifts transmitted to us by these men, we may also be humbly grateful. For it was out of fire and ashes, out of self-destructive rage and sorrow and heartbreak, that our powers of helping our stricken fellow man have been thus extended.

Thus, again, *bonum ex nocentibus.*

Members of this audience will know how strongly I am convinced of the usefulness, the operational "truth" of the Empedoclean-Zoroastrian-Freudian dualism, and how I believe that, in a sense greater than he himself realized, Freud interpreted the microcosm of the personality in terms similarly applicable to the macrocosm of the universe. Freud aspired to keep his data and his formulations as free as possible from unsupported hypotheses and uncontaminated by mystical belief. Yet he must have realized that even the belief that we can or should or do help a fellow creature is unprovable, and represents an act of faith. In this his native optimism overtook the philosophical detachment toward which he consciously aspired. In all his ruminations about the multiple functions ascribed to that internal governor of our lives, the ego, he must have reflected upon the enormous dependence he was placing upon what he called the intellect. Freud was no gnostic, and, for him, reason and intelligence included that mother-wit whereby the ego exhibits the very stuff of life in so manipulating its controls to make the best of every bad bargain and by reconciling conflicting demands at a minimal sacrifice, averts the disintegration of the organism. It is this economic aspect of psychoanalytic personology which most interests me today because from it, I believe, can be derived not only new concepts of the human situation and of those disabilities which we call illness and pain and misbehavior and crime, but new blueprints for the effecting of *social* change as well as *individual* betterment.

Southard was an optimist; he saw great possibilities in a better understanding of motives and thoughts and feelings and behavior. He believed Freud to be a pessimist, who found too much that was dark and unlovely in the depths of the human heart. About this I think my first teacher was mistaken. Freud was a great optimist. He struggled to control too great an expectation from man or life; he strove to be as honest as it is possible to be. But had he lacked faith and hope he could not have gone on; he could not have borne his great sufferings or withstood the impact of his great discoveries.

It is a reflection of Freud's basic faith and optimism, as much as of his courage, that he could face the destructive essence of human personality and assign it a basic role in our existence. Perhaps it was the bravest thing he ever did. And, even in his discouragement over the outlook for civilization, he did not fail to add at the end of his essay about it that "Now it may be expected that the other of the two heavenly forces, eternal Eros, will put forth his strength so as to maintain himself along side of his equally immortal adversary."

It was his optimism that Freud bequeathed to America; and it was the optimism of our youthfulness, our freedom from the sterner, sadder tradition of Europe, which enabled us to seize his gift. It appealed to the idealism of American doctors; it was a new way of helping people and building a better world. Freud was optimistic about human beings being able to *help themselves.* His was an optimism which flowed into action and discovery, and this, too, struck a responsive chord in a pioneer country where we feel that there is nothing which we cannot accomplish if we but put our minds to it. It mobilized the forces of Eros and Agape in the lives of professional workers, and gave them a rationale and a program. It conceded the inevitability of death, not by ignoring it, but by identifying it in all its penultimate manifestations and declaring war against it. For it identified love with life, and death with hate. The clinical axiom, "You can live if you can love," came, thus, not only from the New Testament but from the new psychology, and not only from religion but from medical science.

It is for this that American psychiatry thanks Sigmund Freud on his 100th birthday, him and all those who, like Ernest Jones, brought it to us from him.

9. Footprints

According to a great Bostonian of five generations ago, "the heart of the young man said to the psalmist:

> "Tell me not, in mournful numbers,
>   Life is but an empty dream!
> For the soul is dead that slumbers
>   And things are not what they seem!
>
> "Life is real! Life is earnest!
>   And the grave is not its goal;
> Dust thou art, to dust returnest,
>   Was not spoken of the soul.
>
> "Not enjoyment, and not sorrow,
>   Is our destined end or way;
> But to act, that each to-morrow
>   Finds us farther than to-day.
>
> "Art is long, and Time is fleeting,
>   And our hearts, though stout and brave,
> Still, like muffled drums, are beating
>   Funeral marches to the grave. . . .
>
> "Lives of great men all remind us
>   We can make our lives sublime,
> And, departing, leave behind us
>   Footprints on the sands of time. . . ."

An address given on Nov. 30, 1958, at a meeting celebrating the twenty-fifth anniversary of the Boston Psychoanalytic Society. Previously unpublished.

On an occasion such as this, when we are gathering to take note of the passage of years since the crystallization of some human efforts in a set direction, it is always a question how much and how far we should look back, and how much we should look forward, and how much we should look straight down, straight down into our own hearts and into our present imperfections and our own failures to make our lives sublime. It is a question whether to be nostalgic or euphoric, to devote ourselves to reverencing the achievements of our forebears or a modest evaluation of our own. Actually, there are no whethers about all this, for there is no escape from doing all of these things. It is rather the problem of the essayist how to organize his symbol words of recollection and the lines of his discourse so that the proper mood be created in his kind listeners.

And what is that desired mood, that frame of mind that combines contemplation, commemoration, and rededication?

Whatever it is, I hope that through an unseen grace it will descend upon us now as we, like wayfarers on a vast sandy shore, retrace and identify some of the footprints that have led us to where we are tonight.

Let us stay in this area of Boston and New England, and let us think first of the fierce, heroic, often mismanaged and tragic efforts of the pioneers for whom life in England and Holland had become intolerable. We could, to be sure, think farther back to Indians and Scandinavians and pre-Indians. But time is short and fleeting, and so we must come a long ways forward and begin at a point when what we call civilization was well established.

It was one hundred seventy-six years ago that the Harvard Medical School was founded, which was fourteen years before one Horace Mann was born. This was the Horace Mann who first established state hospitals for the mentally ill, who first had enacted a law prohibiting the use of alcoholic intoxicants, who first created a state board of education, who first built a school for the deaf and for the blind.

It was from the Perkins Institute for the Blind in 1887 that a genius named Anne Sullivan was sent to Alabama to teach another genius, Helen Keller, in one of the most extraordinary instances of everything that is implied in treatment that is anywhere recorded.

But that was long after a raw March day in 1841 when an ex-schoolteacher, fulfilling her conscientious duty of teaching a Sunday School class in East Cambridge jail, observed incidentally and almost by chance, as her biographer says, the suffering of lunatics there detained. This, of course, was Dorothea Lynde Dix. One year later William James was born, and five years later G. Stanley Hall and James J. Putnam (1846).

All this was a little over a hundred years ago, when these great women and men came into the world which they were to do so much to change. Their sublime lives left footprints still clearly visible in the Boston sands.

I am not a historian or a biographer, and I would not undertake the objective evaluation of the contributions of all these leaders to our present knowledge and modes of thought. But on the other hand I have reached a period in life when I realize the tendency of youth—indeed, the tendency of all human beings—to forget the great gifts given to us and to the world by those quaint and picturesque (but *surely* very stuffy, stupid, and old-fashioned) figures who marched across the shores before us, like the jerky figures in an old-time movie run through a present-day speeded-up projector. And so I shall ask your indulgence if I recall some of them to your minds.

Last summer I had a long visit with the ambassador from Burma, who tried to convey to me how their vision of Buddhism envisaged prayer. "You see," he said, "we don't believe in a Creator, or at least one who can be reached by our voice. We don't worship a God, but we pray; for us prayer consists in the reverent contemplation, with gratitude, of how much we owe Gautama for teaching us how best to live. We must reflect upon it so, or we soon get to thinking that it was we who discovered this."

What I should like to do is in this spirit. Reverently, then, I would like to recall that Helen Keller and William James and J. J. Putnam and Horace Mann and Isaac Ray started a train of thought in which we all continue. I shall try to trace the development of that line of thought by describing some personal recollections and experiences.

Boston was the first big city I had ever lived in for any length of time. I was just 22 when I landed, as I well remember, in the old South Station, which, as I later heard, was the busiest depot in the world from the standpoint of trains coming and going. Carrying a suitcase in each hand, I walked out to the busy, dirty cobblestone pavement, the strong smell of roasting coffee assailing my nostrils and the roar of the elevated trains my ears.

I inquired the way to the Y.M.C.A., and following instructions I clambered up the drab, dirty steps to the elevated train and rode to the proper junction point. I was much impressed, as I rode out Boylston and Huntington Avenues, by the Boston Tech buildings, the library, the Opera House and Symphony Hall presided over by the great Karl Muck. I was even more impressed when I learned that from the Y.M.C.A. one must walk—or ride—much farther to reach the Harvard Medical School. Remember, there was little automobile transportation in those days.

Somewhere I met three of my University of Wisconsin friends by appointment, and, traveling as a quartet, for safety, we proceeded to enroll in the great Harvard Medical School. The transition from a closely knit group of medical students in a state university in a small town to the large affairs of a big medical school in a big city was quite a step for us relatively immature and provincial midwestern boys. Inasmuch as this is a psychoanalytic occasion and presumably a psychoanalytically oriented audience, I will indulge myself in the recounting of a recurrent dream which, it seems to me now, I have had at least a half-dozen times since then. It relates in a general way to this matriculation. Curiously enough, the actual steps taken were so obvious and so well planned that I don't recall them. Yet the dream is always to the effect that classes are about to begin, or perhaps have begun, and vast distances are to be traversed in order to get from one class to the next, distances so great, in fact, that time is running out in some way and either I have missed some class, or I am about to, and hence must immediately take "certain steps." What those steps were to be I don't now recall, if indeed, I ever—in my dream—find out.

As so often with a dream, the details elude me, but I know it has to do with that confusing period when we were trying to grasp the relationship of Roxbury, Brookline Village, Coolidge Corner, the Massachusetts General Hospital, the City Hospital, and a few other important landmarks. Later I became so familiar with the map of Boston that I could with pride direct even Bostonians. You must remember that none of us had ever seen curving streets or a subway or a "square," and even the unexpected little trolley dive into the tunnel under the Boston Gardens was a startling experience. Fresh from our midwestern homes and cities, we were almost equally shocked by the drabness and shabbiness of the Roxbury flats where we first stayed and by the style and substance of the food service in the accessible lunch counters.

We Wisconsinites began a search for a steady boarding house, and we settled upon one, the whereabouts of which I cannot recall. I remember that we paid four dollars a week for two meals a day, and that recurrent appearances of finnan haddie, codfish balls, and New England boiled vegetable plate were for us novelties ambivalently appreciated.

We moved from Roxbury to Brookline Village, where two of us roomed on the first floor and two on the second floor of the little apartment at 17 Linden Place. Dr. Victor Jacobson, now professor of pathology at the University of Albany, bunked with me in one double bed; Dr. Robert Parsons, later a rear admiral in the Navy and editor of the *Naval Medical Bulletin,* bunked with Dr. Herbert Dalwig, now of Milwaukee, downstairs. Each of us had a shaky table and a straight chair. I remember that the nights were very cold, and it seems to me the days were always snowy as we trudged through drifts or slush to the car line. But this, of course, was later in the winter.

Before winter came our landlord took us all on an automobile tour through northern and western Massachusetts, Vermont, and New Hampshire, western Massachusetts, and back home. I recall the amazing fall foliage and the winding, hilly roads. I remember, too, that our generous chauffeur got drunk and scared us all nearly to death, but we got back safely, with a better idea of New England topography.

By now we had learned a little of the subway, elevated and surface car system. We had to take many rides daily and through an ingenious scheme of transfer-slip manipulation, passed on no doubt by generations of indigent medical students, we could occasionally manage to make the grand tour from Brookline Village to the Massachusetts General Hospital to the City Hospital to the Medical School for only one fare! This saving was largely dissipated in various ways. My group began its work at the Massachusetts General Hospital, the insignificant appearance of which again shocked us, perhaps by contrast with the glorious pictures we had constructed in our minds of the place where ether was discovered and thousands of Harvard doctors trained.

We had good teachers—Richard Cabot, Louis Newberg, David Edsall, Robert Minot, and others. I remember Cabot confirming my discovery one day of a plasmodium in a blood cell in an outpatient. I remember Newberg teaching me prescribed orderliness for doing a physical examination. I remember Minot showing us the new cresyl-violet stain, and I remember Edsall commending me on my medical histories and suggesting home treatment for some aphthous sores on my tongue.

Perhaps the best-remembered learning experience I had was in obstetrics. We lived for a few weeks in what was called a branch of the Lying-in Hospital, a kind of apartment somewhere in the West End to which the people in that neighborhood would come running when they wanted a doctor. A woman and her daughter, who, it was reputed, had lived there for centuries were in charge of the place, made our beds and gave us our calls and kept track of us generally. It was a wonderful experience. For the first time in my life I saw homes of utter poverty. For the first time I was in the homes of Orthodox Jews who had little except their piety, and in the homes of newly arrived Poles, Italians, and other nationals. We were often given little presents at the end of an obstetrical case, and the Italians outdid everyone. They usually invited us to a home-cooked dinner, which was nothing like any ever served by an Italian restaurant. I can still remember how impressed I was by this, to the extent, indeed, that I importuned one particularly kind family to let me bring a friend of mine the following Sunday!

This friend of mine was a music student, attending the New England Conservatory of Music. Through him I got to see many of the performances at the Boston Opera House with very good seats. He was an usher, and I would buy standing room and wait patiently until near the end of the first act. By this time he knew where to seat me in the parquet.

At this time psychiatry was taught by an exposure of students to the patients and staff of the Boston Psychopathic Hospital (as it was then called) for two weeks in their junior year and Saturday-afternoon visits to some of the state institutions in eastern Massachusetts during the senior year. Like all the other students, I regarded this subject as a curious but unprofitable one, scarcely belonging in the field of medicine. I remember that I objected so strenuously to what seemed to me to be the futility of the treatment program that my later very warm friend, Herman Adler—then head of the department—reproached me for my presumptuousness and gave me C-minus in the course. This occurrence also has frequently come back to my mind.

While I was a medical student I was fascinated by the bound volumes of the publications of the department of neurology, which I got hold of in some way, and the historical library of The Menninger Foundation preserves a memorandum in my handwriting written to my father over fifty years ago, stating that "I have read practically *all* of the articles in all of these volumes and found them nearly all *very* good . . . to be indexed and card-catalogued in our medical library when I ultimately return to Topeka to begin work." Some of these articles were by J. J. Putnam, who until shortly before we came there had been professor of neurology. He had been succeeded by Dr. E. W. Taylor, a man whose exquisite English and dignity impressed me deeply. It was rumored among the students that Doctor Putnam was very broad-minded and Dr.

E. W. Taylor only slightly less so, and that they even tolerated some discussion of the Freudian theories which were being boot-legged around. As a matter of fact, they were not even bootlegged to us medical students; we had a two- or three-hour session with one L. E. Emerson, Ph.D., at the Massachusetts General Hospital. Emerson held the title of psychologist, and was described as an Assistant in neurology in the Harvard Graduate School of Medicine. In 1915 he presented a "Philosophy for Psychoanalysts" before the American Psychoanalytic Association, developing Putnam's felici-tous phrase, "disinterested love." [1] I recently re-read it and decided to reproduce it for all the candidates in our Institute and the Fellows in our School of Psychiatry. I recall his quiet exposition to a small group of us, recommending a little book called *The Psychology of Insanity* by Bernard Hart. I can recall that, logical as all this was, and gentlemanly as Emerson and Taylor were, there seemed to us to be something a little fishy about so much emphasis on the sexual disasters that occurred before a child knew *anything* about sex!

It will be recalled that in the time of which I am writing the world was torn by a great war. We had seen the upsurge of a tremendously dynamic nation which seemed about to take over the world. In that nation there were many great minds, and back about the time I was reading about multiple personalities and psychopathology and hypnosis, one of these great Germans had discovered a method for detecting what was then considered the greatest medical scourge of mankind. The Wassermann test was introduced in 1906, and from that time on we knew that syphilis was even more widespread and more devastating in its effects than anyone had imagined.

Three years after the Wassermann test was introduced, another great German succeeded, after 605 failures, in making an arsenical compound which was more toxic to syphilitic organisms than to human organisms. We gave this 606, neutralized and enormously diluted, by intravenous injection. And then, in those cases in which the nervous system was involved, we withdrew some of this serum while the Salvarsan was still circulating in the bloodstream, and after the proper steps we injected this serum into the spinal canal and into the ventricle. The Swift-Ellis treatment was introduced in

1912 and a year later the Lange gold sol test, this by another German. Then came the war, and James Ayer of Boston, one of my teachers, went on with his classical studies of the spinal fluid here. Meanwhile I was back in Kansas City, making gold sol studies of the spinal and ventricular fluids of patients with various kinds of neuropathology and giving them the possible benefit of intraventricular and intraspinal injections of this new wonder drug.

I want to try to convey something of the spirit of all this. Remember that we had just found out that there was more syphilis everywhere than we had ever imagined. Remember, too, that it, like most other serious infections—including tuberculosis—was considered hopeless—until the wonder drug. Remember that many physicians were skeptical even of the wonder drug, especially as to its effects on neurosyphilis.

Through Lawson G. Lowrey, I learned that at the Boston Psychopathic Hospital Dr. Harry Solomon and others working under Ernest Southard were treating large numbers of hopeless neurosyphilitic patients intensively. Sufficient improvement had been shown by these patients to justify the enlargement of the program.

The imagination of a young doctor can be set on fire by the right man at the right moment. But it is also true that the flames can be blown out by a blast of scornful skepticism. Fortunately, for me, although it was the established belief of every authority that these conditions were hopeless and that they were unaffected by Salvarsan, it was my fate to have escaped the extinction of the flame.

I moved into an unforgettable milieu presided over by the iridescent Ernest Elmer Southard.

William James, probably the greatest contributor to psychological science that America has ever produced, was born in 1842. He wrote his *Principles of Psychology* in 1890. He went to Harvard in 1897, and left there ten years later. It was in 1897 that Ernest Southard received his Bachelor of Arts degree at Harvard. Several years later, when I read the sparkling, flashing letters of William James, I felt as if I were reading letters from Southard—of which I had also read many. James sounded so like Southard in his qualities of naturalness, brightness, grace, and keenness. A week before his death Southard told newspaper reporters, "I give that course [in Harvard] mostly as a tribute to James. . . . I am a pupil of William James." That was twenty years after James had died, but Southard was still "a pupil."

Southard was a merry, kindly, witty fellow whose "greatest jubilation was at the birth of new truth. He was not soberly pleased with a new idea." [2] *Think of a man who could say*—in 1919—"May we not rejoice . . . as psychiatrists, that we, if any, are to be equipped by training and experience better, perhaps, than any other men to see through the apparent terrors of anarchism, of violence, of destructiveness, or paranoia—whether these tendencies are showing in capitalists or in labor leaders, in universities or in tenements, in Congress or under deserted culverts. It is in one sense all a matter of the One and the Many. Psychiatrists must carry their analytic powers, their ingrained optimism, and their tried strength of purpose not merely into the narrow circle of frank disease, but, like Séguin of old, into education; like William James, into the sphere of morals; like Isaac Ray, into jurisprudence; and above all, into economics and industry. I salute the coming years as high years for psychiatrists." [3]

"High years for psychiatrists"! And this was forty years ago!

In 1919 Southard was riding to great peaks of popularity. He became president of the American Neurological Association, president of the American Psychiatric Association, and president of various other groups. He was the discovery of many people all at once. Groups of engineers and artists invited him to New York to address them. It was here that he introduced the notion of industrial psychiatry. He had already introduced the idea of outpatient psychiatry and psychiatric social work in Boston.

Early in February 1920 I went with Dr. Southard to New York, where he gave a series of brilliant addresses. We stayed up quite late after one of them, talking about it and many other things. We had planned to have lunch together next day. A great snow fell in the night, traffic was tied up, and we missed contact. I caught a train for Philadelphia and the next night went on to Washington, arriving very early in the morning. At St. Elizabeths Hospital, while I waited for Dr. William Alanson White, I picked up a newspaper.

On the front page was the news that Ernest Southard had died in a hospital in New York.

It had been Southard's advice that I return to Topeka to the people I knew, where the very lack of many things in Boston was an advantage, as he said, "because you can get them started right without the handicaps of tradition, prejudice, and vested interests. Go out there to the people you know and try to help them," he had said, and so I did. But when I left Boston after the funeral I knew that the little band of disciples was broken up forever. Some of the friendships have remained; I particularly treasure those with Marion Kenworthy and Harry Solomon.

I am sorry to have been so long-winded in discussing my own journey from the hinterlands to the shores of Boston and to the discovery of the footprints which have made this for some of us almost a hallowed city. We think of it—or at least I do—as the place where Whittier and Longfellow lived and spoke, where William James and Josiah Royce taught, where Horace Mann and Dorothea Dix began their inspiring careers, where Morton Prince initiated medical study of "abnormal psychology," where Isaac Ray and Harry Solomon and Frankwood Williams and all the others I have named once lived—especially Elmer Ernest Southard.

Finally, it was Boston and its neighboring city, Worcester, which invited and received Sigmund Freud on his one memorable visit to America! It was not until fourteen years later that the American Psychoanalytic Association, as such, came for the first time to Boston. We met at this very hotel, Somerset.

At the Boston meeting in 1923 I remember Dr. Horace Frink giving a small group of us in a formal meeting a rather intimate account of his experiences on the couch of Sigmund Freud. I also remember that at this meeting Smith Ely Jelliffe reported some unconscious fantasies and psychological determinants in a case involving a bone lesion of some kind, and mentioned either death wish or the death instinct. Whatever it was, I recall the indignant refutation offered by the discussants, whose irritability and impatience with one another was a pattern which I am glad to have seen diminish in public meetings. In those days, however, we were a very small family.

Not until 1933 did the American Psychoanalytic Association return to Boston (and then again nine years later). I am somewhat amazed as I think back upon it that I can so poorly account for psychoanalytic and psychiatric developments in this country, or anywhere else, between 1923 and 1930. Personally, this was an important decade, because my father and my brother Will and I moved our offices into a farmhouse on the outskirts of Topeka and began to develop the Menninger Clinic and the Menninger Sanitarium— which became the C. F. Menninger Memorial Hospital—and The Menninger Foundation. Also in 1925 we established the Southard School, for retarded children—later for children with all kinds of psychiatric conditions.

There was much talk at psychiatric meetings about the necessity of a personal analysis for proper psychoanalytic work. For the most part, this meant going to Europe for a year or more, and few of us younger doctors could afford it. In fact, I had just about concluded that psychoanalysis was forever a financial impossibility when in 1930 the Literary Guild informed me that my book, *The Human Mind,* had been accepted and purchased by them. I spent the proceeds (and much more) for my analysis. But I am getting ahead of my story.

It was also in 1930 that the International Congress of Mental Hygiene was held in Washington, and to this came a man who was to be one of the most important psychoanalytic leaders in America, Franz Alexander. He spoke several times to the Congress, chiefly I recall on the question of criminality. His *Analysis of the Total Personality* had only recently appeared, and the possibility of his coming to America was the exciting news. That fall Franz Alexander became professor of psychoanalysis at the University of Chicago, and Dr. Leo Bartemeier came from Detroit and I from Topeka to join Dr. Helen McLean and others from Chicago in didactic analytic training.

It will be interesting in the future to reflect that Alexander, who from the first emphasized the medical nature of psychoanalysis, was so inhospitably treated by the medical school of the university in which he had been made a professor. Ostensibly, the criticism focused upon the fees charged for didactic analyses, which were considered to be in violation of the Hippocratic oath, a charge which has recently been again leveled against analysts. However, Alexander's personal charm and brilliant lectures attracted a great deal of attention, which was understandably disturbing to some of the more prosaic and conservative faculty members. Like Freud, Alexander had begun his medical work in the laboratory, but, unlike Freud and some other analysts, Alexander maintained his identification with medicine. At the time he and I visited Freud in Vienna in 1934 Freud reproached him bitterly (so Alexander told me) on this very point. This is important in the present context, because the University of Chicago's rejection was Boston's good fortune.

With the help and influence of Ives Hendrick, Martin Peck, Hans Sachs, Henry Murray, William Healy, and others, Alexander was warmly accepted at Harvard and contributed greatly to the work of the Psychological Clinic and the Judge Baker Foundation. The stay here permitted some of us, including your speaker, to finish their personal analyses and continue some of their other didactic training. I mention this because of the occasion which we are celebrating tonight. It was in the fall of 1931 and the spring of 1932. There was a Boston Psychoanalytic Society, many members of which were Rankian-trained—splendid people, some of them, earnest and intelligent and truth-seeking. The coming of Alexander was disturbing to them, in most instances helpfully so.

Franz Alexander probably has analyzed more physicians, more present-day psychoanalysts, than any two other psychoanalysts. He helped Dr. Hendrick to found the Boston Psychoanalytic Institute; later he went to Chicago to found that one; still later he helped us found the one in Topeka. From the beginning he was more interested in teaching and research than in private practice. In teaching he upheld the high standards that he himself had been taught by Eitingon and others in the Berlin Institute. He was indefatigable in his attendance and faithful in his lecturing and supervision of courses. In Chicago, where I knew him best, he inspired a stanch group of psychoanalytic sons and daughters to help him in the development of a training center which has achieved wide influence and popularity.

In 1933 the American Psychoanalytic Association met again in Boston. Coriat was our senior analytic citizen here. A. A. Brill was serving the third of his six terms as president. There had already begun a migration from Europe which was to change the face of American psychoanalysis. The Bibrings came, and the Deutsches, and others—to this city and to other cities. The tragedy of Europe was the great intellectual and scientific gain of America, Boston included! But with the coming of our colleagues from Europe new and conflicting trends began to develop. The next visit of the Association to Boston was in 1942; another war had begun over in Europe and what was almost a war had begun in the American Psychoanalytic Association. I remember it well, because I was your president. I remember that some of you were kind enough to say that, if nothing else was accomplished during my administration, at least schism was prevented, and I am proud to take some credit for that. I have been connected with too many schisms to want to see any more, and of this I was able to persuade some very much divided colleagues. At that time the differences of opinion to which human beings in general and psychoanalysts in particular seem to be prone were already straining the fabric of the Association. Fortunately that was settled. Not since 1942 has there been a meeting in Boston—sixteen years now.

This Institute is twenty-five years old, and we are honoring that achievement with the remembrance of things past. I myself was twenty-five years old when I met Ernest Southard. As I look back upon it, that seems to me to have been the dawning of my intellectual life. Is an institute like a man? Does it come of age or begin to mature at some point like 25? How will the Boston Institute look when it is 50 (maybe I should say, when it is 65)? Will it look back to any influences in 1958 which changed or determined its direction?

New ideas keep coming along, group discussion of problems

leads to their resolution, and to the initiation of new programs, which are often better programs.

And then there is youth—young men and young women accrue to the membership of the institute so that instead of growing older it grows younger. In my presidential address here in Boston sixteen years ago I commented that we were growing rapidly, that we had in training in the United States as many as two hundred students! You know how many more than two hundred we have here today, and many of these two hundred to whom I referred are now our teachers and leaders. Let us hope they have been guided helpfully, in some respects at least by the footprints we have seen together on the sands. Let us ask ourselves where they are going now, with such guidance as we have transmitted to them. What will they do with the scientific heritage—and responsibility—which so quickly falls to them like a mantle from off our shoulders?

During these years vast changes have taken place in psychoanalysis, internally and externally. I am sure many of the older ones in the audience can remember something which no young analyst today can quite understand or appreciate. We all know that there are resistances to the effecting of internal change, whether by psychoanalysis or by some other method. But twenty-five years ago the decision to elect an affiliation with psychoanalysis was an experience quite different from anything comparable to it today. In the first place, the whole business was somewhat mysterious—this European importation which seemed to have been taken up by the *avant-garde* in literary circles but by an extremely small number of medical colleagues. Indeed, its reputation was definitely on the "bad" side. Respectable people didn't want to be preoccupied with theories about sex. To become identified with this movement meant to renounce any ambitions to belong to the conservative tradition of the university, the medical school, the centers of medical research. It was an unpopular, esoteric, peculiar thing to do.

Perhaps most of all we young men were deterred by the requirement of a personal didactic analysis. Treatment, we had always held, was for the patient, not for the physician. Half jokingly or as a mere matter of theory we might be willing to say to the public that all of us have our mental illnesses. But dare we go so far as to demonstrate the truth of this in so far as it affected us personally? What would our patients think of us if we went aside for psychiatric treatment!

Thus, the election of psychoanalysis in those days meant not only the overcoming of the internal resistances but the willingness to risk the loss of reputation, career, income, and everything else. To-day, when psychoanalysis is so popular and psychoanalysts so sought after, it is hard for candidates and young analysts to realize this. But, on the other hand, I often feel that they have been denied the great testing period that we in the earlier day had to go through. And perhaps this reminiscence will help them to be more tolerant with some of our tenaciously held convictions.

Of course some of these convictions are wrong—it must be so. But they seemed right to us once. Perhaps they will always seem right to us. The new generation will have to make new decisions, try out new hypotheses. They will have to do this, overcoming the handicap of the great popularity psychoanalysis has achieved, the thing which Freud so much dreaded as a threat to its intrinsic truths. They will have to overcome enormous secondary gains, financial and otherwise, which now accrue to the espousal of that which was once a costly and unpopular affiliation.

And how, I wonder, will the young men deal with the unsolved questions of the expensiveness of psychoanalytic treatment? If psychoanalysis were free, or very inexpensive, would more people be psychoanalyzed? And even more pertinently, would there be *more* psychoanalysts or *fewer*? Under those circumstances, would there be more interest in group psychotherapy or less?

Do we not all deplore that psychoanalysis is, after fifty years, still a luxury treatment available for the most part to those few who have the means to acquire it as well as the conviction that it is worth whatever it costs?

What will the young men who follow us do with the perennial conflict of centripetal and centrifugal forces affecting the relations of psychoanalysis to psychiatry, to medicine, to psychology, to

sociology, to biology? Will the emphasis swing toward greater
specialization with more intense chauvinism, or toward more integration and diffusion and permeation into the other sciences, even
at the risk of being absorbed by some of them? What in psychoanalysis must be kept unique, and is this for practical purposes or
for theoretical reasons?

How will our successors solve the dilemma expressed to me recently by one of our psychiatric residents: "You put the responsibilities of mental health in our hands. You train us to hear the cries
of sufferers and to go to their help. And psychoanalysis, we are told,
is the supreme science and art of relieving this suffering. Yet we
know that most of us will probably not be able to qualify for or obtain the training for it. You tell us that this is psychotherapy at its
peak, but when we ask the psychoanalysts to guide us in some forms
of psychotherapy with which we, the still benighted, may help our
patients, most of them decline. You propose that for certain patients
a regression can be induced on the psychoanalytic couch, followed
by a reorganization and reconstitution representing recovery. But
is psychoanalysis the only effective way to induce a therapeutic
regression?"

Let us hope that our young men and the young spirit in the
institutes will be able to solve some of these problems in the next
twenty-five years. And let us hope also that they will take a broader
view both of illness and of what we call recovery than did we. Perhaps they will more clearly realize that illness is not a "something"
at all, nor yet recovery, but only aspects of a process. They are the
names applied by some people to what others will describe in
terms of sin and foolishness and crime. The perplexing behavior
of human beings becomes illness only when some sizable group of
the public believes such behavior to be amenable to medical science.
What has psychoanalysis to say about those offenses which are
called illness only metaphorically or through some kind of social
courtesy? If society really felt that the frenzied display of fantastic
violence in some individuals was the evidence of disease, would it
proceed with the medieval mummery of pronouncing one execut-
able and delivering him up to reluctant civil-service employees to

be marched to a grotesque contraption for inducing fatal convulsions?

In the years since 1932 psychoanalytic science has not gone forward in the area of criminology as rapidly as have other methods of study and, indeed, treatment. Perhaps the haunting monstrosity of capital punishment has deterred us from even looking in the direction of these victims of society. Will our young men also look the other way and pass by on the other side?

What will our young men do with psychoanalytic theory? Will they, like some that were once with us, yield to temptation to accomplish self-advancement in the name of intellectual freedom by proclaiming the blunders and omissions of the founder of psychoanalysis? Will they, also, be tempted to distort and misrepresent what Freud said in order to make themselves seem more sensible, more perspicacious, or more trustworthy to the untutored public? It is probably true that Columbus was a narrow-minded and stupid man, restricted by his peculiar Genoese culture, who had the delusion that the earth was round and thought that he had proved it by finding land, land that was neither the East Indies, as he believed, nor the American continent, as others proclaimed. But he was a well-intentioned old fellow, and hence acknowledged duly and formally by the neo-Columbians.

Of course Freud was mistaken about some things, but Columbus *did* discover America and Freud *did* discover psychoanalysis. Perhaps, as J. J. Putnam suggested in several of his great essays, one of Freud's mistakes was at the same time responsible for the vigor of the movement as well as being its chief weakness. You will recall that Putnam was disturbed by Freud's radical positivism. Putnam maintained that one could not dispense with value judgments, to which Freud replied in substance that for solving the problems of human life and motives it was not moral estimates we need but more knowledge. It was Freud's great ideal to substitute intelligent scrutiny for emotional reaction, but this left out of consideration aspects of the human personality not reducible to mechanistic principles. For ten years Putnam and Freud strove together over this difference, a little disappointed each with the other, but never to the extent that the great, elegant, powerful Putnam relinquished his courageous stand in favor of the unpopular, the proscribed and ridiculed new truth discovered by this Viennese colleague.

And so perhaps our reverence and gratitude might well focus to-night on the sturdy footprints of J. J. Putnam (whose daughter graciously honors us by her presence). Let us admiringly recall the great vision which permitted him to detect a precious truth in its incipiency and a great young leader in the midst of unpopularity. Let us reflect upon his own penetrating proposals for liberating man's creative forces and, in the words of Gardner Murphy, the human potentialities for higher development than any of us imagine. Let us reapply to J. J. Putnam the description of his qualities in the words of Ernest Jones: "extraordinarily high ethical standards, [his] upright-ness, honor, fairness and loyalty . . . modesty, amiability, persistence and tenacious adherence to convictions."

In the opinion of many of us Freud, more than Jones, gave evidence of some shift away from his earlier radical positivism toward what some of us consider a more modern point of view. In his later years, I suspect Freud might have been more inclined to agree with the Putnam of his earlier years. Did he not wistfully comment that "now it may be expected that the other of the two heavenly forces, eternal Eros, will put forth his strength so as to maintain himself alongside of his equally immortal adversary"?

When, in 1983 or 1999, our brave young men have grown older and look back at *our* footprints, I hope they will find us worthy of Ray and James and Southard and Putnam and Freud. And yet I hope they will find neither a too deeply worn rut nor a too smoothly traveled plain. I hope they will experience the realization of potentials beyond prediction. I hope that they will have come to believe that, as the stricken man can not only become well, but *weller* than well, so that even he who is not considered ill can transcend himself. I hope they will maintain courage for the enter-tainment of new ideas and flights of imagination, without loss of loyalty to the compass.

I would hope that like us they might have the blessing of great teachers, plus a greater wisdom in the application of their knowledge. And I would warn only against the great error, that daughter of the sin of presumptuousness, the use of knowledge as an immunization against a sense of social responsibility and the need to continue seeking.

"For there must indeed arise a philosophy profounder and more living than our own and endowed with greater spiritual and ethical force. In this terrible period through which mankind is passing we must all keep a look-out for the coming of this more perfect and more powerful form of thought, which will conquer the hearts of individuals and compel whole peoples to acknowledge its sway. It is for this that we must strive" (Albert Schweitzer).

Reference Notes

List of the Published Writings
of Karl Menninger, M.D.

Index

Reference Notes

(Articles by Dr. Karl Menninger which are included in this collection are referred to by page number. His other writings are identified by year of publication only; further information about them can be found in the list of his published writings, page 891.)

PART I: THE MAN

CHAPTER 3

1. Holmes, John. "The Eleventh Commandment." *Harper's Magazine*, October 1956.

CHAPTER 4

1. "Letters of Cyrus Kurtz Holliday," ed. by Lela Barnes, *Kansas Historical Quarterly*, 6:246, 1937.

CHAPTER 12

1. *Best Articles—1953*, selected by Rudolf Flesch. New York: Hermitage House, 1953.
2. Schweitzer, Albert. *Quest of the Historical Jesus.* New York: Harper, 1948.
3. *J. Clin. and Exper. Psycopath.*, 16:281–288, December 1955.

PART II: THE CLINICIAN

CHAPTER 1

1. Osler, William. *The Principles and Practice of Medicine.* New York: Appleton, 1912.
2. Bonhoeffer, Karl. As quoted in *Handbuch der Psychiatrie*, ed. by Gustav Aschaffenburg. Leipzig and Vienna: Deuticke, 1912.
3. Cabot, R. C. *Differential Diagnosis. Presented Through an Analysis of Three Hundred and Eighty-Five Cases,* 2nd ed. Philadelphia: Saunders, 1912.
4. Lowrey, L. G. "An Analysis of the Accuracy of Psychopathic Hospital Diagnoses." *Am. J. Insan.*, 75:351–370, January 1919.
5. Southard, E. E. *J. Lab. and Clin. Med.,* 4:31, November 1918; Transactions of the American Neurological Association, 1918.
6. Kraepelin, Emil. *Psychiatrie,* 8th ed. Leipzig and Vienna: Barth, 1909–1915.
7. Bonhoeffer. Loc. cit.

CHAPTER 2

1. Bonhoeffer, Karl. Loc. cit.
2. McPherson, George E., and Hohman, Leslie B. "The Diagnosis of 'War Psychoses.'" *Arch. Neur. and Psychiat.*, 2: 207–224, 1919.
3. Menninger, Karl. "Psychoses Associated

879

with Influenza": I (supra, p. 110) and
II (1919). "Influenza Psychoses in Successive Epidemics" (1920). "Influenza
and Hypophrenia" (1920).

4. Bond, E. D. "Epidemic Encephalitis and
Catatonic Symptoms." *Am. J. Insan.,*
76:261, January 1920.
   Bourges, H. B., and Marcandier, A.
   "Catatonic Delirium in Epidemic En-
   cephalitis." *Bull. et mem. Soc. Med. d.
   Hop. de. Par.,* 44:685, May 14, 1920.
   Sicard, J. A., and Bollack, J. "Lethargic

Encephalitis." *Bull. et mem. Soc. Med.
d. Hop. de. Par.,* 44:262, Feb. 20, 1920.
Wilson, S. A. K. "Epidemic Encephali-
tis." *Lancet,* 2:7, July 6, 1918.
Hall, A. J. "Epidemic Encephalitis."
British Med. J., 2:461, Oct. 26, 1918.
Batten, F. E., and Still, G. F. "Epidemic
Stupor in Children." *Lancet,* 1:636,
May 4, 1918.
Tilney, F., and Riley, H. A. "Epidemic
Encephalitis." *Neurol. Bull.,* 2:106,
March 1919.

CHAPTER 3

1. Rosanoff, A. J. "Exciting Causes in
Psychiatry." *Am. J. Insan.,* 69:349, 1912.
2. Strecker, E. A. "The Precipitant Situation in 200 Cases of Mental Disease."
Am. J. Psychiat., 1:503, 1922.
3. Skliar, N. "Psychoses in Infectious Diseases, Especially Typhus and Recurrent
Fevers." *Monatschr. f. Psychiat. u.
Neurol.,* 2:21, 1922.
4. Claude, H., and Rose, F. "Étude clinique et anatomique d'une psychose
toxi-infectieuse à forme catatonique au
type de la démence précoce." *Rev. neurol.,* 16:1280, 1908.
5. Gosline, H. I. "The Role of Tuberculosis in Dementia Praecox." *J. Lab. and
Clin. Med.,* 4:186, 1919.
6. Dide, M. "La démence précoce est un
syndrome mentale toxi-infectieux su-
baigu ou chronique." *Rev. neurol.,* 13:
381, 1905.
7. Wolfer. *Dementia Praecox Studies* (Chicago), 3:141, 1920.
8. Lagriffe, quoted by Padeano, G., Paris
Thesis No. 349, 1923.
9. Cotton, H. A. *The Defective, Delinquent
and Insane; the Relation of Focal Infections to Their Causation, Treatment and
Prevention,* Princeton, 1921.
10. Trepsat, L. "Troubles physiques dans la
démence précoce, hébéphrénocatato-
nique," Paris Thesis No. 419, 1905.
11. Urechia, C. I., and Rusdea, N. "Schizophrenoid Cerebral Syphilis," *Encephale,*
Vol. 16, 1921.
12. Gosline, H. I. "Newer Conceptions of
Dementia Praecox." *J. Lab. and Clin.
Med.,* 2:691, July 1917.
13. Ballet, G., and Gallais, A., quoted by
Padeano, G., Paris Thesis No. 349.
14. Southard, E. E., and Solomon, H. C.
Neurosyphilis, Boston: W. M. Leonard,
1917, pp. 442–452; also case 59.
15. Kraepelin, E. *Psychiatrie.*
16. Greene, R. A. "Dementia Praecox and
Syphilis." *Am. J. Psychiat.,* 1:309, 1922.
17. Wilson, S. A. K. "Epidemic Encephalitis." *Lancet,* 2:7, July 6, 1918.

18. Tilney, F., and Riley, H. A. "Epidemic
Encephalitis." Loc. cit.
19. Sicard and Bollack. "Lethargic Encephalitis." Loc. cit.
20. Waterman, Chester, and Folsom, R. P.
"Psychoses Associated with Influenza."
State Hospital Quarterly (New York),
August 1919.
21. Paton, Stewart L. *Psychiatry.*
22. Gosline, H. I. Op. cit.
23. Fell, E. W. "Postinfluential Psychoses."
J.A.M.A., 72:1658, June 7, 1919.
24. Fell, E. W. "Psychoses Accompanying Influenza." *Boston Med. and Surg. J.,* Jan.
29, 1920.
25. Sandy, W. C. "The Association of Neuropsychiatric Conditions with Influenza
in the Epidemic of 1918." *Arch. Neuro.
and Psych.,* 4:171–181, August 1920.
26. Jelliffe, S. E. "Nervous and Mental Disturbances of Influenza." *N.Y. Med. J.,*
Oct. 26, Nov. 2, Nov. 9, 1918.
27. Harris, A. F. "Influenza as a Factor in
Precipitating Latent Psychoses and Ini-
tiating Psychoses with a Brief History
of the Disease and Analysis of Cases."
Boston Med. and Surg. J., 153:610,
1919.
28. Schlessinger, A. "Des délires infectieux
au cours de la grippe." *Revue med. de la
Suisse romande,* 38:489, April 1919.
29. Riese, Walther. "Psychic Disturbances
after Spanish Grippe." *Neurol. Centralbl.,*
Nov. 1, 1918. Abstr. in *J.N. and M.
Dis.,* 56:115–125, August 1922.
30. Harris, I. G., and Corcoran, D. "Psychoses Following Influenza." *State Hospital Quarterly,* 4:469, August 1919.
31. Walther, F. *Ueder Grippepsychosen.*
Berne: Bircher, 1923.
32. Bleuler, E. *Textbook of Psychiatry.* (Berlin, 1923.) Transl. by Brill. New York:
Macmillan, 1924.
33. Kirby, quoted by Waterman, C., and
Folsom, R. P., op. cit. (footnote 20).
34. Menninger, Karl. "Psychoses Associated
with Influenza": I (supra, p. 110). "Influenza and Neurosyphilis" (1919). "Psy-

choses Associated with Influenza": II (1919). "Influenza Psychoses in Successive Epidemics" (1920). "Influenza and Hypophrenia" (1920). "Influenza and Epilepsy" (1921). "Influenza and Melancholy" (1921). "Reversible Schizophrenia" (supra, p. 126). "Epidemic Encephalitis" (1922).

35. Regis, E. Traité de Psychiatrie, 1909.
36. Dide. Op. cit.
37. Bleuler, E. In Aschaffenburg's Handbuch. Section 4, 1st half, p. 280.
38. ———. "Zur Amentia-frage." Centralbl. f. Nervenh. u. Psychiat., 18:815, 1907.
39. ———. Ztschr. f. d. ges. Neurol. u. Psychiat., 13:30 and 450, 1915.
40. Southard, E. E. "A Study of the Dementia Praecox Group in the Light of Certain Cases Showing Anomalies of Sclerosis in Particular Brain Regions." Am. J. Insan., Vol. 67, July 1910. "On the Topographical Distribution of Cortex Lesions and Anomalies in Dementia Praecox with Some Account of Their Functional Significance." Ibid., Vol. 71, January 1915.
41. Bumke, O. "Present Trends in Clinical Psychiatry." München med. Wchnschr., 1:1595, 1924.

42. Bumke, O. "Dementia Praecox." Klin. Wchnschr., 3:437, 1924.
43. Hall, G. W., and Neyman, C. A. "Studies of Schizophrenic Reactions." Am. Neurol. Assn., Forty-eighth Annual Meeting, Washington, D.C., May 1922.
44. Hoch, A. "Problem of Toxic Infectious Psychoses." New York State Hosp. Bull., November 1912.
45. Austregesilo, A. "Cataphrenia." Semana méd., 25:365, 1918.
46. Stransky, quoted by Hoch (fn. 43).
47. Bonhoeffer. "The Symptomatic Psychoses." In Aschaffenburg's Handbuch.
48. Southard, E. E. See note 40, above.
49. Rosanoff. New York State Hosp. Bull., 2:200, 1914.
50. Sioli. Centralbl. f. Nervenh. u. Psychiat., 1909, Vol. 32.
51. Gosline, H. I. See note 12, above.
52. Knapp, P. C. "Confusional Insanity and Dementia Praecox." J. Nerv. and Ment. Dis., 35:609, 1908.
53. Jelliffe, S. E. See note 26, above.
54. Hollos, S., and Ferenczi, S. Psychoanalysis and the Psychic Disorder of General Paresis, New York: Nervous and Mental Diseases Publishing Co., 1925. P. 48.

CHAPTER 4

1. George Savage said, more than fifty years ago, that while the fact that sudden shocks sometimes cured "insanity" had led to great abuses, he was inclined to think that the rough treatment . . . cured some cases that nowadays remain uncured (Practitioner, 16:449, 1876).
2. Pinel. Insanity, English ed., 1806, p. 281.
3. Jacobi. Hauptformen der Seelenstörungen.
4. Koster, Quomodo in insaniam valeat febris intermittens.
5. Fiedler, A. "Ueber den Einfluss fieberhafter Krankheiten auf Psychosen" (The Effect of Febrile Diseases on Insanity). Deutsches Arch. f. klin. Med., 26:275–294, Aug. 3, 1880.
Lehmann, George. "Zur Frage ueber den Guenstigen Einfluss acuter Krankheiten auf den Verlauf von Geistesstoerungen" (The Favorable Effect of Acute Diseases on Insanity). Allg. Ztsch. f. Psychiat., 43:200–210, 1887.
6. Nasse, W. "Typhus und Irresein" (Abdominal Typhoid Fever and Insanity). Allg. Ztschr. f. Psychiat., 26:713–714, 1869.
Fiedler, op. cit., and Lehmann, op. cit.
Rath. "Ueber eine Typhus Epidemie in der provinzial Irrenanstalt zu Osnabrueck" (Notes on a Typhoid Epidemic

at the County Insane Asylum at Oznabrueck). Allg. Ztschr. f. Psychiat., 41:326–338, 1885.
Bach. "Typhus bei Irren" (Typhoid Fever and Insanity). Notizen f. prakt Aerzte (Graevell), 8:601–602, 1855.
Gaye. "Shilderung eines in der Irrenanstalt bei Schleswig in den Jahren 1846 und 1847 epidemisch aufgetretenen gastrischen und typhoiden Fiebers" (Descriptions of an Epidemic of Gastro-Typhoid Fever in the Insane Asylum at Schleswig during 1846–1847). Allg. Ztschr. f. Psychiat., 9:173–199, 1852.
7. Fiedler, op. cit., and Lehmann, op. cit.
8. Nasse, W. "Neue Beobachtungen ueber den Einfluss des Wechselfiebers auf das Irresein" (New Observations on the Effect of Intermittent Fever on Insanity). Allg. Ztschr. f. Psychiat., 21:1–46, 1864.
Fiedler and Lehmann, op. cit.
9. Fiedler, op. cit., and Lehmann, op. cit. Keay, J. "A Case of Acute Mania: Scarlet Fever: Recovery." J. Ment. Sc., 42:267–275, 1896.
10. Sander, A. "Rheumatismus und Geisteskrankheit" (Rheumatism and Insanity). Allg. Ztschr. f. Psychiat., 20:214–228, 1863.
Fiedler, op. cit., and Lehmann, op. cit.
11. Fiedler, op. cit., and Lehmann, op. cit.

12. Fiedler, op. cit., and Lehmann, op cit. Damaye, Henri. "Affections mentales guéris par une grippe et par une angine pultacée" (Mental Affections Cured by Influenza and Pulpy Angina). *Progrès méd.*, 34:501–502, Dec. 6, 1919.
13. Fiedler, op. cit., and Lehmann, op. cit.
14. Fiedler, op. cit., and Lehmann, op. cit. Willerding, W. "Guenstiger Einflusse fieberhafter krankheiten auf Psychosen: Heilung einer Manie in Folge einer Pleuritis" (Favorable Effect of Febrile Diseases on Psychosis: Recovery from Insanity Due to Pleuritis). *Allg. Ztschr. f. Psychiat.*, 46:606–614, 1889–1890.
15. Fiedler, op. cit., and Lehmann, op. cit.
16. Sponholz, Jun. "Ueber den Einfluss somatischer Affectionen auf den Verlauf der Psychosen" (The Action of Somatic Diseases on Psychoses). *Allg. Ztschr. f. Psychiat.*, 30:1–11, 1874. Fiedler, op. cit., and Lehmann, op. cit.
17. Fiedler, op. cit., and Lehmann, op. cit. Schuetze, E. "Heilung einer Manie unter dem Einglusse von Rachendiphtherie" (Insanity Cured by Diphtheria). *Arch. f. Psychiat.*, 20:230–242, 1889.
18. Sponholz. Op. cit.
19. Sponholz. Op. cit. "Die cholera asiatica in der Irren-Heil und Pflegeanstalt zu Sorau" (Asiatic Cholera at the Sorau Insane Asylum). *Allg. Ztschr. f. Psychiat.*, 31:228–234, 1875. Fiedler, op. cit., and Lehmann, op. cit.
20. Fiedler, op. cit., and Lehmann, op. cit.
21. Stenger, C. "Beitrag zur Heilung chronischer Psychosen durch profuse Eiterungen" (The Cure of Chronic Psychosis through Profuse Suppurations). *Allg. Ztschr. f. Psychiat.*, 37:724–729, 1881.
22. Gauster, Moriz. "Die Influenza-Epidemie, 1889–1890, in der Landes-Irrenanstalt in Wien, und ihre Einwirkung auf die Psychopathien." *Wien. med. Presse*, 32:177, 1891.
23. Helweg, K. "Influenzaens Virkninger i en Sindssygeanstalt, saerligt dens Sektions resultater" (Action of Influenza on Insanity According to Autopsy Findings). *Hospitalstidende*, 8:729–745, July 16, 1890.
24. Metz, M. "Heilung einer Paranoia nach Influenza" (Paranoia Cured by Influenza). *Neurol. Centralbl.*, 9:201–204, April 1, 1890.
25. Coveos, G. L. "Mehrjahrige Epilepsie und Idiotismus voellig Geheilt nach einem Anfall schwerer Influenza." *Allg. Wien med. Ztg.*, 45:383, August 1900.
26. Foustenaous, J. *Grèce méd.*, 1900, No. 7.
27. Damaye, Henri. "Troubles mentaux occasionnés par la grippe: troubles mentaux guéris par l'infection grippale" (Insanity Due to Influenza: Insanity Cured by Influenzal Infection). *Ann. méd.-psychol.*, 11:215–220, May 1919. Damaye. See note 12, above.
28. Damaye describes her as having "mystical, melancholy and grandiose delusions, refusing food, assuming obscene postures, blaspheming, alternately singing, weeping and laughing—at times silent and immovable, often agitated, violent and incoherent."
29. Damaye describes the condition thus: "Echolalia, excitement, hears threatening voices, insults everybody, threatening attitude, periods of excitement, alternating with periods of complete indifference, idleness, wandering attention.
30. The author states that the patient could remember his behavior of the previous eighteen months; he also states that the boy's physical condition had begun to improve five months prior to the influenza without having markedly affected the mental state.
31. Latapie. "Quelques remarques à propos de l'épidémie de grippe de 1918—et psychoses favorablement influencées par la grippe" (Some Remarks on the Influenza Epidemic of 1918—and Insanity Favorably Influenced by It). *Ann. med.-psychol.*, 10:350–355, September 1919.
32. Moreira. *Arch. brasil. de med.*, May 1919.
33. Maillard and Brune. "Grippe et epilepsie." *Presse méd.*, 27:70, Feb. 10, 1919.
34. Damaye. See note 12.
35. Ebaugh, F. G. "Mental Health Problems in School Children." *Am. J. Dis. Child.*, 28:265, September 1924.
36. Menninger, Karl. "Influenza and Epilepsy" (1921).
37. Leledy, Albert. "The Grippe and Mental Alienation." Paris thesis, 1891.
38. Jouriac, quoted by Leledy, ibid.
39. Menninger, Karl. "Influenza and Epilepsy" (1921).
40. ———. Ibid.
41. ———. "Influenza and Hypophrenia" (1920).
42. Another feeble-minded child recently under our observation, with a chronological age of 8, a mental age of 5.6, and an intelligence quotient of 63, was discharged from the Southard School in September 1928, to his mother. In November he had influenza and was reported distinctly improved thereafter. According to the mother, he complained of a headache one day and on the noon of the following day had a fever which reached 103. He was restless and ill for several days with this fever and increasing cough. For a few days she thought he was getting pneumonia. He was in

bed altogether ten days. Following this, she says, he did much better school work, talked better (by which she means more clearly, as he had always had a marked speech defect), and seemed more alert. Apparently he was doing passable 2-B work.

43. Courbon, P. C. "The Remission of Men-

tal Disorders Just Before Intercurrent Somatic Diseases." *Rev. neurol.*, 30:237, March 1923.
44. Kubitschek, Paul, and Carmichael, F. A. "Experimental Aseptic Meningitis." *Am. J. Psychiat.*, 8:97–135, July 1928.
45. Menninger, Karl. "Reversible Schizophrenia" (supra, p. 126).

CHAPTER 7

1. Southard, E. E. "A Key to the Practical Grouping of Mental Diseases." *J. of Nervous and Mental Dis.*, Vol. 47. No. 1, January 1918. "Diagnosis per Exclusionem in Ordine; General and Psychiatric Remarks." *J. of Lab. and Clin. Med.*, Vol. 14, No. 2, November 1918. "Recent American Classifications of Mental Disease." *Am. J. Insan.*, Vol. 75, No. 3, January 1919. "The Genera in Certain Great Groups or Orders of Mental Disease." *Arch. Neurol. and Psychiat.*, 1:95–112, January 1919.
2. Menninger, Karl. "Psychoses Associated with Influenza": II (1919).
3. ———. "Psychoses Associated with Influenza": I (supra, p. 110).
4. Seelert. *Archiv für Psychiatrie*, Bd. 55, S. 1, 1915.
5. Wernicke, C. *Grundriss der Psychiatrie.* Leipzig, 1906.
6. Kraepelin, E. *Psychiatrie.* Also "Ueber Paranoide Erkrankungen." *Zeitsch. f. ges. Neur. and Psych.*, 12:510.
7. Ibid.
8. Ziehen, Th. *Psychiatrie.* Leipzig, 1911.
9. See Regis et al.
10. Sander. *Archiv für Psychiatrie*, Vol. 1, p. 387.
11. Kleist. "Die Involutions Paranoia." *Allg. Zeitsch. f. Psych.*, Vol. 70, Pt. 1, p. 1.

12. Westphal. *Allg. Ztschr. f. Psychiatrie*, 34:252, 1876.
13. Lasèque. Quoted by Kraepelin.
14. Falret. Quoted by Kraepelin.
15. Magnan. *Leçons cliniques sur les maladies mentales.* Paris, 1893.
16. See Deny and Roy, *La démence précoce*, Paris, 1903; or Dide and Carras, *Ann. méd.-psych.*, III, 408.
17. Serieux. "La démence précoce." *Gaz. hebd. de med. et de cher.*, 3:10, 1901.
18. Dupré. Quoted by Kraepelin.
19. Neisser, K. "Eroerterunger ueber die Paranoia, etc." *Zentralbl. f. Nervenk. und Psych.*, 1891.
20. Séglas. "La démence paranoide." *Ann. med. psychologiques*, 1900.
21. Bleuler. "Schizophrenia." In Aschaffenburg's *Handbuch.*
22. Snell. *Allg. Ztsch. f. Psychiatrie*, 22:368 and 30:319.
23. Griesinger. *Arch. f. Psychiat.*, 1:143.
24. Kahlbaum. Quoted by Kraepelin.
25. Ziehen, Th. *Psychiatrie.*
26. Kraepelin, E. *Psychiatrie.*
27. Southard, E. E. "On Descriptive Analysis of Manifest Delusions from the Subject's Point of View." *J. Abnormal Psychol.*, August–September 1916.
28. Menninger, Karl. "Delusions Afferent and Efferent." Unpublished.

CHAPTER 8

1. Laird, Donald A. "Case studies in the Mental Problems of Later Adolescence, with Special Reference to the Mental Hygiene of the College Student." *Mental Hygiene*, October 1923.
2. Kerns, Major Harry N. "Management of Acute Hygiene Problems Found among College Men." *Mental Hygiene*, April 1925.
3. Thom, Douglas A. "Moulding Personality in the Pre-School Years." *Mental*

Hygiene of Normal Childhood, p. 40, January–February 1927.
4. Davis, Hallowell and Pauline, *Harvard Alumni Bulletin*, 1928.
5. Heidbreder, E. F. "The Normal Inferiority Complex." *J. of Abnormal and Social Psychol.*, Vol. XXII, No. 3, 1927.
6. Kerns. Op. cit.
7. Robertson, T. M. "Oral Surgery and Radiography." *Int. J. of Orthodontia*, XI, 9, September 1925.

CHAPTER 9

1. Hall, R. W. "Peculiar Personalities." *War Medicine*, 1:383–386, May 1941.
2. Prichard, J. E. *A Treatise on Insanity.*

Philadelphia: Haswell, Barrington and Haswell, 1837.
3. Kraepelin. *Psychiatrie.*

4. Bleuler, E. *Textbook of Psychiatry.*
5. Meyer, A. "Constitutional Abnormality. C. P. Oberndorf's Discussion." *State Hosp. Bull.,* March 1910.
6. Schneider, K. "Die psychopathischen Personlichkeiten." Aschaffenburg's *Handbuch.*
7. Kahn, E. *Psychopathic Personalities.* Transl. from German by H. Flanders Dunbar. New Haven: Yale University Press, 1931.
8. Reich, W. "Der triebhafte Charakter." *Neue Arbeiten Z. arztl. Psychoanalyse,* No. 4. Wien: Intern. Psa. Verlag, 1925.
9. Alexander, F. *The Psychoanalysis of the Total Personality.* New York: Nervous and Mental Diseases Publishing Co., 1930.
10. Karpman, B. "The Problem of the Psychopathies." *Psychiatric Quart.,* 3:495–525, October 1929.
11. Wittels, F. "The Criminal Psychopath in the Psychoanalytic System." *Psychoanalytic Rev.,* 24:276–291, July 1937.
12. Menninger, Karl. *The Human Mind* (1937).
13. Bartemeier, L. H. "The Neurotic Character as a Psychoanalytic Concept." *Am. J. Orthopsychiat.,* 1:512–520, 1931.

14. Levine, M. "The Dynamic Conception of Psychopathic Personality." *Ohio S. Med. J.,* 36:848–850, 1940.
15. Partridge, G. E. "Current Conceptions of Psychopathic Personality." *Am. J. Psychiat.,* 10:53–99, July 1930.
16. Maughs, S. "A Concept of Psychopathy and Psychopathic Personality—Its Evolution and Historical Development." *J. Crim. Psychopath.,* 2:329–356, January 1941, and 2:465–499, April 1941.
17. Kraepelin, E. *Psychiatrie.*
18. Schneider. Op. cit.
19. Partridge. Op. cit.
20. Kahn. Op. cit.
21. Quoted by Maughs, op. cit.
22. See *Ninth Annual Report of the Criminologist.* Dept. of Public Welfare, State of Illinois. July 1, 1925, to June 30, 1926.
23. Dawson, W. S. *Aids to Psychiatry.* New York: William Wood, 1924.
24. Cleckley, H. *The Mask of Sanity.* St. Louis: C. V. Mosby, 1941.
25. Dunn, W. H. "The Psychopath in Armed Forces." *Psychiatry,* 4:251–259, May 1941.
26. Hall. Op. cit.

CHAPTER 10

1. Menninger, Karl. "Paranoid Psychosis with Uremia" (1924).

CHAPTER 12

1. Alexander, Franz. *The Medical Value of Psychoanalysis.* New York: Norton, 1932.

CHAPTER 13

1. Wälder, Robert. "Das Freiheitsproblem in der Psychoanalyse und das Problem der Realitätsprüfung." *Imago XX,* 1934. (Trans. *Int. J. Ps-A. XVII,* 1936).
2. Leshnew, N. F. "Psychogene Erkrankungen und die Urologie." *Ztschr. f. Urol.,* XXII, 1928.
3. Clancy, Frank J. "Urologic Symptoms of Psychogenic Origin." *Urol. and Cutan. Rev.,* 37, 1933.
4. Menninger, Karl. "A Psychoanalytic Study of the Significance of Self-Mutilations" (1935).
5. Mentioned in his discussion of this paper before the Am. Psa. Ass'n.

CHAPTER 14

1. Menninger, Karl. *Man Against Himself* (1938).
2. Leshnew, N. F. "Psychogene Erkrank-M. "Constitutional Factors in Homosexuality." *Am. J. Psychiat.,* 13:1249–1267, May 1934.
3. See, for example, Lilian K. P. Farrar's article on "Prolapse of the Breast," *J.A.M.A.,* Nov. 1, 1930, in which she concludes that "prolapse of the virginal atrophic breast is occurring with alarming frequency in this country owing to the present fashion of dress."
4. Quoted by Mayer, A. "Psychogene Störungen der weiblichen Sexualfunktion," in O. Schwarz's *Psychogenese und Psychotherapie körperlicher Symptome,* Vienna: Springer, 1925, pp. 295–344, bibliography, pp. 469–474.
5. Other authors who believe that sterility may be the consequence of emotional conflict are A. Mayer (op. cit.), and

Kehrer (Kehrer, E. *Ursachen und Behandlung der Unfruchtbarkeit nach modernen Gesichtspunkten. Zugleich ein Beitrag zu den Störungen des sexuellen Lebens, besonders der Dyspareunie.* Dresden and Leipzig: Steinkopff, 1922).

6. Allbutt, T. C. "Gulstonian Lectures on Neuroses of the Viscera." *Lancet,* 1:459–507, 1884. Quoted by Edward Weiss in "Personality Study in the Practice of Internal Medicine," *Annals of Int. Med.,* 8:702–706, December 1934.

7. See Dunbar, H. Flanders. *Emotions and Bodily Changes* (New York: Columbia University Press, 1935, 1938).

Mayer, M. D. "Psychotherapy in a Gynecologic Service." *Am. J. Obst. and Gynec.,* 21:357–364, 1931; disc. 430–431.

8. Groddeck, Georg. *The Book of the It.* New York: Nervous and Mental Disease Publishing Company, 1928.

9. Numerous authors (Forel, Kohnstamm, Schindler, Mayer, Heyer, Brandess, and Stemmer) have reported experiments on clinical observations of suggestion or hypnosis modifying the date of appearance of catamenia, or inhibiting it altogether.

10. Menninger, Karl. *Man Against Himself.*

CHAPTER 15

1. Bryan, Douglas. "Epistaxis in a Man Simulating Menstruation." *Int. J. Psa.,* 7:79–81, 1926.

2. Menninger, Karl. "Some Unconscious Psychological Factors Associated with the Common Cold" (supra, p. 229).

CHAPTER 16

1. Van Ophuijsen, J. H. W. "Contributions to the Masculinity Complex in Woman." *Int. J. Psa.,* 5:42–44, January 1924.

2. See, for example:
Schwarz, Oswald. "Psychogene Miktionsstörungen." In O. Schwarz's *Psychogenese und Psychotherapie körperlicher Symptome,* pp. 273–294.
Sadger, J. "Ueber Urethralerotik." *Jahrb. f. psychoanalyt.,* 2:409–450, 1910.
Abraham, Karl. "Ueber Ejaculatio Praecox." *Internat. Ztschr. f. arztl. psychoanal.,* 4:171–186, 1916.
Stekel, W. *Die Impotenz des Mannes (Die psychischen Störungen der männlichen Sexual funktion).* Berlin and Vienna: Urban and Schwarzenberg, 2 Aufl., 1923.
Fenichel, O. *Hysterien und Zwangsneurosen. Psychoanalytische spezielle Neurosenlehre.* Internat. Psychoanalyst. Verlag, 1931.

3. Anderson, F. N. "Psychiatric Aspects of Enuresis." *Am. J. Dis. Child.,* 40:591–618, 818–850, 1930.

4. Mayer, A. "Ueber gynakologische Scheinkrankheiten — Pseudo-Retroflexio und Pseudo-Zystitis." *Deutsche med. Wchnschr.* (Leipzig), 55:1639–1640, Sept. 27, 1929.

5. See also Alkan, L. *Anatomische Organkrankheiten aus seelischer Ursache.* Stuttgart: Hippokrates-Verlag, 1930.

6. Jelliffe, Smith Ely. "What Price Healing?" *J.A.M.A.,* 94:1393–1395, May 3, 1930.

7. ———. "Psychotherapy in Modern Medicine." *Trans. Am. Neurol. Assn.,* 1923, and *L. I. Med. J.,* 24:152–161, March 1930.

8. Braasch, William F. "Unusual Types of Urinary Lithiasis." *J. of Urology,* Vol. XXIII, No. 1, January 1930. "Hysterical Lithiasis." *Surgery, Gynecology, and Obstetrics,* February 1930, pp. 504–505.

9. Schwarz, O. "Ueber psychogene Nierenschmerzen." *Allg. arztl. Ztschr. f. Psychotherap.,* 1:28–33, 1928.

10. Klemperer, G. "Nierensteinkrankheit als Neurose." *Therap. d. Gegenw.,* 73:14–17, 1932.

11. Groddeck, G. "Ueber die psychische Behandlung der Nierensteinbildung." *Allg. arztl. Ztschr. f. Psychotherap.,* 1:136–141, 1928.

CHAPTER 18

1. Cf. Freud, "The Schreber Case." *Collected Papers.* London: Hogarth, 1925. Vol. III, p. 388.

2. Freud, "Mourning and Melancholia." *Collected Papers.* Vol. IV, p. 156.

3. Alexander, Franz. "The Need for Punishment and the Death Instinct." *Int. J. Psychoanal.,* 10:256, 1929.

CHAPTER 20

1. Menninger, Karl. "Focal Self-Destruction." Unpublished.
2. Alexander, Franz (*The Psychoanalysis of the Total Personality*) called this principle "conscience bribing," and Rado (Rado, S. "Fear of Castration in Women," *Ps.-A. Quart.*, 2:445, 1933), the "choice of the lesser evil."
3. Freud. *Collected Papers*, Vol. III, p. 52.
4. Jones, A. Bassett, and Llewellyn, Llewellyn J. *Malingering*, Philadelphia: P. Blakiston's Son and Company, 1917.
5. Stephen, K. *Psychoanalysis and Medicine: The Wish to Fall Ill.* New York: Macmillan, 1933.
6. Freud. *Collected Papers*, Vol. IV.
7. Alexander, Franz. *The Criminal, the Judge and the Public.* New York: Macmillan, 1930.
8. Duprat, P. E. "Factitious Eruptive Disease." *Rev. méd. d. Uruguay*, 23:123, March 1920; abstract, *J.A.M.A.*, 74:1748, June 1920.
   Short, A. R., and Walker, C. H. "Self-Inflicted Injuries in Civilian Practice." *British M. J.*, 1:298, Feb. 26, 1921.
   Bridge, G. A. "Industrial Malingerer." *Southwestern Med.*, 9:98, March 1925.
   Grindon, J. "Feigned Eruptions." *J. Missouri M. A.*, 26:451, September 1929.
   Feller, A. "Kerosene Phlegmon of Skin in Malingerer: A Case." *Arch. F. Dermat. u. Syph.*, 159:580, 1930.
   Radeli, F. "Pathomimesis; Detection of Pseudotumor Caused by Injection of Lysoform (Formaldehyde Soap Solution)." *Gior. ital. di dermat. e sif.*, 70:1102, October 1929.
   Speschilow, P. W. "Structure of Artificial Granulomas Noted Among Solddiers during World War, Frankfurt." *Ztschr. f. Path.*, 38:513, 1929.
   Fox, H. "Artificial Dermatitis Due to Plants, Irradiations, Medicaments and Malingering." *Proc. Internat. Assemb. Inter-State Post-Grad. M.A. North America*, 5:136, 1930.
   Spillman, L., and Watrin, J. "Cutaneous Self-Mutilation: A Case." *Bull. Soc. franç. de dermat. et syph.* (Réunion dermat., Nancy), 38:350, March 1931.
   Pautrier, L. M., and Silber, J. "Dermatosis Voluntarily Provoked by Cauterization with Potassium Hydroxide and Necessitating Amputation of Fingers; A Case." Ibid., 37:1216, December 1930.
   Gate, J.; Bosonnet, G.; and Michel, P. "Factitia, Cutaneous Pathomimesis; Two Cases." *J. de méd. de Lyon*, 10:351, May 20, 1929.
   Casazza, R. "Cutaneous Pathomimesis in Hysteria." *Boll. d. Soc. med.-chir. Pavia*, 4:547, 1929.
   Stokes, J. H., and Garner, V. C. "Diagnosis of Self-Inflicted Lesions of Skin; Contribution to Physical Diagnosis in Dermatology," *J.A.M.A.*, 93:438, Aug. 10, 1929.
   Ribeiro, H. "Unusual Case of Stimulation of Dermatosis," *Brasil-med.*, 43:229, March 2, 1929.
   Rasch, C. "Cutaneous Pathomimesis." *Ugesk f. laeger*, 91:789, Sept. 19, 1929.
   Mazzant, C. "Cutaneous Self-Mutilation in a Neurotic; A Case." *Dermosifilografo*, 6:505, September 1931.
9. Netherton, E. W. "Dermatitis Artefacta, with a Report of Seven Cases." *Ohio State M. J.*, 23:215, March 1927.
10. Menninger, Karl. "Polysurgery and Polysurgical Addiction" (1934).
11. Klauder, Joseph. "The Cutaneous Neuroses, with Particular Reference to Psychotherapy." *J.A.M.A.*, 85:1683, Nov. 28, 1925.

CHAPTER 21

1. Menninger, W. C. "Psychoanalytic Interpretations of Patients' Reactions in Occupational Therapy, Recreational Therapy and Physiotherapy." *Bull. Menninger Clin.*, 1:148–157, May 1937.
2. Menninger, Karl. "Psychoanalytic Psychiatry: Theory and Practice" (supra, p. 428).
3. ———. *Man Against Himself* (1938).
4. Grinker, R. R., and Spiegel, J. P. *War Neuroses in North Africa.* Prepared and distributed for the Air Surgeon, Army Air Forces. New York: Josiah Macy, Jr. Foundation, 1943.
5. Murray, J. M. "Psychiatry in the Army Air Forces," *Am. J. Psychiat.*, 100:21–24, July 1943.
6. Blain, Daniel. "Personal and Morale Factors in Etiology and Prevention of Traumatic War Neurosis in Merchant Seamen." *Am. J. Psychiat.*, 100:131–135, July 1943.
7. Kubie, L. S. "Manual of Emergency Treatment for Acute War Neuroses." *War. Med.*, 4:582–598, December 1943.
   Potter, H. W. "Physical and Psychologic Aspects of Environment Essential to Treatment of Traumatic Neuroses (Con-

valescent or Rest Homes)." *Am. J. Psychiat.*, 100:120–123, July 1943.

8. Menninger, Karl. "Emotional Factors in Hypertension" (1938).

CHAPTER 23

1. Rasky, Frank. "The Shame of our Nursing Homes." *Tomorrow*, July 1950.

PART III: THE THEORIST

CHAPTER I

1. Quoted from a letter written by Freud to the Vienna lodge of the B'nai B'rith. *B'nai B'rith Magazine*, 50:298, No. 9, June 1936.

CHAPTER 3

1. Knight, Robert P. "Application of Psychoanalytical Concepts in Psychotherapy: Report of Clinical Trials in a Mental Hygiene Service." *Bull. Menninger Clin.*, 1:99–109, March 1937.
2. Crank, Harlan. "The Use of Psychoanalytic Principles in Outpatient Psychotherapy." *Bull. Menninger Clin.*, 4:35–40, March 1940.
3. Auten, Hanford L. "Outpatient Treatment of Sub-Acute Schizophrenia." *Bull. Menninger Clin.*, 3:184–188, November 1939.
4. Menninger, Karl. *Man Against Himself.*
5. Menninger, W. C. "Individualization in Prescriptions for Nursing Care of the Psychiatric Patient." *J.A.M.A.*, 106:756–761, March 7, 1936. "Individualization of Psychiatric Hospital Treatment." *Wis. Med. J.*, 37:1086–1088, December 1938. "Psychiatric Hospital Therapy Designed to Meet Unconscious Needs." *Am. J. Psychiat.*, 93:347–360, September 1936. "Psychoanalytic Interpretations of Patients' Reactions in Occupational Therapy, Recreational Therapy, and Physiotherapy." *Bull. Menninger Clin.*, 1:148–157, May 1937. "Psychoanalytic Principles Applied to the Treatment of Hospitalized Patients." *Bull. Menninger Clin.*, 1:35–43, November 1936.
6. ———. "Therapeutic Methods in a Psychiatric Hospital." *J.A.M.A.*, 99:538–542, Aug. 13, 1932.
7. Knight, Robert P. "The Dynamics and Treatment of Chronic Alcohol Addiction." *Bull. Menninger Clin.*, 1:233–250, September 1937. "Psychoanalysis of Hospitalized Patients." *Bull. Menninger Clin.*, 1:158–167, May 1937. "The Psychoanalytic Treatment in a Sanitarium of Chronic Addiction to Alcohol." *J.A.M.A.*, 3:1443–1446, Oct. 15, 1938. "The Psychodynamics of Chronic Alcoholism." *J. Nerv. and Ment. Dis.*, 86:538, November 1937.

8. Reider, N. "Hospital Care of Patients Undergoing Psychoanalysis." *Bull. Menninger Clin.*, 1:168–175, May 1937.
9. Tidd, C. W. "An Examination of the Recovery Process in Three Cases of Schizophrenia." *Bull. Menninger Clin.*, 1:53–60, November 1936.
10. Hemphill, Robert. "The Aims and Practice of Recreational Therapy." *Bull. Menninger Clin.*, 1:117–122, March 1937.
11. Erickson, Isabel. "The Nursing Problems in the Psychiatric Hospital." *Hospitals*, 11:58–62, May 1937. "The Psychiatric Nurse." *Am. J. Nursing*, 35:351–352, April 1935. "The Psychiatric Nursing Care of Manic Depressive and Schizophrenic Psychoses." *Trained Nurse and Hosp. Rev.*, 98:587–592, June 1937.
12. Anderson, Carl. "Project Work, an Individualized Group Therapy." *Occupat. Therap.*, 15:265, August 1936.
13. Reider, N.; Olinger, Davida; and Lyle, Jeanetta. "Amateur Dramatics as a Therapeutic Agent in the Psychiatric Hospital." *Bull. Menninger Clin.*, 3:20–26, January 1939.
14. Menninger, W. C., and Cutrer, M. "The Psychological Aspects of Physiotherapy." *Am. J. Psychiat.*, 93:909–915, January 1937.
15. McKimens, Dorothy. "Psychiatric Nursing: The Viewpoint of the Nurse." *Bull. Menninger Clin.*, 2:40–46, March 1938.
16. Medd, M. "Individualized Occupational Therapy." *Occupat. Therapy*, 14:47–51, January 1935.
17. Menninger, W. C., and McColl, I. "Recreational Therapy as Applied in a Modern Psychiatric Hospital." *Occupat. Therapy*, 16:15–24, February 1937.
18. Reider; Olinger; and Lyle. Op. cit.
19. Bullard, Dexter. "The Applications of Psychoanalytic Psychiatry to the Psychoses." *Psa. Rev.*, 26:526–534, October 1939.

20. Fromm-Reichmann, Frieda. "Transference Problems in Schizophrenics." *Psychoanalyt. Quart.*, 8:412–426, 1939.
21. Sullivan, Harry Stack. "The Modified Psychoanalytic Treatment of Schizophrenia." *Am. J. Psychiat.*, 88:519–541, November 1931.
22. Simmel, Ernst. "The Psychoanalytic Sanitarium and the Psychoanalytic Movement." *Bull. Menninger Clin.*, 1:133–143, May 1937.
23. Chapman, Ross. "Psychoanalysis in a Psychiatric Hospital." *Am. J. Psychiat.*, 91:1093–1101, March 1935.

24. Sullivan. Op. cit.
25. Chapman. Op. cit.
26. Menninger, W. C. "Individualization in Prescriptions for Nursing Care of the Psychiatric Patient."
27. Fromm-Reichmann. Op. cit.
28. Bullard. Op. cit.
29. Fromm-Reichmann. Op. cit.
30. Sullivan. Op. cit.
31. Zilboorg, Gregory. "Affective Reintegration of the Schizophrenias." *Arch. Neurol. and Psychiat.*, 24:335, August 1930.

CHAPTER 4

1. Trotter, W. *Instincts of the Herd in Peace and War*. London: Ernest Benn, 1916.
2. Freud. *Group Psychology and the Analysis of the Ego*. London: Int. Psa. Press, 1922.

CHAPTER 5

1. Galdston, Iago. *The Metaphysical Basis of Psychoanalysis*. In *Progress in Medicine*. New York: Knopf, 1940.

CHAPTER 7

1. Roe, Anne. "Analysis of Group Rohrschachs of Psychologists and Anthropologists." *J. Proj. Tech.*, 16:212–224, 1952.
2. Thompson, Morton F. *Not as a Stranger*. New York: Scribner, 1954.
3. Edwards, Ward. "The Theory of Decision-Making." *Psychol. Bull.*, 51:380–417, 1954.
4. Kubie, Lawrence. "Some Unsolved Problems of the Scientific Career": Part I, *Am. Sci.*, 41:596–613, 1953; Part II, *Am. Sci.*, 42:104–112, 1954.
5. Severinghaus, A. E. "Selection of Students in the United States." *British Med. J.*, 4885:479–482, 1954.
6. Roe, Anne. Op. cit. Also "Study of Imagery in Research Scientists." *J. Personality*, 19:459–470, 1951.
7. Ginzberg, Eli, et al. *Occupational Choice: An Approach to a General Theory*. New York: Columbia University Press, 1951.
8. Fabricant, Noah. *Why We Became Doctors*. New York: Grune and Stratton, 1954.
Rosen, George, and Rosen, B. C. *400 Years of a Doctor's Life*. New York: Schuman, 1947.
9. Gregg, Alan. "Our Anabasis." *Trans. Assn. Am. Physicians*, 67:47–61, 1954.
10. Mead, Margaret. *Sex and Temperament*. New York: William Morrow, 1935.
11. Menninger, William C. "Characterologic and Symptomatic Expressions Related to the Anal Phase of Psychosexual Development." *Psa. Quart.*, 12:161–193, 1943.
12. Schweitzer, Albert. *Out of My Life and Thought*. New York: Holt, 1949.
13. Rapaport, David. "Autonomy of the Ego." *Bull. Menninger Clin.*, 15:113–123, 1951.

CHAPTER 9

1. Bleuler, Manfred. "Research and Changes in Concepts in the Study of Schizophrenia, 1941–1950." English transl. in *Bull. Isaac Ray Med. Library*, 3:1–132, 1955.
2. Whitehead, A. N. *The Concept of Nature*. London: Cambridge, 1920.
3. Riese, Walther. "History and Principles of Classification of Nervous Diseases." *Bull. Hist. Med.*, 18:465–512, 1945.
4. Menninger, Karl; Ellenberger, Henri; Pruyser, Paul; and Mayman, Martin. "The Unitary Concept of Mental Illness" (1958).
5. Pinel, Philippe. *Traité médico-philosophique sur l'aliénation mentale ou la manie*. Paris: Richards, Caille et Ravier, 1801.
6. Georget, Etienne. *De la Folie*. Paris: Chevot, 1820.
7. Llopis, Bartolomé. "La psicosis unica." *Arch. de Neurobiol.*, 17:1–39, 1954.
8. Guislain, Joseph. *Traité des Phrénopathies*. Bruxelles: Etablissement Encyclographique, 1833.
9. Griesinger, Wilhelm. *Die Pathologie und Therapie der psychischen Krankheiten*. Stuttgart: Krabbe, 1861.

10. Neumann, Heinrich. *Lehrbuch der Psychiatrie*. Erlangen: F. Enke, 1859.
11. Ibid. Quoted by Llopis.
12. Trousseau, Armand. *Clinique médicale de L'Hôtel-Dieu de Paris*, 5th ed. Paris: Baillière, 1877.
13. Janet, Pierre. *La Force et la faiblesse Psychologiques*. Paris: Maloine, 1932.
14. Zilboorg, Gregory. "Freud's Fundamental Psychiatric Orientation." *Int. J. Psa.*, 35:90–94, 1954.
15. Ey, Henri. *Études Psychiatriques*, Vol. 3. Paris: Desclée de Brouwer, 1954.
16. Laignel-Lavastine. *La méthode concentrique dan l'étude des psychoneuroses*. Paris: Chahine, 1928.
17. Leconte, Maurice, and Damey, Alfred. *Essai critique des nosographies psychiatriques actuelles*. Paris: Doin, 1949.
18. Llopis, Bartolomé. Op. cit.
19. ————. *La psicosis pelagrosa*. Barcelona: Editorial Cientifico Medica, 1946, pp. 47–67.
20. Bertalanffy, Ludwig von. "An Outline of General Systems Theory." *British J. Phil. Sci.*, 1:134–165, 1950.

PART IV: THE TEACHER

CHAPTER 6

1. Stearns, Harold E., ed. *American Now*. New York: Scribner, 1938. *Civilization in the United States*. New York: Harcourt, Brace, 1922.
2. Lynd, R. S., and Lynd, H. M. *Middletown* and *Middleton in Transition*. New York: Harcourt, Brace, 1929 and 1937, respectively.
3. Sullivan, H. S. "Psychiatry." In *Encyclopedia of the Social Sciences*. New York: Macmillan, 1937, vol. 6, pp. 578–580.
4. Beers, Clifford. *A Mind That Found Itself*. New York: Doubleday, Doran, 1908.
5. Campbell, C. Macfie. *A Present-Day Conception of Mental Disorders*. Cambridge, Massachusetts: Harvard University Press, 1924, pp. 14–16.
6. Lasswell, Harold D. *Psychopathology and Politics*. Chicago: University of Chicago, 1930.
7. Brown, Junius Flagg. *Psychology and the Social Order*. New York: McGraw-Hill, 1936.
8. Oliver, John Rathbone. *Psychiatry and Mental Health: The Hale Lectures at Western Theological Seminary, 1932*. New York: Scribner, 1932.
9. Boisen, Anton T. *The Exploration of the Newer World: A Study of Mental Disorder and Religious Experience*. Chicago and New York: Willett, Clark, 1936.
10. Menninger, Karl. "Religious Applications of Psychiatry." In *The Human Mind* (1930).

CHAPTER 7

1. Freud, Sigmund. "Contributions to the Psychology of Love. The Most Prevalent Form of Degradation in Erotic Life" (1912). *Coll. Papers*, Vol. 4, pp. 203–216.

CHAPTER II

1. Stone, Leo. "Concerning the Psychogenesis of Somatic Disease: Physical and Neurological Correlations with the Psychological Theory." *Int. J. Psa.*, 19:53–76, 1938.
2. Rasenkov, et al. *Bulletin de Biologie et de Médecine Experimentale de l'USSR*. Moscow, 1936.
3. Bender, Morris B. "Fright and Drug Contractions in Denervated Facial and Ocular Muscles of Monkeys." *Am. J. of Physiology*, 121:609–619, March 1938.
4. Hall, George E. "Experimental Heart Disease." A paper presented at the American College of Physicians session in New York City, April 5, 1938. A report of this address was printed in the New York *Times*, April 6, 1938, p. 24.
5. Gardner, W. W.; Smith, G. M.; Strong, L. C.; and Allen, Edgar. "Development of Sarcoma in Male Mice Receiving Estrogenic Hormones." *Arch. Path.*, 21:504, April 1936.
6. Loeb, Leo. "Estrogenic Hormones and Carcinogenesis." Chapter XIII of *Glandular Physiology and Therapy*. Chicago: American Medical Association, 1935. A brief summary with further references is given in an editorial in the *J.A.M.A.*, 106:1093, March 28, 1936.
7. Lewis, Dean, and Geschickter, Charles F. "Gynecomastia, Virginal Hypertrophy and Fibro-adenomas of the Breast." *Ann. Surgery*, 100:779–795, October 1934. "The Demonstration of Hormones in Tumors." *Ann. Surgery*, 104:787–797, October 1936. An extensive bibliography is appended.
8. Menninger, Karl. *Man Against Himself* (1938), especially Part V, Chapter 3, "The Choice of the Lesser Evil."

CHAPTER 13

1. Séguin. "Concept of Disease." *Psycho-somatic Medicine*, 8:252–257, 1946.

CHAPTER 14

1. Levi-Strauss, Claude. "The Social and Psychological Aspect of Chieftainship in a Primitive Tribe: the Nambikuara of Northwestern Mato Grosso (Brazil)." *Transactions of the New York Academy* of *Sciences*, 7:16–32, Oct. 23, 1944.
2. Marshall, S. L. A. "Men Against Fire." *The Infantry Journal*. New York: William Morrow, 1947.

CHAPTER 16

1. Marquis, Donald G. "Research Planning at the Frontiers of Science." *American Psychologist*, 3:430–438, October 1948.
2. Rapaport, David. "The Future of Research in Clinical Psychology and Psychiatry." *American Psychologist*, 2:167–172, May 1947.
3. Menninger, William. "Research in Mental Health in the National Perspective." *Mental Hygiene*, 33:78–95, January 1949.

PART V: THE PSYCHIATRIST AFIELD

CHAPTER 2

1. Barnes, Harry Elmer, in *Encyclopaedia Britannica*, 14th ed., Vol. 18, pp. 518–519.
2. Editorial, *The Nation*, Dec. 25, 1929.
3. Ibid.

CHAPTER 5

1. Gottlieb, Jacques S., and Tourney, Garfield. "Commitment Procedures and the Advancement of Psychiatric Knowledge." *Am. J. Psychiat.*, 115:109–113, 1958.

PART VI: THE HISTORIAN OF PSYCHIATRY

CHAPTER 7

1. See reports of the New York State Lunacy Commission, November 1905 and January 1906.
2. *Collected Papers of Adolf Meyer*, Vol. II. Baltimore: Johns Hopkins Press, 1950–1952.

CHAPTER 8

1. Frink, Horace Westlake. *Morbid Fears and Compulsions.* . . . New York: Dodd, Mead, 1918.
2. Freud, Sigmund. "Fragment of an Analysis of a Case of Hysteria" (1905). *Collected Papers*, Vol. I. See footnote pp. 28–29.
3. White, William A. *Forty Years of Psychiatry*. New York: Nervous and Mental Disease Publishing Co., 1933. The sections quoted by White are from a discussion of "A Criticism of Psychoanalysis" by Dr. Charles W. Burr, *Proc. Am. Medico-Psychol. Assn.*, 21:322, 1914.
4. Menninger, Karl. "The Contribution of Psychoanalysis to American Psychiatry" (supra, p. 834).

CHAPTER 9

1. Emerson, L. E. "Philosophy for Psychoanalysts." *Psychoanalytic Review*, 2:422.
2. Cabot, Richard C. "An Appreciation of Elmer E. Southard." *Bull. Mass. Dept.* of *Mental Diseases* (Southard Memorial Number), 4:14–29, February 1920.
3. Quoted in ibid.

List of the Published Writings of Karl Menninger, M.D.

1919

"Psychoses Associated with Influenza. I: General Data: Statistical Analysis." *J.A.M.A.*, 72:235–241, Jan. 25.

"Alcoholic Argyll-Robertson Pupils? Alcoholic Psychosis Simulating Neurosyphilis: A Case Report." *Am. J. Syphilis*, 3:232–234, April.

"Cyclothymic Fugues." *J. Abnorm. Psychol.*, 14:54–63, April–June.

"Hysteria in a Male as a Defense Reaction: A Case Report." *Boston Med. Surg. J.*, 180:612–613, May 29.

"Influenza and Neurosyphilis." *Arch. Intern. Med.*, 24:98–115, July.

"Ambulatory Skull Fracture with Delayed Symptoms: A Case Report." *Med. Rec.*, 96:58, July 12.

"The Treatment and Study of Twelve Non-Paretic Neurosyphilitics Treated by Intraventricular Injections of Salvarsanized Serum" (with A. L. Skoog). *J. Nerv. Ment. Dis.*, 50:114–143, August.

"Psychoses Associated with Influenza. II: Specific Data: An Expository Analysis." *Arch. Neurol. Psychiat.*, 2:291–337, September.

"General Psychiatry for the General Practitioner." *J. Kans. Med. Soc.*, 19:212–217, September; 19:243–249, October; 19:271–278, November.

1920

"Influenza Psychoses in Successive Epidemics." *Arch. Neurol. Psychiât.*, 3:57–60, January.

"Paranoid Psychoses." *J. Nerv. Ment. Dis.*, 51:35–40, January.

"The Relations of Feeblemindedness and Tuberculosis." In *Transactions of the Sixteenth Annual Meeting of the National Tuberculosis Association*, St. Louis, April.

"What Can Be Done for the Paralyzed?" *J. Kans. Med. Soc.*, 20:226–232, August.

"A Critique of a Criticism." *J. Abnorm. Psychol.*, 15:278–281, October.

"Influenza and Hypophrenia. The Interrelation of an Acute Epidemic Infection and a Chronic Endemic (Brain) Affection." *J.A.M.A.*, 75:1044–1051, Oct. 16.

1921

"Late Hereditary Neurosyphilis: A Clinical Classification." *Trans. Sect. Nerv. Ment. Dis., A.M.A.,* pp. 93–115.
"Melancholy and Melancholia." *J. Kans. Med. Soc.,* 21:44–50, February.
"Syphilis of the Nervous System." *J. Kans. Med. Soc.,* 21:82–89, March.
"The Dandy Method of Localizing Brain Tumors by the Roentgen Ray: with Report of a Case." *Arch. Neurol. Psychiat.,* 5:438–444, April.
"Influenza and Melancholy." *J. Nerv. Ment. Dis.,* 53:257–281, April.
"Influenza and Epilepsy: Further Studies upon the Relations of Mental Disease and Influenza." *Am. J. Med. Sci.,* 161:884–907, June.
"Ataxic Paraplegia with Pernicious Anemia." *N.Y. Med. J.,* 113:812–813, June 1.
"What is Dementia Praecox?" *J. Kans. Med. Soc.,* 21:381–384, December. Reprinted, ibid., 60:140–142, May 1959.

1922

"Reversible Schizophrenia. A Study of the Implications of Delirium Schizophrenoides and Other Post-Influenzal Syndromes." *Am. J. Psychiat.,* 1:573–588, April.
"Epidemic Encephalitis: A Summary of Present Knowledge." *J. Kans. Med. Soc.,* 22:139–146, May.
"The Washburn College Course in Mental Hygiene." *Kans. Teacher,* 15:22–23, August–September.
"Practical Mental Hygiene: Report of the First Year's Work of the Nervous and Mental Section of the Topeka Municipal Clinic." *J. Kans. Med. Soc.,* 22:355–360, December.

1923

"The Mental Effects of Deafness." *Volta Rev.,* 25:439–445, October. Reprinted in *Psa. Rev.,* 11:144–155, April 1924.
"Treatment of Poliomyelitis." *J. Kans. Med. Soc.,* 23:278–284, October.
"The Thyroid and Psychiatry." *Southwestern Med.,* 7:403–406, November.
"Postencephalitic Manifestations." *J.A.M.A.,* 81:1627, Nov. 10.
Book review:
    The Kingdom of Evils. Psychiatric Social Work Presented in One Hundred Case Histories Together with a Classification of Social Divisions of Evil, by E. E. Southard and Mary C. Jarrett. *Am. J. Psychiat.,* 3:138–141, July.

1924

"Heredosyphilitic Cranial Osteoporosis. A Preliminary Report on a Roentgen-Ray Stigma Found in Late Congenital Syphilis." *Trans. Sect. Nerv. Ment. Dis., A.M.A.,* pp. 164–181. Reprinted in *Radiology,* 4:480–491, June 1925.
"Orpheus and Psyche." *Volta Rev.,* 26:32–33, January.
"Static Seizures in Epilepsy: Report of Two Cases." *J. Nerv. Ment. Dis.,* 59:54–57, January.
"Treatment of Mental Illness." *J. Kans. Med. Soc.,* 24:1–10, January. Reprinted in *Southwestern Med.,* 9:377–386, October 1925.

"Optic Neuritis and Choked Disk in Influenza." *Arch. Neurol. Psychiat.,* 11:328–333, March.

Abstract of Freud's "Group Psychology and the Analysis of the Ego." (Translation by James Strachey, Internat. Psychoanalyt. Library, No. 6, 1923.) *Arch. Neurol. Psychiat.,* 11:334–343, March.

"Drug Addiction." *Quart. Bull. Kans. State Bd. Health,* 2:37–38, April–June.

"Mental Health." *Quart. Bull. Kans. State Bd. Health,* 2:33–35, April–June.

"A Mental Hygiene Clinic: Second Annual Report of the Neuropsychiatric Division of the Topeka Municipal Clinic." *J. Kans. Med. Soc.,* 24:165–173, June.

"Paranoid Psychosis with Uremia." *J. Nerv. Ment. Dis.,* 60:26–34, July.

"The Place of the Psychiatric Department in the General Hospital." *Mod. Hosp.,* 23:1–4, July.

"Nervous Diseases and the General Practitioner." *Southwestern Med.,* 8:417–422, September.

"Mental Health of College Students." *Bull. Kans. Ment. Hyg. Soc.,* 1:1–4, Sept. 15; 1:1–4, Nov. 1.

"Letters of the Alphabet in Psycho-Analytic Formations." *Int. J. Psa.,* 5:462–465, October.

"Three Psychoanalytic Notes." *Int. J. Psa.,* 5:466–467, October.

1925

"Psychiatry and the Prisoner." *Proceedings of the National Conference of Social Work, Fifty-second Meeting.*

"Symptom Analysis in Paretic Neurosyphilis. A Study of One Hundred and Sixty-Six Comparable Consecutive Cases" (with William C. Menninger). *Am. J. Syphilis,* 9:104–112, January.

"The Opportunities of Neuropsychiatry." *Phi Beta Pi Quart.,* 12:116–118, May.

"The Wassermann Reaction in the Blood and Spinal Fluid of Paretic Neurosyphilis. With the Presentation of the Results in One Hundred and Sixty-Six Consecutive Hospitalized Cases" (with William C. Menninger). *Am. J. Med. Sci.,* 170:27–37, July.

"Paretic Gold Curve in Poliomyelitis." *J. Kans. Med. Soc.,* 25:411, December.

Book review:

   The Inheritance of Acquired Characteristics, by Paul Kammerer. *Med. Herald and Physiotherapist.*

1926

"Vengeance—or Vision?" *Survey Graphic,* 8:610–612, March.

"Influenza and Schizophrenia. An Analysis of Post-Influenzal 'Dementia Praecox' as of 1918, and Five Years Later. Further Studies of the Psychiatric Aspects of Influenza." *Am. J. Psychiat.,* 5:469–529, April.

"Psychoanalytic Study of a Case of Organic Epilepsy." *Psa. Rev.,* 13:187–199, April.

"The Psychiatrist in Relation to Crime." *Proceedings of the American Bar Association, Criminal Law Section,* Denver, Colorado. July 13.

"The Course in Mental Hygiene, Washburn College, 1926–1927." *Bull. Kans. Ment. Hyg. Soc.,* 2:1–6, Nov. 1.

1927

"New Treatment Methods in Psychiatry." *Med. Herald and Physiotherapist,* March, pp. 3–6.

"Crime as a Medical Problem." *Tex. State J. Med.,* 23:20–23, May.

"Adaptation Difficulties in College Students." *Ment. Hyg.,* 11:519–535, July.

"Mental Hygiene in Public Health." *Bull. Kans. Ment. Hyg. Soc.,* 3:3–4, July.

"Hysteria." *Hygeia,* 5:394–396, August.

"Medicolegal Proposals of the American Psychiatric Association." *Reports of Am. Bar Assn.,* 52:486–496. Reprinted in *J. Crim. Law Criminol.,* 19:367–377, November 1928.

"The Course in Mental Hygiene, Washburn College, 1927–1928" (with William C. Menninger and Roberta Smith). *Bull. Kans. Ment. Hyg. Soc.,* 3:1–6, September.

"Report of the Committee on the Legal Aspects of Psychiatry." *Am. J. Psychiat.,* 7:333–339, September.

"Depressions." N.Y. *Herald Tribune Magazine,* Oct. 9. Also in *Why Men Fail,* Morris Fishbein and William A. White, eds. New York: Century, 1928.

"Are You a Schizoid?" N.Y. *Herald Tribune Magazine,* Nov. 13.

1928

" 'Queer' Failures." In *Why Men Fail,* Morris Fishbein and William A. White, eds. New York: Century.

"Suicides." *J. Kans. Med. Soc.,* 28:6–10, January.

"Mental Aspects of Tuberculosis." *Tex. State J. Med.,* 24:19–20, May.

"The Schizophrenic Syndrome as a Product of Acute Infectious Disease." *Arch. Neurol. Psychiat.,* 20:464–481, September. Also in *A.R.N.M.D.,* 5:182–203.

Book review:

   The Ways of Behaviorism, by John B. Watson. *Survey,* 61:96, Oct. 15.

1929

"Why Do Students Flunk?" *The Intercollegian,* 46:104–106, January.

"Fundamentalism and Modernism in Psychiatry." *U.S. Naval Med. Bull.,* 27:291–297, April.

"What Is a Healthy Mind?" *Household Magazine,* 29:4, 5, 25, 30, April.

"Psychoanalytic Observations on the Mental Hygiene Problems of College Students." *J. Nerv. Ment. Dis.,* 69:642–650, June.

"The Isolation Type of Personality." *U.S. Naval Med. Bull.,* 27:609–620, July–October.

"College Blues." *Survey Graphic,* 15:549–552, 581–582, September.

"Keeping Your Child's Mind Healthy." *Household Magazine* (On Advisory Council for the Mental Health of Children, November 1929–June 1938.)

"Neurological Pediatrics." *Survey,* 63:229, Nov. 15.

"Sex Education." *Household Magazine,* 29:19, December.

Book reviews:

   The Criminal and His Allies, by Marcus Kavanagh. *Ment. Hyg.,* 13:186–188, January.

The New Criminology: A Consideration of the Chemical Causation of Abnormal Behavior, by Max Schlapp and Edward H. Smith. *Ment. Hyg.,* 13:175–178, January.

("Marriage Under the Microscope") *A Research in Marriage,* by G. V. Hamilton, and *What Is Wrong with Marriage,* by G. V. Hamilton and Kenneth Macgowan. *Survey,* 63:51, Oct. 1.

1930

The Healthy-Minded Child (co-editor, Nelson Antrim Crawford). New York: Coward-McCann. "Sexual Development and Sex Education," pp. 168–182. "What Is a Healthy Mind?" pp. 3–17.

The Human Mind. New York: Knopf. 2nd ed., 1937. 3rd ed., 1945. Japanese translation by Heisaku Kosawa, Tokyo, Nippon Kyobun-Sha Co., 1950. Korean translation by Yong Ho Lee, Seoul, Korea, Minchoong, Vol. 1, 1957; Vol. 2, 1958. Excerpt, "Religious Applications of Psychiatry," in *Pastoral Psychol.,* 1:13–22, April 1950. The following excerpts appeared in *Wisdom:* "Moody Personalities," 2:43, May 1957; "The Neurotic Type," 2:41–42, May 1957; "Psychiatry," 2:72–74, May 1957; "Psychoanalysis," 2:75, May 1957.

"The Amelioration of Mental Disease by Influenza." *J.A.M.A.,* 94:630–634, March 1.

"From the Home to College." *Child Study,* 7:195–199, April.

"Pseudoanalysis." *Outlook and Independent,* 155:353–365, July 9. Summary of this article appeared as "Amateur Dream-Analysis Condemned" in *The World of Dreams,* Ralph L. Woods, ed. New York: Random House, 1947.

"What Is Wrong with Our Prisons?" *Plain Talk,* 7:175–182, August.

"Children and War Movies." *Household Magazine,* 30:25, October.

"Mental Hygiene in the Home." *Ladies' Home Journal,* 27:109, October.

"Amelioration of Schizophrenia Following Dysentery" (with P. E. Kubitschek). *J. Nerv. Ment. Dis.,* 72:535–537, November.

"New Lamps for Old." *Ladies' Home Journal,* 27:101, November.

"As Others See Us." *Ladies' Home Journal,* 27:75, December.

Book reviews:

("Do Doctors Look Like This?") *The Layman Looks at Doctors,* by S. W. and J. T. Pierce. *Survey,* 63:485, Jan. 15.

("The Happy Professor") *The Psychology of Happiness,* by Walter B. Pitkin. *Survey,* 64:102, April 15.

1931

"Parental Attitudes." *Ladies' Home Journal,* 28:61, 87, January.

"Unhappiness." *Ladies' Home Journal,* 28:96, February.

"The Quest for Happiness." *Ladies' Home Journal,* 28:118, March.

"Hard Times and Mental Health." *Household Magazine,* 31:24, April.

"Self-Adoration." *Ladies' Home Journal,* 28:31, 186, April.

"Unprofitable Investments in Love." *Ladies' Home Journal,* 28:120, 127, May.

"Normal People." *Ladies' Home Journal,* 28:98, June.

"Investments of Hate." *Ladies' Home Journal,* 28:83, 93, July.

"Why We Hate." *Ladies' Home Journal,* 28:50, August.

"The Kernel of Hate." *Ladies' Home Journal,* 28:95, September.

"Young Suicides." *Household Magazine*, 31:19, September.
"Starting to School." *Ladies' Home Journal*, 28:107, October.
"High-School Problems." *Ladies' Home Journal*, 28:108, 115, November.
"College-Student Problems." *Ladies' Home Journal*, 28:68, December.
"Mental Hygiene in School." *Household Magazine*, 31:19, December.

1932

"Husbands and Wives." *Ladies' Home Journal*, 29:70, 80, March.
"Those Husbands." *Ladies' Home Journal*, 29:96–97, April.
"Epilepsy and Congenital Syphilis" (with William C. Menninger). *J. Nerv. Ment. Dis.*, 75:473–497, 632–657, May.
"Poor Little Good Child." *Household Magazine*, 32:17, August.
"When Disaster Comes." *Household Magazine*, 32:7, 29–31, October.
"When Women Meet Disaster." *Household Magazine*, 32:6, 31, November.
"Being Honest with Your Child." *Household Magazine*, 32:18, 31, November.
"Temper Tantrums." *Folks*, 2:53–54, December.

1933

"Why Punishment Makes for Disobedience." *Household Magazine*, 33:16, January.
"The Origins and Masques of Fear." *Survey Graphic*, 22:217–220, April.
"Psychoanalytic Aspects of Suicide." *Int. J. Psa.*, 14:376–390, July. Also in *Man Against Himself*, 1938.
Book reviews:
    An Introduction to Analytical Psychotherapy, by T. A. Ross. *Psa. Quart.*, 2:341–343, April.
    Forty Years of Psychiatry, by W. A. White. *Psa. Quart.*, 2:619–620, July–October.

1934

"Polysurgery and Polysurgical Addiction." *Psa. Quart.*, 3:173–199, April.
"Some Unconscious Psychological Factors Associated with the Common Cold." *Psa. Rev.*, 21:201–207, April.
"Symposium on Treatment, 1934." (Participant) *Am. J. Ortho.*, 4:323–358, July.
"Some Psychoanalytic Aspects of Plastic Surgery" (with Howard L. Updegraff). *Am. J. Surg.*, 25:554–558, September.
Discussion of "Evaluation of Statistical and Analytical Methods in Psychiatry and Psychology," by Franz Alexander. *Am. J. Ortho.*, 4:443–444, October.

1935

"Psychology of a Certain Type of Malingering." *Arch. Neurol. Psychiat.*, 33:507–515, March.
"Some Clinical Examples of Indirect Suicide." *South. Med. J.*, 28:356–360, April.
"A Psychoanalytic Study of the Significance of Self-Mutilations." *Psa. Quart.*, 4:408–466, July. Also in *Man Against Himself*, 1938.

Discussion of "Varieties of Homosexual Manifestations," by George Sprague. *Am. J. Psychiat.*, 92:150–151, July.

"Impotence and Frigidity from the Standpoint of Psychoanalysis." *J. Urol.*, 34:166–183, August. Enlarged version appeared as "Impotence and Frigidity" in *Bull. Menninger Clin.*, 1:251–260, September 1937; *Man Against Himself*, 1938; *Elements of Psychoanalysis*, Hans Herma and Gertrud M. Kurth, eds., New York: World Publishing Co., 1950; *Men*, New York: Harcourt, Brace, 1956.

"Unconscious Values in Certain Consistent Mispronunciations." *Psa. Quart.*, 4:614–615, October.

1936

"Psychoanalytic Observations in Cardiac Disorders" (with William C. Menninger). *Am. Heart J.*, 11:10–21, January.

"Purposive Accidents as an Expression of Self-Destructive Tendencies." *Int. J. Psa.*, 17:6–16, January. German translation in *Almanac der Psychoanalyse*, 1936. Also in *Man Against Himself*, 1938.

"Encephalomalacia with Marked Reactive Gliosis." *J. Nerv. Ment. Dis.*, 84:146–151, August.

"Psychiatry and Medicine." *Bull. Menninger Clin.*, 1:1–9, September.

"The Application of Psychoanalytic Methods to the Study of Mental Retardation" (with Leona Chidester). *Am. J. Ortho.*, 6:616–625, October. Abridgment in *Counseling and Psychotherapy with the Mentally Retarded*, Chalmers L. Stacey and Manfred F. DeMartino, eds., Glencoe, Ill.: Free Press, 1957.

"Psychological Factors in Urological Disease." *Psa. Quart.*, 5:488–512, October.

Book review:

> *Emotions and Bodily Changes*, by H. Flanders Dunbar. *J. Kans. Med. Soc.*, 37:82, 84, February.

1937

"The Genius of the Jew in Psychiatry." *Medical Leaves*. Chicago: Medical Leaves, pp. 127–132.

"Organic Suicide." *Bull. Menninger Clin.*, 1:192–198, May. Also in *Man Against Himself*, 1938.

"Combating Man's Destructive Urge." *Survey Graphic*, 26:520–523, October. Also in *Man Against Himself*, 1938.

Book reviews:

> *Psychology and the Social Order*, by J. F. Brown. *Psa. Quart.*, 6:128–132, January. Reprinted in *J.A.M.A.*, 108:1293, April 10.
>
> *Mind, Medicine and Metaphysics: The Philosophy of a Physician*, by William Brown. *J.A.M.A.*, 108:1742, May 15.
>
> *The Problem of Anxiety*, by Sigmund Freud. *Survey*, 73:238, July.
>
> *The Mentally Ill in America*, by Albert Deutsch. *The Nation*, 145:225, Aug. 28.
>
> *Guiding Your Life*, by Josephine A. Jackson. *Survey*, 73:300, September.
>
> *A Mind Mislaid*, by Henry Collins Brown, and *A Mind Restored*, by Elsa Krauch. *The Nation*, 145:385–386, Oct. 9.
>
> *Your Child Faces War*, by Nelson Antrim Crawford. *Household Magazine*, 27:32, November.

1938

Man Against Himself. New York: Harcourt, Brace. Japanese translation by Heisaku Kosawa. Tokyo: Nippon Kyobun-Sha Co., 1952. Spanish translation by Filipe Jimenex de Asua. Buenos Aires: Editorial Losado, 1952. Finnish translation by Sirppa Mikkola. Helsinki: Kustannusosakuyto, Otava, 1955. "Alcohol Addiction" reprinted in *Why You Do What You Do,* R. N. Linscott and J. Stein, eds. New York: Random House, 1956.

"Psychiatry." In *America Now,* by Harold E. Stearnes. New York: Scribner.

"Criminal Behavior as a Form of Masked Self-Destructiveness." *Bull. Menninger Clin.,* 2:1–7, January. Also in *Man Against Himself.*

"Emotional Factors in Hypertension." *Bull. N.Y. Acad. Med.,* 14:198–211, April. Reprinted in *Bull. Menninger Clin.,* 2:74–88, May.

"The Cinderella of Medicine." *N.Y. State J. Med.,* 38:922–925, June 15. Reprinted in *Bull. Menninger Clin.,* 2:180–187, November. Also in *The March of Medicine 1940.* New York: Columbia University, 1940.

"The Psychoneurotic in the General Practice of Medicine." *J. Indiana State Med. Assn.,* 31:442–444, September.

"War Psychology." N.Y. *Herald Tribune* Conference Report No. 8, pp. 173–176, Oct. 26.

Book reviews:

Personality in Formation and Action, by William Healy. *Survey Midmonthly,* 74:298–299, September.

Psychotherapy, by Paul Schilder. *Social Service Rev.,* 12:546–547, September.

1939

"The Psychological Factor in Disease." *Bull. Menninger Clin.,* 3:14–19, January.

"Men, Women and Hate." *Atlantic Monthly,* 163:158–168, February.

"Somatic Correlations with the Unconscious Repudiation of Femininity in Women." *J. Nerv. Ment. Dis.,* 89:514–527, April. Reprinted in *Bull. Menninger Clin.,* 3:106–121, July.

"The Psychiatrist Looks at Birth Control." *Birth Control Rev.,* 23:221–222, June.

"Havelock Ellis." *The Nation,* 149:103–104, July 22.

"Parents Against Children." *Atlantic Monthly,* 164:163–175, August.

"An Anthropological Note on the Theory of Pre-Natal Instinctual Conflict." *Int. J. Psa.,* 20:439–442, July–October. Reprinted in *Bull. Menninger Clin.,* 4:51–55, March 1940.

"Sigmund Freud." *The Nation,* 149:373–374, Oct. 7. Reprinted in *Bull. Menninger Clin.,* 3:161–163, November.

"Intermittent Extrasystole Directly Associated with Emotional Conflict: A Case Report" (with Lewis Gunther). *Bull. Menninger Clin.,* 3:164–176, November.

"Bleeding Kansas." *Kansas Magazine,* December, pp. 3–6.

Book reviews:

New Ways in Psychoanalysis, by Karen Horney. *J.A.M.A.*, 113:356–357, July 22.

Moses and Monotheism, by Sigmund Freud. *The New Republic*, 100:23–25, Aug. 9.

The Open Mind: Elmer Ernest Southard, by F. P. Gay. *Psa. Quart.*, 8:544–546, October.

Alcoholics Anonymous: The Story of How More than One Hundred Men Have Recovered from Alcoholism. *J.A.M.A.*, 113:1513, Oct. 14.

Feet of Clay, by Havelock Ellis. *The Nation*, 149:618–620, Dec. 2.

1940

The Psychodynamics of Abnormal Behavior (with J. F. Brown). New York: McGraw-Hill.

"Scientific Study of Personality from the Medical Standpoint." *Proc. Calif. Acad. Med.*, pp. 70–100.

"The Year in Psychology." *The New Republic*, 102:57–58, Jan. 8.

"Why We Kill." Annual Conference of the American League to Abolish Capital Punishment, April 26.

"Psychoanalytic Psychiatry: Theory and Practice." *Bull. Menninger Clin.*, 4:105–123, July.

Book reviews:

Technique of Analytical Psychotherapy, by Wilhelm Stekel. *The Nation*, 150:547–548, April 27.

Health is Wealth, by Paul de Kruif. *The Nation*, 150:758–760, June 22.

The Psychology of Parent-Child Relationships, by Percival M. Symonds. *The New Republic*, 103:150, July 29.

The Story of Surgery, by Harvey Graham. *The Nation*, 151:97, Aug. 3.

Hugh Young: A Surgeon's Autobiography, by Hugh Young. *The Nation*, 151:307, Oct. 5.

Why Men Behave Like Apes and Vice Versa, by Ernest A. Hooton. *The Nation*, 151:539, Nov. 30.

1941

"Relation of Psychiatry to the Business Man." In *Training for Leadership* (Third Annual Executive Leadership Forum). Indianapolis: Indianapolis Junior Chamber of Commerce, pp. 34–40.

"Psychogenic Influences on the Appearance of the Menstrual Period." *Int. J. Psa.*, 22:60–64, January.

"Some Observations of the Psychological Factors in Urination and Genito-urinary Afflictions." *Psa. Rev.*, 28:117–129, January.

"The Psychological Examination: An Outline of Procedure in the Determination of the Mental Status of the Psychiatric Patient" (with William C. Menninger and Robert P. Knight). *Bull. Menninger Clin.*, 5:97–110, July.

"Civilian Morale in Time of War and Preparation for War." *Bull. Menninger Clin.*, 5:188–194, September.

"Recognizing and Renaming 'Psychopathic Personalities.'" *Bull. Menninger Clin.*, 5:150–156, September.

"Eve and the Flying Dutchman." *Virginia Quart. Rev.*, 17:53–69, Winter.

Book reviews:
> *The Life and Death Instincts,* by Arthur N. Foxe. *Psa. Quart.,* 10:149, January.
> *Germs and the Man,* by Justina Hill. *The Nation,* 152:80, Jan. 18.
> *Must We Grow Old?* by Barclay Newman. *The Nation,* 152:480, April 19.
> *From Thirty Years with Freud,* by Theodor Reik. *Survey Graphic,* 30:310, May.
> *From Orient to Occident: Memoirs of a Doctor,* by Leon Weber-Bauler. *The Nation,* 153:260, Sept. 20.

1942

Love Against Hate (with Jeanetta Lyle Menninger). New York: Harcourt, Brace. Japanese translation by Heisaku Kosawa. Tokyo: Nippon Kyobun-Sha Co., 1951. Spanish translation by Haime Tomas. Buenos Aires: Editorial Nova, 1951. Finnish translation by Toini Havu and Sirppa Mikkola. Helsinki: Kustannusosakuyto, Otava, 1953. Korean translation by Yong Ho Lee. Seoul: Pakcho Co., 1955. "Work as a Sublimation," an excerpt reprinted in *Bull. Menninger Clin.,* 6:170–182, November; Spanish translation appeared in *Rev. Psicoanal.,* 1:168–181, October 1943.

"How to Keep Up Your Morale in Wartime." *Household Magazine,* 42:1, 9, 11, 23, April.

"Chess." *Bull. Menninger Clin.,* 6:80–83, May.

"Psychoanalysis: Past and Present" (Editorial). *Dis. Nerv. System,* 3:133–134, May.

"Recreation for Morale: Some Tentative Conclusions" (with Jeanetta Lyle Menninger). *Bull. Menninger Clin.,* 6:96–102, May.

Presidential Address, American Psychoanalytic Association. *Psa. Quart.,* 11: 287–300, July.

"Play." *Virginia Quart. Rev.,* 18:591–599, Autumn.

"The Kenny Treatment—with a Note on Its Use in Kansas 20 Years Ago." *J. Kans. Med. Soc.,* 43:414–416, October. Reprinted, ibid., 50:158, May 1959.

"This Is Getting Us Someplace." Div. of Child Welfare, Dept. of Kansas, American Legion, December.

Book review:
> *Intelligence, Power and Personality,* by George Crile. *Am. J. Publ. Hlth.,* 32:1403–1404, December.

1943

"Psychiatric Aspects of Contraception." *Bull. Menninger Clin.,* 7:36–40, January. Also in *Therapeutic Abortion,* Harold Rosen, ed. New York: Julian Press, 1954; *Pastoral Psychol.,* 5:27–33, December 1954.

"Emotional Factors in Organic Gynecological Conditions." *Bull. Menninger Clin.,* 7:47–55, January.

"Clinical Psychology in the Psychiatric Clinic." *Bull. Menninger Clin.,* 7:89–92, May.

Symposium: "The Roots of War in Human Nature: Aggression and Hate in Childhood and Family Life." *Child Study,* 20:73–75, Spring.

"They Hate Their Land." *The Land,* 3:17–18, Summer.

"The Dirt Beneath Our Feet: Why Do We Despise It?" *The Land,* 3:137–142, Winter.

1944

"Present Trends in Psychoanalytic Theory and Practice." *Bull. Menninger Clin.,* 8:14–17, January.

"The War Against Fear and Hate." *Bull. Menninger Clin.,* 8:101–106, July. Also in *Rhode Island Med. J.,* 27:387, August.

"The Abuse of Rest in Psychiatry." *J.A.M.A.,* 125:1087–1090, Aug. 19. Reprinted in *Bull. Menninger Clin.,* 9:162–169, September 1945.

"The Man Behind the Badge." *Public Safety,* 26:10–11, 24, August. Enlarged version, "Psychiatric Aspects of Highway Traffic Law Enforcement," in *Bull. Menninger Clin.,* 9:18–26, January 1945.

"Pediatrics and Psychiatry." *Bull. Menninger Clin.,* 8:167–169, November.

Book review:

Health and Hygiene, by Lloyd Ackerman. *Sat. Rev. Lit.,* 27:26–28, May 13. Also in *Quart. Phi Beta Pi,* 41:81–83, Autumn.

1945

"Diagnosis and Treatment of Schizophrenia." *Proc. Interst. Postgrad. Med. Assn. North America,* 1944, pp. 107–111.

"Psychiatry—Opportunity in Medicine." *The Interne,* 11:11, 22, January.

"Graduate Training in Psychiatry." *Bull. Menninger Clin.,* 9:41–46, March.

"The Future of Psychiatric Care in Hospitals." *Mod. Hosp.,* 64:43–45, May.

"Smith Ely Jelliffe, 1866–1945." *Bull. Menninger Clin.,* 9:177–178. November.

"Peter Bassoe, 1874–1945." *Bull. Menninger Clin.,* 9:179, November.

Book review:

Freud's Contribution to Psychiatry, by A. A. Brill. *Sat. Rev. Lit.,* 28:11–12, Feb. 10.

1946

"Psychiatry in Medicine." *The Interne,* 12:25–28, 79, January.

Foreword to the issue by members of the Royal Army Medical Corps. *Bull. Menninger Clin.,* 10:65, May.

"Techniques of Hypnoanalysis Illustrated in a Case Report" (with Merton Gill). *Bull. Menninger Clin.,* 10:110–126, July.

"Winter General Hospital." *Bull. Menninger Clin.,* 10:101–103, July.

"Combat Exhaustion" (with Leo Bartemeier, Lawrence S. Kubie, John Romano, John Whitehorn). *J. Nerv. Ment. Dis.,* 104:358–525, October.

"Mental Patients Predominate at This General Hospital." *Hospitals,* 20:44–46, October.

"The Psychiatrist Looks at the Inferiority Complex." *Encore,* 10:430–436, October.

1947

"The New Role of Psychological Testing in Psychiatry" (with David Rapaport and Roy Schafer). *Am. J. Psychiat.,* 103:473–476, January.

"Psychiatry and Psychology." *Bull. Menninger Clin.,* 11:45–49, March. Condensed version, "Psychology and Psychiatry," in *Am. Psychologist,* 2:139–140, April.

"A Psychiatrist Looks at Custer." (Comments on "Did Cholera Defeat Custer?" by Paul R. Hawley.) *Surg. Gynec. and Obst.*, 84:1012, May.

"Changing Concepts in Medicine and Their Effect Upon Medical Education." *J. Kans. Med. Soc.*, 48:353–355, August.

"Observations of a Psychiatrist in a Dermatology Clinic." *Bull. Menninger Clin.*, 11:141–147, September.

"The Diagnosis and Treatment of Schizophrenia." *Postgrad. Med.*, 2:275–281, October. Reprinted in *Bull. Menninger Clin.*, 12:96–106, May 1948.

1948

Introduction to *The Shame of the States* by Albert Deutsch. New York: Harcourt, Brace. Appeared as "How 'Human' Are We?" in *Menninger Quart.*, 5:4–8, January 1951.

"A Suggested Basic Psychiatric Reading List, 1948." *Bull. Menninger Clin.*, 12:81–89, May.

"Message from Dr. Karl Menninger." *VA Special Services Bull.*, 1B6–86, June 1, p. 2.

"The Veteran—and Don't Forget." *Survey Graphic*, 37:333–337, July.

"Changing Concepts of Disease." *Ann. Intern. Med.*, 29:318–325, August.

"Smith Ely Jelliffe—Father of Psychosomatic Medicine in America" (with George Devereux). *Psa. Rev.*, 35:350–363, October.

1949

"The Doctor as a Leader." *Bull. Menninger Clin.*, 13:9–15, January. Reprinted in *Quart. Phi Beta Pi*, 46:72–76, 82, May; *Menninger Quart.*, 4:11–15, January 1950.

"The Dermatologist and the Psychiatrist" (with A. H. Gottesman). *Arch. Dermat. and Syph.*, 59:367–373, April. Reprinted in *Bull. Menninger Clin.*, 13:119–123, July.

"How Can We Find Personal Peace and Security in Today's World?" ("Town Meeting" radio broadcast on ABC, April 26.) *Town Meeting*, Bull. of America's Town Meeting of the Air, Vol. 14, No. 52, April 26.

"Research in Psychiatry." *Bull. Menninger Clin.*, 13:73–82, May. Also in *Research in Medical Science*, David E. Green and W. Eugene Knox, eds. New York: Macmillan, 1950.

Guest editorial. *The Topeka State Journal*, June 14, p. 4.

"Contributions of A. A. Brill to Psychiatry." *Bull. Menninger Clin.*, 13:185–187, September.

Foreword to the Sigmund Freud Memorial Issue. *Bull. Menninger Clin.*, 13:141–142, September.

"Take Your Choice." *This Week Magazine*, Oct. 16, p. 2.

"James King Hall, M.D., 1875–1948." *Bull. Menninger Clin.*, 13:213–215, November. Also in *Am. J. Psychiat.*, 106:778–779, April 1950.

"Assumptions and Approaches." *Menninger Newsletter*, 3:16–19, No. 4.

Book review:

   The Show of Violence, by Frederic Wertham. N.Y. *Herald Tribune*, May 22.

1950

A Guide to Psychiatric Books with a Suggested Basic Psychiatric Reading List.
Menninger Clinic Monograph Series, No. 7. New York: Grune and Stratton.
2nd ed., revised and enlarged, 1956.

Introduction to *Psychiatric Sections in General Hospitals* by Paul Haun. New
York: F. W. Dodge Corp.

"Looking Ahead in the Fields of Orthopsychiatric Research: Symposium
1949." *Am. J. Orthopsychiat.,* 20:73–114, January.

"The Anatomy and Physiology of the Personality." *Bull. Menninger Clin.,*
14:75–80, March.

Letter to the editor. *Sat. Rev. Lit.,* 33:23, May 13.

"My Favorite Tree." *American Forests,* 56:4, 39, June.

"A Psychiatric Fable." *Bull. Menninger Clin.,* 14:129–130, July. Reprinted in
Quart. Phi Beta Pi, 53:24, October 1956.

"What Is Economy in Mental Illness?" *Menninger Quart.,* 4:12–19, July.

"Adventures in Science." CBS radio broadcast, Aug. 12.

Foreword to "Poetry of Patient." *Bull. Menninger Clin.,* 14:174, September.

"A Guide for Psychiatric Case Study. Part I: The Approach to the Psychiatric
Patient." *Bull. Menninger Clin.,* 14:192–201, November. Reprinted in *Bull.
Tokyo Inst. Psa.,* No. 45, December 1951. Also in *A Manual for Psychiatric
Case Study,* 1952.

"Are Policemen Supermen?" *Kans. State Peace Officer's Mag.,* 15:2 ff., December.

Book reviews:

The Psychoanalytic Study of the Child, Vols. 3 and 4, ed. by Anna Freud
et al. *Fed. Probation,* 14:90–91, June.

The Sexual Perversions and Abnormalities, by Clifford Allen. *J.A.M.A.,*
144:282, September.

Exhibitionism, by N. K. Rickles. *J.A.M.A.,* 144:590, October.

Treatment in Psychiatry, by Oscar Diethelm. *Fed. Probation,* 14:52, December.

1951

"Totemic Aspects of Contemporary Attitudes toward Animals." In *Psychoanalysis and Culture,* G. B. Wilbur and Warner Muensterberger, eds. New
York: International Universities, pp. 42–74.

"Personality Factors in Osteoarthritis" (with Henry Lihn and Martin Mayman). *Bull. Menninger Clin.,* 15:1–5, January.

"*Religio Psychiatrici.*" *Chicago Theological Seminary Reg.,* 41:1–9, March.
Also in *The University of Chicago Magazine,* 43:5–9, March. Reprinted in
Menninger Quart., 5:14–22, July; *Pastoral Psychol.,* 2:10–18, September;
Religion and Human Behavior, Simon Doniger, ed. New York: Association
Press, 1954, pp. 1–19; *Quart. Phi Beta Pi,* 53:25–30, 40, October 1956.

"The Purposive Organization of Case Material." *Bull. Menninger Clin.,* 15:
124–130, July. Also in *A Manual for Psychiatric Case Study,* 1952.

"Prescribing a Therapeutic Program." *Bull. Menninger Clin.,* 15:167–174,
September. Also in *A Manual for Psychiatric Case Study,* 1952.

"A Systematic Consideration of the Homeostatic Functions of the Ego." *Bull. Am. Psa. Assn.*, 7:353–356, December.
Book reviews:
> *Saints, Sinners and Psychiatry*, by Camilla Anderson. *The Humanist*, 11:136–137, June.
> *Fight Against Fears*, by Lucy Freeman. N.Y. *Times*, July 8, p. 7.
> *A Manual for Psychiatric Case Study*, by Karl Menninger. *Psychol. Book Previews*, 1:75–81, October.

1952

A Manual for Psychiatric Case Study. Menninger Clinic Monograph Series, No. 8. New York: Grune and Stratton. Adaptation of Chapter II appeared as "Taking the Psychiatric History" in *State of Mind*. Summit, New Jersey: CIBA, 1956.
"Psychiatric Aspects of Physical Disability." In *Psychological Aspects of Physical Disability*, James F. Garrett, ed. Washington, D.C.; U.S. Government Printing Office, pp. 8–17. Also in *Selected Readings on Rehabilitation*. Illinois Public Aid Commission, Garret W. Keaster, Exec. Sec., 1955, pp. 101–107.
Foreword to *Psychiatric Aide Education* by Bernard H. Hall et al. New York: Grune and Stratton.
"Recording the Findings of the Psychological Examination ('Mental Status')." *Am. J. Psychiat.*, 108:600–609, February. Also in *A Manual for Psychiatric Case Study*.
"A Psychiatrist Replies" (Consultation clinic feature on prevention vs. treatment). *Pastoral Psychol.*, 2:49, February.
"The Philosophy and Technique of Taking a Psychiatric History." *Saskatchewan Psychiat. Services J.*, 1:9–20, April. Also in *A Manual for Psychiatric Case Study*.
"Looking Backward." *Menninger Quart.*, 6:11–17, Spring. Reprinted in *The Land*, 11:251–254, January 1953.
Letter to the editor. *Commonweal*, 26:200–201, May.
Letter to the editor. *Fed. Probation*, 16:31, June.
"What Are the Goals of Psychiatric Education?" *Bull. Menninger Clin.*, 16:153–158, September.
"Citizens and Schools." *Menninger Quart.*, 6:7–10, December. Excerpt in *Better Schools*, 3:6, May 1957.
Book reviews:
> *The Physician Examines the Bible*, by C. R. Smith. *Quart. Phi Beta Pi*, 48:345, January.
> *Cruelty to Children*, by Eustace Chesser. *Fed. Probation*, 16:52–53, December.

1953

"Boom!" In *Music Therapy 1952*, E. G. Gilliland, ed. Lawrence, Kansas: Natl. Assn. Music Therapists.
Mental Health Week statement, May 3–10. Published in various public newspapers.
"A Letter to Men in Prison." *The Inside Story*, Tennessee State Penitentiary, Fall, pp. 13–15. Also in *Menninger Quart.*, 9:8–9, Fall 1955.

"Psychiatry and Medicine." *J. Student Am. Med. Assn.*, 2:28 ff., November.
Discussion of "Dynamics and Classification of Disordered Behavior" by San-
dor Rado. *Am. J. Psychiat.*, 110:417–421, December.
Book reviews:
> *The Second Sex,* by Simone de Beauvoir. *Sat. Rev. Lit.*, Feb. 21, pp. 26–28.
> *Psychiatry and the Law,* by Manfred S. Guttmacher and Harry Weihofen.
> *Iowa Law Rev.*, 38:687–704, Summer.
> *Sexual Behavior in the Human Female,* by Alfred Kinsey et al. *Sat. Rev.
> Lit.*, Sept. 26, pp. 21 ff. Also in *Ill. Soc. Ment. Health Bull.*, 31:4 ff. Enlarged
> version in *GP,* 8:67–72, December; *Pastoral Psychol.*, 5:43–48, February 1954;
> and *The Chaplain,* 11:26–43, August 1954.

1954

Foreword to *Morals and Medicine* by Joseph Fletcher. Princeton: Princeton
University.
"We Hardly Know We Are Alive." *Bull. Menninger Clin.*, 18:17–18, January.
"Psychological Aspects of the Organism Under Stress. Part I: The Homeostatic Regulatory Function of the Ego." *J. Am. Psa. Assn.*, 2:67–106, January; "Part II: The Regulatory Devices of the Ego Under Major Stress."
J. Am. Psa. Assn., 2:280–310, April. Parts I and II reprinted in *General Sys-
tems: Yearbook of the Society for General Systems Research,* Vol. 2, Lud-
wig von Bertalanffy and Anatol Rapoport, eds. Ann Arbor, Michigan: University of Michigan, 1957.
"My Town." *Menninger Quart.*, 8:21–30, Winter. Reprinted in *Look,* 22:89–
92, Sept. 30, 1958.
"The Contribution of Psychoanalysis to American Psychiatry." *Bull. Mennin-
ger Clin.*, 18:85–91, May. Modified version appeared as "Psychiatry and
Psychoanalysis" in *Encyclopedie Medico-Chirurgicale,* Paris, 1955.
"The Dilemma of Psychiatry and the Law." *Menninger Quart.*, 8:16–19,
Spring.
"Reverence for Life." 1954 Ninth Annual Conference of School Administra-
tors, Mt. Rainier Natl. Park, Washington, June.
"The Hydrogen-Cobalt Bomb." *Pulpit Dig.*, 34:38–41, June.
Introductory Remarks to Third Regional Research Conference of the Ameri-
can Psychiatric Association. *Bull. Menninger Clin.*, 18:126–129, July.
Guest editorial. *Winter's Tale,* 1:2, July 28.
"The Meaning of the Hospital." *Menninger Quart.*, 8:9–12, Summer.
"Regulatory Devices of the Ego Under Major Stress." *Int. J. Psa.*, 35:412–420,
part 4.
Book review:
> *The Inside Story,* by Fritz Redlich and June Bingham. *Am. J. Psychiat.*,
> 110:799, April.

1955

"Counseling with Neurotics." In *The Minister's Consultation Clinic,* Simon
Doniger, ed. Great Neck, New York: Channel Press.
Foreword to *Culture and Mental Disorders* by Joseph W. Eaton and Robert
J. Weil. Glencoe, Illinois: Free Press.
Preface to *Love Against Hate,* Korean translation.

"The Psychoanalytic Approach to Alcoholism." *Blue Book*, 7:30–50.
"Psychiatric Responsibilities in Nursing Home Care." *Bull. Menninger Clin.*,
19:16–18, January.
"The First Years of Marriage Are Crucial Years." *McCalls*, 82:53, 90, 91,
April.
"Psychoanalysts Are Indeed Serving in a Sense as Priests." *New Republic*,
132:21, May 16.
Criticism of "Speak Truth to Power." *Progressive Mag.*, 19:12–13, October.
"Freedom." *Bull. Menninger Clin.*, 19:240–243, November. Reprinted in
Menninger Quart., 10:14–18, No. 1, 1956.
"Faith Healing." *Monday Morning*, 20:7–8, Nov. 21.

1956

"Constructive and Destructive Motivation Trends." In *Toward Understanding
Men*, Harry Levinson, ed. Topeka: The Menninger Foundation.
"Thoughts on Bibliotherapy." In *Veterans Administration Sectional Library
Conference*. Topeka: Veterans Administration Hospital, April 5 and 6, pp.
47–53.
Introduction to issue commemorating the centennial of the birth of Freud.
Bull. Menninger Clin., 20:101–102, May. Reprinted in *Menninger Quart.*,
10:4–5, September.
"Episodic Dyscontrol: A Third Order of Stress Adaptation" (with Martin
Mayman). *Bull. Menninger Clin.*, 20:153–165, July.
"Mental Responsibility" (participant, panel). *Army Judge Advocates' Con-
ference*, U.S. Army, Charlottesville, Virginia, Sept. 24–27, pp. 44–59.
"Freud and American Psychiatry." *J. Am. Psa. Assn.*, 4:614–625, October.
"Psychiatric Implications of Surveys on Sexual Behavior" (participant, round
table, 1954). *Psa. Rev.*, 43:485–489, 499, October.
"The Psychiatric View." *The Police Chief*, 23:37, October.
"Psychological Factors in the Choice of Medicine as a Profession." *Quart. Phi
Beta Pi*, 53:12–23, October. Reprinted in two parts in *Bull. Menninger Clin.*,
21:51–58, March 1957; 21:99–106, May 1957.
"Reading Notes." *Quart. Phi Beta Pi*, 53:32–40, October.
"A Psychiatric View of the Police." *The Police Chief*, 23:41–45, December.

1957

Foreword to *Clues to Suicide*, Edwin S. Shneidman and Norman L. Farberow,
eds. New York: McGraw-Hill.
Foreword to *The Human Mind*, Korean translation.
"Listen!" In *Music Therapy 1956*, E. Thayer Gaston, ed. Lawrence, Kansas:
Natl. Assn. for Music Therapy, Inc.
"To Chew or Not to Chew." (Consultation Clinic.) *Pastoral Psychol.*, 8:48,
February.
Letter to the editor ("Sociopetal Building Arouses Controversy.") *Ment. Hosp.*,
8:27, May.
"Reading Notes." *Bull. Menninger Clin.*, 21:167–170, July; 21:220–223, Sep-
tember; 21:259–264, November.

1958

The Theory of Psychoanalytic Technique. Menninger Clinic Monograph Series, No. 12. New York: Basic Books. "The Character of the Therapist" appeared in *Pastoral Psychol.,* 9:14–18, November.

"The Unitary Concept of Mental Illness" (with Henri Ellenberger, Paul Pruyser, and Martin Mayman). *Bull. Menninger Clin.,* 22:4–12, January. Reprinted in *Pastoral Psychol.,* 10:13–19, May 1959.

Letter to the editor. *Christian Century,* 75:316, 318, March 12.

Statement about National Library Week. *The Winter Roundup,* 13:2, March 14.

"Reading Notes." *Bull. Menninger Clin.,* 22:193–202, September.

"Sylvia Allen, M.D. (1892–1958). *Bull. Menninger Clin.,* 22:187, September.

"Isabel Erikson (1908–1958)." *Bull. Menninger Clin.,* 22:232, November.

"Psychoanalysis and the Ministry." *Pastoral Psychol.,* 9:59, November.

1959

"Communication and Mental Health." *Mississippi Valley Med. J.,* 81:18–20, January.

"Reading Notes." *Bull. Menninger Clin.,* 23:31–35, January; 23:71–76, March; 23:114–117, May; 23:158–162, July.

"VA Hospital Dedication." *Bull. Menninger Clin.,* 23:5–6, January.

"Mental Attitudes and Safety: Accidents Are Not Controlled by Chance." *Vital Speeches of the Day,* 25:311–313, March 1; *Best's Insurance News,* 59:67–69, 74, March. Reprinted as "Protecting the Whole Man: Mental Health" in *Occupational Hazards,* 21:29, 66–68, April.

"The Goals of Psychiatric Education." *Menninger School of Psychiatry Catalogue.* Topeka: The Menninger Foundation.

"Human Needs in Urban Society." *Architectural Record,* 126:197–200, July.

"The Psychological Examination." *Bull. Menninger Clin.,* 23:131–143, July.

"Verdict Guilty—Now What?" *Harper's Magazine,* 219:60–64, August.

"Footprints." In *A Psychiatrist's World,* B. H. Hall, ed. New York: Viking.

"Healthier than Healthy." *Ibid.*

"Psychiatry Looks at Religion." *Ibid.*

"To My Father on His Ninetieth Birthday." *Ibid.*

"Toward a Unitary Concept of Mental Health." *Ibid.*

1938

Index

Abbott Laboratories, 71
Abel, 27
Abnormal psychology at Washburn College, 534
Abnormality, individuality and, 799
Abortions, civilization and, 617
Abraham, Karl, 301, 310, 335, 432
Abreaction, 225
"Accident-prone" people, 752
Accidents: hunting and car, 88
   as suicide, 347
Adams, Frank, 548
Adaptation, external and internal, 678
Addiction, alcoholic, 70
Adjunctive therapy, 59, 530, 841, 852
   for inpatients, 724
Adjustment: failure in, 192, 677, 784
   health and, 497
   homeostasis and, 510
   pattern of, 400
   principle, 698
   psychic economy and, 854
   psychosexual, 292
   role rejection and, 288
   of schizoids, 192
   to stress, 842
   techniques of, 665
Adler, Alfred, 204, 431, 827
Adler, Herman, 729n, 862
Adoption, pregnancy after, 291
Advisory Council on the Mental Health of Children, 556n

Aesculapius, 832
Agape and *Eros,* 855
Aggression: control of, 31
   destruction and, 31
   ego rupture and, 507
   erotism of, 333
   femininity and, 618
   groups and, 452
   homeostasis and, 504, 512
   in identification, 484
   indirect, 337
   instinct theory and, 463
   introjection and, 334, 336
   in malingering, 75, 358, 360, 361, 368
   of mother, 622
   "naughty" child and, 556
   organic illness and, 271
   outlets for, 366
   pathology and, 311
   policemen and, 750
   of psychopath, 211
   recovery and, 500
   redirection of, 375, 432
   release of, 355
   role rejection and, 279, 296
   self-directed, 609
   society and, 459
   sports and, 624
   sublimation of, 419
   suicide and, 345
   urethral personality and, 310
   urination and, 304, 308, 309
   in women, 286, 610, 612, 624
Agriculture: vs. animal husbandry, 30
   history of, 27
Aide, *see* Psychiatric Aide

Albany, University of, 860
Alcohol: and cold sore, 234
   prohibition, 17
Alcoholic *Eifersuchtswohn,* 186
Alcoholic psychoses, influenza and, 119, 125
Alcoholism, 70, 72
   hospitalization for, 443
   schizophrenia and, 130
   as self-destruction, 348
Alden-Tuthill Lectureship, 774n
Alexander, Franz, 208, 211, 241, 256, 344, 345, 361, 850, 867, 868
Alienists, 396
Allbutt, Clifford, 293
Allen, Edgar, 656
Alzheimer, Alvis, 121, 128, 145, 147
Amelioration: of mental disease, 156–66
   therapy and, 528
Amenhotep IV, 787
Amenorrhea, role rejection and, 292
Amentia: dementia praecox compared with, 148
   nonparetic, 151
   schizophrenia as, 151
Amentiafrage, 142
American Bar Association, 593, 727, 729n, 736, 757, 761
American Board of Psychiatry and Neurology, 718
American College of Physicians, 670n
American Forestry Association, 94
American Forests, 94